TRANSGENDER

IDEOLOGY &

GENDER DYSPHORIA

A Catholic response

MARYVALE CATHOLIC
PRESS

Printed in the United States of America

Illustrated by Alan Syah

Library of Congress Cataloging-in-Publication Data

Thibault, Jake Ross, 1980—
    Transgender: Science, Nature, & Virtue / Jake Thibault.

        p.   cm.

    Includes bibliographical references and index.

    ISBN- 978-1-7372273-1-1   hardcover

    ISBN- 978-1-7372273-0-4   paperback

    ISBN- 978-1-7372273-2-8   eBook

Transsexualism. 2. Summa Theologica. 3. Moral Theology. 4. Philosophical theology. 5. Pathology—Theories of disease. Etiology. Pathogenesis.

To the Benedictine Monks and Oblates of Pluscarden Abbey

on the Feast of Our Lady of the Rosary 2020

TABLE OF CONTENTS

TABLE OF MEDICAL FIGURES

TABLE OF ILLUSTRATIONS

ABSTRACT

Throughout the previous century, medical professionals aimed to ease the inner tensions found within transgender individuals by conforming their outer appearances to their preferred gender identities. Repeated studies have found a reduction of gender dysphoria through sex reassignment surgeries and hormone therapies. Although well-intentioned, these efforts were on their own insufficient for relieving the underlying distress caused by gender dysphoria. Moreover, transgender individuals, even after sex reassignment procedures, have higher risks of mortality, neoplasms, suicidal behaviors, and psychiatric morbidity than the general population.

Faith-based conversion therapies double the morbidity rates of transgender individuals. A religious approach not based on medical science produces worse outcomes than providing no support at all. A lack of family and communal support of transgender youths leads to increased homelessness, prostitution, and substance abuse. The uncompromising, *tough-love* approach does not lead to positive outcomes for many transgender youths.

Medical evidence from the previous decade suggests a neurodevelopmental cause for transgender identities; however, studies on Rapid-Onset Gender Dysphoria point to social causes for the spike of adolescents identifying as transgender. While high rates of pre-adolescent children diagnosed as transgender desist in their dysphoria, some studies have shown that adolescents who take hormone blockers do not desist into their early twenties. Longer-term follow-up studies are needed to know the effects hormone blockers have on desisting when prescribed early. Nominalist gender theorists have integrated transgender identities into their ideology, whereby the body, mind, and spirit are not essentially united. Although these ideologies attempt to liberate individuals from restrictions of biological realism, this ideology has not offered transgender people an inner sense of peace. According to a 2018 Human Rights Campaign study, individuals who identify as non-binary and other newly named gender identities suffer from the highest levels of depression, anxiety, and suicide attempts.

Under the transgender umbrella are three groups of people: (1) those with early-onset gender dysphoria, (2) those with Rapid Onset Gender Dysphoria, and (3) gender theorists who are part of the 4th wave of feminism. Those with early-onset gender dysphoria suffer from a medical condition that desists at a rate of 80% by adolescence—the 20% who persist benefit from some form of social transformation into the opposite sex. The vast majority of people calling themselves transgender are from the second category who are mostly adolescent females. Like self-harm and eating disorders, this social contagion peaks at seventeen years of age, desisting in adulthood. Autistic young people are significantly affected. This group is primarily looking for an identity and supportive community. The gender theorist has capitalized on this chaos and effectively presented the transgender identity as a way of reinvention. Those with gender dysphoria require support, those with gender confusion need guidance, and gender theorists need to be philosophically challenged.

Thomistic realism offers additional resources for transgender individuals, which secular science cannot offer on its own. Thomism embraces all disciplines of science and the humanities to present a holistic expression of the truth. The Thomistic heuristic utilizes medical science and seeking to restore nature by the least invasive means while depending on virtues and grace to provide wisdom and character to overcome obstacles.

This book argues that using a Thomistic heuristic in line with church teaching is better than medical therapies alone, faith-based conversion therapy, or adopting a nominalist-based gender theory ideology.

CHAPTER 1
INTRODUCTION

Though we labor among the many distractions of this world, we should have but one goal. For we are but travelers on a journey without as yet a fixed abode. We are on our way, not yet in our native land.

— St. Augustine, *Sermon*

Know, then, O beautiful soul, you are *the image of God*.

— St. Ambrose, *Veritatis Splendor*

After Amazon.com de-platformed Ryan Anderson's best-seller, *When Harry Became Sally,* in 2021, the focus shifted to Abigail Shrier's *Irreversible Damage,* a book claiming the existence of a transgender craze seducing teenage girls. The new Amazon.com guideline states that any reference to transgender people being *mentally ill* will be immediately de-platformed. The Amazon policy presumes any book challenging the transgender narrative that *"trans women are women"* must be claiming transgender people are mentally ill. Many critics of these books have not likely read either since neither author calls transgender people mentally ill.

Both Dr. Anderson and journalist Abigail Shrier are notable conservatives who published books from conservative publishing houses. This book is Catholic and Thomistic, leaning neither conservative nor liberal. A Catholic worldview attempts to see issues with the illumination of Christ's incarnational love. The only agenda is to proclaim the truth in love and walk with our brothers and sisters in a spirit of goodwill.

Since many people who try to de-platform a book do not read the whole book, let us address the main premise upfront. ***This book does not claim transgender people are mentally ill***. Instead, this book will make limited affirmative statements using the least rhetoric and the best medical evidence available in 2021. These claims will adapt as medical science evolves. Unfortunately, activists often cancel research due to political pressure if scientists do not frame transgender research according to gender ideology. This censorship is self-defeating since treatments based on ideology rather than data have repeatedly failed.

What we think we know

Androphilic

Some people develop early-onset gender dysphoria (0.1% of the population). These children between the ages of two to four who express an opposite-sex gender expression may be diagnosed as androphilic. An androphilic individual is, crudely speaking, an extreme form of homosexuality. While masculinity and femininity are slightly different and often cultural, some connections between gender expression and gender identity exist.

An atypical neurodevelopmental phenomenon is likely to be responsible for this identification. This use of *the term neurodevelopmental does not mean this is a mental illness*. Left-handedness and autism are also neurodevelopmental conditions and not mental illnesses. A neurodevelopmental cause of gender dysphoria suggests specific brain structures (probably within the hypothalamus) are partially intersexed.

People with gender dysphoria have brain structures most similar to their assigned sex. No evidence suggests a gender dysphoric person has the opposite sex brain; however, the minor opposite sex variations may have a significant effect. Since medical science cannot identify the part of the brain responsible for gender expression, doctors cannot determine if all gender dysphoric people have an intersex condition. The possibility of a partially intersexed brain may express itself in different locations of the sexed brain. The medical community may never understand the complexity of human sexual expression, but their biological etiology may become more evident as they conduct additional studies. All studies on the edges of respectable science in this area should be encouraged.

Many individuals with early-onset gender dysphoria naturally outgrow the dysphoria upon entering puberty and adulthood. Many of these individuals are homosexual and gender nonconforming, but gender dysphoria ceases. The rate of men and women with gender dysphoria is equal in this classification. Although purely observational, people with early-onset gender dysphoria who persist into adulthood appear to be notably different from gender theorists and autogynephilic individuals regarding their opposite-sex gender expression.

Autogynephilic

Some people come out as transgender later in adulthood. These men are typically attracted to women. They do not have classical signs of gender dysphoria, but they have a strong desire to embrace life as a person of the opposite sex. This category is composed nearly entirely of male to female individuals. Ray Blanchard, Ph.D., identified the cause of these desires as an extension of transvestic fantasy, which he called autogynephilic.

The medical community has not found intersex brain structures in autogynephilic individuals. However, this *does not mean these*

individuals are mentally ill. Instead, one can conclude, not all transgender people have the exact cause or experience of dysphoria.

Transgender becomes an umbrella term to describe people with multiple gender dysphoric conditions or no gender dysphoria at all. Transgender people tend to have various types of treatments because the condition is not identical in each person. Since the cause of androphilic and autogynephilic desires are different, the methods for psychic easing cannot be the same. For more on these two categories, see chapter six.

Late-onset

Late-onset gender dysphoria is a new occurrence and much more controversial. This category primarily comprises natal females (75%) who never showed signs of gender dysphoria until puberty or late puberty. People with late-onset gender dysphoria often suffer from general teenage dysphoria with a high comorbidity with eating disorders, cutting, self-harm, and autism. In addition, young people preceded by social interactions in person or online with other transgender people later identifying as transgender themselves.

Nominalist gender activists have infiltrated online spaces pushing personal gender theory. Online forums convince young people that becoming transgender or nonbinary is a way to reinvent themselves as they see fit. This ideology gives young people a sense of identity once occupied by other narratives, such as goths, emos, and neo-punks.[1] ***Young people who experience this generalized late-onset gender dysphoria are not mentally ill.*** Instead, activists have incorrectly convinced these young people, if they change their gender, they will have greater control over their lives and find happiness. The pursuit of happiness in externalities is a false hope which leads to despair, explaining the high rates of stress, depression, and suicide after transitioning or being accepted as a person of their proposed gender.

Gender Theorists

The final group under the umbrella of transgender is nominal gender theorists. This group is an extension of fourth-wave feminism,

---

[1] An aesthetic from the early 2000s characterized by dyed black hair, tight t-shirts and skinny jeans.

which seeks to eradicate all aspects of binary sex. Gender theory is a social and political ideology attempting to deconstruct the family, economy, government, church, and all classical elements of the culture with the hope of rebuilding a superstructure in their own image. Though using the term Marxist can be overplayed, Marxist aspects to this intentional destruction of Western institutions are prevalent. For example, Transgender YouTuber Rose of Dawn claims groups like the *N.U.S. Trans Students Campaigners Network* excludes people with early-onset gender dysphoria while using the public's empathy for transgender people to promote a Marxist agenda (Rose of Dawn 2019).

Gender activists include those with early-onset gender dysphoria in the transgender spectrum. Still, these are primarily individuals who chose this identity to bring down the alleged patriarchy. This group has politicized the medical conditions of gender dysphoria and intersex and has claimed them for their own to legitimize their movement. Some gender theorists are dysphoric about life, so they are thus gender dysphoric. Others claim the label of dysphoria for oppression points. Still, others claim dysphoria is not needed to be transgender since they assert the binary system is a social construction. Consequently, one can choose to be transgender.

When a group does not have the virtue of building up society, they express their agency by tearing society down. Although people in this movement may be well-intentioned, the consequences of their actions are toxic. **Gender theorists are not mentally ill**, but this book primarily reacts against their ideology while affirming the reality of gender dysphoric people and youth who are generally dysphoric about life.

Four Proposals

This book advocates for four changes to the current way of looking at the transgender issue: first, early-onset gender dysphoria is real; yet, very rare. Not all children with gender dysphoria grow up to be adults with gender dysphoria; hence, the Dutch Protocol (a wait-and-see approach) is better than a gender affirmation approach.

Second, youth with late-onset gender dysphoria should be listened to and receive therapy from professionals who seek to uncover the underlying cause of the dysphoria. Occasionally, doctors can treat the symptoms of dysphoria with antidepressants and cognitive-behavioral therapy. Doctors should follow the Dutch Protocol since, like Body Dysmorphic Disorders (BDD), the symptoms usually cease on their own upon reaching adulthood.

Third, this book challenges the philosophy of gender nominalism and a personal gender theory. A particular philosophy should not be protected as a special class of thought, validated by academic censorship. Philosophies exist to be debated, not doctrinally enforced by either the left or the right. As the adage goes, if you have the facts on your side, pound the facts; if you have the science on your side, pound the science; if you have neither the facts nor the science, pound the table. This book attempts to pound the facts and science more than the table. Facts and science should lead to the truth and not censorship.

Fourth, this book recognizes transgender as an umbrella ideology incorporating many feelings and attitudes towards gender nonconformity. The integration of these groups, while politically beneficial, is not appropriate when offering medicalized treatments or pastoral care. Identifying the etiology is essential when seeking the least invasive means of restoring the natural order. For example, doctors cannot treat someone with early-onset gender dysphoria the same as late-onset gender dysphoria. Likewise, doctors cannot treat androphilic patients like an autogynephilic patient; or a gender theorist like someone diagnosed with gender dysphoria. Treating all transgender patients alike is an eyes wide shut approach to medicine deserving criticism.

The Catholic Approach

The key to maintaining healthy relationships with others is patience and loving people where they are. Within any relationship, one should focus on the person rather than their social identities: masculine, feminine, educated, uneducated, old, young, a person of color, white, fat, skinny, gay, straight, believer, unbeliever, cat lover, dog lover, vegan, carnivore, woke, redneck, local, foreigner, Democrat, Republican, trans, cis, et cetera. Despite these categories providing helpful descriptions in certain situations, their owners should not construe them as identities.

While affability is a virtue, good counsel, followed by proper judgment, is necessary for a prudent person to give what is due to another justly. Being aware of specific underlying medical, psychological, philosophical, and spiritual issues related to the transgender condition is vital in being a faithful friend, a competent pastor, an attentive parent, or a just and prudent policymaker. Pastorally, one must understand transgender people and act justly towards them.

Commutative justice deals with a certain kind of correlation between equals within society. When neighbors are in a relationship, neither has authority over the other. Therefore, judging one another is not appropriate. Citizens of the commonweal should not tell a transgender barista their beliefs about the transgender issue at their local coffee shop. One's duty is to be an affable neighbor, seeking peace and goodwill. Showing beneficence towards one's neighbor is sufficient as the proper Christian virtue. This approach supports a person and not necessarily their ideology.

Suppose one has authority over another, as a pastor of souls, parent, or representative of the commonweal. In that case, the attitude of *who am I to judge* becomes an abnegation of God-given responsibilities and the public trust. Parents who do not make proper judgments for their children are negligent. How about when dealing with rational adults rather than children?

Faithfully exercising authority becomes more complicated when the authority figure is the politician, an institutional administrator, or a pastor of souls. Society no longer agrees with the precept that leaders of church and state must guide their members towards virtue and proper ends. Nevertheless, if those in authority reject their responsibilities, the necessity of their existence is called into question. The gender theorists, by contrast, think nothing of asserting the authority laid down by the church and commonweal.

The first response of Catholics when encountering a person with gender dysphoria should not be chastisement but compassion. Archbishop Robert Carlson of St. Louis wrote in a pastoral letter, the starting place for addressing transgender people is compassion, *"But if compassion is the first (and the last) thing to say, it's not the only thing to say"* (Carlson 2020, 4). The church has to say that gender dysphoria must be rooted in biological realism and the rational sciences rather than any form of faith-based conversion therapies by well-meaning pastors and laypeople.

The ethicists of the National Catholic Bioethics Center teach, *"Persons claiming to be transgender must be accompanied on their difficult journey with true charity, and should be offered ethical, effective therapies based on sound anthropology and scientific evidence"* (The Ethicists of The National Catholic Bioethics Center 2016, 599). The Catholic response must be both rooted in scientific as well as anthropological truths.

This book has a twofold purpose for Catholics. First, to give the citizens of the commonweal a better understanding of the complexities of the transgender issue from a non-modernist perspective. Second, this book may help those in authority reasonably act with good counsel based on solid medical science and philosophy.

Ethical Considerations

Even if transgender expressions are not a common occurrence naturally, the medical approach to transgender individuals raises new ethical and legal realities not only for transgender people but for society. Calls from proponents of non-cognitivist[2] gender ideologies to create a third sex or seventy-six genders reject the natural necessity of the complementarity of the sexes for the generation of the species. Instead, materialistic anthropology views the human body as raw flesh, which skilled surgeons can mold into any desired form.

In an age of secularity, the loss of Christian theological principles applied to human sexuality is not a concern for most lay Catholics, who want to be likable and not considered judgmental in any way. Nevertheless, the violation of the normativity of nature results in high rates of suicide for transgender individuals 10 to 15 years after surgery, with deaths from tumors and heart disease 2.5 times greater and psychiatric hospitalizations 2.8 times greater than the general population (Dhejne, Lichtenstein et al. 2011). Thus, the rose-colored glasses that tint the framing of transgender identities as a celebrated occurrence are opaque to the reality that transgender people will face when receiving their desired medical treatments.

If a diagnosis is philosophically, theologically, and medically unsound, there is reason to pause. When medical science cannot cure the patient alone, one should consider if the medical approach is their

---

[2] Those who use emotions or non-universal ideas to determine ethics.

best option. Similarly, well-intentioned people of faith created unhelpful treatments in an attempt to heal transgender people of their dysphoria. As a result of these amateur attempts of Christian healers, transgender people are at a higher risk of suicide than those who did not receive their assistance (Meyer, Teylan, and Schwartz 2014).

No medical cure exists for gender dysphoria, so managing the effects of these feelings is the best solution. While no singular explanation for how early-onset gender dysphoria develops, significant breakthroughs in the last ten years point to a neurodevelopmental cause (Rajkumar 2014) (Guillamon, Junque, and Gómez-Gil 2016).

Many genetic, hormonal, and environmental factors contribute to the psyche's formation as the brain develops in the womb. By the time of one's birth, the brain crystalizes many of these structures and pathways. Then, within five years, the brain fully develops the remaining identity-controlling centers. Thus, before any concern about a child expressing a transgender identity arises, a child has a nearly fully formed immutable brain.

Until the 1990s, physicians at the Gender Identity Clinic of Johns Hopkins operated under the false belief that a child's sex was mutable for the first three years of life. The following faux science based on nominalist gender theories rather than on biological realism was never successful. After the disastrous results of these surgeries and treatments were made public, the medical community discredited the false ideology of the sexual mutability of children. Despite the medical evidence, some trans-feminists, like Rachel Anne Williams, claim that they were boys and evolved into women in adulthood (R. A. Williams 2019, 100). This concept of sex and gender mutability in midlife is an anomaly consistent with personal gender theory but inconsistent with the realism of 800 million years of evolutionary human biology.

During puberty, young brains are flooded with elevated estrogen and testosterone levels triggering the last period of significant structural changes within the brain. Social pressure is being put on parents to rush into hormonally and surgically transitioning their children as early as eight years of age (Ruttimann 2013) (Olson-Kennedy 2014). This book argues that the Dutch Protocol (wait-and-see option) appears to be the most practical, considering 63 to 84% of prepubescents diagnosed with gender dysphoria desist naturally before 15 years of age (Steensma, McGuire, et al. 2013). Those who claim properly diagnosed transgender youth do not desist must acknowledge that far more children are being diagnosed with gender dysphoria than those who persist later in life.

In an Assembly Bill (AB2218) for transgender health, the State of California suggested that 27% of youth between the ages of twelve and seventeen were in some way transgender (CA 2020). The national average of transgender people is 0.4% (Flores et al. 2016). The number of transgender people who receive reassignment surgeries is only 25% of those who consider themselves transgender (Nolan, Kuhner, and Dy 2019, 188). Vastly different results occur if gender clinics approach youth with the philosophy that 27% are gender dysphoric. These false statistics lead to the false belief that puberty needs to be stopped *"early in the process,"* as Johanna Olson-Kennedy, M.D., of the Children's Hospital of Los Angeles claims (Olson-Kennedy 2014). When doctors use the philosophy that 0.1% of the population will ultimately seek sex reassignment surgeries as adults, they come to a different set of therapeutics. Some studies show that children who use hormone blockers are more likely to persist with gender dysphoria, begging the question of whether desisting would naturally occur if left hormonally untreated (de Vries et al., 2011).

Over the previous decade, the rate of teenage late-onset gender dysphoria has exploded as a social contagion, suggesting desisting rates will also explode within the following decade. In cases involving youth, the farther they progressed socially, legally, and medically, the greater the risk of being unable to admit a mistake. In addition, embarrassment, shame, and despair of no external cause of happiness at the end of the rainbow may lead to destructive self-harm.

In the lack of straightforward procedures that could help transgender people work through their brokenness, the church has an opportunity to assist individuals who would otherwise have no viable medical alternatives. The data shows that if a person feels content with sex reassignment surgery, it is not without serious side effects. Transexuals must live with high cancer rates, heart disease, blood clots, and other medical issues resulting from transitioning. Studies have arguably found that sex reassignment also does not heal any of the underlying psychological conditions.

Application of Virtue Ethics

Neo-Thomism points toward a unification of the person and an inner sense of peace with its cosmology, anthropology, epistemology, theology, and ethics. Happiness, according to virtue ethics, is a result of moral luck and the practice of virtues. For example, gender dysphoria may be bad luck since one does not choose or expect this debilitating condition. Therefore, one can focus on being virtuous to achieve happiness rather than hoping to become happy through good luck. Aristotle considered the role luck and virtue play in achieving *eudaimonia,* or a flourishing life. He wrote in the *Nicomachean Ethics*:

> Now many events happen by chance, and events differing in importance; small pieces of good fortune or its opposite clearly do not weigh down the scales of life one way or the other, but a multitude of great events, if they turn out well, will make life more blessed while if they turn out ill, they crush and maim blessedness; for they both bring pain with them and hinder activities. *Yet even in these nobility shines through, when a man bears with resignation many great misfortunes, not through insensibility to pain but through nobility and greatness of soul.* (Aristotle *NE,* 1100b22–32)

Pope Leo I echoed this greatness of soul when he preached, "*Virtue is nothing without the trial of temptation, for there is no conflict without an enemy, no victory without strife*" (Leo I *Sermo.*). Aristotle also recommends friendship as a means of happiness. No one has to carry their burdens alone, but with the help of their friends and the Holy Spirit.

The life of virtue for the Christians is when they unite their minds and souls to Christ, becoming the *imago Christi.* Self-help in a Christian sense is not ego-centric, but following the advice of Fr. W. Norris Clarke, S.J., *giving and receiving leads to becoming.* A Christian never finds happiness staring in the mirror for too long. Fr. Clarke wrote in *Person and Being,* "*To be fully a person consists in living out to the full the alternating rhythm of self-possession and openness to others, or as Jacques Maritain explains, self-mastery for self-giving*" (Clarke 2016, 113).

Lastly, this method requires the openness to the grace of God to allow His love and mercy to transform feelings of dysphoria. Grace-filled hope becomes an opportunity to love God in solitude and use one's energy to serve others.

1.1 INTERDISCIPLINARY ANALYSIS

An interdisciplinary approach is required to analyze transgender experience within its historical, cultural, and biological contexts. The reader needs to examine the medical evidence to appreciate the transgender experiences better. In addition, the reader must also be knowledgeable about societal and ecclesiastical perspectives related to sex and gender. The purpose of this book is to examine the evidence using the humanities and the sciences to find the truth about the transgender phenomenon.

To understand the transgender issue properly, one must understand the biology and psychology affecting patients with gender dysphoria. A more nuanced medical and pastoral response can be provided by understanding the science of gender dysphoria. A threefold approach to understanding the transgender phenomenon includes: (1) sexual desire, (2) ontology, and (3) gender theory

Sexual Desire Argument

The first is related to identity and sexual orientation. Many social activists place sexual identity and sexual attractions in different boxes, but one should not presume these categories are unrelated. The Thomistic approach considers the living relationships between organic categories and how all aspects of life are interrelated. Could sexual attraction and orientation affect sexual identity? The answer from a Thomistic perspective is, of course! One's attractions could point to an etiology for sexual identity. As an example, gynephilic individuals possess a different etiology than androphilic people. The coping process would be entirely different if the transgender person's feelings result from transvestitism versus homosexuality. For a gynephilic person, the feeling of being feminine and wearing women's clothing, makeup, and apparel has an alluring effect. By contrast, homosexual-type transgender people wish to become another sex, and cross-sex objects do not appeal to them. Hence, the pastoral approach will be different in both of these cases. Dysphoria based on the desire to become something is different from dysphoria for being something. Judith Shapiro, Ph.D., explains, transsexuals are *"more a royalist than the king"* (J. Shapiro 1991, 250).

Ontology Argument

The second is the ontological approach to transgender identities, which holds that a transgender mind resides in an opposite-sex person. Ontology considers the totality of a person. The existence of feminine or masculine features or a penis or breasts does not always fully explain the ontological reality of the person. The totality of the person includes the person morphologically, hormonally, and mentally. If a man is trapped in a woman's body or a woman is trapped in a man's body, this would require a wildly different response than if these feelings originate in sexual desires. Being a male or female is different from desiring to be a male or female.

Gender Theory Argument

The third is sociological and cultural. If gender identity were a personal choice or part of a breakdown, the patriarchy would require a different pastoral response. Unfortunately, the response from well-meaning people has often been only to address this third category, excluding the biological and psychological foundations within the previous two categories.

One must also consider if a person is gender dysphoric from a biological cause, dysphoric in general as a social contagion, or is part of a nominalist gender theorist ideology. When considering if a person suffers from gender dysphoria, one needs to address the sexual desire and ontological arguments. When considering the nominalist gender theory, the biological element becomes irrelevant, and accordingly, anyone can become transgender according to this philosophy. The gender theorists are often well-intentioned; however, the consequences of their unnatural ideology imposed upon disconnected youth can be detrimental.

The importance of medical research

The biological foundations of a neurodevelopmental disorder may also give insights into better treatments of the condition without using opposite-sex hormones, hormone blockers, and surgery. Based on the medical evidence, many scientists believe some forms of gender dysphoria have a neurodevelopmental cause.

Like other neurodevelopmental disorders such as Schizophrenia, Body Dysmorphic Disorder, and Autism, non-surgical and non-hormonal treatments are available. Gender dysphoria is most like Body Dysmorphic Disorder or its counterpart, Body Identity Integrity Disorder, yet no studies approach gender dysphoria with similar therapies. The treatment options available for gender dysphoria are narrower and based on the patient's wants, namely, to make the body match one's gender identity.

Transgender identities appear across diverse cultures around the world, but their treatments differ. In most cultures, people with transgender identities are integrated within a society and given a particular function. In the latter part of the twentieth century, medical advances provided a medicalized approach for transgender identities. Despite this, suicide was an abnormal occurrence in the West during the preindustrial age (Zell 1986, 303). Furthermore, some records show that famous people lived as members of the opposite sex throughout the nineteenth and eighteenth centuries. So why does the modern era convert gender nonconformity into a disorder, ending in a high suicide rate?

1.2 METHOD AND STRUCTURE

T his book divides the qualitative analysis into eleven chapters. First, the inquiry will examine the biological factors which may contribute to feelings of gender dysphoria. Second, the encyclicals of Leo XIII encourage the church to embrace truth from the secular sciences but understood through the lens of St. Thomas Aquinas (Leo XIII 1879) (Leo XIII 1893). Third, the analysis will carve out creative pathways for placing people with transgender identities within a Biblical and Magisterial context using Neo-Thomism. Finally, by combining virtue ethics with a theology of disability, the book offers a vision of *eudaimonia* as an alternative to the medicalization of transgender people.

Unlike most philosophical books, this book is full of illustrations. This use of art is intentionally twofold. First and foremost, Catholic objects should be *true, good*, and *beautiful*. The illustrations are an attempt to entice the reader into accepting the beauty of the truth. Secondly, humanity must be present in this dialogue. Too often, interlocutors dehumanize their opponents. St. Thomas Aquinas, in contrast, fortified the objections in the *Summa Theologica* since, through strong objections, St. Thomas most clearly defines truth. Strawmen's arguments may be helpful for sophists, but they are of little use to philosophers. Showing people's faces on both sides of the debate should help the Catholic love the interlocutors in this conversation. One can disagree with someone philosophically and theologically without losing sight of the person's humanity. As a face is more difficult to hate than a name, this book is full of faces to decrease the hate.

Chapter one will be an introductory chapter containing the method and structure of the book and a statement of the problem.

Chapter two defines the gender terminology used to discuss sex and gender. The section also explains the medical procedures used in sex reassignment surgeries and presents the church's teaching on cosmetic surgeries. The document, *Women's Culture: Equality and Difference* (Pontifical Council for Culture, 2015) raises the ethics of elective surgeries. John Paul II's *Theology of the Body* (John Paul II, 2006) also comprises an essential source for understanding twentieth-century Catholic anthropology. Chapter two addresses three approaches to gender theory: biological, personal, and social. This section examines the diverse understanding of transgender people, giving context to the gender variances over time and place. Lastly, this section discusses the normativity of creation and epistemology. This section helps create the context for understanding transgender issues. Chapter two addresses multiple epistemological perspectives within each of these fields of knowledge.

Chapter three addresses the cultural divide surrounding the transgender issue. This section briefly examines the culture war ensuing in the Western world between nominalist gender theorists and anti-transgender legislators. In addition, this chapter addresses the silencing of medical researchers who do not repeat the politically correct narrative concerning transgender issues. Despite the division concerning the transgender matter, Pope Francis and the Congregation for Catholic Education address the problems from a pastoral perspective. Pope Francis rejects gender theories that promote the unnatural division between sex and gender, yet he does not cease showing support for individuals coping with the condition of gender dysphoria. Finally, chapter three affirms the positive relationship between science and faith and how both benefit from this relationship.

Chapter four begins an investigation into the science of sexual abnormalities. Nature includes anomalies as part of every species. Despite the importance of not overstating the intersex phenomenon (1.6% of the world's population), the church needs to recognize those 120.48 million people. The parameters of what constitutes intersex are broad, ranging from infertility to two sets of genitalia and genotypes, which are neither XX nor X.Y.

These abnormalities are prevalent in lower species, which suggests nature allows for variability and abnormalities. Unfortunately, intersex people have become politicized and used as proof of sex as a spectrum. The politicizing of a sexual abnormality is an example of a medical condition becoming an ideology. The church has accepted the difference between intersex people with a medical condition and gender ideology that uses intersex people as a weapon. Likewise, the church can distinguish between people with gender dysphoria and those using transgender people as a fulcrum to raise their nominalist gender ideology.

Chapter five examines the beginning of the medicalization of transgender people in the twentieth century and the early diagnosis of this disorder. This historical section narrates the history of transvestitism, an earlier term to describe transgender people. Next, this chapter discusses transgender people's persistent demand for a medical sex assignment and the response from medical professionals using modern technology. Finally, the rapid progression of medical science in sex and gender led to the rise and fall of the first Gender Identity Clinic. The consequences of what this book will argue is an inaccurate philosophy of the human person. This event exemplifies why sound biology and upright philosophy must go hand in hand to help people with an atypical sexual disorder.

Chapter six examines the theories of transgender identification developed during the 1980s and 1990s by Ray Blanchard, Ph.D. (1945–), a clinical psychiatrist at the Clarke Institute of Psychiatry in Toronto, and a member of the Gender Identity committee for the *DSM.- 4* and *5*. Even though the transgender community typically disavows Dr. Blanchard's work, his observational reports created insights into two possible etiological foundations for transgender desires. The two-etiology approach breaks down the barrier between sexual identity and sexual orientation and desires. This approach is not popular with nominalist gender activists firmly rooted in the siloed approach to sex, gender, sexual orientation, masculinity/femininity, and gender roles. However, neurodevelopmental research 30 years later validates some of Dr. Blanchard's observations. So, this material is included not to promote division but because these theories remain indirectly part of ongoing medical research.

Chapter seven examines contemporary medical studies related to transgender identities and the correlation between identity, the brain, and hormones. This section chronologically shows the evolution of medical research, which constructs the best contemporary understanding of the *transgender brain*. The medical research on the transgender brain has only just begun and should continue without political interference. If these foundational studies become outdated by future studies, they will likely only further define what science has already established. Conversely, if future studies create a paradigm shift to a different understanding of human sexuality, many original pastoral elements will remain relevant. For example, although Einstein replaced Newton through a paradigm shift, Newton's physics put a man on the moon (Kuhn 2012, 115). Likewise, if science replaces these theories in the future, they will still be helpful, and many of their truths will carry over from theory to theory.

Chapter eight concludes the brain research sections. This chapter finishes with the claims of a neurodevelopmental etiology. This section also considers plausible medical causes of this occurrence. Chapter four focuses on genetic abnormalities and the hormonal effects on human development, while chapter eight links these genetic, hormonal, and structural abnormalities to probable causes of gender dysphoria. There may be a link between intersex bodies and intersex brains— which is part of the body.

One must consider the correlation between gender dysphoria, neurodevelopmental disorders, and their comorbidity. Some proud transgender people will interpret this section as polemic since the language is similar to language describing intellectual and psychological disorders, but this is not the book's intention. Besides, *the correlation between mental illness and gender dysphoria does not claim that transgender people are mentally ill.* Instead, these studies claim a possible link to a common neurodevelopmental cause for both, an idea confirmed by multiple studies.

Chapter nine claims that a significant rate of teens with late-onset gender dysphoria do not have a genetic or biological foundation for transgender feelings or desires. Instead, evidence in this section suggests a strong link between gender dysphoria and a social etiology among teenage girls. This section also examines biological reasons why a child with early-onset gender dysphoria may naturally desist from these feelings after the completion of puberty. While nominalist gender theorists strongly dispute the theories presented in this section, it is nonetheless one of the most important sections in the book. This topic is grave since it involves children who depend on well-informed adults to make sound medical decisions based on confirmed medical science.

Children are also reliant on their parents to be examples of faith and solid philosophical judgments. Children can learn about being a boy or girl by witnessing a parent's clear vision of life, their teleology, and how to live a life morally pleasing to God, leading to human flourishing. Regrettably, nominalist gender theorists have invested immense energy and money into using children to promote their ideology. Nevertheless, many gender theorists sincerely believe their actions are liberatory. Parents, pastors, and public officials should be aware of these philosophical differences to respond appropriately to difficult situations.

Understanding transgender issues correctly leads to a complex dilemma addressed in chapter ten. This section approaches the medical problems associated with sex reassignment surgeries and cross-hormone treatments. Finally, the section culminates in the medical research and the Obama Administration's memo on denying sex reassignment surgeries under the Medicare and Medicaid programs in 2016.

Chapter ten concludes with a heuristic approach, which, if applied, may offer guidance for ecclesiastical authorities, pastors, parents, and gender dysphoric individuals. This five-step approach incorporates science, moral theology, and grace from a Neo-Thomistic perspective. This Neo-Thomistic framework provides an understanding and identifies the crucial elements in a transgender person's experience while placing these events within the larger Christian cosmology.

Chapter eleven turns to a pastoral approach consistent with Dr. Vanier's approach to assist those dealing with gender dysphoria. This heuristic design helps those in the church with a simple step-by-step approach rather than allowing pastors to offer advice with incomplete knowledge of the disorder. Chapter eleven is indebted to the Thomism of Fr. Cessario, whose commentary on the *Summa Theologica* and virtues is essential to this book. This section addresses medical research merging with a classical Thomistic understanding of virtues and grace to create a healing pathway and human flourishing.

1.3 PHILOSOPHY AND TECHNOLOGY

At the heart of the transgender dilemma is the philosophical question: Is there a difference between males and females? What is a man or woman biologically, personally, spiritually, and socially? This book asks what it means to be *hylomorphic*—a person of matter and essence?

Before the scientific method can be applied, a philosopher first proposes a scientific hypothesis. Dan Dennett wrote, *"There is no such thing as philosophy-free science—there is only science whose philosophical baggage is taken on board without examination"* (Dennett 1996, 157). Questions of science ask why something occurs, how this happens, or the possible relationship between two objects? To create the scientific hypothesis, a person needs to observe the natural world, discover something unknown, and finally consider, using intellect and wisdom, to create a reasonable hypothesis. Thus, the scientific method originates with a philosophical proposal based on rational observations of the world.

The best use of science begins by asking the right questions. What are the right questions to ask about people who experience transgender identities? The most asked question by transgender people during the twentieth century was if *"surgeries existed to alter men who wanted to be women"* (Ettner 1999, 11). The earliest request for a medical solution was never *"how do I get my mind to conform to my body,"* but rather, *"how do I get my body to conform to my mind?"* This starting point shapes the treatment of this disorder. A worthwhile philosopher challenges these assumptions.

The issue presented is also an ethics of technology question since the current treatment plans for people who experience transgender feelings rely on a medicalized approach. In his encyclical, Praise Be to You (*Laudato Si'*), Pope Francis wrote,

> *Technology tends to absorb everything into its ironclad logic. Those surrounded by technology fully understand that it moves forward in the final analysis, neither for profit nor for the well-being of the human race* (Francis 2015a, sec. 108).

These ethical considerations would never have manifested until advances in endocrinology and cosmetic surgeries, but do these medical advances better humanity?

1.4 STATEMENT OF PROBLEMS

Is there a transgender brain?

The situation before the church is two-fold. First, the church must be open to the medical sciences, which inform her understanding of the human person. Second, the church must offer motherly guidance to support transgender individuals and help guide the commonweal to support lives of virtue and proper ends.

When looking at the science, two divergent interpretations of the data emerge, that of Dr. McHugh's and Katherine Wu's. First, Dr. McHugh claims a weak connection between transgender identities and a neurodevelopmental cause (McHugh and Mayer 2016). However, medical research from the previous decade challenges Dr. McHugh's claim (Hare et al. 2009), (Rametti et al. 2011), (Diamond 2013), (Fisher et al. 2013), (Rajkumar 2014), (Strang et al. 2014), (Ostgathe, Schnell and Kasten 2014), (Fernández 2014), and (Guillamon, Junque and Gómez-Gil 2016).

Second, in juxtaposition, medical studies have shown Katherine Wu to be incorrect in her assertion of transgender people being born *"with brains more similar to the gender with which they identify, rather than the one to which they were assigned"* (K. Wu 2016). The studies have definitively shown that the brains of transgender people are most like those of other people of the same assigned sex. Researchers in each study would find one site out of hundreds whereby one section was like the opposite sex (Henningsson et al. 2005), (Hare et al. 2009), (Rametti et al. 2011), and (Fernández 2014).

Uniquely one study determined transgender people have certain portions of their brains dissimilar to those of cis males or cis females but most similar to other transgender people (Guillamon, Junque, and Gómez-Gil 2016). The stance taken within this book is between the two extremes of Dr. McHugh and Katherine Wu. A transgender person's brain only contains small segments, unlike those of the assigned sex, making it difficult to know exactly how certain brain sections affect sexual identity. Within medical science, slight differences can have far-reaching consequences.

How is transgender part of the LGBTQIA+ alphabet?

The leaders of the commonweal and those in authority have misunderstood the distinctions between sex, gender, sexual orientation, gender identity, and gender expression. In an attempt to include homosexual people, politicians have created protections for the whole spectrum of LGBTQIA+. While intending to protect sexual orientation, lesbian, gay, bisexuals [LGB], they have included people questioning [Q] their orientation (who are straight or homosexual) and allies [A] (who are straight) and intersex people [I] (who are straight people with medical conditions). They have also included transgender people [T], which is about gender identity and not sexual orientation. To protect transgender people under its expansive definition is to protect (1) people with gender dysphoria, a medical condition. The proper law to protect people with a disability is the Americans with Disability Act (A.D.A.). (2) People are furthering a gender ideology that is political in nature. In June of 2020, The Supreme Court codified into the 1964 Civil Rights Act the protection not only of homosexual people but transgender people. For people in the latter category of being transgender, this is now a federally protected ideology.

Is gender dysphoria innate?

Genetics alone does not explain gender dysphoria since when identical twins are born with one being transgendered, there is a 70% chance that the other will not be transgender (Diamond 2013). The twins' study would suggest that epigenetic, hormonal, and environmental influences both within and outside the womb are factors in determining if a person is gender dysphoric.

Archbishop Carlson relies on The Ethicists of The National Catholic Bioethics Center's *Brief Statement on Transgenderism* for his conclusion that Catholic institutions cannot support sex reassignment procedures. This document definitively and without any equivocation rejects any possibility of any form of sex reassignment procedures, but they leave a sizeable exception within their argument. At the beginning of the document, the ethicists claim that they are only addressing people who are emotionally transgender and not those with ambiguous sexual indeterminacy. They wrote,

For the purposes of the present statement, it should be stressed that we are not addressing the complicated cases where various congenital disorders of sexual development resulting in *uncertainty regarding a person's biological sex,* for example, situations involving *ambiguous genitalia.* (The Ethicists of The National Catholic Bioethics Center 2016, 600)

The bioethicists' statement is only for those with *unambiguous* and *"clearly defined sexual identity as male or female."* The bioethicists claim that nature embeds sex determination in secondary sex organs. Twenty-first-century brain scientists and endocrinologists are now claiming that one's biological sex is more accurately determined by one's hormones and brain structures rather than by the existence of a penis or vagina.

Biological reality might be closely connected to psychological reality, creating an identity that is not part of gender ideology but instead part of biological reality. Some people who identify as gender dysphoric may have an intersex brain, which could cause sexual indeterminacy and not be purely emotional (non-cognitive). Catholics can fully agree that easing one's desire to be of the opposite sex cannot be the grounds for receiving a sex reassignment surgery. Nevertheless, Catholics can still be open to some form of medicalized treatment since many, if not most, early-onset transgender people do not participate in a gender theory experiment but react to some biological sexual ambiguity with natural origins.

Should those in authority encourage a medicalized approach?

If transgender identities are naturally occurring within the human species, should transgender identities be embraced as a third gender, or should society encourage individuals to choose either gender or should society encourage people to switch between genders as they deem fit? Although the church should be open to new ways of understanding the human person, she cannot violate her own philosophical and theological principles to be inclusive or popular. Is this a topic the church should become involved with at all? This book argues that the church should be involved in this issue (though cautiously) and offer support for transgender people and their families. A particular pastoral concern for detransitioners is also essential and often overlooked.

People with early-onset gender dysphoria deserve compassion, youth with late-onset gender dysphoria require prudent guidance, and nominalist gender theorists require adequate rebuttal. The suicide attempt rate for MtF adolescents is 29.9%, adolescent FtM attempts are at 50%, and 41.8% for non-binary adolescents (Toomey, Syvertsen and Shramko 2018). The rate of tumor formation is also 2.5% higher due to hormone therapies (Knight and McDonald 2013). One study found that even 15 years after surgery, the suicide rates were 19.1% higher than cis individuals (Dhejne, Lichtenstein, et al., 2011). Dissatisfaction rates from the 610 follow-up surveys conducted in Germany between 1995 and 2015 are as high as 79% (Hess et al. 2018).

Suppose these adverse outcomes from the Dhejne study are statistics for people with early-onset gender dysphoria. In that case, the data for those with late-onset gender dysphoria will likely only be worse. Nevertheless, after a sufficient wait-and-see period, those with early-onset gender dysphoria would have the most to gain by having their social gender expressions match their gender identities since their brain has fully crystallized their psyche.

People with late-onset gender dysphoria are especially vulnerable because gender ideology has captivated their hopes, which cannot deliver the liberation they seek. Late-onset gender dysphoric people will desist from their dysphoria in adulthood; the only question is, will they still have their bodies intact? Secondarily, will the shame and embarrassment of falling for this ideology allow them to reintegrate into society as their natural sex?

Is it possible to treat transgender people without surgeries?

When dealing with Body Dysmorphic Disorder (BDD) and Body Integrity Identity Disorder (BIID)—disorders with psychological and neurodevelopmental origins, the treatments never involve making the body match the mind. Still, they treat the mind to match the body. The treatments for BDD and BIID involve learning to love and accept one's body as one exists (Body Dysmorphic Disorder Foundation n.d.).

Spirituality, becoming less self-absorbed, and practicing self-acceptance reduces anxiety and depression until the individual can live a flourishing life. Nevertheless, given the shortcomings of the medical treatments currently available for transgender individuals: can BDD and BIID treatments offer any relief, particularly in young people who already experience a 63 to 84% desisting rate by 15 years old (Steensma, McGuire, et al. 2013) and young females who suffer from elevated rates of eating disorders and other forms of body dysmorphia? Alternative treatments exist despite the trend to quickly transition a person using hormone blockers, opposite-sex hormones, and surgeries.

What should be the church's approach?

The church approaches this issue with several principles intact. First, a common argument among Catholic ethicists against sex reassignment surgery and hormone treatments is that they violate the totality principle, resulting in direct sterilization. Second, mutilating the human body is inconsistent with the theology of the incarnation. Third, the practice of dualism calls into question the unity of body and spirit when it asserts that humans are ghosts inside machines and that human bodies are raw flesh that doctors can manipulate.

John Paul II notes in The Splendor of the Truth (*Veritatis Splendor*), *"A freedom which claims to be absolute ends up treating the human body as a raw datum, devoid of any meaning and moral values until freedom has shaped it in accordance with its design"* (John Paul II 1993, 46). The church believes humans are bound to their biology and God's natural order as means rather than stumbling blocks to salvation. When a person is born with a neurodevelopmental disorder or is a victim of fate, these conditions hinder a person's ability to flourish (Tessman 2005).

People do not control their moral luck (B. Williams 1981), but people control their virtues. Living a virtuous life leads to a life of happiness. Whatever one's circumstances, one can find meaning in life, making life worth living (Frankl 2007). Likewise, Dr. Vanier practiced this theology in the communities of L'Arche for half a century and found peace and happiness in people regardless of disability.

The church does not need to reject medical science, and medical science does not need to reject the church's gifts. Modern medicine works best when combined with spirituality and the practice of virtue (Terruwe and Baars 1981). Likewise, the church is not needed to condemn gender dysphoria, a concept preached by Pope Francis (Francis 2016) and the Congregation for Catholic Education (Congregation for Catholic Education 2019). Still, she needs to help heal individuals who cannot find all their answers in surgeries and hormone supplements.

A 2017 study found religious affiliation as a *"significant predictor"* in the happiness of transgender individuals (Barringer and Gay 2017). In addition, a 2013 Pew Study discovered that a significant rate of transgender people considers religion, including Christianity—*"very serious"* (Bautista, Mountain, and Mackenzie-Reynolds 2014). Thus, the church does not have to shy away from the issue of transgender identities; instead, she possesses a tremendous gift to offer transgender people.

Religious beliefs and religious counseling have not served to reduce the suicide rates for transgender youth. After receiving religious-based counseling, those individuals' suicide rates increased (Meyer, Teylan, and Schwartz 2014). The church should not get involved in psychological counseling on matters with which she is not familiar. This book proposes a heuristic dissimilar to religious counseling or conversion therapies and more similar to the twelve-step program at Alcoholics Anonymous. Suicide rates do not increase due to the twelve-step program since the process also focuses on grace and virtues.

CHAPTER 2
GENDER FRAMEWORK

To believe it is possible to know a universally valid truth is in no way to encourage intolerance; on the contrary, it is the essential condition for sincere and authentic dialogue between persons.

— Pope St. John Paul II, *Fides et Ratio*

Hence, a self is gendered—not essentially but unavoidably.

— Charlotte Witt, Ph.D., *The Metaphysics of Gender*

2.1 SEX AND GENDER

S ex refers to one's biological status as either male or female. A person is a member of a sex based on five physical variables: (1) chromosomal, (2) gonadal, (3) hormonal and pubertal feminization or virilization, (4) the internal accessory reproductive structures, and (5) external genital morphology (Money, Hampson, and Hampson 1957, 333). Transgender activist Rachel Anne Williams adds to this list; sex is (6) reproductive, (7) social, and (8) psychological as well (R. A. Williams 2019, 204). Traditionally these first six would be sex while seven and eight would be gender.

Gender is one's psychological sex, a set of *"socially constructed roles, behaviors, activities, and attributes that a given society considers appropriate for boys and men or girls and women"* (Money, Hampson, and Hampson 1957, 333). Whereas the concept of sex is uncomplicated for most individuals,[1] gender expressions can vary across cultures, religions, and times since it involves culture and psychology.

Until Johns Hopkins' Sexologist John Money, Ph.D., coined the term *gender role* in 1955, most people used sex and gender relatively interchangeably (Money 1955, 253). Figure 2.1 shows the relationship between sex and gender roles, as understood traditionally throughout the twentieth century.

Rachel claims *"it is not only possible but relatively straightforward to change one's sex"* (R. A. Williams 2019, 203). How straightforward is *it?* One cannot change one's chromosomal sex. Some morphological structures of sex can be modified through cosmetic surgeries, for example, the addition or subtraction of breasts. In contrast, medical professionals cannot change other structures like the skeletal frame, gonads, the size of a person's heart, or create a womb. Pharmacists can change endocrinological sex artificially through hormone blockers and

---

[1] Except for an exceedly rare minority of individuals who are born with an intersex condition so severe the individual's sex cannot be determined.

supplements, which patients must take for the rest of their lives. The individual will never produce the necessary testosterone or estrogen needed for the body's healthy functioning. Doctors can create non-reproductive genitals by reconfiguring already existing tissue. A cosmetic surgeon can give a person breasts, but not breasts that will be able to feed babies. A transexual can sometimes use these genitals for intercourse but not for reproduction. Reproductive sex is immutable. The idea that one can change one's sex to have sexual intercourse without any possibility of offspring misses the essential nature of having a sexed body.

The only straightforward way in which a person can change one's sex is psychologically and socially, and then, only after a remarkable amount of effort. The psychological and social elements of sex are otherwise called gender. Therefore, changing one's sex is not *straightforward* and is instead impossible.

Anatomical and Social Facets of Sex

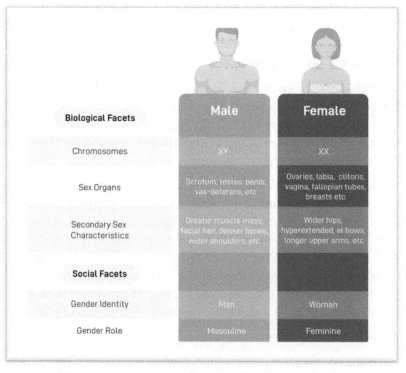

Figure 2.1 Anatomical and Social Facets to Sex

What is gender?

Gender differentiates between the necessary relationship between biological sex and self-expression. The church promotes gender realism, a concept which affirms the essential link between biology and behavior. Sister Mary Prudence Allen, R.S.M., uses the etymology for the word *gender* to support gender realism theory. The root, *gen,* means to produce or beget, as in *gen*erations or to *gen*erate. Other uses of *gen* include *gen*ealogy, *gen*es, *gen*esis, *gen*ital, and pro*gen*y. Thus, sister Allen claims, *"the radical separation of the concept and word 'sex' from the concept and word 'gender' suggested by some twentieth-century authors is artificial indeed"* (Allen 2014, 26–27).

Some nominalist gender theorists like Indigo Fox currently claim *"medical diaries,"* and medical experts state the prevalence of more than two genders (B. White 2017). This talking point is within the common parlance of left-leaning individuals and, in particular, within the cultural mindset of the youth. In contrast, conservative transgender YouTuber Blaire White in an online debate with Indigo Fox responded to this ideology claiming, *"there are only two genders… separating gender from sex is like separating waves from the ocean"* (B. White 2017).

The etymology may show the original intent of the word gender, but what is its meaning from a scientific perspective? In 1968, UCLA Medical psychiatric researcher Robert Stoller, M.D. (1924–1991), introduced three criteria in the establishment of gender identities (1) biological and hormonal influences, (2) sex assignment at birth, and (3) environmental and psychological influences with effects similar to imprinting (Stoller 1968, 383). Dr. Stoller defined gender identity as *"one's sense of being a member of a particular sex"* (Stoller 1968, 115). Ambiguity exists within this scientific criteria since the first two criteria, *biological/hormonal* and *sex assigned at birth,* are objective standards. In contrast, *one's sense of being a member of a particular sex* is entirely subjective. So what happens when the objective conflicts with the subjective?

The reader must reconsider the definition of gender. Gender can be considered in two ways (see figure 2.2); the first is gender as an expression of one's sex and inseparable from sex. Second, gender is however one identifies. According to the first approach, the predominant psychiatric outlook inextricably links sex and gender as inseparable. Even if one views gender as principally social, one could not deny the influence of biology and sex assignment. The second definition of gender bases its understanding on *one's sense of being a member of a particular sex.* Under this definition, there are no additional criteria for claiming to be a member of a particular gender.

When claiming science proves the existence of countless genders, Indigo makes a logical error since medical science cannot prove someone's gender under her definition since gender is thus subjective. Within the traditional framework, gender is an expression of one's sex and can be verified medically. Under the modern framework, gender is whatever a person considers themselves to be. Frequently, those who argue that gender is non-binary argue from the latter definition of gender but somehow claim scientific validity for their claims. One might ask whether the term gender can be defined by consensus any longer?

 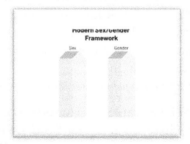

Figure 2.2 Sex and Gender

How is gender formed under the modern framework?

Whatever they desire to be, they are in reality. If people call themselves women, they are women, while if they call themselves men, they are men. If people say they are neither or both, that becomes their gender. Gender is a mega essential identity, superior to one's sex.

How is gender formed under the traditional framework?

Social philosopher and educational consultant Michael Gurian distinguishes, *"Gender is inborn, and then it becomes socialized by culture"* (Gurian and Stevens 2005, 57). Thus, how one behaves within a society is biologically grounded but culturally driven in the specific expressions of their sex. In *The Minds of Boys,* Michael establishes a three-stage formation of gender from biological and psychological factors of child development (Gurian and Stevens 2005, 56–58). Hence, the process of creating a person's gender includes these three stages: genetic, endocrinologic, and psychological.

Stage One

At conception, babies are genetically XX or XY unless a genetic defect exists, causing an intersex child with XXX, XXY, XO, or others. One of these atypical formations could cause any number of intersex disorders. Chromosomal markers within these genes launch the development of male or female fetal brains and hormones (Dewing et al., 2003). If a Y chromosome is present, a *"gene cascade"* initiates, causing the previously undifferentiated gonads to become testes; in the absence of a Y chromosome, an alternate cascade leads to the differentiation of ovaries (Austriaco 2013) (Bowles and Koopman 2013).

Stage Two

The genetic markers induce estrogen and testosterone release in varying amounts between the second and fifth months of gestation. In addition to one's sex genotype marked by XX and XY chromosomes, two hormonal factors determine a person's sex: testosterone governs males, and estrogen governs females. If nature inflicts a woman with infertility or disformed morphology, the dominance of estrogen in her system would indicate the individual is female; however, exceptions to these rules exist.

In typical formation, the testes produce testosterone for a brief prenatal period, and this hormonal exposure is responsible for the masculinization of the external genitalia and internal duct systems (Jost 1978, 6). Testosterone also enters the developing brain and acts via androgen receptors or, after aromatization to estrogen, via estrogen receptors to cause many recognized neural sex differences in animals (Forger, Strahan, and Castillo-Ruiz 2016, 75).

The intense bath of hormones surrounding the developing brain affects neuron migration to specific brain regions and creates pathways different in males and females. For example, the density of neurons in the hypothalamus affects the glands, which are instrumental in sexual development, a process extending through puberty. When the development process unfolds as expected, XX and XY chromosomes signal the release of the correct testosterone and estrogen levels to create organs in accord with one's sex; however, biology does not follow laws perfectly, and abnormalities regularly occur (Schore 2001, 11–15).

Stage Three

Male infants receive a testosterone surge between four to eight weeks after birth, sometimes called a *"mini-puberty"* (G. Butler 2017, 173). Children with abnormal pituitary development or deficient pituitary gonadotropin secretion may lack this mini puberty. These children would have fully formed male bodies but may lack early masculinization. No established data links this occurrence to gender dysphoria, but this topic appears to be still unexplored. These large hormone bursts during twelve to fourteen weeks of gestation followed by the first three months postnatally play a role in setting neutral apoptosis (death cells that form brain patterns) later in neural development (Hutchinson 1997).

Within a few weeks of the child being born, the child sends *"nonverbal and then verbal cues to parents, the nurturing community, and the culture at large. These cues are biological cues—based on the child's genetics and hardwiring"* (Gurian and Stevens 2005, 57). The visual cortices in children are differentiated by four days old, and girls start making twice the eye contact as boys. By four months old, girls can better differentiate strangers from recognized people while boys spend more time observing objects moving through space. Girls develop verbal skills faster than boys, while boys use objects as tools (Rhoads 2004, 22). Most social scientists accept the definition of gender as a *"system that restricts and encourages patterned behavior"* (Risman 2018, 202). Some of these restrictions and encouragements are social, although many more are psychological and, once crystallized, are impossible to undo.

Gender in the traditional sense is the subconscious wiring which affects the way people encounter the world socially. Thus, gender has nothing to do with identity and everything to do with a subconscious pattern of behavior.

The Tanner Scale of Sexual Maturity

The Tanner Scale or Sexual Maturity Rating (SMR) was developed in 1969 by James Tanner, M.D., a British Pediatrician (see figure 2.3). Although the Tanner Scale focuses predominantly on external factors of sexual development, these morphologies and functions have a causal element. These stages do not happen with time alone but due to bursts of hormones, further masculinizing and feminizing the body, including the brain. Consequently, the body morphologically witnesses the effects of these masculinizing and feminizing hormones.

Some females do not develop breasts or start their menstrual cycle before Tanner Stage 5, which can occur as late as 18. The onset of these final stages of feminization occurs when the final burst of estrogen floods her body. This feminization of her body directly correlates to the feminization of her brain. The brain is the most crucial sex organ in the body.

A similar process occurs in teenage boys. An individual being entirely male or female depends on the outcome of hormone bursts in sexual development. Masculinization and feminization continue, marking the end of puberty and the start of adulthood. Before adulthood, it would be premature to claim that one does not have an adequately masculinized or feminized brain. If one removes the bread from the oven halfway through baking, one cannot complain that it is not light and fluffy. Once puberty is complete, gender dysphoria usually disappears. Puberty leads to a proper feminization and masculinization of the brain. The reduction in hormone bursts also helps reduce mood swings, allowing people to settle into their adult bodies. Gender dysphoria naturally desists when hormone levels are not spiking, and sex takes a secondary place within one's adult life.

Stage		Female				Male			
	Age range (years)	Breast growth	Pubic hair growth	Other changes	Age range (years)	Testes growth	Penis growth	Pubic hair growth	Other changes
I	0–15	Pre-adolescent	None	Pre-adolescent	0–15	Pre-adolescent testes (≤2.5 cm)	Pre-adolescent	None	Pre-adolescent
II	8–15	Breast budding (thelarche); areolar hyperplasia with small amount of breast tissue	Long downy pubic hair near the labia, often appearing with breast budding or several weeks or months later	Peak growth velocity often occurs soon after stage II	10–15	Enlargement of testes; pigmentation of scrotal sac	Minimal or no enlargement	Long downy hair, often appearing several months after testicular growth; variable pattern noted with pubarche	Not applicable
III	10–15	Further enlargement of breast tissue and areola, with no separation of their contours	Increase in amount and pigmentation of hair	Menarche occurs in 2% of girls late in stage III	11½–16.5	Further enlargement	Significant enlargement, especially in diameter	Increase in amount; curling	Not applicable
IV	10–17	Separation of contours; areola and nipple form secondary mound above breasts tissue	Adult in type but not in distribution	Menarche occurs in most girls in stage IV, 1–3 years after thelarche	Variable: 12–17	Further enlargement	Further enlargement, especially in diameter	Adult in type but not in distribution	Development of axillary hair and some facial hair
V	12.5–18	Large breast with single contour	Adult in distribution	Menarche occurs in 10% of girls in stage V.	13–18	Adult in size	Adult in size	Adult in distribution (medial aspects of thighs; linea alba)	Body hair continues to grow and muscles continue to increase in size for several months to years; 20% of boys reach peak growth velocity during this period

Figure 2.3 Tanner Scale

Are humans sexually dimorphic?

Although society divides gender into male and female expressions based on biological and social influences, how different are men from women in the human species? Fr. Benedict Ashley, O.P., in his comprehensive book, *Theologies of the Body,* claims

> Sexual differentiation also leads to a varying degree of dimorphism between the sexes, adapting them to the reproductive and educative roles as described. In the case of the human species, this dimorphism is moderate. (Ashley 1985, 434)

This moderate dimorphism is a result of 800 million years of human evolution. Thus, female fertility is cyclical, but women's *"readiness for intercourse is not,"* which led the human species to *"monogamous and relatively permanent bonding"* (Ashley 1985, 435).

Monogamous relationships led to a diversification of labor and allowed for more extended childcare periods and the father's active role in child-rearing. Darwinian biologist Helena Cronin, Ph.D., and clinical psychologist Simon Baron-Cohen, Ph.D., made similar claims of the relatively small yet still important distinction between males and females in the human species (Cronin, Rippon, and Baron-Cohen 2016).

Chimpanzees and humans are 99% genetically similar, showing that a 1% difference genetically may be the difference between a species that eats lice in trees and a species that can reach outer space. These differences between the sexes are even more minor but can have a significant effect. Jordan Peterson, Ph.D., argues that although men and women are nearly the same psychologically, nearly all prisoners in the United States guilty of violent crime are male. All mass shooters are male. Nearly all serial killers are male or are women instructed by alpha males. Most men are not violent murderers, but nearly all violent murderers are men. (Peterson 2018). The correlation between sex and violence cannot be purely cultural differences between men and women since these rates are consistent throughout time and culture. Instead, these minor genetic differences can have a significant cumulative effect.

St. Theresa Benedicta of the Cross, O.C.D. (1891–1942), taught the differences between men and women were few but also complimentary:

> I believe that the human species develops as a twofold species, "*male*" and "*female*." That essence of the human being, which no trait should be absent from, is expressed in both, and that the entire structure of being highlights this specific mould. (Bello 2016, 12)

The saint affirms that each human being, male or female, can obtain all the same traits yet manifest differently. Men have the trait of courage, but so do women. Men are strong, and women are strong. Men are intelligent, and women are intelligent. Men are sensitive, and women are sensitive. The Catechism teaches the complementarity of the sexes, *"Each of the two sexes is an image of the power and tenderness of God, with equal dignity though in a different way"* (*CCC*, 2205). Men and women may manifest courage and sensitivity differently, but neither sex lacks these virtues.

What is the classical understanding of sex?

Aristotle's theory of sexual difference is biological and cosmological. Aristotle addresses sex differentiation, *Metaphysics,* the *History of Animals,* and the *Generation of Animals.* Aristotle defines male and female based on generation:

> A male animal generates in another, and a female generates in itself. Men think of the earth as a mother in the macrocosm and address heaven, the sun, and other like entities as progenitors and fathers. (Aristotle Generation of Animals, 716a 10–15)

Aristotle distinguished between the sexes based on differing faculties and physical organs:

> A male and a female are defined differently by having individual faculties. By definition, a male is an animal that can generate in another; a female is an animal that can generate in itself and then produce offspring who already existed in the generator. For the union and birth of offspring, certain parts need to exist. Moreover, these must differ from each other so that consequently, the male will differ from the female. In the female, this is the uterus; it is the testes and the penis in the male. (Aristotle *Generation of Animals,* 716a 20–30)

Aristotle describes various attributes he categorizes as belonging to men or women, some physical (sex), and others emotional or temperamental (gender):

> The male is larger and longer than the female. Again the female is less muscular and less compactly jointed and more thin and delicate in the hair. Moreover, the female is more flaccid in texture of flesh and more knock-kneed, and the shin bones are thinner than males. Women are more compassionate than men, more easily moved to tears, and are more jealous, more querulous, more apt to scold and strike. As was previously stated, the male is more courageous than the female and more sympathetic in the way of standing by to help. (Aristotle History of Animals, 538a 22–38b 10; 608b 8)

Aristotle recognizes males and females are contraries and privations of the other. This privation *"provided the early metaphysical framework for sex polarity"* (Allen 1985, 89). The sexes are privations of each other, as the yin and yang are privations. What each lacks provides the space for communion with another. Neo-Thomism will help update Aristotle's biology while holding on to the metaphysics of complementarity between the sexes.

Aristotle is renowned for his metaphysics; he is also a natural biologist, studying every species he could examine. His understanding of species is based on his observations in nature. In his observations, Aristotle tries to generalize what something is by its standard features within its category. For example, when Aristotle claims an octopus possesses eight legs, he uses deductive reasoning rather than witnessing every octopus. Since he observed many octopuses and, in general, they all have eight legs, he claims octopuses have eight legs.

Using deduction, Aristotle makes certain general statements about the nature of males and females within species. Using biological realism to understand transgender identities, one must consider biological factors and their actions to validate these identities. Gender nominalists often claim that since some people are born with the anomaly of intersex, then sex and gender do not exist. These gender theorists also conclude that whatever gender one claims *is* one's gender. If readers were to consider the gender nominalists' rationale seriously, they would have to reject deductive reasoning outright. For example, the existence of any seven-legged octopus would mean a cod could be an octopus since the number of legs is not a requirement of being an octopus. This logic misses the understanding of the totality, which also considers additional biological factors and the formal cause of a being.

In *Metaphysics*, Aristotle states that *"male and female are indeed modifications peculiar to 'animal,' not, however, in virtue of its essence but in the matter, i.e., the body"* (Aristotle *Metaphysics*, 1058b 21–23). Aristotle locates the creation of one's sex in the matter provided in the mother's womb and not the father's form. [2] Neo-Aristotelians define sex biologically as *"a differentiation that occurs in animals of the higher types and renders each individual either male or female"* (von Hildebrand, Shivanandan, and Latkovic 2013, 1405).

The transgender debate hinges on the interlocutor's understanding of sex and gender, making them the most controversial terms to define.

---

[2] In contrast, modern genetics shows that virtually always, the father's sperm determines sex.

The Aristotelian perspective is that the only way to be a woman (gender) is to be a female (sex), and the only way to be a man (gender) is to be a male (sex). While pop culture, emotivist philosophers, and experimental gender theorists like Dr. Money differentiate between sex as a biological reality and gender as a societal role, Aristotelian anthropology uses gender and sex interchangeably.

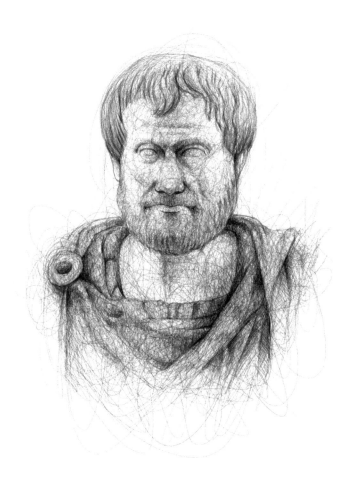

[Aristotle, 384—322 B.C.]

Essence and accidental qualities

Using Aristotelian principles, one can argue that gender is an accidental character of sex and can be applied differently given social or cultural norms (gender norms). One example of this could be the domestic responsibilities in child-rearing. In cultures relying on hunting, women's domestic responsibilities included gardening close to the home, while men did the farming in agricultural societies. Farming is not predicated on the sex of the farmer.

A father in one society might teach his son how to fish, while the father in another culture might teach his sons how to shave or use a computer. These actions are all accidental qualities of fatherhood. Likewise, colors of clothing, types of shoes, career paths, favorite foods, parenting styles, and hundreds of other social factors are not intrinsically male or female. The attraction of one style over another can be confused as being gender non-conforming or transgender. From an Aristotelian perspective, these are all accidental qualities and have little in common with men's and women's essences. The summation of its accidents does not determine the essence. The faculty which determines maleness and femaleness is singular, whether the generation of species occurs internally or externally.

Journalist Amy Nickell appeared on *Good Morning Britain* to argue, *"Anybody including men can mother"* (Nickell 2019). Aristotelians would disagree with this sentiment, not because men cannot be sensitive or nurturing parents, but because a sensitive and nurturing male progenitor is called a father. The sex of the person derives some of its properties. Such characteristics are the property of a specific sex. Fatherhood is the property of men, while motherhood is the property of women. Men and women are not essentially fathers or mothers, since a person with no children is neither, but fatherhood is predicated upon being a man. Motherhood is predicated on womanhood.

Despite Amy Nickell's claim, a woman could never be a father, even while having the ability to teach gender-specific roles or actions. For example, a mother teaching her son how to hunt does not make her a father. Likewise, certain biological powers associated with a property exist only in a male or female as a relationship, not merely as a function. Any teaching to the contrary would require a redefining of the terms mother and father.

Therefore, when a man with gender dysphoria desires involvement in feminine activities, these actions do not determine a man is a woman. The accidental functions do not determine sex. For example, giving birth is a property of femaleness, whereas clothing, apparel, mannerisms, and attractions are all accidental qualities, not essentially determining gender ontology. Archbishop Carlson affirmed the Aristotelian perspective when he taught:

> How we live our masculine and feminine identity is certainly diverse, and there needs to be room for that. There is a wide variety of personalities, and they do not always fit gender stereotypes. (Carlson 2020, 4)

Many features society considers an essential property of one sex or another may be an accidental quality, utterly detached from a particular sex's nature and more ascribed to custom or preference. However, simultaneously, some sole dependant properties of sex are treated as accidental properties, detached from biological sex altogether.

Laura Erickson-Schroth, M.D., and Laura Jacobs, LCSW-R's book *You're in the Wrong Bathroom,* provide many examples of gender confusion. For example, within the text, the authors describe an FtM individual who became pregnant, claiming, *"Pregnancy and childbirth were very male experiences for me. When I birthed my children, I was born into fatherhood"* (Erickson-Schroth and Jacobs 2019, 59).

From a classical perspective, a male is *"that which is able to generate in another"* while *"the female is that which is able to generate in itself and out of which comes into being the offspring"* (Aristotle *Generation of Animals,* 716a 20–24). Therefore, a person who gives birth is a female by definition. The parental property of females is motherhood. No matter the accumulations of accidental male qualities, the essence and properties of a person who gave birth are femaleness and motherhood.

2.2 GENDER DYSPHORIA

S ome people are gender nonconforming, where their behaviors and mannerisms are contrary to the social expectations of their respective sexes, e.g., a tomboy, sissy (feminine male), or transvestite—these individuals are not necessarily gendered dysphoric. Gender nonconforming individuals may have homosexual orientations, or these expressions may be part of the wide variety of heterosexual cis expressions related to one's sex. Atypical sexual expressions are not *per se* signs of gender dysphoria.

If people identify as genders different from their biological sex, they typically identify as *transgender*. However, a person may identify as a member of the opposite sex for several reasons; consequently, not all transgender people are gender dysphoric. For instance, if a person is transgender to promote a nominalist gender theory, the individual may not be gender dysphoric.

The opposite of gender theorists who claim to be transgender and do not experience gender dysphoria are people who experience distress concerning their gender without being transgender. Nearly all teenagers experiencing puberty go through some degree of gender dysphoria when their changing bodies become a source of embarrassment, and they experience puberty-related anxiety.

Gender dysphoria is the *"clinically significant distress or impairment in social, occupational, or other important areas of functioning"* and *"a marked incongruence between one's experienced/expressed gender and assigned gender"* (American Psychiatric Association 2013, 452).

Usually, after their first menstruation and when they develop breasts, teenage girls often desire not to be a female. Gender dysphoria can originate at this stage of development if the young girl concludes that her dislike of breasts and menstruation means that she is instead a teenage boy. Similarly, a homosexual male youth may interpret his feminine disposition and attraction to his male classmates to indicate that he is a teenage girl. These typical teenage anxieties are mild forms of gender dysphoria, but these youth are not transgender.

Paul McHugh, M.D., describes gender dysphoria in the following way: the individual *"begins by feeling like they are the opposite sex but know they are not. They then struggle with those feelings until they come to believe they are the opposite sex and try to act accordingly"* (McHugh 2014a, 20).

Norman Fisk, M.D., an early pioneer in transgender medicine, wrote, *"originally, the concept of gender dysphoria syndrome grew out of clinical necessity very much in an organic, naturalistic fashion… I readily agree that classical transsexualism is best described [as] the most extreme form of gender dysphoria"* (Fisk 1974).

People who are genuinely transgender are those with diagnosed gender dysphoria. This distinction of real versus fake transgender people is called *gatekeeping* by the extreme fringes of gender theorists. However, as Dr. Fisk explained, to radically change one's body hormonally and surgically, the person would have to suffer from an extreme degree of gender dysphoria or be unaware of the challenges of undergoing sex reassignment surgery.

Likewise, no one amputates a limb due to a paper cut. A person who does not suffer from gender dysphoria but chooses to have these invasive procedures, regardless, maintains these procedures are just their preference. Although irrational and self-destructive, the latter is not unthinkable, considering many people act as if their bodies were completely malleable.

What is the maximal approach to transgender ideology?

Since the 1990s, separate groups of gender variant people came together under the single heading of *Transgender*. Some of these groups were willing to come together under the language of being trans for the sake of political activism, which *"marked an important shift away from the identity categories derived by doctors and psychiatrists and imagined a future for transgender as an explicitly public and political identity"* (Murib 2015, 387). This approach of making a large umbrella to cover all gender variant people is titled maximalism.

Janice Raymond, Ph.D. (1943–), a Gender Critical feminist, notes in her new introduction to *The Transsexual Empire*, 1994,

> The issue of transsexualism has been largely superseded by debates over transgenderism or what has been called 'sexuality's newest cutting edge.' The term transgender covers preoperative and postoperative transsexuals, transvestites, drag queens, crossdressers, gays and lesbians, bisexuals, and straights who exhibit any kind of dress and/or behavior interpreted as 'transgressing' gender roles. (Raymond 1994, xxv)

When considering the vast rainbow of options within the gender spectrum, one can quickly become lost in the terminology and complex postmodern anthropologies of the gender variant community. Dr. Raymond's list relates to personal identities or gender expressions, but not necessarily individuals diagnosed with gender dysphoria. Gender dysphoria is not a sexual orientation, a political movement, or a social construct—this disorder should be wholly unrelated to gender theory—unlike many other identities included in this grouping.

In an attempt to challenge nominalist gender theories, churchmen have condemned transgenderism without clarifying some of these sub-categories of transgender people. It is accurate to claim the transgender umbrella is an ideology whereas gender dysphoria is a disorder, but many people with gender dysphoria are unaware of this distinction. When a doctor diagnoses a person as gender dysphoric, one often *comes out* as transgender as an identity, not having any other type of guidance.

Gender dysphoria is a transgender condition with diagnosable adverse psychological effects requiring a medical or psychiatric therapeutic response. In addition, whereas sexual orientation is crystalized and does not change, gender dysphoria often desists over time and with the help of behavioral therapy.

What is the *DSM-5's* definition of gender dysphoria?

The DSM-5 gives insights into the experience of gender dysphoric individuals. Having a *strong desire* is a necessary attribute of gender dysphoria. The diagnosis is as follows:

1. A marked incongruence between one's experienced/expressed gender and primary and/or secondary sex characteristics

2. A strong desire to be rid of one's primary and/or secondary sex characteristics
3. A strong desire for the primary and/or secondary sex characteristics of the other gender
4. A strong desire to be of the other gender
5. A strong desire to be treated as the other gender
6. A strong conviction that one has the typical feelings and reactions of the other gender

According to the 2013 statistics in the *DSM-5*, the *American Psychiatric Society* estimates between 0.005 and 0.014% of adult males, and between 0.002 and 0.003% of adult females experience gender dysphoria (American Psychiatric Association 2013, 454). These statistics only include individuals seeking help from a licensed mental health professional before the transgender issue had mainline support. These statistics from the *DSM* are before *Time* magazine's claimed American society had reached *The Transgender Tipping Point;* before Diane Sawyer had interviewed Caitlyn Jenner in April 2015; and the launch of the reality TV show about transgender youth, Jazz Jennings. The rates of people diagnosed with gender dysphoria, particularly young people, skyrocketed in this social phenomenon.

It is common for transgender people to claim they have always believed they were gender dysphoric since early childhood. When people imagine a young transgender youth, they can picture a little boy wearing his mother's shoes and makeup. However, another form of gender dysphoria is more prevalent than early-onset gender dysphoria; this is so-called late-onset gender dysphoria. One FtMtF detransitioner with a YouTube channel titled *Grayson's Projects* explained her experience with late-onset gender dysphoria,

> When I was fourteen or fifteen, I was not really great mentally, but I was also really insecure about myself. I always felt ugly and or like I didn't feel comfortable in my body. I was also socially awkward, and I had a lot of anxiety and stuff like that. Around this time, I became more active on social media and learned more about the **LGBT** community, the transgender community in particular. And being insecure about my body and confused with a lot of parts of myself. I interpreted that insecurity as me being in the wrong body and not a girl at all. (Graysons Projects 2021)

49

These forms of gender dysphoria are somewhat different from one another. For the majority of individuals with early-onset gender dysphoria, their dysphoria ceases in late puberty. Statistically, 84% of early-onset gender dysphoria remits independent of intervention (Steensma, McGuire, et al. 2013, 582). The statistics for late-onset gender dysphoria, the type of generalized dysphoria experienced by Grayson, is wholly undetermined. Late-onset gender dysphoria is a new concept and only taking on prevalence within the last several years. The reader may presume that as the generalized dysphoria fades into adulthood, gender dysphoria will also cease.

Grayson lived socially as a male with hormone blockers and testosterone for six years and now, in her early twenties, realizes she was never transgender. This book predicts rapid rates of detransitioning as youth with late-onset gender dysphoria mature into adulthood. The result will be widespread infertility and women with deep voices, which will never reverse.

For individuals with permanent life-long early-onset gender dysphoria, the church must be concerned about not stigmatizing those who make up 0.01% of the population. Simultaneously, she must be a gatekeeper, not accepting the testimony of every person who claims to be transgender as if every person has persistent early-onset gender dysphoria. The particular pastoral concern is appropriate for each category of transgender people, including those with gender dysphoria, yet those in authority cannot treat them all the same.

[Caitlyn Jenner, 1949—]

2.3 SEX REASSIGNMENT

U nderstanding what sex reassignment surgery entails is vital when discussing patients undergoing the procedure. Nevertheless, one must also acknowledge that most transgender individuals do not receive all or any of these types of medical treatments. Whereas the term transsexual requires some medical transitioning, the term transgender only relates to gender identity and not gender expression. This section will address the various stages of transitioning.

This book refers to individuals assigned male at birth but who later self-identify as females as MtF (male to female) individuals. Similarly, this book refers to people whom doctors assigned females at birth but self-identify as male, as FtM (female to male) individuals. This identification system does not consider if the person has received medical treatments or is just self-identifying as a member of that sex. This nomenclature alerts the reader how doctors assigned the person at birth and how the person currently identifies.

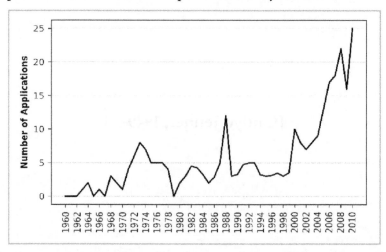

Figure 2.4 Applications for sex reassignment surgeries 1960–2010

A less politically correct approach would be to call the individual by one's assigned sex at birth or use MtT and FtT, meaning male to trans and female to trans. However, people who use these terms are firm in their resolve of sexual immutability and claim the most one can do is *"trans yourself"* (R. A. Williams 2019, 107). Thus, the most politically correct term would be transman/ transwoman or just man/woman. Therefore, this book takes the middle path of using the terms MtF and FtM to show the slightest bias possible to either ideology while avoiding confusion for an audience not specialized in and accustomed to the terminology.

Another question of terminology exists over the naming of the medical procedure provided for transgender individuals. The term used throughout this book is *sex reassignment surgery* (SRS), the most common phraseology. The most politically correct term is *gender confirmation surgery*. Transgender people, in particular transmedicalists, [3] assert that surgery does not change one's sex. Instead, it aligns one's gender with that which is more socially acceptable, thus functioning as a member of that gender. Another term is *gender reassignment surgery*, although it appears misguided since gender is an internal sense of being and cannot be changed through surgery.

A 2014 report in a Swedish journal recounted a rapid increase in applications for sex reassignment surgeries, particularly after the year 2000 (Dhejne, Öberg, et al. 2014, 1540). This trend appears to have increased since 2010. The *American Society of Plastic Surgeons* submitted a report claiming sex reassignment surgeries increased 20% between 2015 and 2016 in the United States (American Society of Plastic Surgeons 2017a). The Williams Institute of UCLA School of Law claimed that in 2016, 0.4% of Americans identified as transgender (Flores et al. 2016). Statistically, there are 1.4 million self-identified transgender Americans.

---

[3] A topic which will be covered further in section 2.4. People who are transgender who claim being transgender is a medically diagnosable condition with a biological etiology similar to being intersex. They often react against nominalist gender theorists and people who believe one can choose their gender.

Usually, MtF individuals who receive sex reassignment surgery receive hormone blockers called anti-androgens, including spironolactone, 5-a reductase blockers, androgen receptor blockers GnRH analogues. Once the testosterone is blocked, the individuals also receive estrogen to replace the lost male hormones. After about one year of transitioning hormonally and socially, a doctor can determine if a person is suitable for surgery. If a doctor is willing to perform the surgery, the patient must withdraw from hormone therapy for at least one month.

Surgically, the MtF individual receives orchiectomy and penectomy procedures, removing the testes and penis, respectively. The surgeon conducts a genital construction of vaginoplasty, clitoroplasty, labiaplasty, and urethrostomy. More common are the non-surgical therapies, which include intramuscular injections or transdermal patches and gels. Non-hormonal treatments are the most common, including laser hair removal, electrolysis, and hair transplants. An orchiectomy costs approximately $5,000, while vaginoplasty is around $30,000 (Erickson-Schroth and Jacobs 2019, 20).

For FtM, individuals undergoing sex reassignment procedures, doctors prescribe androgens for testosterone, and one year later, taking progestins/GnRH analogues will suspend menstruation and begin the onset of menopause. Vaginal atrophy can become a lifelong effect. An FtM individual undergoes both male puberty and menopause simultaneously.

After one year, a doctor can determine if the patient is suitable for sex reassignment surgery. Two to four weeks before the surgery, the patient ceases taking the hormone supplement and blockers. A mastectomy is the most typical procedure for FtM individuals. A minority of individuals also receive metoidioplasty, inflatable/rigid penile prosthesis, insertion, and scrotal reconstruction. Phalloplasty costs approximately $100,000 (Erickson-Schroth and Jacobs 2019, 21).

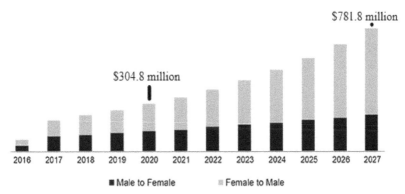

Figure 2.5 Market Size of Sex Reassignment Surgery Industry in the United States by Sex (Data from Grand View Research 2000)

According to self-reporting surveys, 25 to 35% of people who identify as transgender undergo some type of sex reassignment surgery (Nolan, Kuhner, and Dy 2019, 185). Within the transgender community is a hierarchy of pre-op, non-op, and post-op individuals with added shame and stress on low-income people who cannot afford the surgeries. In 2018, 9,576 sex reassignment surgeries took place-of which 6,691 were FtM. In comparison, MtF individuals received only 2,285 surgeries (ASPS National Clearinghouse of Plastic Surgery 2019).

Studies assessing transgender men and women as an aggregate reported chest surgery comprising 8 to 25% of surgeries, while genital surgery comprised 4 to 13% (Kailas et al., 2017). According to medical market research performed by Grand View Research, the *"U.S. sex reassignment surgery market size was valued at USD 267.0 million in 2019 and is expected to expand at a compound annual growth rate (CAGR) of 14.4% from 2020 to 2027"* (Grand View Research 2020). Global Market Insights predicts a 24.5% compound annual growth rate (CAGR) between 2020 and 2026 within the United States (Ugalmugle and Swain 2020). Sex reassignment surgeries have become a profitable field of medicine for a booming 300 new gender clinics (Shrier 2021).

Doctors conducted chest surgeries at about twice the rate of genital construction. Referring to the 9,576 individuals in 2018 who had sex reassignment surgery, half of those would have only received chest surgeries, either mastectomy or breast augmentation. Some prominent SRS medical centers in the United States include Mount Sinai (New York, NY), Transgender Surgery Institute of Southern

California (Santa Monica, CA), Cedars Sinai (Los Angeles, CA), Moein Surgical Arts (Los Angeles, CA), Boston Medical Center (Boston, MA), Cleveland Clinic(Cleveland, OH), CNY Cosmetic & Reconstructive Surgery (East Syracuse, NY), and Plastic Surgery Group Rochester (Rochester, NY).

A progressive society like Sweden with national healthcare and no out-of-pocket costs for surgeries received 767 applications (289 natal females and 478 natal males) for sex reassignment surgeries between 1960 and 2010. Sweden's population averaged 9 million people in 50 years, with the rate of sex reassignment surgeries around 0.007% of the population (Dhejne, Öberg, et al. 2014, 1540). Even when societies are liberal and the surgeries are free, sex reassignment surgeries are incredibly uncommon.

Are SRS's a large percentage of all cosmetic surgeries?

Despite the overwhelming media coverage on transgender issues, the actual rate of sex reassignment surgeries is low. The total cost of SRS in 2020 was $304.8 million, with forecasts of a 14.4% annual growth rate (Grand View Research 2020). Global Market Insights is forecasting SRS to be a $1.5 billion industry by 2026 (Ugalmugle and Swain 2020), while the cosmetic surgery industry is forecast to be around $50.92 billion by 2028 (Inkwood Research 2020). The plastic surgery industry is worth $16.5 billion a year in the United States in 2018, with $930 million spent on facelifts annually. In 2018, 313,735 breast augmentations and 10,246 vaginal rejuvenations were performed. The rate of cosmetic surgeries was a concern of the *Pontifical Council for Culture* in its working document *Women's Culture: Equality and Difference,* which warned about women's objectification through a false appreciation of femininity.

Suppose the primary ethical issue for transgender people is the unnatural manipulation of the physical body. In that case, the church should consider these surgeries within the broader context of medicalizing body dysphoria experienced globally. The number of sex reassignment surgeries performed in 2018 was 9,576 compared to cisgender surgeries, including mainly breast augmentation and mastectomy procedures (ASPS National Clearinghouse of Plastic Surgery 2019). Cis women had 43,591 cosmetic breast reduction surgeries, and cis men had 24,753 cosmetic breast reductions

(Gynecomastia). Women had 313,735 breast enhancements. Not only is 9,576 a meager rate compared to the American population of around 340 million people, but a low rate compared to the 1.8 million Americans who underwent plastic surgery for vanity and psychological comfort. Transgender surgeries only comprised 0.55% of all cosmetic surgeries nationally in 2018. Thus, a degree of hypocrisy exists when Christian women with $100,000 worth of plastic surgery appear on live television to complain about the evils of gender theory. While conservatives stigmatize transgender people for having surgery to find psychological comfort and peace, let those without plastic surgery cast the first stone.

The *American Medical Association* asserted that sex reassignment surgeries are not strictly *'cosmetic,'* stating, *"It is important to stress that surgery is not a cosmetic intervention, but one that attempts to reconcile an individual's core identity and physical characteristics"* (Best and Stein 1998). The New York Supreme Court also agrees with the concept, ruling, sex reassignment surgeries *"cannot be considered to be of a strictly cosmetic nature,"* noting *"Cosmetic surgery is deemed optional or elective"* (*Davidson v. Aetna Life & Casualty Insurance Company* 1979, 453).

What is the church's response to cosmetic surgeries?

What is the church's stance on cosmetic or elective surgeries? Surprisingly, the church does not have a universal teaching on this matter. In 1958, Pope Pius XII proclaimed that the morality of such surgery *"depends on the specific circumstances of each case"* (Pentin 2010). Nevertheless, Pius XII praised surgeons claiming, *"many faces of God's children, whom misfortune has refused them the gift to reflect their beauty, regain their lost smile by your [plastic surgeon's] science and your art!"* (Pentin 2010). In 1989, John Paul II praised the *"noble mission"* of dental and maxillofacial surgeons, stressing that the *"indissoluble unity of the person means that what is defective or deficient in the body also has a serious indirect impact on the human psyche."* He told the doctors that their work is *"a true art,"* that it is *"a very noble mission"* and *"a service to the harmonic composition and good functioning of various parts of the body."* (Pentin 2010).

The document *Women's Culture: Equality and Difference* promulgated by the Plenary Assembly of the Pontifical Council for Culture ("Pontifical Council") in 2015 is non-magisterial yet provides some insights into the mindsets of present high ranking clerics in the Vatican.

The Pontifical Council, composed of Italian laywomen and clergy, declared, *"Plastic surgery can be counted as one of the many manipulations of the body."* The Pontifical Council continued, *"Plastic surgery that is not medico-therapeutic can be aggressive toward the feminine identity, showing a refusal of the body in as much as it is a refusal of the 'season' that is being lived out"* (Pontifical Council for Culture 2015, sec. 7).

This Pontifical Council echoes the sentiment of John Paul II and Pius XII in their approval of the medico-therapeutic use of cosmetic surgery. Still, as did the *Catechism of the Catholic Church* 2289 & 2297 and *Enchiridion Symbolorum* 3722, cautions about an attitude that *idolizes physical perfection* and intends *amputations, mutilations,* and *sterilizations* for non-therapeutic purposes is strictly prohibited. The committee recalls one woman's account, *"Plastic surgery is like a burqa made of flesh. Having been given freedom of choice for all, are we not under a new cultural yoke of a singular feminine model?"* (Pontifical Council for Culture 2015, sec. 9)

This section can apply to the transgender issue in three ways. First, some mutilate or deform their bodies out of some ideology or mental illness, i.e., people who tried to alter their bodies to resemble snakes or cats. The second way includes people who are using surgery to enhance their sexual attractiveness and increase lust. The third way is transgender people who are not attempting to mutilate their bodies but consequently do so. Gender dysphoric people tend to fall into the third category, seeking to fit into society better. The desire to be more attractive is universal, yet gender dysphoric people are not getting the surgeries to become attractive. Thus, the purpose of SRS for transgender people is for psychic easing alone.

The church document *Women's Cultures: Equality and Difference* rejects the concept of cosmetic surgeries for the sake of vanity, although the line between vanity and therapeutic treatment is faint. Rabbis and Imams have had the same challenges[4]. Are the therapies

---

[4] David Shabtai, a rabbi, doctor, and professor of bioethics at Yeshiva University tries to explain the Jewish position by explaining, *"If a girl doesn't think she is going to be able to find a husband because she is so ugly, the rabbis will end up saying, 'If it really, really, really bothers her so much, it'll be okay'"* (Oppenheimer 2015). Imam Suhaib Webb's teaches Muslims do not embrace cosmetic surgery and even ban it, yet exceptions exist. He explains, *"My question is, 'How deeply rooted is this in your personal well-being?'"* Imam Webb

limited to physical causes, or can psychological issues be addressed as well?

If a woman were to have a breast removed due to breast cancer, could she have a breast implant to remain balanced, proportional, and not disformed? How about cosmetic skin grafts for a person who was the victim of a fire burn? How about someone with a *"beak of a nose,"* a term frequently used to describe the face of St. Charles Borromeo (Yeo 1938, 113)? How about a person with ambiguous sex organs? What about a person with a neurodevelopmental disorder, causing them to identify as someone of the opposite sex? How about if an English man wants to appear Korean? In all these cases, the therapeutic efforts are psychological rather than medically necessary. Nevertheless, to what degree can a person physically modify oneself to become psychologically healed? Is the philosophy of the culture which created the faces of Jocelyn Wildenstein, Donatella Versace, and Michael Jackson fundamentally different from the personal philosophy of Caitlyn Jenner?

Archbishop Robert Carlson in *Compassion and Challenge* comes to a definitive moral stance. The archbishop draws the moral line, *"On the topic of Cross-Sex Hormones and Surgery, I must say, very simply: the Church does not and cannot approve this"* (Carlson 2020,11). The archbishop does not speak with the Holy See's authority on this issue; however, his viewpoint would be prevalent among the church's leadership.

Whereas cosmetic surgery for cisgender individuals may be vanity, the aim is to be a more *"perfect"* female or male. The surgery for a transgender individual is, *"in the end, a false hope because it is not rooted in the truth about the body"* (Carlson 2020, 12). Conversely, one may argue, sex reassignment surgery creates the didactic truth which existed in the biology of the transgender person's brain. The question hinges on the ontology of the transgender person. Is the gender dysphoric person intersex, which would trigger a different set of ethical considerations

---

said. *"My feeling is, if you talk to your physician and your physician says, 'This is rooted in your well-being and personal health,' that is up to you"* (Oppenheimer 2015). There appears to be a universal acceptance of surgeries performed for medically necessary reasons, a rejection of it for vanity reasons, and a middle ground for discretion. How discretion is defined is open to interpretation.

when evaluating psychic easing? What defines the actual sex of someone with gender dysphoria?

2.4 GENDER IDENTITY

The topic of gender presently hinges on the topic of identity. The term identity began to be popular in the 1960s, but in the mid-1980s, the concept skyrocketed (see figure 2.6). Identity comes from the Latin *identitās,* which connotes *sameness,* or the distinct personality of an individual regarded as a persisting entity. The identity of an individual is an immutable property. Like race or biological sex, an individual's identity persists throughout their lifetime.

In common parlance, *identity* has lost its classical meaning. James Baldwin describes identity using its common contemporary understanding, *"An identity would seem to be arrived at by the way in which the person faces and uses his experience"* (Chang 2007, 186). Identity, according to James Baldwin, evolves as a person responds to personal experiences.

In the field of nominalism, one's identity becomes sacrosanct and an infallible source of knowledge. To question a person's identity is to *'erase'* them. In contrast to identities derived from the original *identitās,* the Baldwin approach to identity is a subjective concept derived from how individuals internalize their experiences.

Shuvo Ghosh, M.D., defines gender identity as a *"personal conception of oneself as male or female"* (Ghosh 2020). People's conception of their gender identity can be subjective and may change over time, or they may be mistaken based on gender stereotypes.

One cannot truly internalize what it is like to be the opposite sex, so their beliefs merely perceive this identity. The best way to evaluate one's perceptions is to shine a light on them and allow people to question them. Unfortunately, questioning a person's conceptions about being one sex or another is now considered a hate crime in several Western countries, so the process of discovering the truth through empirical investigation is being eliminated. Instead, one must naively believe the conceptions of another person as reality. Accepting a person's self-identification may be an acceptable approach when strangers in society deal with each other, but how about when one is a parent, pastor, teacher, or leader of the commonweal? Can personal conceptions be understood as unquestionable facts?

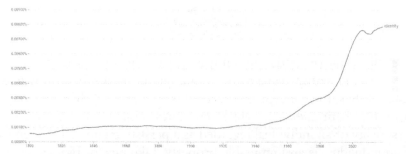

Figure 2.6 Ngram for the use of Identity in literature
(Book Ngram Viewer 2019)

Three forms of gender ideology

Transgender activist and gender theorist Natalie Wynn (1988–) uses three gender classifications to identify gender. A person possesses a gender in three ways: (1) biological, (2) personal, and (3) social (Wynn 2019). These three categories mirror what Charlotte Witt, Ph.D. (1951–), describes in the *Metaphysics of Gender* as *"the tripartite ontological complexity of our existence"* (Witt 2011, 57). Natalie Wynn approaches gender primarily through the frame of personal experience, while Dr. Witt's primary frame is social. The Thomistic approach roots the social and personal in the biological reality.

A thorough analysis of the separate approaches to gender and a proper understanding of the complexities of gender theory ideologies is essential for building bridges between the church and popular culture. This philosophical understanding is also essential to dispel ideologies inconsistent with a rational and realist worldview.

Fr. Dan Horan, O.F.M., who holds the Duns Scotus Chair of Spirituality at the Catholic Theological Union in Chicago, claims the church does not clearly define gender identity or, more broadly, gender theory. Fr. Horan argues that the church's lack of understanding of gender theory indicates a vacuum of Catholic experts in the field of gender theory. Fr. Horan writes in the *National Catholic Reporter,*

It is demonstrably clear that those who invoke 'gender ideology' generally don't know what they are talking about. Such folks would do well to listen to leading scholars on the subjects of sex and gender, like Judith Butler of the University of California, Berkeley, instead of attacking her and other experts. (Horan 2020)

Feminist Philosophers like Judith Butler, Ph.D. (1956–), claim an essential difference *"between sex, as a biological facticity, and gender, as the cultural interpretation or signification of that facticity"* (J. Butler 1988, 522). However, Aristotelians and Thomists object to Dr. Butler's assertion, insisting on a necessary unity of sex and gender.

The biological gender theory (1) is closest to Thomistic Realism. This theory requires harmony between the phenomenal (physical) and the pneumenal (spiritual).

Personal gender theory (2) heavily relies on one's ideas of a personal pneumenal ontology and gender identity. Gender identity only requires a personal sense of one's gender with no requirements of any phenomenological (bodily) manifestation. Using layman's terms: personal gender theory solely bases itself on what one thinks about oneself regardless of the physical reality.

Social gender theory (3) is related to gender expression and society accepting a person as a member of their social classification. For the social gender theory, one expresses oneself as a member of the opposite sex. A person received into a class of people creates a successful gender expression. For example, when a person is *"clockable"* (noticeably transgender), the personal gender identity might be present, but the gender expression was a failed attempt. When a person is unintentionally misgendered, this results from insufficient gender expression and an inability to be part of the desired social gender class. By displaying a convincing gender expression, a person is accepted socially into their preferred gender class.

Those who claim personal or social gender theories, divorced from biological realism, align with what Pope Francis calls *'gender theory.'* Clinical psychologists Jordan Peterson, Ph.D., does not consider biological realism an ideology but rather reality (Peterson 2021). Dr. Peterson argues that once society categorizes realism as one ideology among many, the principles of realism become one more object of relativism. This book is willing to argue that uniessentialism with roots in biological realism is superior to any other ideology based on its metaphysics and not the authority of nature. The church bases its perspective upon biological realism, which differs significantly from most transgender activists; however, this is arguably still a form of gender theory.

Transgender transmedicalist YouTuber Blaire White claims her dysphoria as an MtF individual makes her want to conform to the gender binary. She recognizes the differences between men and women but believes elements within her brain caused her to have a female gender identity (B. White 2021b). Blaire White claims her transitioning as a social female alleviated most of her dysphoria, and her quality of life greatly improved.

The people who recognize the biological basis for sex, but are experiencing genuine dysphoria, are most likely to benefit from *social* transition when they are allowed to do so. This transition is also not a deception since a transmedicalist is aware that their natal sex is incongruent with their psyche. An MtF transmedicalist does not claim to *be* a female but instead seeks psychic easing by socially becoming a member of the female class as a *transgender woman*. If a person successfully transitions socially, society is not aware of their presence as a transgender person.

Debbie Hayton, Ph.D., an MtF teacher, and journalist controversially wore a shirt, *"Trans women are men,"* at an event organized by Fair Play For Women (Hayton 2021). Dr. Hayton advocates for the preservation of women-only spaces based on biological sex rather than gender identity. When the interviewer challenged her position, she stated, *"I would say that the only validation that really matters is from within. We validate ourselves as who we are — and also, I guess from our friends and family, people we love and care about. If somebody on social media says, 'You're a man, Hayton,' why should that bother me?"* (Hayton 2020).

As a physicist, Dr. Hayton points to the facts of the body, which are height, weight, age, and sex. She claims, sex is binary, and there is nothing anyone can do about it. According to Dr. Hayton, sex is objective and biological, while gender is entirely individual. One could argue there are as many genders as there are people, but this does not give anyone the right to expect others to conform to their gender. Although Dr. Hayton follows the modern approach to gender, she consistently follows it to its natural ends, abolishing gender as a practical qualifying class.

In an interview with *Triggernometry,* Dr. Hayton revealed she receives an abundance of criticisms from her assertion that gender is not a categorization but rather how one lives in the world, which is unique and individual. For example, one does not need a classification of being asexual; if a person is not interested in a romantic relationship, just abstain from having one. No categorization is needed (Hayton 2021). Dr. Hayton challenges the gender theorist assumption that desire creates identity. According to Dr. Hayton, the need for categorization and the further need for other people to validate these categories is narcissistic and insecure.

Four books written by MtF individuals who ascribe to personal gender theories are used as examples throughout this section: *Gender Outlaw* (1994) by Kate Bornstein, *You're in the Wrong Bathroom* (2017) by Laura Erickson-Schroth and Laura Jacobs, *Everything You Ever Wanted to Know About Trans** (2018) by Brynn Tannehill, and *Transgressive* (2019) by Rachel Anne Williams.

These four texts present an overview of the personal gender theory, the leading theory among transgender activists. Within these texts are chapters dedicated to laws, sports, politics, religion, surgeries, hormones, loneliness, fetishes, gender liberation, sexual intercourse, and sexual liberation. These books are entirely silent on how their transition to medicalized womanhood psychologically and socially allowed them to become more naturally women. Notably, with over one thousand pages of text on sex and gender, the only reference to reproduction was an extremely brief passage concerning the ability of FtM individuals to give birth as a father.

Their emphasis on becoming a woman appears devoid of the values of real women. Professionals and laypeople speculate that gender dysphoria may indicate a gender-intersex brain, meaning these men have a feminized psyche. However, should not this female essence manifest itself in a feminized approach to sexual intercourse, intimacy, and family? Contemporary understandings of sex and gender do not require an objective expression of what it means to be a member of that gender, either biologically or psychologically.

What appears consistent throughout these texts is the inordinate emphasis of MtF transgender activists on the *desire to be perceived by others* as a woman rather than living as an actual woman. For individuals like Blaire White, Debbie Hayton, and India Willoughby, who do not ascribe to the personal gender theory, interest in marriage and children appear to be more prevalent.

What is the Biological Theory of gender?

Transgender YouTuber Natalie Wynn explains how the transgender community divides itself across different gender theory ideologies in a YouTube video titled *"Transtrenders"| Contrapoints* (Wynn 2019). Natalie explains that some transgender people are *"transmedicalists"* or *"truscum,"* referring to transgender people who believe transgender identity includes having a biological etiology, diagnosed as gender dysphoria. Transmedicalists claim to have a form of intersex brain, making them at least partially the biological sex to which they ascribe. Blaire White, a transmedicalist, states that gender dysphoria is a neurological medical condition requiring medical treatment. Blaire claims the treatment for this dysphoria includes hormone blockers, hormone supplements, and surgery to alleviate their distress and align her body with the biological sex within her brain. Transmedicalists assert that doctors should follow the neurology of the patient rather than the presence of gonads. This is the policy used by doctors in cases of intersex people. The transmedicalists adhere to the binary sex system but believe they have an intersex brain. In general, transmedicalists ascribe to biological realism and the tenants of the traditional sex/gender framework established in section 2.1. Pope Francis and the Congregation for Catholic Education have shown pastoral support for transmedicalists (without explicitly using the term) while denouncing gender ideologies based on personal and social foundations.

[Debbie Hayton, Ph.D., 1968—]

The church has not determined which medical solutions currently offered are morally consistent with the church's teaching. Still, the church recognizes gender dysphoria exists, and some individuals suffer from this medical disorder. Thomistic realism requires a foundational belief in biological reality. Therefore, the totality of the person and the human body's teleology must remain an essential factor when considering options for treating transgender identities. Peter Geach, Ph.D., wrote in *Virtues*, *"A moral code 'freely adopted' that ignores the built-in teleologies of human nature can only lead to disaster"* (Geach 1977, vii).

If an intersex condition exists, doctors undertake a medical approach to affirm the natural order to restore personal totality. Does gender dysphoria exist because the person *desires* to be the opposite sex or because the person *is* mentally the opposite sex? This distinction is key to understanding the totality of the person. If a patient has the brain of a person of the opposite assigned sex, realigning secondary sex characteristics to match their brain is restoring the totality of the person. Suppose gender dysphoria is the inordinate desire to be the opposite sex, even if there is a chemical cause for this desire. In that case, the totality of the person is their assigned sex. Aligning the body to match desire would be supporting a lie, opening the door to trans-species, trans-racial, or whatever the mind can imagine. Medical science that has identified different brain morphologies within the brains of gender dysphoric individuals has not studied if these abnormalities create a desire or align with the opposite sex in praxis.

If an intersex brain condition causes gender dysphoria, what is the best treatment? Is the best approach to offer sex reassignment procedures to mask the body so one can transition socially? Or should gender dysphoria be treated like Body Dysmorphic Disorder or Body Integrity Identity Disorder—conditions that confuse one's sense of phenomenal expression? All other things being equal, the preferable option is to heal the psyche rather than mask the body.

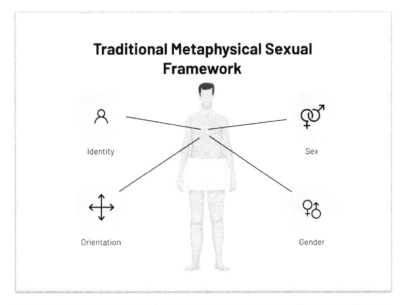

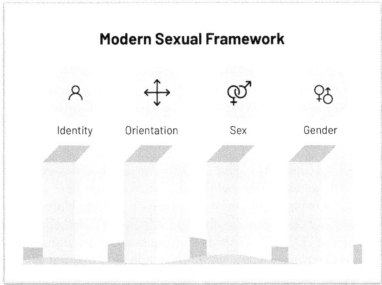

Figure 2.7 Traditional/Modern Sexual Frameworks

The unity of sex and gender within the biological framework

When contrasting the male and female sexes, the manifestation of these differences appears in the forms of masculinity and femininity. Pope Francis, in his encyclical Praise Be to You (*Laudato Si'*), wrote: *"valuing one's own body in its femininity or masculinity is necessary if I am going to be able to recognize myself in an encounter with someone who is different"* (Francis 2015a, sec. 155). Sex, to some degree, is uncomfortable since one is encountering a privation in oneself to fulfill a privation in another. Returning to the book of Genesis, Adam has the privation of his rib, which only Eve can fulfill, and only Adam can complete Eve. The deprivation leads to an encounter as expressed by Pope Francis and thus leads to communion.

Nominalist gender theorists like to silo the categories of gender expression (masculine/feminine), sexual orientation (homosexual/heterosexual), gender identity (male/female), and sex (man/woman). Sexual dimorphism may encompass a wide range of variations; however, these categories are not silos as the gender nominalists claim but integrated into the human person (see figure 2.7). Women, by nature, are female, marry men, and act feminine. This pattern does not deny some women being more attracted to other women than to men (or vice versa), but the natural order determines normativity. The metaphysical framework integrates the human person but still possesses a longing for the opposite sex.

Feminist, Charlotte. Witt, Ph.D., ascribes and develops the concept of gender uniessentialism whereby gender unites the biological, personal, and social elements of gender. Uniessentialism asks the Aristotelian question about *quiddity*, what is *it*? What makes a house a house? Dr. Witt explains that the house's functional property (teleology) determines why a new unified individual exists at all. Finally, Dr. Witt examines the causality of the metaphysics:

> Hence there is reason to think that these are two different theories of individual essentialism in the sense that they respond to different questions about individuals. Aristotle explains why a new individual exists at all over and above the sum of its material constituents of

parts—that is, its teleology. In contrast, Prof. Kripke[5] begins with an existing individual and asks about which of those individual's properties are necessary to be that very individual. (Witt 2011, 6)

Without the Aristotelian teleology, Prof. Kripke, as a modernist, approaches quiddity as a naming process. With his contingent *a priori* approach of existence preceding essence, Professor Kripke may ask: *"what piece of the person is necessary to remain a member of a particular sex?"* The uterus, hormones, gonads, mental functioning? For Dr. Witt and other Aristotelians, a woman is not a matter of any individual part but how the parts work together to create the whole being, which exists socially in the world. Posie Parker (A Gender Critical person[6]) likewise proposed it is not one's breasts or any other physical feature which makes a person a woman. When discussing MtF cyclist Rachel McKinnon, Posie claimed, people become wrapped up in specific body parts when explaining why it is unfair for a natal male to compete in female sports. People say, *"It's the lungs, the muscle fibers, the...."* Posie replies emphatically, *"no, it is because he is a man"* (Parker 2019). This response is incredibly Aristotelian, focusing on the totality of the person rather than any one individual part.

The teleology of biological sex

Francis Marshall, DS.c. (1878–1949), defines the *doctrine of internal finality* as a theory whereby *"each individual, or at any rate each species, is made for itself, that all its parts conspire for the greatest good of the whole, and are intelligently organized in view of that end, but without regard for other organisms or kinds of organisms"* (Marshall 1937, 3). This concept is instrumental in St. Thomas's final cause, or teleology of the parts. All parts work towards the greater good of the whole: one's body parts work for the benefit of the person, each person works for the splendor of the church, and the church works for the glory of God.

---

[5] American philosopher Professor Saul Kripke (1940–) advocated for a different form of essentialism. Professor Kripke uses a lectern as an example of essentialism. What about the lectern is essential to it still being called a lectern? How much can you remove before it ceases to be called a lectern? This reductivist approach differs from Aristotle whose approach considers all the parts working together.

[6] She choose not to identify as a feminist.

The external finality is an extension of the inner finality. All parts work together and lead to the deification of creation. Teleology leads humanity back to the Creator; one describes the Thomistic *reditus,* the return to God. What is teleology for transgender people? What is their usefulness offered to the Body of Christ, which will glorify God? How does the lack of a clear *reditus* affect transgender people's understanding of themselves and their place within the cosmology of the universe?

The church teaches sex from its totality becomes functional and relational in the forms of fatherhood and motherhood. John Paul II explained, *"the mystery of femininity manifests and reveals itself in its full depth through motherhood,"* as the text says, *"who conceived and gave birth"* (John Paul II 2006, sec. 210). The woman stands before the man as a spouse and mother. Her being is the origin of new human life, conceived and developing within her. Through the woman, one is born into the world. *"In this way, what also reveals itself is the mystery of the man's masculinity, that is, the generative and 'paternal' meaning of his body"* (John Paul II 2006, sec. 211). This difference in a relationship is also different in its most essential properties. The pope restates, woman's constitution differs from man's: *"The whole exterior constitution of a woman's body, its particular look, the qualities that stand, with the power of a perennial attraction, at the beginning of the "knowledge" about which Genesis 4:1–2 speaks ("Adam united himself with Eve"), are in strict union with motherhood"* (John Paul II 2006, sec. 212). The teleology of sex is relational. Sex draws people outside of themselves into a relationship with another, creating a bond of husband, wife, mother, father, son, daughter, et cetera.

In the 2015 document *Women's Culture: Equality and Difference,* the authors from the Plenary Assembly of the Pontifical Council for Culture repeated the teachings of John Paul II. The physiological complementarity of male-female sexual difference assures the necessary conditions for procreation. The Plenary Assembly states, *"The physicality of women – which makes the world alive, long-living, able to extend itself – finds in the womb its greatest expression"* (Pontifical Council for Culture 2015, sec. 5). The greatest expression of femininity is not breasts, makeup, long hair, soft voices, and the like. Using this pattern, one can find multiple ways in which one can be feminine and masculine. Femininity and masculinity are predominantly socially constructed, but not entirely. When gender theorists say *gender is a social construct,* they essentially mean that femininity is a social construct.

According to biological realists, these attributes and relationships rooted in sex and gender have a biological basis.

According to the church's documents, the most significant expression of femininity is the womb and motherhood. Feminists who want the church to view women as more than just wombs routinely attack this naturalist position. Mary Hunt, Ph.D., a Catholic feminist theologian, wrote in response to this document, *"What about women's brains?"* (Hunt 2015). This oppositional perspective misses an essential element of Catholic anthropology, which states, *"the essence of the human being, of which no trait should be missing, is present in both, manifesting itself in two ways"* (Bello 2016, 12). The church could not identify women's brains as the greatest expression of femininity since men and women equally share in the *ratio entis*. Men and women are likewise rational beings and have brains equally capable of intellectual pursuits.

Women's Culture: Equality and Difference did not deny the differences between men and women. Instead, the document stated that the most significant physical difference between men and women is the womb because the human person comes into the world through the womb. Dr. Hunt asks, *"Would we say that men's physicality finds in the penis its greatest expression? Sadly, in some circles, but I hope not. Such objectification of persons, such reduction to the purely physical is never appropriate"* (Hunt 2015), but this would not be too far from the church's position. No other physical quality of a man *makes the world alive* other than his genitalia and gonads. In its statement, the church perhaps exemplifies the womb over the penis for two reasons, the first because the document was about women; second, any man can impregnate a woman in minutes. Still, a mother nurtures a baby for nine months in the womb. Although both are necessary for reproduction, the church, with its knowledge of the history of negligent fathers, rightly praises women for their more vital role in reproduction and the continuation of human life.

When the church claims the physicality at the center of being a woman is the womb (uterus), feminists label the church as part of the patriarchy, yet this is a double standard when for nearly two decades, the same feminists hailed the *Vagina Monologues* as liberating women. For an increasing number of progressive students, the *Vagina Monologues* are being abandoned, have become anti-transgender and anti-intersex. Erin Murphy, president of the Mount Holyoke College theatre company, announced they would no longer perform the *Vagina*

Monologues in 2015. The reason given was because gender is *"one that cannot simply be reduced to biological or anatomical distinctions, and many of us who have participated in the show have grown increasingly uncomfortable presenting material that is inherently reductionist and exclusive"* (Kingkade 2015).

Since the *Vagina Monologues'* inception, the church protested against the performance claiming the show reduces women to vaginas, something materialistic and sexually objectifying. Ironically, the *Vagina Monologues* were only shut down following the outrage of MtF individuals. People with penises forced women to stop talking about their vaginas as a public spectacle. The church does not enjoy a victory since there is no acknowledgment of the womb as the center of a woman's physicality or the epicenter of all human existence. Instead, this only results in the broader gap since their ideology erased the concept of womanhood completely.

Lastly, Judith Butler, Ph.D., claims the concept of transgender identities is so difficult for people because the transgender person's image is often the feminized biological man. Dr. Butler stated, *"Trans women have relinquished masculinity, showing that it can be relinquished, and that is very threatening to a man who wants to see his power as an intrinsic feature of who he is"* (J. Butler 2015). Contemporary transgender social philosopher Julia Serano, Ph.D. (1967—), harps on this same theme claiming *femmephoibia*, the fear of anything feminine. The concept of a man being feminine is repulsive in ancient and modern societies because of *femmephobia* (Serano 2007).

A Victorian ideal of femininity exists solely to please the *male gaze*. This false womanhood or *femmephobia* is not the underlying disagreement Thomists have with changing one's sex. Although sexism exists, even informally within the church, the church's teachings are always a result of fortified reason rather than fear or any appetites. Pope Francis embraces some advancements in gender equality in his defense of the natural family seen in the apostolic exhortation The Joy of the Gospel (*Evangelii Gaudium*). In this document, Pope Francis rejects the *machismo* culture of alcoholism and physical and mental abuse of women (Francis 2013a, sec. 69). As the apostolic exhortation The Joy of Love (*Amoris Laetitia*) explained, *"[Our] history is burdened by the excesses of patriarchal cultures that considered women inferior"* (Francis 2016, sec. 54). The pope's critique of personal gender theories, which detach sex from the natural order and denies its biological origins, is not an approach synonymous with the patriarchy or restrictive gender roles, reducing women to characters in the *Handmaid's Tale*. Instead, a biological realist recognizes the unity of the human person as a *hylomorphic* being with a specific teleology.

What is the Personal Theory of gender?

The second category includes those who believe gender is personal or psychological. As some transgender activists point out:

> While some in trans communities believe that transness is biological and the foundation of their true selves, others feel that they have come to their trans identity out of an ongoing exploration of gender and that their understanding of themselves has been influenced by culture and gender norms. (Erickson-Schroth and Jacobs 2017, 30)

Proponents of this ideology claim a scientific diagnosis is not needed to validate one's own personal feelings. Dr. Serano explains, *"Identify[ing] as something, whether it be as a woman, a Democrat, a Christian, a feminist, a cat person or a metal-head, seems to be a conscious, deliberate choice on our part, one that we make in order to better describe how we think we fit into the world"* (Serano 2007, 56). Thus, Dr. Serano's approach to gender theory aligns gender with identity.

Is anything essential to gender? What is necessary to be a woman? One could say the ability to bear children, but not all women can bear children. One could say having breasts and a uterus, but not all women have breasts and a uterus, either due to congenital disabilities or cancer. One could say having XX chromosomes, but as in instances of intersex, not all women have XX chromosomes. In response to this, many feminists maintain that women do not possess any essential characteristics of womanhood. This type of feminist ascribes to nominalism, which claims the only element binding all women together is the title woman, which they all use. Is womanhood a matter of straightforward self-identification?

Transgender people have correspondingly used the nominalist argument, *"I am a woman because I call myself a woman; no other explanation is needed"* (Wynn 2019). Nominalists regard gender as a non-essential attribute of the individual, meaning no physical characteristics specify a gender or gender role. Thus, a woman can have any job, do anything socially, be masculine or feminine, define herself in any way she likes, or become pregnant or impregnate another—nothing determines gender other than self-profession. Even the *Center for Disease Control* (CDC) began using the term *pregnant people* in 2019 to accommodate FtM individuals who become pregnant since now both men and women can be pregnant and can breastfeed. Continuing with the trend, some liberal schools, when running sex education, have divided the class into *"people with a penis"* and *"people with a vagina"* rather than *"boys"* and *"girls"* (Soh 2020,26).

Genderqueer activist Mey Valdivia Rude describes herself as a *"bisexual Latina trans woman living in Los Angeles. She's a writer, comic consultant and a trans activist. She's a bruja, a femme, a pop princess and she loves comic books, witches, dinosaurs and crying. She has a cat named Sawyer and a very successful twitter"* (Rude 2014). Identity is abundantly crucial to Mey. She proclaimed, *"There's nothing intrinsically male about XY chromosomes, testosterone, body hair, muscle mass or penises… Sex, like gender, is indeed socially constructed and can be changed"* (Rude 2014). These statements often attract the most attention, leaving people with gender dysphoria feeling excluded from the conversation. Therefore, Mey would be considered a gender activist and perhaps a *transtrender*. Typically, transmedicalists are frustrated with *"transtrenders"* individuals they perceive using the transgender movement as part of a broader sexual liberation designed to undercut the values of gender itself (Wynn 2019). *"Maximals"* is another term for transtrenders who would like the term *"trans"* to be inclusive to progress trans politics.

Under gender nominalism, if a natal male believes he is a woman, she is a woman. Amnesty International adopted this ideology with statements like, *"A transgender woman is a woman who was assigned the 'male' sex at birth' but has a female gender identity"* (Amnesty International 2014, 17). Dr. McHugh, a biological realist, responds to this, stating, *"The language of 'assigned at birth' is purposefully misleading and would be identical to an assertion that blood type is assigned at birth. Yes, a doctor can check your blood type and list it. But blood type, like sex, is objectively recognizable, not assigned"* (McHugh 2014a, 6). The term *assigned* suggests someone else could assign the child differently and based on a separate set of standards. These same activists now claim biology is just a *"scientific construction"* (Soh 2020, 26). Although doctors use various categories to describe a child at birth, such as length, weight, race, ableness, et cetera, sex is still one of the most important factors worth noting.

Similar to Amnesty International's definition, actor Daniel Radcliffe wrote after one of J.K. Rowling's gender realist Tweets,

> Transgender women are women. Any statement to the contrary erases the identity and dignity of transgender people and goes against all advice given by professional health care associations who have far more expertise on this subject. According to The Trevor Project, 78% of transgender and nonbinary youth reported being the subject of discrimination due to their gender identity. It's clear that we need to do more to support transgender and nonbinary people, not invalidate their identities, and not cause further harm. (Radcliffe 2020)

Daniel Radcliffe's statement is an example of the subjective emotivist approach to ontology and epistemology. If one *feels* like a woman, then one *is* a woman. Therefore, the only knowledge worth considering is one's *personal truth*. The Congregation for Catholic Education in the 2019 document *Male and Female He Created Them* addresses this ideology. The CCE critiqued: *"Gender theory (especially in its most radical forms) speaks of a gradual process of denaturalization, that is a move away from nature and towards an absolute option for the decision of the feelings of the human subject"* (Congregation for Catholic Education 2019, sec. 19).

Gender theorists have weaponized empathy against nature. Pope Benedict XVI likewise stated in his message to the German parliament. The pontiff claimed, *"[Man] is intellect and will, but he is also nature, and his will is rightly ordered if he respects his nature, listens to it and accepts himself for who he is, as one who did not create himself"* (Benedict XVI 2011). Pope Francis, in a 2016 meeting with Polish bishops, complained about ideological colonization, *"Today, in schools they are teaching this to children— to children!– that everyone can choose their gender...We are living a moment of annihilation of man as the image of God"* (Francis 2016b).

How many genders are there?

Some proponents of this ideology advocate for the personal selection of one of the two genders, while others advocate for 76-genders (M. Stewart 2020) or an unlimited number of genders (Brusman 2019) or a genderless world (Joel 2019). Kate Bornstein, in her own extreme example, reflects,

> My identity as a transsexual lesbian whose female lover is becoming a man is manifest in my fashion statement. I identify as neither male nor female, and now that my lover is going through his gender change, it turns out I'm neither straight nor gay. (Bornstein 1995, 3–4)

Rachel Anne Williams, a fellow transfeminist, asserts, *"My body is an act of terrorism. It confuses those who cannot see the body for what it is: a field of potential"* (R. A. Williams 2019, 121).

An increasingly popular trend is neopronouns, where a person uses terms such as ze/zer, tree/treeself, and bunny/bunnyself instead of the traditional pronouns. Although localized, this personal approach of gender is popular within a small community of gender theorists. For example, actor and musician Keiynan Lonsdale asked the public to refer to him as Tree and Treeself. In an Instagram Live Q&A, Keiynan stated, *"I want people to call me 'tree,' because we all come from trees, so it doesn't matter if you're a he or a she or a they or a them. At the end of the day, everyone's a tree"* (Bote 2018). In addition, celebrities coming out as non-binary is a 2020 trend to grab the spotlight for 15-minutes of fame and support the transgender community. Jonathan McDonald Van Ness from *Queer Eye* and musicians Sam Smith, Harry Styles, and Miley Cyrus have all come out as non-binary or genderfluid. The predictable next step within the personal gender theory will be personalized verbs and adjectives.

[Kate Bornstein, 1948—]

This self-identification approach to gender is growing in the United States but while being defeated across Europe. The United Kingdom started restricting puberty blockers for children after the Kierra Bell case in the latter part of 2020. In May of 2021, leftist parties in Spain and Germany proposed implementing self-identification laws that parliaments defeated by wide margins. In Spain, the Podemos party proposed a law allowing gender transition for minors at twelve years. In addition, the bill proposed that teens could change their legal sex without medical or psychological checks to prove they were suffering from gender dysphoria. The conservative party, as well as feminists, objected to this bill. Correspondingly, the liberal party FDP in Germany proposed a bill to bring down the age of gender self-identification to fourteen. In both cases, 70% of parliamentarians voted against these bills.

Non-binary youth

The most extreme form of a personal gender theory is of non-binary youth. Non-binary individuals feel as if they do not conform to either of the binary clearly defined categories. Some examples of gender non-binary expressions include genderqueer, gender fluid, demigender, bigender, agender, and gender unicorns. Genderqueer is often used to show political significance. A genderqueer person can play with gender and social norms. For example, a genderqueer person might be a male who presents as a woman but includes a glitter beard. This expression intentionally violates social norms.

Genderfluid is a concept growing in popularity whereby a person may express more masculine or feminine on any given day. For example, pronoun usage may fluctuate frequently. A demigender is connected to both genders but is partially connected more to one gender than another. A bi-gender person tries to incorporate both genders. Someone who identifies as agender or non-gender does not claim either a male or female gender. A gender unicorn is a *"rare and fantastical creature who might seemingly defy the laws of nature and cannot exist, yet do"* (Erickson-Schroth and Jacobs 2017, 15).

Non-heterosexual young women comprise the largest group of people who claim to be non-binary (Whyte, Brooks, and Torgler 2018, 2403). The term non-binary describes individuals who identify as genderqueer or *"genderfluid, bigender, agender, gender creative, and others"*

(Yarhouse and Sadusky 2019, 108). These individuals adopt gender non-conformity as gender identity. Often those who are part of the non-binary categories of transgender do not experience *"clinically significant distress or impairment in social, occupational, or other important areas of functioning"* (American Psychiatric Association 2013, 452) and is, therefore, not gender dysphoric. Unlike transsexuals, there is no commitment to undergoing surgery or sterilizing hormones, so one can be transgender one day and cease to be the next without permanent consequences. This characteristic is a blessing and a curse. Although non-binary activists may have few long-term repercussions from their ambiguous identities, they are a vocal group within activist circles. Their rhetoric often becomes codified in transgender protections and policies. As social media has become a dominant force in society, many teenagers cling to this ideology and adopt these identities as their own. The youth may make long-term life decisions by using hormone blockers and opposite-sex hormones due to this non-binary activism.

Early versions of the *Standards of Care* published by the Harry Benjamin International Gender Dysphoria Association required transgender persons to have a binary presentation to receive medical treatments. This stance changed with the seventh version in 2014, which accepted various genders outside the binary system. This change is an example of gender theory influencing standards of medical care.

Gender theorist Judith Lorber, Ph.D., negates the entire construct of sex and gender, claiming an extreme form of non-binariness. She writes, *"For human beings, there is no essential femaleness or maleness, femininity or masculinity, womanhood or manhood, but once gender is ascribed, the social order construct holds individuals to strong gender norms and expectations"* (Lorber 2018, 278). Under Dr. Lober's theory, all people are born non-binary and with full plasticity. According to Dr. Lorber, being transgender would be impossible since gender would merely be, as Ru Paul claims, *"You're born naked, and the rest is drag."* (Raymond 1994, 31). However, Dr. Raymond writes, unlike drag, *"They purport to be the real thing. And our suspension of disbelief in their synthetic nature is required as a moral imperative"* (Raymond 1994, xxiii). Although this sophistry does not fool most adults, youth without proper prudence and shrewdness gravitate to this ideology.

Diane Ehrensaft, Ph.D., the director of mental health at the University of California San Francisco's gender clinic, rejects the term *"persist and consistent"* found in the *DSM-5* since those terms imply binary sex is fixed in children. In an interview with Jon Brooks, Dr. Ehrensaft claims, *"younger generations of transgender people—and even younger generations in the general population—see gender as more protean, even customizable"* (Brooks 2018). The 2016 report from the National Center for Transgender Equality found that more than one-third of nearly 28,000 transgender youth respondents claimed they were of some form of non-binary gender (National Center for Transgender Equality 2016). Dr. Ehrensaft argues that children naturally identify as *"both male and female, neither male nor female, or sometimes male, sometimes female"* (Brooks 2018).

Dr. Ehrensaft's idea of children effortlessly flip-flopping between genders contradicts the shared experience of adults who work with children. If one calls a little boy a girl or a little girl a boy, misgendering produces an immediate adverse reaction by a child. Children are more aware of gender than race or religion. Gender for children is a mega essential role. Teenagers, in contrast, are experimenting with sex, gender, and sexual orientation but ultimately, they settle on a stable sexuality.

Some individuals in the non-binary movement use the term *'trans'* with an asterisk (*trans**) to indicate the inclusion of all individuals who do not identify as members of the gender-conforming group. This identification originated in the 1980s in message boards, whereby people used *"t*"* to identify transgender (Ryan 2014). *Trans** is now rejected in some transgender circles since the asterisk indicates trans (transsexuals) are more valid than trans* (meaning non-binary). As one activist site avers, *"Claiming the asterisk itself is fundamentally oppressive denies accountability and ignores the culture of binarism and transmisogyny that affects the community"* (Trans Student Educational Resources n.d.).

Non-binary people are transgender because they do not have a gender identity, experienced in the same way cisgender people experience sex. Although traditionally, non-binary identities would not be *"transgender"* since they do not *cross*-gender identities, they reject the binary sex categories. The use of *trans* without *gender* furthers the idea that personal identities do not need to be binary. The word transgender suggests a person is switching from one gender to another, whereas many people who identify as non-binary reject this concept outright (Ryan 2014). A person can be non-binary for numerous reasons, including experimenting with feelings of transgender identity, gender nonconformity, or a social/political stance against patriarchy. One study found, *"Among non-binary people assigned male at birth, one percent have had vaginoplasty or labiaplasty, and 11% desire these in the future"* (James et al., 2016, 103). Most of the transitions for nonbinary people involve the breasts. Natal females most frequently seek a double mastectomy, while natal males seek estrogen to obtain breasts and stop virilization (G. Butler 2017, 176).

Although this theory is at the center of the church's critique of gender theory ideology, non-binary does not carry the same pastoral concerns since nonbinary identification does not frequently manifest in any specific actions. Paradoxically, non-binary ideology is the most significant concern since it is a proselytizing philosophy detrimental to both transgender and cisgender people. Compared to any of the LGBTQ subgroups, youth who identify as non-binary (90%) and gender non-conformity (91%) self-report the highest levels of stress (Human Rights Campaign 2018, 6). Also, 41.8% of non-binary adolescents attempt suicide (Toomey, Syvertsen and Shramko 2018).

Non-binary identities may be a trend term for confused youth, or some people may be lifelong non-binaries. However, not enough time passed since people began using the term to determine its fecundity. For example, a survey of Minnesota high-schoolers found that 41% of transgender respondents identified primarily as non-binary (Rider et al. 2018, 2). Notably, older people who identify as transgender do not frequently identify as non-binary, suggesting this may be associated with a trend rather than a form of gender dysphoria with a biological etiology.

Non-binary individuals are naturally the most extreme form of personal gender theorists since social politics typically drive their non-binariness rather than a medical condition. Within society, one finds Republicans with gender dysphoria, a notable example being Caitlyn Jenner. Conversely, one does not find Republican or conservative people who identify as non-binary or genderfluid.

Gender theorists pretend that youth are coming up with these expressions independently, but this is not true. Trans Student Education Resources (TSER) is one of the transgender activist sites which, because of their use of abstraction and hyperbole, draws the most criticism (Anderson 2018a, 31–33) (Anderson 2018c). One example of a hyperbolic response of TSER is this statement, *"Biological sex is an ambiguous word [sic] that has no scale and no meaning besides that it is related to some sex characteristics. It is also harmful to trans people"* (Trans Student Educational Resources n.d.). The belief that using the term *"biological sex"* is *"harmful to trans people"* is the type of victim mentality that incites cisgender individuals to reject all transgender issues as a type of extremist gender ideology.

In an article titled *Transgender Youth: ways to be an ally and advocate*, the authors recommend emphasizing role models of gender-benders in art, history, and curriculum, in addition to advocating for youth to change their identities more effortlessly. The authors recommended allowing a child to choose: *"male, female, prefer not to say, to be discussed when I meet you, genderqueer, gender flux, gender neutral, gender fluid, genderless, transgender, or other"* (Gary-Smith and Steinhart 2016, 215). Unfortunately, this approach to gender identity is being manufactured and promoted by gender theorists.

What is the Social Theory of gender?

The social approach to gender is more nuanced than the personal theory and merits more philosophical analysis. What does being a man or woman mean socially? Humans never interact with one another on a chromosomal level. Seldom do humans interact with society using their genitals. Instead, humans constantly interact in society using their sexuality. If a person performs as a woman within society and society receives the person as a woman, then socially, that person is a woman. United with the social gender theory is the theory of gender expression. To be received as a member of a gender class requires more than an internalized sense of identity; membership requires a manifestation in the social world, convincing other people that they are members of this group.

Transgender YouTuber, Blaire White in a 2018 debate with Ben Shapiro, Esq. claimed adoptive parents do not biologically beget or bear offspring, yet, society would not doubt adoptive parents are parents (B. White 2018). An adoptive parent takes the role socially as a child's parent. In contrast to the psychological or personal approach, the social theory focuses on relationships. Social gender theory is not about the feeling of being a parent, a concept unmeasured and unobserved. For example, suppose a woman felt like a parent because she treated a doll as a human baby. In this situation, a doll-mother is a parent personally, but not biologically or socially. Although society often tolerates this language, laws, rituals, or culture do not encourage these practices.

Juxtaposed to the woman with a baby doll would be the exceedingly rare exception that someone would disagree with the premise that *an adoptive parent is a parent.* Biological and adoptive parents act in the same way. Parents raising their biological children is the same performance as adoptive parents; therefore, both rightly deserve to be called parents. Using the Aristotelian language, an adoptive parent is formally a parent but not an efficient parent. The person is a parent in action and intention but not the material cause of the child's existence. The act of parenting a doll is substantially different and, therefore, not considered parenthood formally or efficiently.

The social gender theory can also be a tool for the benefit of gender dysphoric individuals. Suppose a person with early-onset gender dysphoria finds psychic easing by being perceived as a member of a particular sex. It is the social gender theory that is more relied upon than the personal and biological theories. Many transmedicalists know they cannot change biological aspects of their sex regardless of the surgeon's skill or the hormones they receive. However, they find ease and comfort by being perceived as a member of the opposite sex.

MtF transgender YouTuber Rose of Dawn (Transmedicalist) asserts, *"You don't change biology when you transition. You do everything you can to fit into that biology and make yourself as comfortable as possible"* (Rose of Dawn 2019). Although transmedicalists often recognize this reality, differentiating between a social transition and a biological one is a distinction silenced by the media and social media platforms. For example, Rose of Dawn claims Twitter banned other MtF gender dysphoric individuals for claiming they (themselves) were still biological males (Rose of Dawn 2019).

Feminist insights

For gender, Dr. Witt does not categorize females as women because of a purely biological deduction; instead, she considers how women perceive themselves and how they exist within society. If two categories are the most universal in humans, they are categories of man and woman. Many categories define people in society, but Dr. Witt claims the *"mega essential social role"* is gender (Witt 2011, 80). Even if one wanted to deny having a gender, society constantly would remind individuals of their sex. Transmedicalist may agree with Dr. Witt, being perceived socially as a member of a particular gender is more important than the biological transformation when relieving dysphoria. Blaire White, as an example, transitioned as an MtF individual socially but is not orchiectomized. She does not deny her biological reality, but her surgeries and hormones are only an attempt to socially transition her into womanhood.

Dr. Witt's metaphysics of gender aligns itself with the concept of being socially a woman. A transsexual person who passes socially as a woman may have all the socially acceptable appearances of a woman, long hair, breasts, no Adam's apple, lower hairline, makeup, female clothing, softer voice, et cetera. Transgender MtF individuals often imitated these characteristics to a comical degree when first *"coming out"* to *"pass"* as women but eventually adopt a more neutral presentation. This persona is a uniform they put on to become a social member of a particular sex. Proponents of personal gender theory, like nonbinary people with glitter beards, often refuse to put on that uniform yet demand recognition as a member of the female class. In contrast, interlocutors from social gender theory claim one must ascribe to the social contract to become a member of a gender class.

Voluntarism is the theory that gender is in no way determinative and is something out of which people can reject. Another term is non-ascriptivist which states a woman is not held to the standards of her sex if she does not ascribe to them. The woman herself must make the decision. Dr. Witt, who ascribes to the social gender theory, rejects both the non-ascriptivist and voluntarist claims. The document *Male and Female He Created Them* follows the same distrust for voluntarism, stating, *"This combination of physicalism and voluntarism gives rise to relativism"* (Congregation for Catholic Education 2019, sec. 20).

Humans are born, and social gender norms frame everything a child does from the earliest moments of life. These norms are so ingrained that if a woman rejects the social norms, she cannot honestly claim that she is not still affected by them. A woman cannot voluntarily opt out of her experience of being treated as a woman. A woman who does not follow gender social norms will still suffer social consequences for violating social norms; therefore, sex is *"ascriptive"* (Witt 2011, 43). Dr. Witt claims gender forms how men and women interact with the social world, and no matter how much a woman tries to reject her sex, society will not allow her.

In contrast to this social understanding of womanhood, second-wave feminists claim one cannot assume a gender later in life. Using the social model, an MtF individual might feel like a woman, but one cannot understand what it feels like to be a woman if one did not grow up experiencing what it was like being a young girl. Janice Raymond, Ph.D., similarly claimed, *"To deny that female history is, in part, based on female biology is like denying that important aspects of Black history are based on skin color."* (Raymond 1994, xx). A criticism of autogynephilic individuals is that they claim to be women, but they cannot help but act like men when entering women's spaces.

The male privilege of being seen and heard by women and other men continues after medically transitioning. One cannot quickly abandon one's socialization and life-long maleness, even when one desires to be a woman and believes he is a woman. As an example, MtF individual Zoey Tur, during a debate with Ben Shapiro, J.D., leaned over, look him in the eye, calmly threatened to send him home by ambulance if he misgendered her again (Tur 2015). The nature of this threat of violence is a socialized male behavior.

As an adult, one could be a woman in the conventional social imitation of the Western ideal of femininity, but this is what the Gender Critical feminist Germaine Greer, Ph.D. (1939–), calls *"fake femaleness."* She claims, *"Femininity is the fake version of femaleness. Female is real, and it's sex; femininity is unreal, and it's gender. It's a role you play and for that to become the given identity of women is a profoundly disabling notion"* (Greer 2018).

Dr. Greer claims an authentic woman is not about breasts and perfectly soft skin, as Western society asserts in its commercial marketing. The Pontifical Council agrees with Dr. Greer's stance that femininity is betrayed in gender when gender detaches itself from the reality of one's sex. Here the document *Women Culture: Equality and Difference* would coincide in part with Dr. Greer,

> The physicality of women–which makes the world alive, long-living, able to extend itself–finds in the womb its greatest expression. The body of the woman is the starting point for each

human person. If the body is the place of the truth of the feminine self, in the indispensable mixture of culture and biology, it is also the place of the *"betrayal"* of this truth. (*Women Culture: Equality and Difference,* 5)

Does the church have an alternative narrative?

In Persona Humana, the Congregation for the Doctrine of the Faith (CDF) states, "In fact, it is from [their] sex that the human person receives the characteristics which, on the biological, psychological and spiritual levels, make that person a man or a woman, and thereby largely condition his or her progress towards maturity and insertion into society" (Congregation for the Doctrine of the Faith 1975, paragraph 1). Thus, the CDF unites the theories of biological, psychological, spiritual, and social. This unitive theory holds all of these elements together in the reality of sex. As the heresy of partialism falsely divides God's nature into artificial categories and roles, human partialism artificially divides the persona humana into disunified psyches, bodies, and spirits. Pope Benedict XVI warned of this nominalist non-ascriptive rationality as a *"new philosophy of sexuality... [where sex is] no longer a given element of nature [but rather] a social role that we choose for ourselves"* (Benedict XVI 2012).

The church rejects men and women being sexless beings like angels, a concept promulgated by Tertullian in his teachings on the afterlife. Tertullian wrote, *"I am classed with angels—not a male angel, nor a female one. There will be no one to do aught against me, nor will they find any male energy in me"* (Tertullian, *Adversus Valentinianos,* sec. 32. 5). Consequently, Rachel Anne Williams and nominalist gender theorists would find themselves at home in the gender theory of Tertullian.

Apart from Tertullian, the church fathers condemned this bodiless theology, which resembled Gnosticism's unison of voice. St. Augustine called this first-millennium gender theory *"astonishing madness!"* (Augustine, *Monachorum,* sec. 32) St. John Chrysostom called this the *"Devil's work...[castration] injures God's creation and allows men to fall into sin"* (Chrysostom, *Homily XXXV* on Gen. 14). St. Ambrose claimed, *"The Church gathers those who conquer, not those who are defeated"* (Ambrose, *De viduis,* sec. 13.75–77). St. Basil responded to the clerical eunuch as one *"damned by the knife and that although he is chaste, his chastity will go unrewarded"* (Ringrose 2004, 116).

The church is familiar with experimental gender theories. The councils have embedded these experiments into the *memoria* of the church. In the first century, *"Holy men dreamt of being castrated angels"* (Tougher 2004, 94). In this period, castrated men grew their hair long to accentuate the renunciation of their masculinity. They showed their shame as pride. Women likewise uncovered their heads to renounce their femininity and their new identity in Christ. Early Christian clergy, with the zeal of the Gospel, castrated themselves to be servants of Christ. During the early church, other clergy committed suicide to show their faith in the afterlife and rapidly enter heaven. The church responded by condemning suicide and castration as a sin against creation. The First Council of Nicaea (325 AD), which established the Creed, also forbade all bodily mutilations. The first canon states,

> If anyone in sickness has been subjected by physicians to a surgical operation, or if he has been castrated by barbarians, let him remain among the clergy; but, if anyone in sound health has castrated himself, it behooves that such a one, if [already] enrolled among the clergy, should cease [from his ministry], and that from henceforth no such person should be promoted. (The Canons of the First Council of Nicaea, Canon 1)

The first canon of the First Council of Nicaea condemns self-castration, a four-century gender theory. The Council of Nicaea's declaration is relevant to address the non-binary ideology, but this canon is not didactic when considering gender dysphoric people. In contrast, the first canon acknowledges anyone who in *"sickness has been subjected by physicians to a surgical operation… let him remain among the clergy."* This decree is not against medical castration for therapeutic purposes but only those who do so because of a false ideology of the human body. Surgical operations as a means of restoring the totality of a person would be acceptable, even for the clergy.

In contrast, gender theorists advocating that being non-binary is a type of enlightened virtue is synonymous with clergy self-castrating to obtain holiness. Holiness and enlightened virtue result from charity put into practice and not within the body's flesh. *Circumcise your hearts, not your foreskin* (Deut. 10:16).

The church is also not naive to the effects of visual and narrative-based propaganda. Right-wing Christian movements are tempted to fight transgender propaganda with cisgender hyper-heterosexual propaganda. Instead, the Catholic Church presents a better option; she shares her depository of thousands of saints of every age, nationality, and race. These saints include married people, celibates, virgins, widows and widowers, and people of every complexity level. The lives of the saints reveal the underdog spirit of the persecuted minority. Their sacrifices become virtues and a display of integrity.

The church freely exemplifies her own role models for youth, which helps create a cosmology for their own lives while steering clear of an ideology that, at times, is tragic and lacks hope. Unfortunately, the church is yet to find a way to incorporate LGBT young adults into the universal church. A 2015 study showed that LGBT youth who *"mature in religious contexts have higher odds of suicidal thoughts, and more specifically 'chronic suicidal thoughts,' as well as suicide attempts compared to other LGBT young adults"* (Gibbs and Goldbach 2015, 472). When the fruit of religious experience is committing suicide, one can reasonably conclude the religious *praxis* has failed, but the following nominalist gender ideology is also failing. The seeds of the Gospel fall among the briars, and the birds eat them; yet, authentic discipleship will cultivate a space for fruitfulness.

2.5 GENDER VARIANCE

G ender nonconformity, as understood by Western society, is not a recent phenomenon and cannot be reduced to a passing liberal fad. Catholic missionaries from the colonial era recorded other gender-nonconforming social structures among non-European peoples. Some gender non-conforming people may be intersex, others transgender, and others homosexual—these distinctions are not always clear. What do examples of these practices confirm? The point is unclear since one cannot defend the ahistorical maxim that non-European cultures are better, more humane, or more ethical than many European cultures. In many cases, human sacrifice and ritualized orgies were still present during colonialism, suggesting modern people should not blindly copy ancient traditions.

In 2018, archeologists discovered the ritually sacrificed remains of more than 140 children in the Chimú Empire before the colonial conquests (Romey 2018). History does not support the romantic view of a pre-colonial utopia. Being familiar with these other cultures and practices is advantageous because they are part of the non-binary narrative, which asserts that being transgender is not a trend but an original approach to sexuality free from colonization.

In contrast to this claim of an uncolonized utopia, Pope Francis refers to nominalist gender theories as *"ideological colonization that destroys"* (San Martín 2016). Despite notable examples of sexual abnormality outside the Western Christian world, the binary model is also widely supported. In the 2008 *Journal of Personality and Social Psychology*, Dr. David Schmitt reported data from fifty-five countries revealing women tend to be more agreeable, conscientious, nurturing, cautious, and neurotic while men are usually more competitive and risk-taking (Schmitt et al. 2008, 172). Looking for homogeneity would require investigating people's entire life cycles and cultures and not just snapshots taken out of context. In most cases, cultures are more similar than dissimilar. If Dr. Schmitt is correct, then advancing nominative gender theory constitutes colonization rather than decolonization.

The last part of this section includes the United States, an exception to the older cultures listed in this section. The United States is a tribal nation, not just in its indigenous cultures but also in present-day politics. Some parts of the United States are deeply conservative, whereas other parts are wildly liberal. The recent data shows no correlation between the number of people who consider themselves transgender and the cultural liberality of an area.

This data, along with the other accounts, presents a perspective that gender non-conformity is not new or isolated. In addition, these narratives illustrate how other cultures have successfully woven gender outcasts into their religious and social fabric. The normative consequence of this exploration is not clear but worthy of a cursory investigation.

American Two-Spirit and Machi

In the sixteenth century, Spanish missionaries, along with the conquistadors, were *"outraged by widespread homosexuality and transvestitism they found to be so prevalent among the Native peoples"* (Taylor 1996, 17). Timothy Taylor, Ph.D., in his book, *The pre-history of sex: Four million years of human sexual culture,* claims that the colonizers *"systematically destroyed sculptures, jewelry, and monuments that depicted and celebrated such practices"* (Taylor 1996, 17) although one may ask how he would be aware of this when someone deliberately destroyed the evidence 500 years ago.

Although Dr. Taylor's account of the destruction of taboo art may lack evidence, a similar history of widespread homosexuality and transgender identities made by French Jesuits gives credence to his statements about gender variation within these societies. For example, observations were made and documented of a group of tribal members in the Great Plains called the *Berdache,* a term most literally translated, *"young prostitute."* In the 1990s, the title *Berdache* was exchanged for two-spirit or *wergern* to avoid the negative connotation of prostitution. Nevertheless, they held a prominent role within society, according to Fr. Jacques Marquette, S.J.:

[Mahu]

> Through what superstition I know not, some Illinois as well as some Nadouessi; while yet young, assume female dress and keep it all their life. There is a mystery about it, for they never marry and glory in debasing themselves to do all that women do, yet they go to war, though not allowed to use a bow and arrow, only a club. They are permitted to sing but not to dance; they attend councils. Nothing is decided without their advice; finally, by profession of an extraordinary life, they pass for *manitous* or persons of consequence. (Shea 2015, 34)

Anthropologists recorded these activities among other tribes, such as the Choctaws and Delaware, and the tribes in Florida, the Pueblo of New Mexico, and upper Missouri's tribes. (Carr 1883, 33). Jesuit priest Pierre François Xavier de Charlevoix, in his letters to Duchess of Lesdiguières, surmised this activity to be part of the religious rituals of the tribes which reserved certain men for this place within society (Charlevoix 1851, 213). However, Fr. Charlevoix makes no speculation whether this commission was voluntary or predetermined.

The *machi* in tribal South America showed the same observations in the *Mapuche* indigenous groups near Chile and Argentina. The *machi* have a highly religious and ritualized purpose within their society (Vincent and Manzano 2017, 24).

Hawaiian Mahu

In Hawaii, the *Mahu* are the Polynesian equivalent to the two-spirit people. The Polynesian cultures also consider this role within society to be religious, as an embodiment of spiritual duality. Still, the *Mahu* has a unique position within society, often as caretakers of children given their virtues of being compassionate and creative. The entire Polynesian culture attempts to embody some element of this spiritual duality. Names in Polynesian culture are not gendered as in western culture so that a man may have the same name as a woman. When addressing homosexuality, intersex, or transsexualism, the Hawaiians have the myth, *"Sometimes Mother Nature cannot make up her mind, whether to make a man or a woman, even in Polynesia, so she mixes up a little of the male with some of the female element"* (Robertson 1989, 313). This idea of being comprised of mixed elements is reminiscent of Aristotle's interpretation of intersex people. Aristotle taught that congenital disorders occur when a woman produces too much material to make

94

one person but not enough material to make two people; consequently, a child is born with extra parts or both sets of sexes. In Polynesian cultures, this is considered natural and a benefit for society.

Kathoey and Toms

Asian societies include gender variant people in various ways throughout their cultures. Thailand boasts *kathoey* and *toms,* while Indonesia includes *waria* (Vincent and Manzano 2017, 11). The *kathoey* are sometimes referred to as *'ladyboys,'* although some *kathoey* take offense to the term since cis men use it pejoratively to identify them as sex workers. *Toms* are natal females who present as men. *Toms* usually date more feminine women. *Toms* often identify as lesbians or transgender men (Erickson-Schroth and Jacobs 2017, 125). The term *waria* originates from the words *wantia* (woman) and *pria* (man). In the 1820s, westerners called them *"transvestite performers,"* and by the 1960s were primarily renowned as sex workers (Boellstorff 2004, 164).

Men who dress like women play an essential role in the Burmese's religious life. The Western concept of physically changing one's body through surgery to match the gender expression would be foreign in cultures that embrace the sanctity of the paradox (Coleman, Colgan, and Gooren 1992, 313). The *Kama Sutra* dedicated a chapter to eunuch courtesans, including two kinds of eunuchs who appeared like men and others who imitated women. Men who act as females *"imitate their dress, speech, gestures, tenderness, timidity, simplicity, softness and bashfulness"* (Vatsyayana 1961, IX). Within this Indian culture, male and female transsexuals were sexually active as courtesans, seducing their partners with sexual nonconformity.

Indian Kinner

Likewise, the *Hirjas,* or as they prefer to be called in India, the *Kinner,* the mythological beings who excel at song and dance, are famous for their transgender identities. They comprise an essential part of Indian culture while remaining taboo and not discussed within proper society. An estimated 5 to 6 million *Kinners* live in India, with only an 8% rate of castration (Swain 2006, 57). In India's subcontinent, they are officially recognized as a third sex, being neither man nor woman. Within their cultures, they bring good luck to newlyweds, but some accuse them of being kidnappers. They show up to weddings without invitation and dance, performing unusual gestures and jeering at guests. Finally, the wedding party pays them to leave (Jaffrey 1996, 73).

Iran

After Thailand, Iran has the highest rate of sex reassignment surgeries worldwide (Barford 2008). If liberality were the singular cause for transgender surgeries, Iran would not have the second-highest sex reassignment surgery rate. One probable reason for the high number of surgeries in Iran may be because homosexuality is punishable by death. The 1979 fatwa instituted by Iran's revolutionary leader Ayatollah Khomeini legalized intersex surgeries without necessitating any physical defect. The Iranian government provides grants of $1,240 and loans up to $1,500 to help pay for the surgeries (The United States Department of State 2017, 43). Hojatol Islam Muhammad Mehdi Kariminia, the religious cleric responsible for gender reassignment surgeries in an interview with the BBC, asserted,

> The discussion is fundamentally separate from a discussion regarding homosexuals. Absolutely not related. Homosexuals are doing something unnatural and against religion. Our Islamic law clearly states that such behaviour is not allowed because it disrupts the social order. (Barford 2008)

The *United States Department of State*, in a 2017 report, affirmed this claim stating, *"authorities pressured LGBTI persons to undergo gender reassignment surgery"* (The United States Department of State 2017, 43). Clerics can pressure feminine males to accept sex reassignment surgery—to act feminine without consequences and to be able to marry a man. The social component of this is challenging, as well. Families do not rejoice when their sons become women, and the young person becomes isolated. Communities of transsexuals come together and often survive by becoming prostitutes. FtM individuals could exist in theory, although it appears to be exceedingly rare.

[Kinner]

Italian Castrati

Despite the condemnation of the practice of castration by the church to become like holy angels, castration remained an essential part of Italian dioceses for centuries until 1870, when outlawed by secular authorities. The *castrati* reached the height between 1650 and 1750, holding the necessary theatre, opera, and church choirs. Frequently the castrati came from orphaned children of the Italian peninsula. During the eighteenth century, 4,000 castrati operations were recorded (Barbier 1996, 11). The last Roman castrati, Alessandro Moreschi, *Direttore dei concertisti* (Director of soloists) of the Sistine Chapel Choir, died in 1922.

Contemporary USA

Within the United States, the prevalence of transgender people would not be what many expect. Data does not support the presumption that transgender issues affect primarily middle and upper-middle-class people in liberal states. In the Williams Institute 2016 report (Flores et al. 2016), 0.58% of the country identifies as transgender. Conservative states outnumber liberal states when looking at per-capita averages of people who identify as transgender, see figure 2.8.

Besides Vermont, no other state from socially liberal New England is above the national average. Based on Polynesian culture without sex discrimination, Hawaii maintains a 0.03% difference with Georgia, a moderately conservative state. Of the top ten most conservative states identified by a 2017 Gallup Poll (Newport 2017), five of them have higher than average rates of people who self-identify as transgender. Of the ten most liberal states, only five have higher than average rates of people who identify as transgender. Conservative and liberal cultures may affect people's identity, but not significant enough to show liberal causation for transgender issues as a trend.

States above the national average	Percentage (Nat. Avg. 0.58 %)
Hawaii	0.78
California	0.76
Georgia	0.75
New Mexico	0.75
Texas	0.66
Florida	0.66
Oregon	0.65
Oklahoma	0.64
Deleware	0.64
Tennesee	0.63
Washington	0.62
Arizona	0.62
Mississippi	0.61
Nevada	0.61
Alabama	0.61
Arkansas	0.6
Louisiana	0.6
North Carolina	0.6
Vermont	0.59
Minnesotta	0.59

Figure 2.8 States with above-average rates of people who identify as transgender. Grey boxes are considered conservative states, according to World Population Review 2021 data. The bold print identifies states which are in the top ten most liberal or conservative states.

According to a Playboy magazine report, 25% of the 5,000 British men surveyed claimed to have cross-dressed at some point in their lives, and 8% claim to do so weekly (Ettner 1999, 28). Thus, gender variation within cultures is a principal element when considering the transgender phenomenon. However, even in a culture like Great Britain, with no history of cross-dressing, no religious traditions of gender variation, or any notable trans-trending before the twentieth century, men are still interested in experimenting with femininity in publicly taboo ways.

Small communities of transgender people find a place within societies throughout the world. Whether they are part of Babylonian priesthood, Indian courtesanship, or a Roman choir, there is a place for this sexual outcast. Another sign of the universality of transgender identities is their prevalence worldwide despite the negative consequences one faces for being a transgender person. Cases of people seeking transsexual surgeries exist in the USA, Canada, Sweden, Netherlands, Singapore, China, Germany, France, Southeast Asia, Japan, East Africa, et cetera. The near-universal occurrence of transgender subcultures suggests an innate explanation is more likely than a cultural one. Their roles may differ from culture to culture, but their existence appears widely prevalent. These individuals are universally rare and seen as atypical, which is likely why they hold sacred and taboo roles within their cultures. Western Christian cultures now need to discern what vocations are encouraged for people with atypical gender expressions.

2.6 Human Nature

Aristotle in the *Rhetoric* also claims the *"law of nature"* or the *"common law"* is an eternal, immutable principle (Aristotle, *Rhetoric* 1373b2–8). Personal identity is deeply rooted in this law of natural biology, but this is not solely biological, as Pope Francis remarked in his apostolic exhortation, The Joy of Love (*Amoris Laetitia*),

> The configuration of our one mode of being, whether as male or female, is not simply the result of biological or genetic factors, but of multiple elements having to do with temperament, family history, culture, experience, education, the influence of friends, family members and respected persons, as well as other formative situations. (Francis 2016, sec. 286)

Human biology and sex are united. Nevertheless, overemphasizing biology is to fall into genetic predestination, whereby biology eliminates free will. Now human nature is not just guided by the natural law but is also contained in free will. Human free will exists in a fallen state, yet Adam and Eve had absolute freedom to voluntarily follow the serpent or God. As sinless humans, they had no passions or concupiscence. In short, they had no bad habits. Although adult humans are free, they carry the baggage of habits created in their youth and the fall. Original sin is inherent to the nature of humanity. Although original sin may not be a popular topic in the modern world, its effects explain many of our most profound problems.

One cannot understand human nature illuminated by Scripture without contrasting the two vastly different realities found between chapters two and three in the Book of Genesis. In the first instance, *"The man and his wife were both naked, yet they felt no shame" (Gn 2:25 NAB) and then only a few verses later, "I heard you in the garden; but I was afraid, because I was naked, so I hid"* (Gn 3:10 NAB). Thus, there was no shame at first, and in the second, *I was afraid because I was naked, so I hid.* These events stand on either side of the fall of man: prelapsarian innocence vs. postlapsarian shame.

St. Thomas (*ST* IIa–IIae q. 164, a. 2) claimed that the punishment of original sin includes three universal parts.[7] First, the confusion they experienced as a rebellion of the flesh leads to embarrassment and confusion about the body. As stated in Genesis chapter 3, *"They perceived themselves to be naked."* Second, by the reproach of their sin, they are burdened with the knowledge of good and evil. Whereas other animals follow their nature instinctually and involuntarily, humanity must voluntarily follow what is rational (*ST* Ia–IIae q. 91, a. 2, ad 3). Third, man is aware of death's proximity, which leads to an existential crisis about the meaning of life and matters of faith. Humanity is constantly aware *"Dust thou art and into dust thou shalt return."* A combination of anxiety over shame, confusion about life, free will concerning how to live, and fear of mortality leads humanity into a personal psychological dystopia. People find peace in submitting to God's will rather than one's ego.

In the *Theology of the Body*, John Paul II focuses on original sin, describing the shame of Adam and Eve, *"Thus shame is not only one of man's original experiences, but is also a 'boundary' experience"* (John Paul II 2006, sec. 172). The pontiff explains that this boundary is not a transition from *"not knowing"* to *"knowing"* about nakedness as a form of *gnosis*; instead, this knowledge changes the relationship between men and women. Carnal knowledge is the nakedness of man before woman and woman before man. John Paul II creates a challenge for Christians, *"we must ask ourselves whether we can in some way reconstruct the original meaning of nakedness"* (John Paul II 2006, sec. 173). Can man, now after the resurrection of Christ, be redeemed in his fallen nature to stand naked before woman, with no shame? Sex, in a covenantal bond of love and with the original unity restored, in union with the Trinity, in the *imago Dei:* man and woman standing before God and one another with no shame.

The restless heart

Catholics believe the normativity of creation is ingrained in every cell of the human body. St. James describes this when he writes, *"But everyone who gazes into The Perfect Law of Liberty and continues in it, he is not a hearer who heard what is forgotten but is a doer of the works, and this one shall be*

---

[7] In addition to six special punishments which are sex specific.

blessed in his work" (Jas 1: 25 ABPE). Obedience to the laws of nature leads to freedom and the preservation of the human person's dignity. Pope Francis, in his first encyclical Praise Be to You (*Laudato Si'*), proclaims human ecology implies the profound reality of *"the relationship between human life and the moral law, which is inscribed in our nature and is necessary for the creation of a more dignified environment"* (Francis 2015a, sec.155)

The feelings of unsettledness are also part of this human experience. St Augustine explains this in two ways—the first is the result of original sin in the world; the second is the famous line, *"cor nostrum inquietum est donec requiescat in Te"*[8] man's destiny is heaven. The Catechism teaches,

> Because man is a composite being, spirit and body, there already exists a certain tension in him; a certain struggle of tendencies between *'spirit'* and *'flesh'* develops. But in fact, this struggle belongs to the heritage of sin. It is a consequence of sin and, at the same time, a confirmation of it. It is part of the daily experience of the spiritual battle. (*CCC*, 2516)

Dr. Raymond acknowledges this and calls feelings of transgender *"gender dissatisfaction,"* a term she uses 257 times in her book *The Transsexual Empire*. However, to be at odds with our body is not necessarily a sign of being transgender but a sign of being human. Christians have recognized this division between heart and body for millennia. However, St. Thomas wrote, man possesses an immortal soul, and since the fall of his first parents, his body is moral. This paradox means man is *composed of contraries:* he is aware he is called to eternity and will die a natural death (*ST* IIa–IIae q. 164, a. 1, ad 1). Man divided is restless indeed.

A principal element of Catholic epistemology and ethics reflects the normativity of creation. Br. Jacques Maritain, P.F.J., describes the ontological element of the normativity of creation as an out-of-tune piano. By ontological, he means the *"normality of functioning, which is grounded in the essence of that being"* (Maritain 2001, 29). The piano must be either tuned or thrown out since a piano that cannot make the

---

[8] You have made us for yourself, and our hearts are restless until they rest in You (Augustine *The Confessions*, chap. 1).

proper notes violates its ontology. Humans endowed with intelligence can discover their true nature. Br. Maritain explains, *"This means that there is, by the very virtue of human nature, an order or a disposition which human reason can discover and according to which the human will must act in order to attune itself to the essential and necessary ends of the human being"* (Maritain 2001, 27).

Everything expresses a natural way of functioning, which, if put into action, is beautiful and gives joy. A genuine understanding of nature and freedom establishes the proper understanding of the normativity of creation. Joseph Cardinal Ratzinger writes in The Gift of Life (*Donum Vitae*), *"The natural moral law expresses and lays down the purposes, rights and duties which are based upon the bodily and spiritual nature of the human person"* (Ratzinger 1987, sec. 3). The restless heart finds its home in the natural law, found within the recesses of a person's human nature.

How didactic is the normativity of creation?

The church's focus on nature can often become misused by individuals who overgeneralize nature's didactic elements. Like a preacher who tries to win an argument with the trump phrase, *"The Bible says..."* Catholics are sometimes guilty of the same appeal to authority with the line, *"Natural law says..."* or *"It is clear from looking at nature that..."*. Nature is not clear about very much. However, despite the shortcomings of nature as a source of human ethics, applied carefully as, with proper exegetical Bible study, this process may help give insights into the meanings behind being a man, woman, or human. Moreover, Br. Maritain highlights the unknowingness of creation's normativity, or what he calls *"gnoseological elements."* He refers to the *Summa Theologica* (*ST* IIa–IIae q. 45, a. 2) where St. Thomas calls this, *"Knowledge by inclination .... [which is] knowledge that is not clear, like that obtained through concepts and conceptual judgments."* Br. Maritain explains, *"All this leads to a judgment—not to a judgment based on concepts, but to the judgement which expresses simply the conformity of reason to tendencies to which it is inclined"* (Maritain 2001, 35). This normativity of creation is not *a priori* knowledge but insights through inclinations. The normativity of creation gives greater insights and sets up dynamic schemes of how life works in the natural world. Through natural inclinations, divine patterns inscribe normativity upon human reason.

Is humanity chained to nature?

Although human's common ancestry does not enslave humanity, Fr. Ashley wrote, *"The mark of civilization is that we 'naked apes' put on clothes, but although we might cover our bodies, we could not improve them. Our bodies remained the same archaic, savage bodies that evolution has given us"* (Ashley 1985, 6). This normativity of creation perspective is in contrast with nineteenth and twentieth-century thinkers like Karl Marx, who wrote,

> Man is now God because he creates himself—he makes his own essence, and he also decides what values will be placed upon his life and his actions and even upon the life and actions of others. He is God, but a God chained; he is condemned to make these decisions. He has not chosen to play God, and yet no matter what he does, he cannot escape his role. (Marx 1975, 305–306)

At first, it sounds as if Karl Marx promotes an anthropological arrogance—almost like Lucifer's pride against the heavens—but the latter identifies the tragic reality of human life. Karl Marx echoes the writings of Milton or Dante: *man is a chained God, condemned.* Marx could be describing original sin and the *"unreality of nature and of man"* (Marx 1975, 305–306), but the Christian theology of grace and the redemption of nature and man by Jesus's incarnation and resurrection, liberates both from the chains of being a (false) God.

The consequence of this personal identity ideology for John Paul II in The Splendor of the Truth (*Veritatis Splendor*) is *"when all is said and done man would not even have nature; he would be his own personal life-project"* (John Paul II 1993, 46). Naturally, proponents of the non-cognitive and non-ascriptivist schools of thought would rejoice in having a *"personal life-project"* rather than a nature. Nevertheless, this personal life project is imprisonment, chained to the limitations of one's ego.

Jean-Paul Sartre, a humanist existentialist, likewise shares views of human destiny with Karl Marx, writing a cynical view of nature,

> Man, the creator and recreator of his own and all human life, the creator of meaning and values, the only factor actively managing history, increasingly conquering an existing situation to his objectivization, is man's future, as well as his immediate present.

> Man is man's problem, but he is also his neighbor and brother. (Sartre 1965, 139)

The reader can mistakenly take this Sartrian/Marxist view out of context to support a triumphalist anthropology of man as the singular creator of his destiny, which implies nature no longer applies to man. This perspective also means man is not bound to normative ethics of nature but only accountable to his individuality. Like Karl Marx, this interpretation of Jean-Paul Sartre would miss their writings' tragic tone. Modern people claim to be free from the constraints of nature, but this has led to their *objectification*. People are liberated from nature, freed from being a *naked ape*, only to be enslaved by social constructions.

Does enmity with nature create a dystopia?

Fr. Ashley, reflecting on the dystopian relationship between man and technology in Jacques Ellul's book *The Technological Society* (1965), describes the modern person's tragic but familiar vision. Fr. Ashley describes:

> Our advance in technology control has not been matched by social and ethical control, so that technology, instead of liberating, is more and more enslaving us through environmental pollution, the *"population explosion," "the energy crisis,"* iatrogenic disease, totalitarian social domination, and the threat of nuclear obliteration. Perhaps the new definition of the human being should be not *"the animal who creates itself,"* but *"the animal who self-destructs."* (Ashley 1985, 7)

In response to this dystopia, Fr. Ashley does not argue that men should return to primal states of existence. In his praise of the noble savage and the natural state, not even Jean-Jacques Rousseau recommended society go backward since this is undeniably impossible. Time only travels in one direction. Nevertheless, humans can capitalize on their natural properties, *ratio entis*, creativity, sociability, and, importantly, risibility. In general, dysphoria would decrease if people laughed more. Humanists and Christians alike can agree upon these common human traits built upon human nature.

Br. Maritain, in 1936, warned about pseudo-realism, which creates a dystopia of science and technology. He writes, *"It, too, in practice, denies that man is a creature of God, but this is because it does not wish to recognize that which comes from nothingness is man."* Br. Maritain continues, *"but from the moment they have taken apart with the powers of darkness and have renounced nature, they have become strangers to the values connoted by the name of man"* (Maritain 1968, 227).

When reflecting upon transgender issues and the normativity of creation, immediately, some concerns become apparent. Hormone blockers, opposite-sex hormone supplements, and surgical procedures are not natural. Whether the feelings of gender dysphoria are natural requires practitioners of the normativity of creation to listen deeply to transgender people's experiences. As Br. Maritain observed, humans attempt to comprehend the normativity of creation but can find themselves in trouble when they assume they grasped it without the humility to keep listening. Nature points towards the divine will, which should be followed not as an absolute commandment but as a guide.

How does human nature lead to solitude?

The most notable advocate of the link between sex and gender was John Paul II's *Theology of the Body*. The pontiff developed a vigorous philosophical and theological anthropology which dramatically influences the Catholic interpretation of morality and ethics. John Paul II began his treatise of the *Theology of the Body* by introducing humanity's complementarity and solitude. In his exegesis of Genesis, *"The man gave names to all the tame animals, all the birds of the air, and all the wild animals; but none proved to be a helper suited to the man"* (Gen. 2:20 NAB). The pope raises the concept of the *proximate genus* and *specific differentia,* using the anthropology of Aristotle. The *proximate genus* groups together similar beings, while the *specific differentia* notices the ways in which beings are different from one another (John Paul II 2006, sec. 149 n.10). With man understood as a *ratio entis*—a rational being—the *proximate genus* is *"being,"* which makes humanity like every other animal or substance. Rationality is man's *specific differentia,* the quality of being that distinguishes man from other living beings. This *specific differentia* makes him a solitary being in the world, *but none proved to be a helper suited to the man.*

[Br. Jacques Maritain, P.F.J., 1882—1973]

God responds to man's isolation stating, *"It is not good for the man to be alone. I will make a helper suited to him"* (Gn 2:18 NAB). The man looked to all the species of the earth and concluded he was alone. He was a *"body among bodies"* in his *proximate genus,* but he was alone as a rational being. God is the other *ratio entis;* God is man's *proximate genus* and no other. This theological mystery points to an anthropological reality; God made the man a partner of Himself alone. Through his humanity, John Paul II concludes that man is alone, but at the same time, *"set into a unique, exclusive, and unrepeatable relationship with God himself"* (John Paul II 2006, sec. 151). People's feelings of loneliness are part of the divine plan to draw humanity into Himself. Either one can disappear down the rabbit hole looking for meaning or look up to the heavens in *beatitudo.*

Man's solitude led to his subjectivity and self-knowledge. As a result, man becomes aware of his own body in his search for communion. John Paul II states, *"that division of solitude through which man has from the beginning in the visible world as a body among bodies and discovers the meaning of his own bodiliness"* (John Paul II 2006, sec. 153). God's response is to divide man into male and female. Using the theology of St. Theresa Benedicta of the Cross, John Paul II echoes her theology of two paths for one ontology. He writes this is *"based on masculinity and femininity, which are, as it were, two different "incarnations," that is, two ways in which the same human being, created "in the image of God (Gn 1:27), is a body"* (John Paul II 2006, sec. 157). Anthropologically, what does this mean? First, man's ontological essence is the human being. Secondly, one is either male or female through a necessary accident or property of the essence. Ultimately, the purpose of this creation is to draw the person into divine unity, from *solitudo* to *communio,* not despite one's body but through it.

2.7 EPISTEMOLOGY

Biological and cultural factors contribute to the transgender issue as well as epistemic considerations. Pope Francis wrote in his post-synodal apostolic exhortation, The Joy of Love (*Amoris Laetitia*), *"To show understanding in the face of exceptional situations never implies dimming the light of the fuller ideal, or proposing less than what Jesus offers to the human being"* (Francis 2016, 307). Truth illuminates the mind through *recta ratio* or right reason. Gender dysphoria is the *strong desire* of an individual to be received as a member of the opposite sex. This desire believes that if one were to be the other sex, the significant distress and impairment would cease. Rachel Anne Williams writes of her own experience,

> Am I a special type of man or a special type of woman? I do not know. It does not seem important to me. What matters more is self-knowledge concerning my desire to continue transitioning. I desire to keep using female pronouns, shopping [sic] in the women's section, take HRT, using [sic] the name *'Rachel,'* and so on… I am aware of my desire to keep transitioning. (R. A. Williams 2019, 184)

Rachel Anne Williams, an MtF individual, is driven by her desire more than knowledge of being a woman. In terms of self-knowledge, Rachel Anne Williams claims to be agnostic about gender. These beliefs are based on the innate feelings of being perceived as the wrong gender. Which *epistēmē* is true, one's biology (realism), or one's feelings (emotivism)?

John Paul II holds the view that gender identity must be rooted in the truth. He writes in *Acting Person, "Self-determination and the closely related self-governance often require that action be taken in the name of bare truth about the good, in the name of values that are not felt. It even may require that action be taken against one's actual feelings"* (Wojtyla 1979, 233). Therefore, when a person is experiencing gender dysphoria, one must examine their feelings by the standard of the *bare truth*. Due to humanity's fallen nature, concupiscible desires are no longer the truth. Desires, according to the pontiff, must be judged by reason since desires can deceive humanity.

The desire to be a man or woman raises the question: if one is not a woman or a man, how does one come to realize what it feels like to be a man or woman? Feeling like a man or woman is a statement of experiential knowledge that cannot be verified even subjectively, let alone by any objective criteria. For example, society would outright dismiss subjective identity statements if a white man said he profoundly understands what it is like to be a black woman. Alternatively, a person born into wealth claiming to understand what it is like to be poor or someone who does not experience loss knows what it feels like to lose a child or a spouse. This contradiction is what St. Edith Stein called the phenomenology of empathy or the primordial given. These statements are either ridiculous or offensive, but they could never be accurate according to reason.

In 2021, a self-obsessed British youth named Oli London had surgery to make himself look Korean, claiming he *was* Korean. Despite claiming to be trans-racial, Oli cannot speak Korean and Korean people have not kindly responded to the appropriation of their nationality. This false identity exemplifies Edith Stein's principle that being someone else is a metaphysical impossibility. So how do people who adopt a personal gender theory or hold a nominalist worldview reject transracial claims without proper gatekeeping? Once the floodgate is open, everyone must accept all statements of beliefs as reality. Only people who adhere to the superiority of rational realism can rightly oppose these ideological fallacies.

[Archbishop Robert Carlson, 1944—]

Epistemological need for a Creator

Modern epistemological skeptics do not trust their experience of external reality; as such, they trust their perceptions and intuitions. John Locke (1632—1704) claims, meaning requires a meaning maker, so if there is no creator, there is no creation, and all material bodies exist as a raw datum. The rejection of God by John Locke entails a negation of life's inherent value. An intentionally designed universe rationally entails natural phenomena with inherent purposes, concepts that gender theorists reject. Gender theory takes the Lockean perspective of rejecting Aristotelian kind essentialism, stating nothing is essential about being a male or female. This rejection of essentialism leads to fluidity between males and females, as well as masculinity and femininity. John Locke claimed the normativity of creation could not exist without a lawgiver; therefore, nothing is essentially true about being male or female. Second-wave feminists are particularly fond of Lockean ethics since John Locke makes no positive claims about sex and the system's foundation is a godless relativism.

Is emotivism the best epistemological approach?

Archbishop Robert Carlson of St. Louis, in his 2020 pastoral letter, *Compassion and Challenge,* addresses three tenets of modern philosophy that have made their way into gender theory:

1. Feelings define our identity: *"How you feel is who you are."*

2. Human integrity means acting on our persistent desires. *"I have to be true to myself."*

3. Anyone who does not affirm our feelings and actions hates us. (Carlson 2020, 6)

In his letter, the archbishop asserts, feelings are part of being a human person, but they do not define the individual. Feelings change, so one cannot base one's life on what one feels at the moment. The archbishop also calls for people to sift through their desires rather than follow them without proper discernment. Archbishop Carlson claims,

> For gender ideology, a feeling or desire is authentic and good if it is persistent, insistent, and consistent. But any number of examples can tell us that sinful and unhelpful desires—desires and feelings that are contrary to our identity as God's children and lead us away from

Heaven—can be persistent, insistent, and consistent. (Carlson 2020, 6)

Lastly, the archbishop stresses, love, and disagreement can co-exist and, in many ways, must exist for evangelization to occur. According to the archbishop, when Catholics and secular culture mutually disagree, only the church is labeled as hateful, but not the secular culture is hateful of the church. In his encyclical, Fraternity, and Social Friendship (*Fratelli Tutti*), As Pope Francis mentions, those who want to achieve chaos by interfering with civility are capitalizing on and promoting entrenched disagreements. Pope Francis wrote,

Political life no longer has to do with healthy debates about long-term plans to improve people's lives and advance the common good, but only with slick marketing techniques primarily aimed at discrediting others. In this craven exchange of charges and counter-charges, debate degenerates into a permanent state of disagreement and confrontation. (Francis 2020, sec. 15)

For decades feminists have been silencing men *because* they are men. With irony, feminist Posie Parker notes that women are now being silenced in women-only spaces if they disagree with the ideology that *trans women are women* (Parker 2019). As a cis woman, the gender theorists silence her for having an opinion about being a woman while not recognizing the experience of transgender women. Identity politics came full circle, substituting rational realism with emotivism. Sophists use identity politics to shut down debate, leading to an especially dangerous epistemology whereby people cannot challenge an idea unless they belong to the correct gender, race, orientation, or unique form of victimhood. Identity rather than truth becomes authoritative.

Cardinal Karol Wojtyła, in *Love and Responsibility*, writes, "*one's ability to discover the truth gives man the possibility of self-determination, of deciding for himself the character and direction of his own actions, and that is what freedom means*" (Wojtyla 1981, 115). One's self-determination is not based on one's emotions or feelings but instead based on truth. The Christian needs truth to be free and to choose a path leading to happiness. In the absence of truth, emotions and desires rule people's actions. St. Thomas advocated for *rectitudo appetitus* or a rectified appetite. This principle states, all emotions, and appetitive capacities must remain disposed to their proper teleology. The objects of emotions take possession of the individual until the individual ceases to have freedom over their actions, which is why the *rectitudo appetitus* liberates humanity through the practice of being *ratio entis*. Through the virtue of fortitude, the individual overcomes fear and the irascible appetite. In contrast, the virtue of temperance controls concupiscence and the desire for inordinate pleasures.

René Descartes'(1596–1650) *cogito ergo sum*[9] and the invention of idealism and skepticism, which rejected the exterior world's concrete reality, tore the scholastic philosophers' realism asunder, emphasizing the causality of the material universe. The *cogito* emphasizes the mind as the sole principle of truth. René Descartes's theory contains two parts: thought and externalities. The mind is thought without externalities, while matter is externalities without thought. This cogito approach greatly influences nominalist gender theory ideology, making space for the idea that the mind and body can be disjointed.

Are the body and soul unified?

The phenomenological influence in John Paul II's *Theology of the Body* recognizes the body's profound meaning. This phenomenology does not minimize the importance of the rational soul. Instead, phenomenology highlights the human person's anthropological necessity as both body and soul. The body-soul unity is the essence of the Thomistic principle of *hylomorphism*, whereby people do not merely *possess* bodies; they *are* bodies. As proposed by Cartesians, an amorphous gendered spirit would be impossible under the Thomistic approach to gender theory.

The Cartesian theory does not provide a metaphysical bridge between externalities and thought. If the mind is more valid than the body, how does the body mirror the mind's reality? How does the mind comprehend that the concrete externalities are real? Seventeenth-century Dutch philosopher Baruch Spinoza (1632–1677) solves this problem by claiming everything is spirit, and externalities do not exist (Spinoza 2001, 162–163). In the opposite direction, modern science claims there is only mechanical positivism—meaning, only the body exists and not the mind, and if the mind exists, it is the organ of the brain. The organ of the brain and the biology of the human senses are

---

[9] Descartes *Discourse on Method and Meditations on First Philosophy*, 18.

interpreting a physical reality. This latter approach leads to a materialist worldview where matter is identified only by quantifiable properties. Br. Maritain rejects both of these epistemologies, claiming, *"There is no worse philosophy than a philosophy that despises nature. A knowledge that despises what is itself nothing; a cherry between the teeth holds within it more mystery than the whole of idealistic metaphysics"* (Maritain 1959, 335). Thomistic realism, on the other hand, contains truth and profundity.

What theory is more didactic, idealism or realism?

The Realist approach considers abstraction the finality of a being. Being might be a lump of flesh, but it is also a man, a father, brother, son, or friend. The substance is more than a quantifiable piece of raw datum. Realism considers the teleology of the being. How does a realist experience the world? First, the intellect grasps the external nature, then the intellect by reflection grasps the act, and finally, the intellect by examination grasps oneself. This knowing of something is an encounter, an experience, and a relationship with the external world. This existence is individual and singular and understood through the senses, *"For sense judges of particular objects, while reason judges of universals"* (*ST Ia, q 59, a. 1, ad. 1*).

Cardinal Wojtyla similarly writes in *The Acting Person*, *"The fusion of sensitivity with truthfulness is the necessary condition of the experience of values"* (Wojtyla 1979, 233). The senses are essential as the *nucleus for crystallizing* one's experience, but the intellect integrates sensitivities with reason, expressing authentic realism. In the forward to *Thomistic Realism*, Dr. Frederick Wilhelmsen (1923–1996) explains the historical evolution of this philosophy, *"The foundations of realism is the unity of the knowing subject. This unity of sense and intellect within a knowing subject had been ruptured by the cogito; the resulting discontinuity had been accepted by Kant as a fait accompli"* (Wilhelmsen 2012, 18).

René Descartes's idealism cannot break out of its non-realism, and the logical consequences lead to Berkeley or Kant. Philosopher Ayn Rand called Kant *"the real villain of our age"* because he

> Preached that man's mind is not valid, that the things you perceive are not there. Things that you perceive are in the phenomenal world and the pneumenal world, which you cannot perceive in any way, and the (mystical) pneumenal is the true reality. (Rand 1979)

Ayn Rand claims, according to academics, *"we all must follow it based on faith in Kant, and not based on reason"* (Rand 1979). John Paul II took up the debate of the phenomenal vs. pneumenal in his understanding of *"psychosomatic"* and *"psychophysical"* unity. This integration refers to a higher level of unity than psychosomatic unity in the empirical sense (Wojtyla 1979, 191).

When using realism and idealism to consider the transgender issue, the degree to which a Neo-Thomist could understand this issue hinges on reality—something existing in the external world. If an MtF individual claims through one's impressions he is a she, this belief could be perfectly valid under the *cogito ergo sum* epistemology of René Descartes: I *think* I am a woman; therefore, *I am* a woman or rather *sentio ergo sum*—I *feel* like I am a woman; therefore, I *am* a woman. From a realist perspective, one does not start with one's impressions or intuitions but instead with the concrete reality of being which exists. How does concrete material reality manifest itself? This answer is not as straightforwardly answered for transgender people since one cannot merely look inside one's brain to extract the material reality.

[René Descartes, 1596—1650]

What does Skepticism look like
in a transgender ideology?

This pneumenal approach taken to the extreme absurdity is found in Rachel Anne Williams concept of sex and gender. She argues,

> [T]here is nothing *'male'* about a trans woman—the term *'male'* is simply not appropriate as applied to trans women. They don't have 'male' body parts because only males have male body parts, and in my view, trans women are not males but females, so any parts of the body or physical characteristic they have is only appropriately described as female.

She continues,

> Penises are not *'male'* because some women have penises. Vaginas are not 'female' because some men have vaginas. XY chromosomes are not *'male'* because some women have XY chromosomes, and some men have XX chromosomes. (R. A. Williams 2019, 174)

Rachel's position is not just the extreme position of a transgender activist. To celebrate Men's Day in 2019, the ACLU Tweeted out, *"There's no one way to be a man. Men who get their periods are men. Men who get pregnant and give birth are men. Trans and non-binary men belong. #InternationalMensDay"* (ACLU 2019). The feminine product brand *Always* responded by taking all feminine imagery off its feminine product packaging (Murphy 2019). This pneumenal theory goes as far as claiming transwomen's penises are *"girl penises"* (R. A. Williams 2019, 175). This nominalist gender theory bases its principle of gender on the concept of pneumenal gender—one's feelings are the grounds for judging reality.

To bend physical reality to accommodate a person's feelings and desires, one would call the male sex organs female sex organs. This ideology not only calls biology by the opposite names but also essentially sex-determined actions. For example, when a transman ovulates, becomes pregnant, and gives birth, he is a father under this pneumenal theory. Those opposed to this ideology are dubbed transphobic, but fear of transgender people does not drive Catholics to reject this ideology but realist-based epistemology.

What is the epistemological divide?

In his reflections in *Our Journey Home*, Jean Vanier, Ph.D., also recognized this epistemological divide in the 1990s. Dr. Vanier identifies those who wish to change the world through realism versus those trying to change the world through ideology. He recognizes these two categories:

> My experience shows me that there are two kinds of ideals: one which focuses on structures; another which is more directed towards people. The first tends to be militant, seeking to reform social structures and relying on good organization and a form of propaganda. The other stresses the importance of listening, presence, and kindness, changing one heart at a time. (Vanier 1997, 97)

These two paths have drastically different results for the people involved as well. Non-cognitive activism leads to anger and frustration since utopias are not for this world. Realism leads to peace and understanding since realism is rooted in relationships with real people. Realism accepts real people on their road to life. Dr. Vanier remarked,

> Young people who focus their energies on people tend to live closer to human reality than those who seek change through theories, structures, and a perfect way of life. The latter can quickly become ideologies that crush people instead of leading them to greater freedom, wisdom, and compassion. (Vanier 1997, 97)

Although those who seek to liberate society from oppression are noble in their liberatory goals, its non-cognitive utopian approach falls short of reality. As a result, the reader must leave the halls of academia, the echo chamber of social media, and the safe spaces designed for youth. Instead, working in a community of disabled people like *L'Arche,* establishing friendships with people in nursing homes, or becoming friends with people who are transgender or any number of other hands-on activities, meets the goals of liberation, not just for the other person, but for him or herself.

The *cogito* epistemology is not consistent with the Neo-Thomistic perspective. Many future problems concerning personal identity will fall into either of these two epistemologies: reality on one side and impressions or intuitions on the other? What if someone feels like a different animal species, a person of another race, age, et cetera? Are these feelings based on what is real, or are the feelings based on one's imagination? The Catholic approach states, the unfolding of one's life needs to be based on concrete reality and not on one's feelings alone. The reader must judge feelings with reason.

2.8 CONCEPT REVIEW

Chapter two explored the concepts of sex and gender within the context of transgender issues existing culturally, medically, and philosophically. This section also explored concepts of gender from a biological, social, and personal ideology. The church remains firm in her stance *"Because man is a composite being, spirit, and body, there already exists a certain tension in him"* (*CCC*, 2516). This tension is a result of man's *"heritage of sin."* Despite this tension, biology binds humanity to herself—her flesh and alive socially and in the spirit. Aristotle calls the unification of mind, body, and action essentialism, whereby the essence or soul causes the material or parts to become a unified whole (Witt 1989, 103). Thomistic realism ensures humans are not just material parts and disembodied spirits but are a unified whole.

Lastly, this section examined what Pope Francis means by gender theory, which is part of a *global war against the family* and *ideological colonization.* Pope Francis is not criticizing gender dysphoric people in his writings since gender dysphoria is a medical condition; instead, he raises objections to the ideology of personal gender theory. The movement of nominalist gender theorists is not an isolated phenomenon since its fundamental ideology is rooted in the enlightenment and René Descartes's skepticism, which persisted for 400 years. Skepticism creates a chasm between impressions and reality, which can never be crossed, creating two different world views today – materialism, which is material with no essence, and Spinozism, which is essence with no material. As a result, modern science became principally materialistic, while gender theorists and academics within the humanities have become mostly followers of Spinoza, Hume, or Kant.

Another reason this ideology is troubling is the indoctrination of non-realism within the culture. This skepticism leads to relativism, which becomes part of the educational curriculum and the media's common parlance. Regardless of one's stance on gender dysphoria, the more significant issue for the church is society's rejection of realism.

Gender Framework

The church must again combat a Gnostic culture to approach Christ's incarnational truth. Ironically, the church found partnerships with anti-ecclesiastical philosophers like Ayn Rand and Gender Critical feminists like Dr. Greer and Posie Parker since they hold realism as their epistemological foundation.

CHAPTER 3
THE CULTURE AND THE CHURCH

Males are privileged, and females are oppressed: that's the narrative we must stick with if we want to survive in academia.
— Anonymous University Administrator, *Saving Our Sons*

They did not want to look on the naked face of luck (*tuchè*), so they turned themselves over to science (*technè*). As a result, they are released from their dependence on luck but not from their dependence on science.
— Author of the Hippocratic Treatise, *The Fragility of Goodness*

In his 1981 book *After Virtue,* Alastair MacIntyre, Ph.D., commented on the cause of social division—without a unifying cosmology, anthropology, religion, philosophy, or ethics, society will fall apart. Dr. Macintyre argues that personal ethics are wedded to an overarching narrative: *"I can only answer the question 'What am I to do?' If I can answer the prior question 'Of what story or stories do I find myself apart?"* (MacIntyre 1981, 250). Nominalism and emotivism lead to relativity and subjectivity—which carries an arbitrary command. A worldview that lacks a cohesive philosophical framework creates internal chaos and disorder when living within ordinary life.

Western cultures struggle to establish a dominant cosmology: one side is rational realism, and the other is relativism. The Catholic cosmology rooted in rational realism revolves around an ordered ecclesiastical and celestial hierarchy with a singular heavenward trajectory. The secular cosmology is postmodern, egalitarian, morally relativistic, and anti-hierarchical. This battle over cosmological framing manifests itself in a culture war that incorporates politics, the judiciary, pop culture, entertainment, spirituality, and the historical narrative.

The two sides mirror the Hindu deities of Vishnu (the preserver) and Shiva (the destroyer). The chaos can break false illusions and idols, while the preserver provides peace and stability. The Hindus may be wise in recognizing the necessity of both powers but what is prudently required is discernment over the correct proportion. Christianity manifests this paradox, both in adherence to Divine precepts and openness to the Holy Spirit. In this vision, a narrow gate is open for the church to pass through, not entrenched in conservatism or liberalism, but guided by the light of Christ—who is the Truth.

How should the church engage in the culture war?

In an interview with *Triggernomitry,* Posie Parker (A Gender Critical person), founder of *Standing for Women,* questioned, where will the line be drawn for people going along with the transgender narrative? She quipped, *"Every place you go to where you think it will stop there, no one is going to go along with that, surely it will stop there. This is insane…And yet, everyone is going along with it"* (Parker 2019). Ordinary people, feminists included, are looking for authoritative guidance based on common sense and realist principles.

The church chooses to engage in this culture war by actively fighting against its ideological adversaries and through the Franciscan method of *Preaching the Gospel at all times and, when necessary, using words.* However, once the church decides the best approach to fight the culture war is to be quietly authentic, some push-back against the culture is still necessary if she takes her responsibility seriously as a spiritual and ethical leader.

The church guides her faithful through the narrow gate with the grace of God. Ego and pride burden the reader with a weight that makes the passage impassible. *Church* in Greek is *ekklēsía: ek (out of)* and *kaleein* (to call). The role of the church is to call away from worldliness. The church is not to become an imitation of the world. Instead, the church calls its members to higher principles and be prophetic to those not yet members of the Body of Christ. The church creates a pathway through the dangers of modern culture. The Christian must live *in the world* and not be *of the world.* How is this possible? *"What is impossible for human beings is possible for God"* (Lk 18:27). The Christian life is only possible through the Holy Spirit.

In his 2020 encyclical, Fraternity and Social Friendship (Fratelli Tutti), Pope Francis compares the present time to 800 years ago during the crusades. The example for Christians today is to be like St Francis, who, with *"his openness of heart, knew no bounds and transcended differences of origin, nationality, colour or religion"* (Francis 2020, sec. 3). Like St. Francis of Assisi, Pope Francis attempts to avoid the culture wars and live in the light of the Good News. This path is the narrow way and the eye of the needle. It is authentic discipleship without pride. When addressing the transgender issue, the culture is polarized and toxic. The victims of this culture war campaign are often experiencing gender dysphoria and the youth raised without a clear cultural or religious identity. Pope Francis called for a return to a common *social friendship.* This approach equally angers those looking for an endorsement of sexual liberation and those looking for a clear and decisive declaration against LGBT people. Pope Francis instead attempts to address people directly and walk with them as a fellow sinner. The result is that no one is completely satisfied. This dissatisfaction builds a bridge of fellowship and keeps communication open between liberals and conservatives. This delicate balance is the work of the new evangelization.

Are millennials at odds with the church?

The church is facing a crisis with its response to the transgender issue. The Public Religion Research Institute found that 70% of *"Millennials believe that religious groups are alienating young adults by being too judgmental about gay and lesbian issues"* (Jones, Cox, and Navarro-Rivera 2014). According to the Public Religion Research Institute, 31% of millennials claim to have left the mainline faiths because of religious intolerance towards LGBT people. In a 2007 study by the Barna Group, millennials' most common word to describe Christianity is *"antihomosexual."* When asked, 91% of non-Christians and 80% of young churchgoers used the term when describing key Christian qualities. Common negative perceptions include that present-day Christianity is judgmental (87%), hypocritical (85%), old-fashioned (78%), and too involved in politics (75%). In comparison, only 55% claimed that it is a faith that they respected (The Barna Group 2007). These results are a far cry from what Tertullian claimed drew people to the church in the first centuries, *"'Look,' they say, 'how they love one another' 'and how they are ready to die for each other'"* (Tertullian *Apologeticus,* chap. 39, sec. 7).

Alexander Griswold in *The Federalist* wrote that becoming LGBT—affirming is the fastest way to *"shrink your church in one easy step"* (Griswold 2014). Griswold cites the rapid decline of the Episcopal Church, Evangelical Lutheran Church, United Church of Christ, and the Presbyterian Church U.S.A. Notably, the churches that are better at maintaining their members are the Assemblies of God, Roman Catholic Church, Mormons, and Southern Baptists. Self-proclaimed transgender activist Brynn Tannehill responded that Griswold is missing the overall trend that *"Conservative faiths are declining more slowly while moderate progressive ones are shrinking more quickly."* Brynn Tannehill claims that conservative faiths *"are making all of Christianity toxic to moderate and progressive Millennials"* (Tannehill 2019, 249).

The opposite might also be true, and liberalism is destroying Christianity. Western Christianity as a whole no longer aspires to produce magnanimous saints. It is less likely that high standards are shrinking Christianity. Rather effeminacy and pusillanimity are overtaking liberal Christianity and slowly decaying the Catholic Church from the inside. When Christianity becomes religious entertainment, it cannot compete with the secular forms of entertainment in the world.

Venerable Fulton Sheen notably said that religion which demands nothing *"becomes a luxury like an opera, not a responsibility like life."*

The claim that the church must conform to modern Western principles to draw people in is contrary to the heart of authentic evangelization. The church does not intend to be popular; however, it should not be unpopular because the culture considers it judgmental, hypocritical, old-fashioned, political, and anti-homosexual. Anne Hendershott, Ph.D., Director of the Veritas Center for Ethics in Public Life at Franciscan University, responded to the Pew Study 2015, which showed the exiting of millennials from religion: *"While the LGBT community does not want to be reminded of biblical injunctions or of sin, it appears—ironically—that the churches which refuse to acknowledge sin are not deemed worth attending."* Dr. Hendershott also noted that *"If there is no creed or doctrine beyond 'we are all good,' there is no reason to attend church; any group activity will suffice"* (Hendershott 2015). Although the culture is antithetical to authentic expressions of religion, the only path forward for the Catholic Church is to reside in the truth. The unpopularity of truth is not new; St. John wrote, *"Jesus then said to the Twelve, 'Do you also want to leave?' Simon Peter answered him, 'Master, to whom shall we go? You have the words of eternal life. We have come to believe and are convinced that you are the Holy One of God'"* (John 6:67—69 NAB).

Does a Catholic cosmology create greater happiness?

Does the Catholic approach to sexual morality create more significant meaning in life, increase happiness, and result in holiness? Unfortunately, the quantitative analysis does not quickly answer the question since the laity and many clergy are unfaithful to the church's teaching on sexual morality. Moreover, American Catholicism is in a state of *Catholic nominalism*, whereby identifying as Catholic is not predictive of belief nor action. Nevertheless, the teachings of the Catholic Church take a robust stance against artificial birth control methods, premarital cohabitation/premarital sex, that marriage is exclusively between one man and one woman, and that celibacy is linked with holiness.

Despite the church's moral teaching, Catholics accept homosexual marriage at a higher rate than the United States' general population, around 62 and 58%, respectively (Piacenza and Jones 2017). A 2014 Univision Poll found that 79% of American Catholics believe birth control is morally acceptable (Culp-Ressler 2015), and 98% of American Catholic women use it (Guttmacher Institute 2008). Sixty-one percent of Catholics believe that couples cohabiting before marriage should receive communion, and 62% believe that divorced and remarried Catholics should be able to receive communion without an annulment. Beliefs about cohabitation and divorce are statistically identical between American Catholics and the general public (Lipka 2015). The reader may agree more with the culture than the church on some of these hot topics, which only affirms the point.

A study of all self-identified Catholics is not accurate when predicting practices of sexual morality. Therefore one cannot judge the overall happiness of self-identified Catholics when adherence to moral teaching is the basis for happiness. No one has conducted studies on the overall happiness of transgender Catholics who adhere strictly to tenants of faith, including sexual morality.

The church's sexual abuse crisis did not assure society that the church's teaching on human sexuality is healthy and based on the youth's best interest. On the contrary, certain churchmen's insensitivities when handling these scandals only led to a more severe undermining of the church's moral authority and the faithful abandoning Catholic moral principles. Therefore, it is difficult to grasp if Catholics who are transgender are happier than non-Catholics who are transgender since formal membership seldom results in practicing the church's moral code.

Mormons[1] adhere to their code of morality with a higher degree of faithfulness than Catholics. So does this moral code help transgender Mormon youth better adapt to society? The result since 2011 is the doubling of suicides by youth aged fifteen to nineteen. Benjamin Knoll, Ph.D., found a 95% correlation between suicide rates and the Mormon Church (Knoll 2016). The leading cause of death for kids in Utah, ages eleven to seventeen, is suicide, a rate increasing 141% since the Mormon Church fought against Proposition 8. In response, in August 2017, the Mormon Church supported the *LoveLoud Festival*, a concert raising money for charities that support LGBTQ youth (M. Jones 2017). In 2018, *The Church of Jesus Christ of Latter-day Saints Foundation*

---

[1] The Church of Jesus Christ of Latter-Day Saints

gave $25,000 to *Affirmation: LGBT Mormons, Families & Friends* for a new suicide prevention initiative (Walch 2018). The Mormon Church did not change its theology, but it responded to the crisis concretely.

The Catholic Church's response does not necessarily require a change in theology (like the Mormon church's response), but to more effectively preach the Good News of Jesus Christ, may need a different framing of contemporary moral issues appearing more supportive. Like the Mormon Church, the Catholic Church may want to put energy towards supporting the mental health of transgender youth, not because justice requires it, but because of mercy. Detransitioner Jamie Shupe noted that many LGBT support groups are available when transitioning, some meeting in churches, but detransitioning happens alone (Shupe 2019). Ministries offering pastoral support for people detransitioning would be a natural niche for the church, without worrying that the faithful would misunderstand the church's moral teachings.

People who engage in gender ideology will be critical of whatever the Catholic church does, so attempting to please them is futile. Transgender activist Brynn Tannehill claims that when LGBT Catholics hear the advocacy of faithful Catholics like Paul McHugh, M.D., what they perceive is *"the treatments they recommend are provided by exactly the same ex-gay organizations, with exactly the same people, using exactly the same religious perspective, and using the exact same methods (and theories) as were performed on gays for decades (with absolutely no success)"* (Tannehill 2019, 257). Sexologists like Ray Blanchard, Ph.D., and J. Michael Bailey, Ph.D., quickly point out that sexual orientation rarely changes, but sexual identity frequently changes through life stages. Helping people ease their gender dysphoria is nothing like conversion therapy (Blanchard 2019)(Bailey 2019).

How are public institutions addressing the transgender issue?

The commonweal also faces the challenge of addressing the transgender issue. Many Republican politicians rally their base and remain publicly relevant by focusing on transgender people in public facilities and sports. The fear of transgender people in public restrooms had a brief spotlight in the media, followed by liberal states passing laws to make gender-free restrooms available. Conservative states created laws to prohibit restroom use for transgender people, but this is not a primary concern of most cisgender people.

Most gender dysphoric people avoid situations that make other people uncomfortable. Gender dysphoria involves an inordinate amount of anxiety and fear over not *"passing."* Consequently, they avoid these potentially embarrassing situations. The type of sexual predators using the transgender umbrella to prey on women are often forced out of these spaces by women and charged with voyeurism when appropriate. People who are part of a gender theory and make no efforts to transition socially are of more significant concern, not because they are predators but because their presence may make women uncomfortable. For example, women in stages of undress may naturally be uncomfortable around strangers with beards who are also in a state of undress.

When women who have been abused or raped by men in the past raised these concerns, gender nominalists shouted, *"Transwomen are women,"* effectively ending the conversation (Family Policy Institute of Washington 2016). Any conversations women want to have concerning women-only spaces become framed as a debate over *"extinguishing a trans person's right to exist"* (Erickson-Schroth and Jacobs 2017). Ironically, identity politics has come full circle against feminists who first created identity politics.

The focus shifted to transgender people in competitive sports. This area is still irrelevant for most cisgender people, but it is much more interesting since it affects even high school sports leagues and college athletic scholarships. Many doctors and laypeople believe a man who benefited from decades of testosterone, denser bones, larger muscles, et cetera should not be able to compete as a woman in athletic competitions (Lowry 2019) (Aschwanden 2019) (Heyer 2020) (Milanovich 2019). Nevertheless, a regularly cited 2017 study claims *"no direct or consistent research suggesting transgender female individuals (or male individuals) have an athletic advantage at any stage of their transition"* (B. Jones et al., 2017). This response is being undermined every season by MtF athletes who are dominating their sports leagues.

In a Connecticut lawsuit, three ciswomen sued the United States Department of Education for allowing MtF students the ability to compete in female sports. As a result of the state's nondiscrimination policy, two transgender athletes Terry Miller and Andraya Yearwood won fifteen of the women's state championship titles. In addition, these two individuals took more than 85 opportunities to participate in higher-level competitions from female track athletes from 2017 to 2019 (Maxouris 2020). In April 2021, U.S. District Court Judge Robert Chatigny dismissed the case on procedural grounds, although the underlying issue will not go away by refusing to adjudicate the case.

Chapter three also reviews the church in relationship with the culture. This section examines *The Congregation for Catholic Education's* 2019 document titled *Male and Female He Created Them,* a non-magisterial letter addressing gender theory and cross-gender expressions. Again, the church demonstrates many signs of mercy, where clergy, religious, and laity effectively navigate the culture wars and shepherd transgender individuals. The faithful approach to transgender people is to reject nominalist gender ideology and to minister to the people. This chapter also briefly examines insights from Scripture and the relationship between science and the church.

3.1 Cancel Culture

The term cancel culture became the call of the boy who cried wolf too many times. Cancel culture is a wedge issue and the last desperate tool of a politician unwilling to govern the commonweal with constructive policies. Despite being overused, the term is still valid. One can see why the term cancel culture is common when reviewing its history. At the heart of cancel culture is the belief that the institutional systems of justice do not work to create real justice for their victims. Many situations are out of the individual's control, such as war, poverty, prisons, and government bureaucracies. Solving these problems with elections every 2 to 4 years requires intense, prolonged activism against money interests. In response, those involved in cancel culture try to bring down those people and corporations which are small enough or dependent on public opinion.

Within cancel culture, nuance and listening to both sides of an argument are becoming a lost skill. Cancel culture, at its worst, demonizes the other side to exaggerate their point. Through the lens of cancel culture or wokeness, disagreeing with someone becomes *'erasing'* someone and *'committing violence'* against them. A rational, civil debate degrades playing the victim and shaming the other side into submission or silence. This technique is not limited to political liberals or conservatives, Christians or atheists, or any other dichotomy within the shared society. Each side believes the other is more guilty of *canceling*, but it is insidious in whatever manifestation it takes. Cancel culture's vast influence silences experts with opinions contrary to *pro multis* (the many). The subsequent sections relay stories of people being canceled over the transgender issue, the worse being medical professionals.

Does cancel culture affect public discourse?

On December 19, 2019, the author of the popular Harry Potter series, J.K. Rowling tweeted, *"Dress however you please. Call yourself whatever you like. Sleep with any consenting adult who'll have you. Live your best life in peace and security. But force women out of their jobs for stating that sex is real? #IStandWithMaya #ThisIsNotADrill"* (Rowling 2019).[2] J.K. Rowling wrote that she did not think it was right to fire women who stated that sex is real. Through abstraction, this becomes, *"J.K. Rowling is defending transphobia."* Through essentialism, this becomes, *"J.K. Rowling is a transphobe."*

Abstract essentialist statements become emotionalized by ordinary people on social media with tweets like *"her decision, to support people that hate me, and want to do me harm. It brings me to tears... Why? Why?"* (Lilly 2019). Mainline media, such as Vox, featured posts like Lilly's as evidence of a social movement. The media posted stories like, *"J.K. Rowling's latest tweet seems like transphobic BS. Her fans are heartbroken.: JKR just ruined Harry Potter, Merry Christmas"* (Romano 2019). J.K. Rowling makes a statement to *live your best life but do not fire women for stating their beliefs that sex is real.* Cancel culture reports J.K. Rowling is a transphobe who destroys childhoods and Christmas (and implicitly), she must be silenced and stopped.

Actor Daniel Radcliffe posted a response to J.K Rowling's comments on the Trevor Project website. Daniel wrote, *"To all the people who now feel that their experience of the books has been tarnished or diminished, I am deeply sorry for the pain these comments have caused you. I really hope that you don't entirely lose what was valuable in these stories to you."* (Radcliffe 2020).

In the media, cancel culture silences varying opinions on transgender issues. For example, in May 2014, journalist Kevin Williamson released a story in the culture section of the conservative publication *National Review* with the headline, *Laverne Cox Is Not a Woman: Facts are not subject to our feelings* (K. Williamson 2014). This article responded to *Time* magazine's cover of Laverne Cox appearing in stunning feminine beauty, much like the *"Blonde Bombshell"* Christine Jorgensen appearing on the *New York Daily News* 62 years prior (*infra-*5.2). A conservative headline on a social issue in a conservative

---

[2] Maya Forstater won her appeal on June 10, 2021.

publication would not typically be notable; however, the *Chicago Sun-Times* reprinted Williamson's news story as an Op-Ed.

A majority of the mainstream press condemned the article's opinions and the Chicago Sun-Times for reprinting them. Change.org, a website dedicated to petitions against organizations and companies they would like to see canceled, created a petition titled, *Retract Your Disgusting and Transphobic Op-Ed on Laverne Cox.* The site stated, *"Stand with me in demanding that The Chicago Sun-Times remove and apologize for this disgusting example of transmisogyny in America"* (O'Keefe 2014). The *Chicago Sun-Times* published an opinion piece to show both sides of an issue. Instead, they become a newspaper that needs to be stood against through abstraction because they promote *"transmisogyny."* The *Chicago Sun-Times* responded by removing the Op-Ed and apologized. The only opinion allowed in mainline newspapers must, without any wavering, support the gender ideology that transwomen are real women.

Does cancel culture affect medical research?

Worse than the cancel culture affecting pop culture and news is the canceling of medical science and research. For example, Debra Soh, Ph.D., reported to the Oxford Union in 2021 that her fellow researchers need to avoid topics that are not politically correct for transgender activists. Dr. Soh claims *"left leading science denial was taking over the field,"* and she abandoned academia upon releasing her op-ed about gender dysphoria desisting rates for youth (Soh 2021).

The commonweal should keep science and politics apart, but this is not practiced in the current political climate. Thus, for example, Van Meter, M.D., wrote as an expert witness in the case of *United States of America v. State of North Carolina, et al.*:

> Mainstream clinicians and scientists who consider gender discordance to be a mental disorder have been deliberately excluded in the makeup of the steering committees of academic and medical professional societies, promulgating previously unheard-of guidelines. (Van Meter 2016)

Examples of Dr. Meter's claims are too numerous to list, but this section will reveal the stories of a few of these notable cases, including doctors Marcus Evans, Ray Blanchard, Kenneth Zucker, and Lisa Littman.

In 2019, Marcus Evans, Ph.D., one of The Tavistock and Portman NHS Foundation Trust governors, resigned. Dr. Evan stated his reason, *"In my 40 years of experience in psychiatry, I have learned that dismissing serious concerns about a service or approach is often driven by a defensive wish to prevent painful examination of an 'overvalued system'"* (Doward 2019). Dr. Evans claims transgender activists are shouting down debate and discussion while anyone questioning any aspect of gender ideology is reported as *'transphobic'* by the press. Thirty-four other psychiatrists also resigned from Tavistock over its policy of transitioning children hormonally (Sky News 2019).

Removing Lisa Littman, Ph.D.'s study for seven months from *PLoS One* is not an isolated event. If something is upsetting and enough activists become involved, public relations offices remove that person or idea from public view. Jeffrey Flier, M.D., the former dean of Harvard Medical School, wrote of Dr. Littman's situation, *"I have never once seen a comparable reaction from a journal within days of publishing a paper that the journal already had subjected to peer review, accepted, and published. One can only assume that the response was in large measure due to the intense lobbying the journal received"* (Flier 2018).

Ray Blanchard, Ph.D., worked for the Clarke Institute of Psychiatry while teaching at the University of Toronto. Dr. Blanchard led the Clinical Sexology Services in the Law and Mental Health Programme at the Center for Addiction and Mental Health in Toronto and worked on the *DSM-4*; yet, when appointed to the paraphilia chair sub-workgroup of the *DSM-5*, transgender activists rallied to remove him.

The American Psychological Association Task Force on Gender Identity, Gender Variance, and Intersex Conditions, appointed Kenneth Zucker, Ph.D., as a member in 2007. Dr. Zucker became the chair of the American Psychiatric Association sub-group *"Sexual and Gender Identity Disorders"* for DSM-5. In addition, Dr. Zucker chaired the Center for Addiction and Mental Health in Toronto and used medical research studies to determine how to treat young children suffering from gender dysphoria. Dr. Zucker's approach was to give the prepubescent children therapies to encourage them to accept their assigned genders until they were at an age when they could decide upon their own identity. Then, upon assessing the youth for several years and concluding that they were fully aware of the specifics of gender reassignment surgery, Dr. Blanchard might prescribe hormone blockers.

Dr. Zucker attempted to support the children and help them cope with their condition and cautiously waited before making life-altering decisions on a prepubescent child (the standard Dutch protocol). However, in responding to Dr. Zucker's failure to transition the child immediately, the transgender activist community viewed his interventions as synonymous with conversion therapy for homosexuals (O'Leary 2018). After pressure and false reviews about Dr. Zucker's practices, the university fired him, and the clinic permanently closed in March of 2015. Upon realizing the accusations against Dr. Zucker were untrue, the administrators apologized for their mistreatment (Singal 2016).

In August 2016, Paul McHugh, M.D., and Lawrence Mayer, M.D., from Johns Hopkins, released a 143-page literature review of what modern science knew about transgender issues and what was still unknown. Journalist Jonathan Last summarized the essence of the paper in one sentence: *"Human sexuality and gender are incredibly complicated, a lot of what's presented as 'fact' has no sturdy basis in scientific research, and we really ought to study the entire subject more rigorously"* (Last 2017). Johns Hopkins Medical Center, which just started treating transgender patients again after a thirty-eight-year hiatus, was threatened by the Human Rights Campaign (HRC) with backlash from the LGBT community if it did not condemn the report prepared by doctors McHugh and Mayer. Despite receiving a perfect score on the Healthcare Equality Index in 2016, a ranking given by the HRC, Johns Hopkins' refusal to denounce Drs. McHugh and Mayer's study resulted in a lower ranking in 2017.

The growing trend of activist communities silencing science that does not fit into their narratives is a form of cancel culture of which everyone should be wary. In response to this problem of the separation of science from politics, Jesse Singal wrote, *Why Some of the Worst Attacks on Social Science Have Come from Liberals,* claiming:

> We should want researchers to poke around at the edges of *"respectable"* beliefs about gender and race and religion and sex and identity and trauma, and other issues that make us squirm. That's why the scientific method was invented in the first place. If activists — any activists, regardless of their political orientation or the rightness of their cause — get to decide by fiat what is and isn't an acceptable interpretation of the world, then science is pointless, and we should just throw the whole damn thing out. (Singal 2015)

Jesse Singal paints a bleak picture of the relationship between science and activism. The ability to obtain funding for important and timely research on controversial topics is exceedingly challenging. Doctors Littman, Blanchard, Zucker, et cetera all faced the consequences because they were practicing unbiased secular scientific research, and the results went against the agenda of the gender activists. To better understand the transgender issue and offer better treatments, the research into these critical topics must continue unhindered by ideology.

[Kenneth Zucker, Ph.D., 1950—]

3.2 WOMEN'S SPACES

Intentionally throughout this book, there is an attempt not to demonize those who ascribe to a gender ideology or create an image of transgender people as criminal or mentally ill. Within this section are notable criminals who likely have a mental illness. Notable transgender activists, particularly transmedicalists, have distanced themselves from many of these people and their approach to being transgender. So-called *gatekeepers* like Blaire White, Debbie Hayward, and Rose of Dawn clarify that these criminals do not represent transgender people. This section does not try to conflate mentally ill criminal cross-dressers with people authentically suffering from gender dysphoria. However, it is an important topic since many jurisdictions are turning to self-identification (self-id) laws to determine who is transgender. These laws offer no gatekeeping, allowing anyone who claims to be transgender to be given the same rights and privileges as fully transitioned, life-long transsexuals.

Throughout this book are illustrations of people within the transgender conversation in an attempt to humanize the discussion. Within section 3.2, there are no images of publicly recognized people as criminals or mentally ill. There is, of course, morbid curiosity for what these people look like, and it would be sensational to show their failures at transitioning into women, but doing so would not respect either the dignity of the person shown or the transgender community. These individuals are easily searchable online for anyone genuinely interested in learning more about them.

This section contains two illustrations of transgender people, one of Rachel McKinnon, Ph.D., and Addison Vincent Rose. Although Addison's image is sensational, showing it is not to make fun of them but to illustrate the gender non-conforming challenge in women-only spaces. Moreover, this book draws sharp opposition to the philosophical premises held by Addison and Dr. McKinnon. Still, there is no attempt here to demonize the character or appearances of either of them.

The bathroom debate

The North Carolina House Bill 2 (H2), which passed in March 2016, was one of the most publicized transgender battles which further entrenched liberals and conservatives against one another. This bill required people in public institutions, including in public schools, to use the restrooms that coincided with the sex on their birth certificates. Three months later, the *U.S. Departments of Justice and Education* responded by claiming a Title IX violation, interpreted by the Obama administration. The consequence of a Title IX violation is a lawsuit or a loss of federal funding (Ehrenhalt 2018).

The legal debate over the North Carolina law continued until February 2017, one month after Donald Trump took office as President of the United States. At that time, he revoked the Obama administration's interpretation of Title IX, which protected transgender people in government institutions. The *North Carolina Department of Health and Human Servic*es claimed, *"Anyone who has undergone a sex change can change their sex on their birth certificate"* (North Carolina Department of Health and Human Services 2016). Therefore, H2 does not discriminate against transsexuals but transgender people who do not legally change their sex. Non-binary people who choose not to identify as male or female are restricted to their natal sex by default. If the person physically appears as a person of the opposite sex, H2 would prohibit that person from entering women or men-only spaces. Thus, the law balances both parties' comfort, the transgender person and the other public facility users.

In May 2018, the issue resurfaced when a federal judge ruled in favor of a transgender student in Virginia, given the alias Gavin Grimm. The student's family sued the school board for their *"insistence on his using bathrooms corresponding to his biological sex"* (G.G. [Gavin Grimm] v. Gloucester County School Board 2018). In August 2019, the U.S. District Court for the Eastern District of Virginia granted Gavin's motion for summary judgment, ruling that the school violated Gavin's rights under Title IX and the Fourteenth Amendment.

Cancel culture is in contrast to compromise and understanding. As part of the cancel culture, the mayor of San Francisco barred any publicly funded travel to North Carolina after passing House Bill 2. IBM, Apple, Facebook, Google, and Salesforce also came out against the law, while PayPal went further and halted a $3.6 million expansion in the state. Ryan Anderson, Ph.D., in *How Harry Became Sally,* responded by noting that when PayPal opened its international headquarters in Singapore, a country where people who engage in *private, consensual homosexual acts can face two years in jail.* Dr. Anderson noted, they did not appear to be concerned; or in 2012 when opening *"in the United Arab Emirates, which reportedly jails people who identify as gay or transgender"* (Anderson 2018a, 15).

On June 15, 2020, the United States Supreme Court ruled transgender people will receive protections under the 1964 Civil Rights Act in a six to three decision. The future Catholic president, Joe Biden, praised the Supreme Court's decision. He released a statement, stating: *"Today, by affirming that sexual orientation and gender identity discrimination are prohibited under Title VII of the Civil Rights Act, the Supreme Court has confirmed the simple but profoundly American idea that every human being should be treated with respect and dignity"* (Totenberg 2020).

Response from Jeff Shafer, Esq., in *First Things,* stated,

> Transgender ideology instructs that the body does not reveal the person; the mind does. Except that the mind is invisible and so reveals nothing. While aiming to replace sex with gender identity, Gavin [the plaintiff] insists on access to the male facilities that exist only because the public acknowledges the meaningfulness of bodies that she denies have meaning. Her novel theory of identity and her claim for restroom access are mutually refuting. (Shafer 2017)

This debate is politically motivated by conservatives trying to rally their base around traditional values and liberals pushing sexual liberation and a theory of equality. The underlying theological and philosophical argument is about epistemology and ontology—what defines one's being, how one feels, or what one is. Again, this is a matter of phenomenal vs. pneumenal. The separate restrooms are due to the phenomenal differences between men and women, not pneumenal differences. In other words, sex-specific restrooms are for the two sexes, not the two genders. From a realist perspective, a person enters a public facility bodily and not pneumenally.

This issue of women-only spaces is of particular concern to feminists in the UK. Although left-wing feminists commonly unite with the LGBT community, many feminists broke from the left-wing over the transgender issue. Gender-Critical activist Posie Parker claims that women are particularly vulnerable in women-only spaces like changing rooms and restrooms. Men can change their clothing or use the restroom with relative ease and speed, while women often require a greater degree of undress to use the restroom. Women require more time in the changing rooms due to more complicated garbs and sometimes have difficulties taking care of feminine issues that men do not consider.

The vulnerability of women in these spaces conjoins with women's high rate of experiences of sexual abuse. When young women develop breasts, they are objectified and sexualized by men and need to protect themselves from male predators. Posie Parker notes that not all men are predators, but plenty of predators are looking for an opportunity to prey on women. Women, particularly women with experiences of sexual abuse, should be given access to safe, women-only spaces when in vulnerable situations. Historically, women's access to public and professional life owes a great deal to the formation of women-only spaces.

Posie Parker and most Gender Critical feminists are not against a personal restroom for transgender people or anyone who wants privacy, but this proposal is now considered transphobic since *separate but equal is never equal* (Rosen n.d.). Furthermore, Posie Parker claims that women victimized by men should not be required to *get over it* so that MtF individuals gain the privilege of feeling equally like real women (Parker 2019).

Individuals like Addison Rose Vincent, who identifies as nonbinary but presents as a person with makeup, women's clothing, and a full beard, create a challenge. Although Addison may feel more comfortable in a woman's facility, the other women experience a man. Addison may also be unsafe in a men's facility since women's clothing and makeup challenge gender norms. Addison's self-expression creates an affront to the cultural gender norms of Western society, a path that is less safe for them and threatening to women within women-only spaces. A personal expression that makes one less safe and vulnerable people uncomfortable is akin to an exhibitionist who is most comfortable naked in public spaces or a person who likes to dress in military garb when never having served in the military. One who violates the social contract violates the virtue of affability, which is a component of justice. Adults who live within the commonweal realize that their behaviors affect other people and thus modify their desires out of respect for their neighbors. In contrast, children or vain adults do whatever they like without regard for how their actions affect others.

For feminists like Posie, whether the individual is gender dysphoric or a non-binary gender theorist is irrelevant if women are uncomfortable with male bodies in a female-only space. Women's comfort level raises the question of a person *"passing"* as someone of the assumed gender. The likelihood of any woman feeling unsafe is unlikely if one cannot tell whether a person is transgender. Androphilic MtFs are not sexually attracted to females and are often the most passable as natural women. The uneasiness is chiefly over autogynephilic individuals who, as Posie describes, look like *"truckers in a dress"* (Parker 2019). Autogynephilic people are typically heterosexual type individuals, being attracted to women and fetishistic about femininity. Shauna "Sean Patrick" Smith, an MtF individual, without any attempt to transition, was arrested in a Target changing room for voyeurism, explicitly taking pictures of an 18-year-old girl changing (Chokshi 2016).

Genderqueer Non-binary activist Alok Vaid-Menon (1991—), influential in celebrity circles, claims that society does not need to be concerned with transgender people in women-only spaces because little girls are kinky. He tweeted,

> The narrative is that transgender people will come into bathrooms and abuse little girls. The supposed *'purity'* of the victims has remained stagnant. There are no fairy tales and no princess here. Little girls are trans, queer, kinky, devious, kind, mean, beautiful, ugly, tremendous, and peculiar. (Vaid-Menon 2021)

Alok also called the Exorcist movie a coming-of-age movie for a *"young little girl [who] was really exploring her sexuality."* Despite their pedophilic comments, the critics of Alok are being blocked on social media since one cannot criticize a transgender person online. Lauren Witzke, a conservative politician and Republican from Delaware, retweeted Alok's quote with the caption *"demonic,"* and Twitter immediately and permanently suspended her account for hate speech (Masiello 2021).

144

As another example, a Canadian MtF activist named Jessica Yaniv (1987—), submitting the sex change application without transitioning, went into the female restroom and took pictures of teenage girls. Jessica also reportedly asked teenage girls if they needed help putting in their tampons (B. White 2019b). Jessica attempted to host an *"all-bodies swim"* topless event for youth twelve and up, and parents were prohibited (Wood 2019). Jessica booked appointments at women-only spas so she could force female estheticians to wax her male genitalia. If an esthetician refused, Jessica would sue the spa and demand the government shut it down for being transphobic. Jessica filed fifteen lawsuits against spas, gynecologists, and a beauty pageant for not treating her as a natural woman (Naylor 2020).

The *British Columbia Human Rights Tribunal* dismissed each of her cases (Larsen 2019). Jessica Yaniv and Shauna Smith represent the concerns of people toward transgender individuals. These activists place socially transitioned gender dysphoric people in a negative light. Transgender individuals are statistically far more likely to be victims of violence than the perpetrator; therefore, society needs balance and proportion to ensure the comfort and safety of MtF individuals and ciswomen. Reasonableness and compromise are two features missing in the typical dialogue. Regardless of the interlocutor's position, both sides need protection against senseless violence and exploitation of the innocent.

[Addison Vincent Rose, 1987—]

The prison debate

The most recent issue related to the masculine invasion of women's spaces is jailing. A British MtF individual, Stephen Wood, a.k.a. Karen White, despite being convicted of raping women, was held at a women's facility since he identifies as a woman. Stephen is notorious for wearing a wig, make-up, and false breasts, while never receiving opposite-sex hormones or SRS. Imprisoned for raping women, he continued to rape two women while in jail. Judge Christopher Batty told Stephen Wood, *"You are a predator and highly manipulative and in my view you are a danger... You represent a significant risk of serious harm to children, to women and to the general public"* (BBC News 2018). Currently, the state is confining Stephen in a male facility. The female prisoner raped by Stephen is now seeking a judicial review of placing MtF individuals in female facilities.

The High Court will rule on this review in 2021. The complaint listed several statistics concerning the issues raised in the complaint:

» A majority of female prisoners are victims of domestic violence (57%) and emotional, physical, or sexual abuse during childhood (53%) (the figures are probably a lot higher but for under-reporting);

» In the year ending March 2017, victims of those convicted of rape or assault by penetration reported that 99% of offenders were male, and 1% were female;

» Of the 125 transgender prisoners in prison in 2017, 60 (48%) had convictions for sexual offenses. Of those, 27 (45%) had been convicted of rape (Peirce 2020).

Placing MtF individuals, 48% of whom are convicted of sexual offenses in a female environment, with women who are overwhelmingly victims of sexual abuse, is not properly balancing the needs of vulnerable populations. In addition, due to the small number of female prisoners, the facility does not divide inmates based on their crimes as done with the male population. Consequently, a woman who was an accomplice in a drug-related offense may be cellmates with a serial rapist or a violent criminal.

Within the United States, some states place MtF individuals in women's facilities and some in men's facilities, with neither option being safe. For example, female cellmates have made allegations of MtF individuals abusing them in Illinois prisons, where the state houses transgender inmates with females (Masterson 2020).

Alejandro Gentile, who goes by Barbie Kardashian, demonstrated a long pattern of severe abuse against women in Ireland. Barbie had experienced years of abuse as a child. In turn, Barbie spent her teenage years abusing girls and female social workers while in group homes. Reports claim Barbie *"displayed violent and extreme sexual behaviors toward female care staff during his early teens, and maintained a list of care staff he intended to harm"* (Shaw 2020). As a teen, Barbie began identifying as a female. At eighteen, the state convicted Barbie for assaulting two women. Despite a therapist's conclusion that Barbie was not gender dysphoric, the state still placed her in a women's prison because of the Irish Self-Identification Policy. In addition, Ireland's reporting restrictions stopped the Irish press from mentioning that Barbie is transgender and instead had to refer to her as a teenage girl.

On the other side, MtF individuals placed within the male prison population are at a high risk of being the victims of rape. For example, in Georgia, MtF inmate Ashley Diamond alleges being raped fourteen times by male inmates and correctional officers (Kelleher 2020). In addition, the state of Michigan was sued in 2020 in a similar case when the state placed an MtF inmate with a male sex offender who raped her within the first 24 hours (N. Clark 2021).

Better use of prudence is necessary when considering the complexities of incarcerated transgender people. For instance, the state should not treat an autogynephilic sex offender the same as an androphilic. Likewise, the courts should not treat partially or fully transitioned non-violent offenders the same as non-transitioned violent offenders. These distinctions are self-evident at face value but challenging to codify into law.

[Rachel McKinnon, Ph.D., 1982—]

The sports debate

An increasing number of people believe sport's leagues should not accommodate transgender people in competitive sports due to biological differences between men and women. However, a Gallup poll conducted in May 2021 discovered that only 34% of Americans support the inclusion of transgender people in sports (McCarthy 2021).

One of the reasons competitive sports are single-sex is the physical inequities between men and women. For example, testosterone's effect in the male body results in stronger muscles, denser bones, a thicker skull, a bigger heart, more oxygen in the bloodstream, and a larger amygdala, which increases aggression. Males also have a frontal lobe designed for impulsivity, and a stronger cerebellum helps with balance, more adrenaline. In addition, the more competitive the sport, the more subtle differences are between the players' skills and abilities. Races, for example, are won by fractions of a second; therefore, any of those masculine advantages can significantly affect outcomes. This information is well established by male and female athletes and the ordinary observer, resulting in sports leagues creating men and women's competitions.

While some may agree with these observations, others claim there are too many variations within individuals to make *"overgeneralizations about a group's potential for athletic greatness, [which] can lead to widespread discrimination"* (Yerke and Fortier 2016, 151). FtM Harvard athlete Schuyler Bailar is an example of this exception whereby he placed in the top 13% of all college athletes in the breaststroke (Mineo 2019). Schuyler is a notable exception, but if the ideology that male and female athletes are equal in ability were actionable, one would abolish all-female sports leagues. Furthermore, no female athletes are promoting the end of female clubs. These examples raise the issue, are sex-based sports leagues separate due to differences in sex or differences in gender? The leagues exist not because of gender differences but due to the morphological differences between men and women.

Although MtF athletes possess natural advantages over most natal females, there are also some unnatural disadvantages. Women typically produce more estrogen than testosterone, but women still produce testosterone, which derives from their ovaries. MtF individuals without testes or ovaries do not produce any testosterone and are thus disadvantaged compared to cisgender females.

The International Olympic Committee in 2016 established three rules for transgender individuals: (1) they must legally be recognized as their gender, (2) they must be on hormone replacement therapy for at least one year (although surgery is not a requirement), and (3) for female sports, testosterone levels must fall within the range of female norms (Zeigler 2016). Nevertheless, the Olympics has permitted transgender athletes to participate in the Olympics since 2004. Laurel Hubbard, a weightlifter at the 2021 Tokyo games, is the first transgender person to qualify. Although this argument about transgender women not monopolizing positions at the Olympics can be persuasive, transgender women consistently dominate women's sports outside of the Olympics in recent years. Eventually, this trend may percolate into Olympic sports as well.

Athletes like Rachel McKinnon (also called Veronica Ivy), an MtF cyclist, won the gold medal in the 2018 Women's world championship in Los Angeles and again in 2019 in Manchester. Responding to criticisms that a natal male had won the women's world championship for two consecutive years, Dr. McKinnon tweeted:

> I have yet to meet a real champion who has a problem with trans women. Real champions want stronger competition. If you win because bigotry got your competition banned… you're a loser, and also, that debate is over. You lost (Dr. Veronica Ivy 2019).

Mary Gregory, an MtF weightlifter, won nine out of nine competitions at the 2019 100% Raw Weightlifting Federation competition, breaking four world records in the process. When the league discovered that Mary was born male, they revoked her medals. Paul Bossi, the president of the federation, released a statement,

> Our rules, and the basis of separating genders for competition, are based on physiological classification rather than identification. On the basis of all information presented to the Board of Directors for this particular case, the conclusion made, is that the correct physiological classification is male. (Bossi 2019)

MtF athlete Fallon Fox won five out of six professional martial arts competitions she competed in between 2012 and 2014 in featherweight championships (under 145 lbs). Podcaster Joe Rogan responded,

151

> First of all, she's not really a she. She's a transgender, post-op person. The operation doesn't shave down your bone density. It doesn't change. You look at a man's hands, and you look at a woman's hands, and they're built differently. They're just thicker; they're stronger, your wrists are thicker, your elbows are thicker, your joints are thicker. Just the mechanical function of punching, a man can do it much harder than a woman can, period. (Rogan 2018)

The notion that an athlete with male puberty and 31 years of testosterone might fairly compete against women is patently unfair. A woman can defeat a man in mixed martial arts since Ashlee Nicole Evans-Smith beat Fallon Fox on October 12, 2013. Still, there is an apparent advantage of being biologically male when competing in martial arts. The *National Gay and Lesbian Sports Hall of Fame* inducted Fallon Fox in 2013. Honors like being inducted in the hall of fame are awarded to people having done something exceedingly notable. Honoring Fallon Fox celebrates someone with a masculinized body beating a woman at mixed martial arts. A biological male beating a biological female in a combat sport is not something particularly remarkable.

Caster Semenya, a cis woman with naturally high testosterone levels, has been compelled by the Court of Arbitration for Sport to take hormone suppressants to compete. The International Association of Athletics Federations (IAAF) reaffirm the court's findings. The court decided the IAAF rules were *"necessary and reasonable,"* claiming the regulations *"do not infringe any athlete's rights"* but rather preserve *"fair and meaningful competition within the female classification"* (Gstalter 2019). This decision aims to establish some fair guidelines about who can compete in women's sports. Unfortunately, the collateral damage is a cis woman excluded from her own league. Furthermore, these rulings anger natal female athletes since the protocols force natural women to take hormone blockers to become *"real women."* This infringement on their natural womanhood accommodates biological men who want to enter this women-only environment (Pape 2019).

Every female athletic league is addressing this issue, and the outcomes of these rulings are frequently contested. Each week during the second half of 2019 and the beginning of 2020 (until sports were halted due to the pandemic), a new association was forced to redefine the term *"female athlete."*

[Ryan T. Anderson, Ph.D., 1982—]

3.3 Responding to the Transgender Moment

The most famous Catholic authored book on transgender issues is *When Harry Became Sally: Responding to the Transgender Moment* (2018), written by Ryan Anderson, Ph.D. This book arms Catholics with statistics, stories, and plenty of fear about how the culture war will change our lives and threaten Western culture. Although the underlying philosophy is consistent with a Catholic cosmology, the book is (arguably) pastorally insufficient.

The reviews on the back of the book include remarks like *"a government-enforced tyranny of false presumptions about nature besieges the American family"* from Dr. McHugh. Mary Ann Glendon, Esq., a Harvard law professor, warns about the *"human costs and their political implications."* Margaret Hagen, Ph.D., a professor of psychology and brain science at Boston University, warns, *"Everyone concerned with the welfare of children should read When Harry Became Sally."* Maureen Condic, Ph.D., a professor of neurobiology and anatomy at the University of Utah, also warns of the *"human costs"* of the transgender moment (Anderson 2018a, cover).

Although Dr. Anderson devotes several pages to real-life individuals suffering from gender dysphoria, his main focus is on the culture war. Gender ideology is easy to attack, especially within a crowd of similar-minded people; however, the book does not give any pastoral insights to help those who are not part of the ideology and are suffering from dysphoria. Though Dr. Anderson's pastoral approach lacks, his realist position is commendable. Dr. Anderson understands sex as something fixed and binary.

What is the opposition to *When Harry Became Sally?*

Throughout the twentieth century, several different definitions of gender developed. Abigail Favale, Ph.D., in contrast to Dr. Anderson, claims, *"Gender is a spectrum; Gender is fluid; Gender is innate; Gender is in the brain; Gender is a construct"* (Favale 2019, 2). Divergently, Dr. Anderson provides his view explaining, *"Gender is socially shaped, but is not a mere social construct,"* instead, he argues, *"It originates in biology and is how we give social expression to that reality"* (Anderson 2018a, 49). He writes, *"Sex is a bodily, biological reality"* and quotes Princeton philosopher Robert George, Ph.D., *"Changing sexes is a metaphysical impossibility because it is a biological impossibility"* (Anderson 2018a, 100).

Dr. Favale claims that society now uses the word sex to refer to a type of behavior, not just a property of the person. Dr. Favale reveals her materialist outlook stating, *"A surgeon can make a vagina out of a wound because the vagina is no longer seen as the door to a womb"* (Favale 2019, 3). She believes these linguistic changes change the way people understand themselves, *"The concept of gender, then, has ultimately served to pry a wedge between body and identity"* (Favale, 2019, 2).

Kelly Novak, M.S., responding to Dr. Anderson, claims his assertions are false and wrote *Let Harry Become Sally: Responding to the Anti-Transgender Moment.* Kelly argues against natural law by pointing to examples of defects in nature, such as the example of diabetes, *"If God made someone diabetic, should they be refused insulin?"* (Novak 2018, 10) Though this occurred naturally, we still instinctively recognize that the person should receive treatment. Kelly is implicitly asking a question pertinent to the transgender debate: who defines a good body? Natural law states, nature inherently has good ends, while critics of natural law eliminate the principle of natural goodness altogether.

Kelly devotes a significant portion of her book denouncing scientific sources used by Dr. Anderson. Her rhetoric is inflammatory and at times polemical, utilizing the term *hate group* twenty-four times throughout *Let Harry Become Sally*, such as *"the hate group American College of Pediatricians"* (Novak 2018, 25) and the *"hate group Family Research Council"* (Novak 2018, 8). Kelly also calls Dr. Anderson's studies *"opinions"* and *"propaganda"* (Novak 2018, 28). Skepticism towards science, defensive rhetoric, and inclusive politics are significant aspects of Kelly's book, indicating a postmodern perspective. Furthermore, postmodern philosophy contributes to the transgender movement by subjectivizing truth, demonstrated when the individual's internal identity is more accurate than external bodily reality.

Both Dr. Anderson and Kelly appear aware of the different foundational assumptions on either side of the transgender debate and focus their arguments accordingly. Dr. Anderson appeals to the concept of natural good in describing the body, stating the natural law approach is *"a basic principle of sound ethical reflection"* (Anderson 2018a, 158). Likewise, his essentialist understanding of sex is grounded in an objective source of meaning. In reference to an emphasis on family time and work-life balance, Dr. Anderson claims, *"You might think we could all support those values"* (Anderson 2018a, 147). These values about family life presume his audience agrees with these principles. However, many feminists and progressive organizations like Black Lives Matter advocate for something different, stating, *"We disrupt the Western-prescribed nuclear family"* (Black Lives Matter 2020), and Simone de Beauvoir, who states, *"the family must be abolished"* (Anderson 2018, 152). Thus, finding common ground becomes increasingly tricky. Dr. Anderson writes to an audience who believes in an objective source of morality, a teleological universe, a *hylomorphic* person, and a realist epistemology, while Kelly's audience does not.

Though most readers will not be familiar with these terms, as the preceding chapter demonstrates (*supra* chapter two), these are all in keeping with a theocentric worldview. On the other hand, *Let Harry Become Sally* assumes a postmodern approach to science, a nominalist approach to sex, a gnostic approach to human ontology, and a mechanical universe, keeping with an anthropocentric worldview. As a consequence, each author appeals to their intended audience instead of finding common ground.

Why did *When Harry Became Sally* get canceled from Amazon.com?

In February 2021, Amazon.com, the world's largest book distributor without warning, decided not to carry *When Harry Became Sally*. After members of Congress inquired with Amazon about their reasoning to silence this speech on their platform, Amazon.com responded it is because of a new policy whereby they *"have chosen not to sell books that frame LGBTQ+ identity as a mental illness"* (Huseman 2021). Dr. Anderson, in a Tweet, responded,

> Gender dysphoria is listed in the APA's Diagnostic and Statistical Manual of Mental Disorders, which Amazon sells. So the real deciding factor seems to be whether you endorse hormones and surgery as the proper treatment or counseling. (Anderson 2021)

One may note *Let Harry Become Sally* is still available on Amazon.com, once again proving there is only one acceptable viewpoint on this topic, not based on medical science but rather a social agenda.

3.4 SIGNS OF MERCY

The belief that the church only embraces one narrow vision of what sex and gender roles require is far from reality. Throughout the church's history, women religious and devout Catholic laywomen became the backbone of the Western commonweal and the church, despite being, what Simone de Beauvoir in 1949 called, *The Second Sex*. Women like the Blessed Mother as well as Ss. Theresa of Avila, Elizabeth of Hungary, Catherine of Siena, Claire of Assisi, Helena, Eleanor of Aquitaine, Theresa Benedicta of the Cross, Scholastica, Saint Brigid of Kildare, Hildegard of Bingen, Flannery O'Connor, Dorothy Day, Elizabeth Anscombe, and Mother Teresa of Calcutta exemplify being Christian women, contrary to their cultures. This list does not prove there are no historical disparities between men and women throughout the history of the Western Catholic world. Instead, these women are icons of the many ways of being Catholic beyond the gender stereotypes. In the lives of the saints, the reader finds true feminism. Their lives provide the groundwork for holiness, not always despite being the second sex, but by persevering through it to their proper ends.

The church accepts this reality and, to varying degrees, embraces this diversity. Therefore, the bridge between concepts of sex, gender, and gender nonconformity exists within the church already. Adapting this flexibility to transgender people is a delicate task assigned to people of mercy. It is essential to distinguish what is philosophically and biologically integral to the transgender issue and what is culturally optional. Women saints are examples of people having done this well before. Now gender minorities must also tread this path of holiness, perhaps as fellow members of this second sex. Their guides are often women of fortitude and, in a unique way, our Blessed Mother.

Theologian David Albert Jones, Ph.D., in an article in *Blackfriars,* recalls a narrative about Catholic apologist and philosopher Elizabeth Anscombe (1919–2001), who notably defended the church's teaching on marriage and the family, but is also *"notoriously for her disregard for conventional gender norms in manners and in dress. She kept her maiden name, smoked cigars, frequently sported a monocle, and habitually wore trousers"* (D. A. Jones 2018, 763). Dr. Jones also noted a ninth-century papal letter to the Bulgars who were seeking to become Christian but did not conform to the cultural norms of the Holy Roman Empire. Pope Nicholas I (820–867) wrote,

> We [do not] desire to know what you are wearing except Christ— for however many of you have been baptized in Christ, have put on Christ… pants are ordered to be made, not in order that women may use them, but that men may… but really do what you please. Whether you or your women wear or do not wear pants neither impedes your salvation nor leads to any increase of your virtues. (Nicholas I 1925, LIX)

The pope's call to *put on Christ* (Gal 3:27) becomes of far greater importance than what clothes one wears. The more significant concern is what is occurring in the heart rather than what is external. Within the church are living stones, who, through their church ministries, offer hope for transgender people. Like Pope Nicholas, they are reminders that it is not what one puts on that matters; instead, it resides in the heart. The individuals listed below are signs of mercy within the church. They bridged the divide between classical theology and transgender people, ignoring the culture war and embracing charity.

[Sr. Monica Astorga, O.C.D., 1967—]

Sister Monica Astorga, O.C.D.

Since 2006, Sister Monica of Neuquen has been serving MtF individuals at her Carmelite convent in Argentina. Throughout her ministry, she served approximately 90 transgender individuals. Most of the transgender people Sister Monica works with are involved in prostitution because they lack opportunities and family support because of being transgender. Upon meeting the first transgender woman, Sister Monica recalls her conversation with her, *"I invited her to search for others who wanted to leave prostitution, and she came back five days later with four more. I invited them to pray and then asked them to tell me their dreams."* One transgender woman, Katy, replied, *'I want a clean bed where I can die'"* (San Martín 2017).

Sister Monica is in the process of building a fifteen-bedroom house for these young people to keep them safe. Already, she faces strong opposition from the neighborhood for her work with these outcastes. In his letter to Sister Monica, Pope Francis encouraged her: *"In Jesus's times, the lepers were rejected. They are the lepers of today. Don't leave the frontier work you were given."*[3] Sister Monica's work is fruitful as she explains, *"They've always told me that 'without believing in God, we wouldn't survive. Each night, before going out on the street, we light a candle and ask God to take care of us"* (San Martín 2017). Sister Monica has not successfully found employment for her girls, so she wants to open a nursing home to hire many of them since their natural abilities are physical strength and emotional sensitivity vital to nursing.

---

[3] Though indistinct in English, that time Francis used the female pronoun when saying that the transgender persons are the lepers of today.

[Sr. Pavithra, C.M.C]

Sister Pavithra, C.M.C.

In December 2016, Vijayaraja Mallika, a transgender activist in southern India, with the help of the Congregation of the Mother of Carmel, opened a school for transgender people in Kerala. Vijayaraja Mallika had visited 700 properties without being able to secure a location for the school. Finally, six of the Provincial Council's Sisters approved the project with the local bishop's blessing. In Kerala, 20% of the state is Catholic, so obtaining the church's involvement was helpful. This project launched the first school to educate transgender people in India, where 58% of transgender people drop out of school before finishing the tenth grade. The most common profession for a transgender person is prostitution. Only 11.6% of transgender people maintain regular jobs in India, and 89% report mistreatment at work (Mathew 2017). This school is the first time the Catholic Church became explicitly involved in transgender education in India.

The school faces many problems, including social stigma, the difficulty getting sex workers to leave their professions to enter an unaccredited school with no certainty of employment following, and Vijayaraja Mallika's lack of experience running a school. Nevertheless, Sister Pavithra does not want to give up because she acknowledges, *"Once they are into sex work, it is very difficult to get them back on track."* Sister Pavithra advocates, *"We cannot blame them because society never accepts [them]. We have not given them any earning system other than sex work or begging"* (Mathew 2017).

Although Vijayaraja Mallika's school is struggling, the sisters began a new initiative to help trans youth by teaching them in their Carmelite-run schools. There are 6,000 Sisters in this community, and they run many institutions. With their schools' programs, they hope to *"foster empathy for trans people in the Catholic community and encourage trans students in their schools to come to them for support and counseling"* (Mathew 2017).

[Vijayaraja Mallika, 1985—]

Sister Luisa Derouen, O.P.

The ability to be out of the closet about ministering to transgender people is different in the United States. Over 20 years, a now 74-year-old sister has been ministering, praying, and listening to transgender people. In 2015, she released her story using the pseudonym Sister Monica David. In 2019 she revealed herself as Sister Luisa Derouem, O.P. She wrote about her experience living with transgender people, transforming her life. She also recalled times when her love for people had not been enough to save them. She recalled the story of Carol,

Carol wanted to believe that choosing to end her own life—out of love for those whose lives she was disrupting—would be acceptable. She believed she was a freak and evil, and her family's life would be better without her. While Carol was one of the first transgender persons in my experience who grappled with these distorted notions, she was certainly not the last.

During her retreat time, Carol experienced a deep sense of peace and the power of God's grace in her life. But soon after her return home, she again fell into patterns of self-hatred. She continued to isolate herself from contact with anyone sympathetic to her transition. Although I've reached out many times, I have not heard from Carol in years. I fear she has ended her life...

When love and respect lead the way, understanding easily follows. I had never before ministered among those who were rendered so invisible by society. Even now, I experience excruciating pain as I confront the fear and hostility directed toward members of the transgender community—people I so love and respect. For many years I have lived with the heavy burden of this conflict... To protect my religious community from censure, I have to keep my ministry with the transgender community hidden. (David 2015, 32–33)

In her 2019 article posted on globalsistersreport.org, Sister Luisa explains, *"I have been trying to help transgender people stay close to God and stay in the Catholic Church. Most of them are staying close to God but staying in the Catholic Church is quite another matter"* (Derouen 2019). She claims the Congregation for Catholic Education's document *Male and Female He Created Them* did not help create meaningful dialogues with transgender people; instead, this is another example of the church talking *about them* without talking *to them.*

[Sr. Luisa Derouen, O.P.]

Tia Michelle Pesando

The story of Tia Pesando, although somewhat sensationalized, presents an interesting case that could have ended in various ways. Tia is, as the news stories claim, transgender, but she is also intersex.[4] Tia, a convert to the Catholic Church, tried to become a religious sister at the age of 35 in London, Ontario. Tia claimed she was under private vows of chastity, poverty, and obedience received by her parish priest. Tia authored a book while discerning her vocation, titled, *Why God Doesn't Hate You* (2014), a book for LGBT readers who experience alienation from Christianity (Kellaway 2014). In the years following Tia's story, she ceased to seek entrance into religious life and is persisting in a celibate vocation.

Fr. George Almeida

In 2000, Fr. George Almeida, who served in the Navy during the Korean War, was close to retirement. Every morning after the daily Mass, two old ladies, a young man and Fr. Almeida would gather for breakfast at a local restaurant. At the table, one of the elderly ladies would push Fr. Almeida to explain why he associated with this older, not convincingly female transsexual. Fr. Almeida explained, this man was once an altar server for him many decades ago. He married and had children. A few years ago, she came out as transgender (autogynephilic) but remained married to her wife. They were poor people, and when a sixty-year-old poor autogynephilic man transitions, the effects are not consistent with Western feminine beauty. She had been cross-dressing on and off for many years. At the time, she mainly wore female clothing and had been diagnosed with cancer. Not knowing where to turn, she found Fr. Almeida and started returning to church.

The old ladies warned Fr. Almeida that people talked and asked why he talked to this *man*. Fr. Almeida responded to the women, *"I really don't care what people think,"* which ended the conversation. Twenty years later, he has since passed to eternal glory; still, Fr. Almeida exemplifies the Catholic Church's integrity in his courage. Fr. Almeida could have easily denied her in person or at least behind her back. However, Fr. Almeida did neither, knowing this person, no matter how

---

[4] Is it possible to be transgender if one is intersex?

ridiculous she looked to everyone else, is a human being with feelings and a soul, and nobody who seeks God with an open heart should be shunned.

[Fr. George Almeida, 1931—2012]

POPE ST. JOHN PAUL, II

At the Madison Square Garden on October 3rd, 1979, to a crowd of 20,000 cheering youth, Pope John Paul II proclaimed, *"John Paul II, he loves you!"* The saint went on to issue a challenge to the young people, *"When you wonder about the mystery of yourself, look to Christ who gives you the meaning of life. When you wonder what it means to be a mature person, look to Christ who is the fullness of humanity"* (John Paul II, 1979a, sec. 2). This pastoral message of Pope John Paul II, one month into his four-year series, now called the *Theology of the Body,* created a new chapter in how the church talked about the unity of the human person.

In his *Theology of the Body,* John Paul II explains this divine reality of *communion personarum* analogously using Scripture. When Jesus is asked whether divorce should be legal, he turns to *the beginning* for answers. Jesus cannot answer the question of divorce without first considering the meaning of marriage, which further leads to questions of what it means to be man and woman in communion with each other and with God. St. Matthew recalls Jesus's teaching:

> Some Pharisees approached him and tested him, saying, *"Is it lawful for a man to divorce his wife for any cause whatever?"* He said in reply, *"Have you not read that from the beginning the Creator 'made them male and female' and said, 'For this reason, a man shall leave his father and mother and be joined to his wife, and the two shall become one flesh'? So they are no longer two, but one flesh. Therefore, what God has joined together, no human being must separate."* They said to him, *"Then why did Moses command that the man give the woman a bill of divorce and dismiss [her]?"* He said to them, *"Because of the hardness of your hearts, Moses allowed you to divorce your wives, but from the beginning, it was not so."* (Mt. 19:3–8 NAB)

Jesus pointed to the beginning to illuminate the Pharisees. Still, one can extract more from this analogy, which goes beyond divorce to the broader question of the human person. What do the earliest narratives about the origins of man say about our specific nature?

As the image of God, humanity begins first in Scripture, *"God created humanity in his image; in the image of God he created them; male and female he created them"* (Gn 1:27). The concept of the *imago Dei* illuminated saints Augustine and Thomas Aquinas. In the *Summa Theologica* Ia q. 93, a. 1, ad 2, St. Thomas quotes St. Augustine in answering whether the image of God is found in man or only in Jesus. St Thomas explains:

172

> Since the perfect likeness to God cannot be except in an identical nature, the Image of God exists in His first-born Son, as the image of the king is in his son, who is of the exact nature as himself. Whereas God's likeness exists in man through an alien nature, as the image of the king is in a silver coin. (Augustine, *Augustinus Magister*, Ser. IX)

All of God's creation has a trace of the divine. Do intersex and transgender people also express a trace of the divine? All living beings are, in part, a member of the *imago Dei*. In a particular way, the distinguishing feature that makes humanity in the *imago Dei*, even if just as a king copied on a silver coin, is the *ratio entis*. St. Thomas quotes St. Augustine from *Gen. ad lit*. vi. 12: *"Man's excellence consists in the fact that God made him to His own image by giving him an intellectual soul which raises him above the beasts of the field"* (*ST* Ia q. 93, a.2). To be clear what is meant by an intellectual soul, St. Thomas means *"So we find in man a likeness to God by way of an image in his mind; but in the other parts of his being by way of a trace"* (*ST* Ia q. 93, a. 6).

In all other ways, man mirrors animals, but man shares the divine image within the *ratio*. The more one is rational, the more one mirrors the divine. Fortitude removes any obstacles that prevent a person from following reason. The transgender people become the *imago Dei* to the degree to which they are rational. Man is not only in the *imago Dei* through his mind, but in trace ways as well. Since Christ is in the form of a man, humanity shares a body with the second person of the Trinity. Man is the *imago Dei* because the *imago Christi* is a man.

The *Theology of the Body* goes beyond St. Thomas's idea of man being the *imago Dei*. Instead, John Paul II focuses on the *communio personarum*, that *"man became the image of God not only through his own humanity but also through the communion of person, which man and woman form from the very beginning"* (John Paul II 2006, sec. 163). By the recreation of the original unity of the two sexes, men and women *reproduce their own prototypes*. Not in solitude, but in the moment of communion, man becomes the *imago Dei*. Thus, John Paul II explains, the *imago Dei* becomes a theology of masculinity and femininity.

For many people, one is only an ally if they wave the flag and promote particular activist agendas. By this definition, Pope John Paul II is not an ally. The banner held by the pontiff is of Christ; however, this is a greater hope. By promoting the truth and pointing to a way of life that leads to wholeness and unity, Pope John Paul II is an ally of transgender people. Although the challenge of Pope John Paul II may not be what people want to hear, they are words spoken in the love of God and neighbor. The transgender person can always recall Madison Square Garden and be assured, *St. John Paul II loves you too.*

Out of John Paul II's commissioning of the youth to become a new springtime in the church and to establish a new evangelization, *Life Teen* was born. This Catholic youth ministry responded by reaching out and transforming the culture from within. Christina Mead, a member of *Life Teen,* released a statement to transgender youth reminding them, *"Our model is Jesus Christ. He let anyone sit and share a meal with Him. He saved the outcasts from the shame of isolation. He welcomed those whom others had judged and labeled as sinners. And He spoke the truth in love. We're trying to do those things"* (Mead n.d.). Christina continues with six truths *Life Teen* wants every young person to grasp. These truths echo St. John Paul II's *Theology of the Body* and apply to all Christians, not solely transgender youth.

1. You are precious and loved and worthy of good things.

2. We are all called to holiness

3. Medical advances are to heal, not hurt

4. Your body doesn't have to define your personality

5. The greatest good in life is not genital sexual expression

6. The Catholic church is a place for us to call home

The voice of St. John Paul II and his ongoing ministries led by the church's youth he inspired embodies Christ's call of preaching the truth in love. In Christ, honesty is never *brutal,* only loving. Neither Christ nor His church allows those they love to live in ignorance and disorder, but instead, they light a path towards liberation.

[Pope St. John Paul II, 1920—2005]

POPE FRANCIS

In 2016, Pope Francis stated in his post-synodal apostolic exhortation, The Joy of Love (*Amoris Laetitia*), *"It needs to be emphasized that 'biological sex and the socio-cultural role of sex (gender) can be distinguished but not separated"* (Francis 2016). Pope Francis provides insights into helping young people not enter the culture war. On one side of the culture war is the nominalist gender theory, which states there is no difference between men and women and gender is a social construction. On the other end of the spectrum are church groups accentuating the differences between men and women to enter the culture war. For example, they create masculine Christian hunting activities for *real* men and feminine Christian knitting parties for *real* women. This method attempts to help children gain a clear understanding of what it means to be a man or woman.

Pope Francis promoted an alternative in his post-synodal apostolic exhortation, The Joy of Love (*Amoris Laetitia*), where he recognizes *"history is burdened by the excesses of patriarchal cultures that considered women inferior"* (Francis 2016, 54). According to the Catechism, the church affirms both equality and the separation of the sexes. The Catechism states, *"Each of the two sexes is an image of the power and tenderness of God, with equal dignity though in a different way"* (*CCC*, 2205). Pope Francis continues his critique of the culture war and false dichotomies of masculinity and femininity in The Joy of Love (*Amoris Laetitia*),

> A rigid approach turns into an over-accentuation of the masculine or feminine and does not help children and young people to appreciate the genuine reciprocity incarnate in the real conditions of matrimony. Such rigidity, in turn, can hinder the development of an individual's abilities, to the point of leading them to think, for example, that it is not really masculine to cultivate art or dance or not very feminine to exercise leadership. This, thank God, has changed, but in some places, deficient notions still condition the legitimate freedom and hamper the authentic development of children's specific identity and potential. (Francis 2016, 286)

If gender stereotypes are too rigid in their definition of masculinity and femininity, the dichotomy could confuse young people who may not naturally conform to them. Germaine Greer, Ph.D., made similar claims about *"false femininity"* described in *supra-2.4*. If a male child is sensitive and caring, non-violent, and an effective communicator, he would be a caring father and husband; therefore, he should not be shamed into becoming someone he is not. Strict dichotomies may create confusion because if he is not stereotypically masculine, he may believe he is homosexual or transgender. In the apostolic exhortation The Joy of the Gospel (*Evangelii Gaudium*), Pope Francis criticizes *machismo* and sexist behavior as false masculinity (Francis 2013a, sec. 69). Pope St. John Paul II raised up ideals of masculinity and femininity without defining what they mean. Christians speculate what is meant by the terms masculinity and femininity. Pope Francis has not yet defined these terms but stresses what they are not.

The pontiff had plainly spoken when he called gender theory *ideological colonization that destroys*. Although Pope Francis does not clarify what he means by these statements, they hold within their words the idea that the unity of gender and sex is a cohesive biological, social, and religious natural reality. The concept of ideological colonization refers to overthrowing the natural order with an artificial fiction contrived by academics and activists. Colonization is exploitative of a social, cultural, linguistic, and religious group of people. Pope Francis is building on what Cardinal Joseph Ratzinger similarly understands as the *ideological colonization that destroys*. Cardinal Ratzinger preached in his last homily before becoming pope, *"We are building a dictatorship of relativism that does not recognize anything as definitive and whose ultimate goal consists solely of one's own ego and desires"* (Ratzinger 2005).

Pope Francis frames the transgender element of the gender theory as a moral problem. Still, gender theory is only a tiny part of a much larger *global war against the family,* not founded on a small transgender minority (Wooden 2016). Cardinal Robert Sarah, prefect of the Vatican's Congregation for Divine Worship, repeated this sentiment at a Washington prayer breakfast. In 2016, the cardinal remarked, *"Nowhere is this clearer than in the threat that societies are visiting on the family through a demonic 'gender ideology,' a deadly impulse that is being experienced in a world increasingly cut off from God through ideological colonialism"* (Sarah 2016).

In contrast to the ideological culture war, Pope Francis' welcomes transgender people into the church family. When interviewed about transgender people in October 2016, Pope Francis recalled a story about a Spanish-born woman who wanted to transition to become a man. The woman's mother asked her to wait until she died before having the surgery performed. After the mother died, she had sex reassignment surgery and visited the bishop. Pope Francis showed appreciation of the bishop's willingness to meet with the individual even though he could easily dismiss him. Pope Francis recalled, *"He who was a she, but is a he,"* asked for help from that Spanish bishop to visit the Vatican with his wife (San Martín 2016). Pope Francis's non-political tone and respectful reflection on the pastoral nature of the request set a standard for others approaching transgender people within the church's context.

Pope Francis, in the same interview, recalled two priests, one older and one younger. The eighty-year-old priest offered to hear the confession of a transgender person so he could receive communion. Instead, the young priest shouted at both the older priest and the transgender person, *"You'll go to Hell."* In the telling of this story, the pope is aware of the tensions within the church. The reality is there are no easy answers, but he does appear more open to the welcoming approach of the older priest.

In the interview, the pope stated his belief, *"Life is life. Things have to be accepted as they come. Sin is sin. Tendencies, hormonal imbalance, have and cause so many problems... we must be attentive. Not to say that it's all the same, but in each case, welcome, accompany, study, discern, and integrate. This is what Jesus would do today"* (San Martín 2016). Before moving on to the next question, Pope Francis added, *"Please don't say that the pope will sanctify trans [transgender people] because I read the headlines in the newspapers. I want to be clear; this is a problem of morals. It's a problem. It's a human problem that has to be resolved as it can, always with God's mercy"* (San Martín 2016). Pope Francis claims the church must welcome, accompany, study, discern, and integrate transgender people as Jesus would while warning of a moral problem. The pope also accepts that hormonal problems are concrete problems in need of medical attention, and this is not antithetical to the church's goal to include all people.

In Pope Francis's most recent encyclical, Fraternity and Social Friendship (*Fratelli Tutti*), the pontiff noted, *"[St.] Francis did not wage a war of words aimed at imposing doctrines; he simply spread the love of God. He understood that 'God is love and those who abide in love abide in God' (1 JN 4:16)"* (Francis 2020, sec. 4). Pope Francis warns of deconstructionism.

If someone tells young people to ignore their history, to reject the experiences of their elders, to look down on the past, and to look forward to a future that he himself holds out, doesn't it then become easy to draw them along so that they only do what he tells them? He needs the young to be shallow, uprooted, and distrustful so that they can trust only in his promises and act according to his plans. (Francis 2020, sec. 3)

People who promote these ideologies need the young to be ignorant of their cultural, spiritual, and historical contexts. These ideologies erase the past and invent a narrative of personal nihilism that is easily exploitable. Pope Francis challenges those of goodwill to consider the parable of the Good Samaritan instead of the narrative of exploitation. He explains,

Now there are only two kinds of people: those who care for someone who is hurting and those who pass by; those who bend down to help and those who look the other way and hurry off. Here, all our distinctions, labels, and masks fall away: it is the moment of truth. Will we bend down to touch and heal the wounds of others? Will we bend down and help another to get up? This is today's challenge, and we should not be afraid to face it. In moments of crisis, decisions become urgent. (Francis 2020, sec. 70)

The challenge before Catholics is to become involved in the lives of others. Catholics do not need all the answers to every worldly and medical problem—this is not what Christ asked. Instead, those in the church can show compassion and accompany those who are suffering.

3.5 MALE AND
FEMALE HE CREATED THEM

The document *Male and Female He Created Them* promulgated by the Congregation for Catholic Education (CCE) in 2019 is not a universally binding magisterial doctrine. However, this document acknowledges certain ancient heresies resurfacing in modern gender theory, and in this regard, the issues are magisterially related. As one of the few Vatican documents addressing transgender issues specifically, it deserves serious consideration.

Male and Female He Created Them begins by emphasizing its orientation towards dialogue and, therefore, is not doctrinal, rather the beginning of the conversation regarding *"gender theory in [Catholic] education."* (Congregation for Catholic Education 2019, cover). The document lays out three points of agreement with gender theory, all of which address feminism and none of which relate to transgender people. The document also raises five critiques of gender theory, all of which are related to transgender ideologies. The critiques are of the radical forms of gender theory trying to denaturalize sex, *"that is a move away from nature and towards an absolute option for the decision of the feelings of the human subject"* (Congregation for Catholic Education 2019, sec. 19). The CCE also criticizes gender theory by asserting it ignores the relationship between sexuality and the family as a natural reality. The CCE warns,

> The view of both sexuality [sic] identity and the family become subject to the same *'liquidity'* and *'fluidity'* that characterizes other aspects of post-modern culture, often founded on nothing more than a confused concept of freedom in the realm of feelings and wants, or momentary desires provoked by emotional impulses and the will of the individual, as opposed to anything based on the truths of existence. (Congregation for Catholic Education 2019, sec. 19)

The CCE challenges gender theory advocates, who claim each person should subjectively determine their own sex and gender without regard for concrete reality. This practice *"actually negates the relevance of each one [sex]. This has particular importance for the question of sexual difference"* (Congregation for Catholic Education 2019, sec. 20). If sex and gender are only adjectives and adverbs individually chosen, they cease to be interesting descriptors of any vital reality. The CCE cites Pope Francis to combat sexism while maintaining the reciprocity between the sexes being intrinsically right and just. The CCE writes,

> Instead of combatting wrongful interpretations of sexual differences that would diminish the fundamental importance of that difference for human dignity, such a proposal would simply eliminate it by proposing procedures and practices that make it irrelevant for a person's development and human relationships. But the utopia of the *'neuter'* eliminates both human dignity in sexual distinctiveness and the personal nature of the generation of new life. (Francis 2017, 3)

In this document, several themes deserve attention: the unity of body and soul, moral relativism, and its pastoral foundations in St. John Paul II's *Theology of the Body*.

What does the CCE say about the Cartesian System?

The CCE identifies the theological inconsistencies between the church's epistemology and gender theory: *"The underlying presuppositions of these theories can be traced back to a dualistic anthropology, separating body (reduced to the status of inert matter) from human will, which itself becomes an absolute that can manipulate the body as it pleases"* (Congregation for Catholic Education 2019, sec. 20). In the seventeenth century, René Descartes, through Plato, came again to this division between the *res cogitans* (thinking thing) and the *res extensa* (thing extended in space). René Descartes taught that the former belonged to a higher and more privileged dimension, while the latter is legitimately the object of manipulation and re-organization. Transsexuals change their bodies to be in line with their personal identities.

The modernist claim is that the inner self—the mind, will, soul—is the authentic self, and the body is a lesser mutable entity that must conform to the *res cogitans*. Christianity is a rejection of the concept that the body is a machine or a piece of flesh. In Christianity, the human person is integrated holistically and with a final cause in the resurrection. The incarnation of Christ points to the holiness of the body. Cartesianism is heretical since it is a product of dualism and universal Docetism, whereby humans are defined principally as immaterial beings. Being a bodiless soul or a soulless body might be one of the conflicting goals of gender theorists. Nevertheless, this requires an abnegation of the concrete realism that humans have an immortal soul and a mortal body.

What does the CCE say about modern Gnosticism?

Gnosticism is an early Christian heresy that states that matter is a fallen inferior form of being. Matter traps the soul, so one's sex does not define them. Gnosticism is a broad term for various Church heresies that challenged the early Christian understanding of the person, united by common anthropology that divides the physical from the spiritual and the bodily from the mental. To the Gnostic, only the internal sense of self matters: the physical body is inferior and not the actual individual. Gnostics believe that humans are *"non-bodily persons inhabiting non-personal bodies"* (George 2016, 5). More generally, the material world is evil, in contrast with the spiritual realm, which is good. Bishop Robert Barron of the Archdiocese of Los Angeles links this to the transgender worldview because *"the body is presented as an antagonist which can and should be manipulated by the authentic self"* (Barron 2015).

Robert P. George, D.Phil. (1955–), in *Gnostic Liberalism* writes that this mirrors the Gnostic self, whereby *"no dimension of our personal identity is truly determined biologically"* (George 2016, 3). Here a person is no longer an inner sense of self, intertwined with an external body; instead, one is merely an internal identity. In this light, transitioning would be proper to help align the physical body with one's feelings. This modernist approach is radically different from the Christian perspective. In response to those who hold the belief that one's body or sex is indeterminate, the *International Theological Commission* overseen by Cardinal Joseph Ratzinger reiterated, *"Biblical anthropology clearly presupposes the unity of man, and understands bodiliness to be essential to personal identity"* (International Theological Commission 2002).

Theologians call the unity of body and soul *hylomorphism,* and the Catholic understanding arose from St. Thomas Aquinas's incorporation of Aristotle. From this view, *"the living body, [instead of] being our vehicle or external instrument, is part of our personal reality"* (George 2016, 2). Consequently, from a Catholic perspective, one should not, and ultimately cannot, change one's sex to correspond with their gender identity. A person *is* either male or female. The gnostic emphasizes the inner self as accurate against the false external bodily self. A Gnostic could believe the inner self can be female compared to the outer male self. Thus, from the Gnostic-transgender understanding of a person, a transition is beneficial, while a transition is harmful and impossible from the hylomorphic perspective.

One can ask, is this Gnosticism, Universal Docetism, or Cartesianism still relevant? In a 2013 TED Talk in Ohio, Decker Moss proposed that children should not be sexed at birth and allowed to choose independently when the person is ready to decide. Decker Moss claims, *"[Sex] is assigned to us the moment we are born by a doctor based solely on what is between our legs, but I think that this needs to change"* (Moss 2013).

Freedom for self-expression and creativity is a gift of the *ratio entis*—something uniquely beautiful, which only God and man possess. Pope Francis wrote, *"[I]t is easy nowadays to confuse genuine freedom with the idea that each individual can act arbitrarily as if there were no truths, values, and principles to provide guidance, and everything was possible and permissible"* (Francis 2016, 34). On the contrary, the church teaches, human nature and freedom cannot be rooted in truth, and scientific truth cannot contradict philosophical truth.

What does the CCE say about relativism?

The CCE also warns, *"This combination of physicalism and voluntarism gives rise to relativism, in which everything that exists is of equal value and at the same time undifferentiated, without any real order or purpose"* (Congregation for Catholic Education 2019, sec. 20). Physicalists claim, cosmology without a causality minimizes all reality to materiality. They are simultaneously claiming the absolute plasticity of materiality. What one feels about their sexual identity becomes more important to their identity than the concreteness of their sex. The CCE warns that the subsequent step towards sexual relativism is public recognition of personal realities. They write, *"a juridical revolution since such beliefs claim specific rights for the individual and across society"* (Congregation for Catholic Education 2019, sec. 20). In section twenty, the *Congregation for Catholic*

Education affirms the Thomistic principle of the unity of the body and soul taught in Aristotle's *De Anima.*

Does this document affirm the *Theology of the Body?*

At the heart of section twenty-one is John Paul II's *Theology of the Body,* which seeks to reclaim original unity through marriage's sacramental bond. The grace of God creates this unity on complimentary beings as set out in Genesis, *"God created mankind in his image; in the image of God he created them; male and female he created them"* (Gn 1:27 NAB). The difference between men and women, masculinity, and femininity is a gift from the creator when effectively used. These differences are the source of discrimination—a corruption of God's design. However, used correctly, they are a gift of love uniting man and woman with God as co-creators of new life. By neutering the sexes, humanity is diminished rather than liberated.

The document *Male and Female He Created Them* explains the *Theology of the Body,* considering the furthering of the sexual liberation ideology in the twenty-first century. The document states,

> This ideology inspires educational programmes and legislative trends that promote ideas of personal identity and affective intimacy that make a radical break with the actual biological difference between males and females. Human identity is consigned to the individual's choice, which can also change in time. (Congregation for Catholic Education 2019, sec. 22)

While these heretical concepts may appear far-reaching to many people, popular gender theorists have already incorporated them into their social agenda.

What is at the heart of *Male and Female He Created Them?*

Section twenty-three of *Male and Female He Created Them* directly responds to people trying to use gender theory to create a relativistic society. Nevertheless, this directly responds not to transgender people suffering from an identity disorder but to a culture war against the church and Thomistic realism.

Most of the concerns related to gender theory in *Male and Female He Created Them* are ideological. This section considers transgender people beyond the ideology and addresses those suffering from *sexual indeterminacy,* which may include those with gender dysphoria.

The most crucial part of the document is in the reasoning section, which is long but worth quoting:

> » From the point of view of genetics, male cells (which contain XY chromosomes) differ, from the very moment of conception, from female cells (with their XX chromosomes).

> » That said, in cases where a person's sex is not clearly defined, it is medical professionals who can make a therapeutic intervention. In such situations, parents cannot make an arbitrary choice on the issue, let alone society.

> » Instead, *medical science* should act with purely therapeutic ends and intervene in the least invasive fashion, on the basis of objective parameters and with a view to establishing the person's constitutive identity. (Congregation for Catholic Education 2019, sec. 26)

This section plainly states that in cases *where a person's sex is not clearly defined, medical professionals can make a therapeutic intervention... in the least invasive fashion ... with a view of establishing the person's constitutive identity.* This section acknowledges that some people are born with sexual ambiguity, and a medical professional should determine the sex of the person. Doctors must use appropriate medical treatments, which are the least invasive, so the person's body aligns with one's sexual identity, either masculine or feminine. This process is neither relativistic nor political. This first half of section twenty-six is apparent, while the second half recognizes nuance and complexity.

> » *The process of identifying sexual identity* is made more difficult by the fictitious contract known as *"gender neuter"* or *"third gender,"* which has the effect of obscuring the fact that a person's sex is a structural determinant of male or female identity.

> » Efforts to go beyond the constitutive male-female sexual difference, such as the ideas of *"intersex"* or *"transgender,"* lead to masculinity or femininity that is ambiguous, even though (in a self-contradictory way), these concepts themselves actually presuppose the very sexual difference that they propose to negate or supersede.

» This oscillation between male and female becomes, at the end of the day, only a *'provocative'* display against so-called *'traditional frameworks,'* and one which, in fact, ignores the suffering of those who have to live in situations of sexual indeterminacy.

» Similar theories aim to annihilate the concept of *'nature'* (that is, everything we have been given as a pre-existing foundation of our being and action in the world) while at the same time implicitly reaffirming its existence. (Congregation for Catholic Education 2019, sec. 26)

Here the CCE claims *"structural determinants"* determine sex, and *"ideas"* like intersex and transgender are efforts to go beyond constitutive male-female-sexual differences. Most intersex people would not be classified as activists, although some intersex people align with activists. This early-onset gender dysphoria is possibly caused by several different developmental syndromes or genetic anomalies and is not something chosen. The personal gender theorists reject sexual differences and seek to deconstruct biological sex entirely. Thus, an important distinction exists between those with early-onset gender dysphoria and promoters of gender ideology. Further, no medical professional would ever call intersex an *"idea."*

This section also claims structural determinants form one's sex, but since the CCE raises both intersex and transgender people in this section, do they intend to include both? Physical ambiguity exists within the structural determinants of intersex individuals. Therefore, according to this document, a medical professional should determine the sex. Suppose the medical community determines neurodevelopmental disorders can cause discordant sex-brain structures within gender dysphoric people. Are ambiguous brain morphologies enough of a structural determinant to allow a medical professional to determine the sex of the persons and the appropriate therapeutic treatment for them, as would be done with other forms of intersex abnormalities? Medical professionals often decide the sex of intersex people by waiting and listening to how they feel and identify themselves later in life.

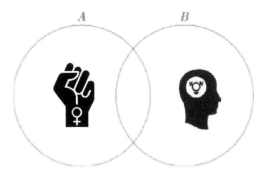

Figure 3.1 Transgender People / Gender Theorists Venn diagram

When section twenty-six shifts back to the position that intersex and transgender people are part of an ideology, this *"ignores the suffering of those who have to live situations of sexual indeterminacy."* However, the only people with sexual indeterminacy *are* intersex and transgender people. The authors claim intersex and the transgender idea are self-contradictory and implicitly affirming. The CCE was trying to demonstrate that gender theory, which does not believe in the differences between men and women, is contradicted by claims of intersex and transgender people, who claim sex is real and they want to be a member of a particular sex. The CCE recognizes that one cannot be both gender-neutral and biologically determined to be transgender. Unfortunately, by trying to show the inconsistency of thought, without realizing it, they join together two different warring tribes: people with gender dysphoria and gender activists. Some people with gender dysphoria are also nominalist gender theorists, but this is not the majority of gender dysphoric people.

Most intersex and transgender people are not claiming gender neutrality and oscillating between sexes. For example, these concepts never apply to intersex people who were born with a physical medical condition. Transgender people likewise are divided into two classifications, those who suffer from gender dysphoria (Truscum/transmedicalists) and those who are part of a gender theory movement of sexual liberation (Maximals). Using a Venn diagram in figure 3.1, A. are gender theorists; B. are transgender people; the middle is both transgender and gender theorists.

Chair of the U.S. bishops' committee on education, Bishop Michael Barber, S.J., responded to the document Male and Female He Created Them in a press release. The bishop praised,

> In a difficult and complex issue, the clarity of Church teaching, rooted in the equal dignity of men and women as created by God, provides the light of truth and compassion that is most needed in our world today. (United States Conference of Catholic Bishops 2019)

Fr. Dan Horan, O.F.M., responded in the *National Catholic Register*,

> Call it what you like, but such claims appear tantamount to a physically or emotionally abusive parent, spouse, or partner claiming that their violence is grounded in a place of *'tough love.'* In the end, it's still simply abuse, adding the church must stop promoting the *'boogeyman of gender ideology.'* (Horan 2020)

The divided response to this document further emphasizes the liberal/conservative division within society and the church. The only way forward pastorally is to overcome the culture war and encounter Christ in the medical, philosophical, and theological truths since all truth leads to *the* Truth.

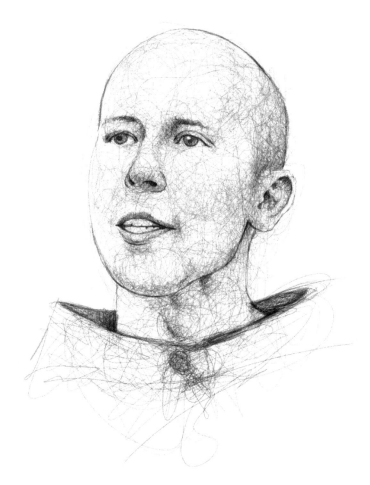

[Fr. Dan Horan, O.F.M., 1983—]

3.6 SCRIPTURAL RELEVANCE

S cripture correctly interpreted reveals the Spirit of God at work in the world. Pope Francis announced in his 2019 *motu proprio*, He Opened (*Aperuit illis*), *"without the Scriptures, the events of the mission of Jesus and of his church in this world would remain incomprehensible. Hence, St. Jerome could rightly claim, 'Ignorance of the Scriptures is ignorance of Christ'"* (Francis 2019, sec. 1). The term transgender is not found within the Scriptures, while the texts address two related themes: cross-dressing and eunuchs. Within the prohibitions of cross-dressing, the Scriptures reject the pagan orgy cults of their times and directs the believer towards humble and sober fidelity to the virtuous life.

Cross-dressing prohibitions also address issues of truthfulness, whereby one accurately presents oneself publicly. Secondly, the section on eunuchs is more didactic since the teaching evolves over the Old and New Law. Third, Christ addresses the topic of natural, involuntary, and voluntary eunuchs and their role within the Kingdom of God. Fourth, the link between eunuchs, intersex, and transgender people is particularly illuminating and may be a sign of God's Divine Providence. Lastly, Pope St. John Paul II's teachings on the *imago Dei* and the original nakedness of man and woman illustrate the call of deification of humanity through adoption into the Body of Christ.

Before applying an exegetical approach to the transgender issue, the reader must first explore ethical considerations. This section does not consider if a transgender person can marry a person of the same assigned sex. Whether or not it is a homosexual relationship is determined by an ontological conclusion. If the gender dysphoric person has an intersex brain, then perhaps the relationship is heterosexual. [5] If gender dysphoria only creates the *desire* to be a member of the opposite sex, it is a homosexual relationship. When considering the androphilic and autogynephilic arguments, both have origins within sexual orientation and paraphilia. Therefore, both would

---

[5] Some notable Muslims take this stance. *Supra-2.5 Iran.*

likely constitute homosexual relationships. Whether someone with gender dysphoria has the capacity to enter into marriage with someone of the opposite assigned sex is an additional canonical question not addressed in this section.

This section narrowly considers the vocation of a eunuch within Scripture. A natural eunuch is an intersex person or someone with a sexual defect. This category generally applies to transgender people. This section also considers cross-dressing since this generally applies to gender theory or those with paraphilia. If a person is not entirely a natural eunuch, Jesus calls all of his followers to be eunuchs for the sake of the kingdom if they can bear this vocation. Whatever their form, eunuchs have an essential vocation in the church. In light of this calling, transgender people, modern-day eunuchs, are called in a particular way to unite themselves to God's espousal love.

Christianity has a preferential option for virginity, but it is not absolute. John Paul II wrote, *"the decision about continence or the life of virginity must be voluntary, and that only such continence is better than marriage"* (John Paul II 2006, sec. 445). Fr. Ashley similarly writes, *"Christian ethics of sexuality is creative because it seeks to use human intelligence and freedom to enable human beings to use their sexuality well, rather than to submit to the widespread abuses built into our sinful world and encouraged by it"* (Ashley 1985, 449). Sexuality, whether expressed in marriage or celibacy, requires people to act with creativity. Creativity is necessary to maintain a happy marriage. Although celibacy takes many forms, the happiest celibates are the ones with creative outlets.

What does the Bible say about cross-dressing?

The Pentateuch proclaimed a prohibition against what appears to be cross-dressing thousands of years before the invention of gender ideology. The Book of Deuteronomy states, *"A woman shall not wear a man's garment, nor shall a man put on woman's clothing; for anyone who does such things is an abomination to the LORD,[6] your God"* (Dt 22:5 NAB).

Although this is *"not a text which has ever been interpreted literally by the Rabbis,"* the origins and original interpretation of this passage remain unknown (Gilchrist 2015). Rabbi Shlomo *"Rashi"* Yizchaki (1040–

---

[6] The use of *"LORD"* piously refers to YHWH of the Old Testament.

1105) gave the oldest recorded interpretation, which still exists. He wrote, *"A man's item should not be on a woman so she can go out among men, for this is only for adultery"* and also, *"A man shall not wear a woman's garment: so he can go and be among the women"* (Rashi 1985).

The Shulhan Arukh, a sixteenth-century law code which is a standard text for most observant Jewish people, agrees with Rabbi Rashi that the purpose is to *"prevent men and women from associating with what would normally be a single-sex group of the other gender under false pretenses in circumstances which might lead to adultery or for 'abhorrent' behavior"* (Gilchrist 2015). This interpretation is particularly relevant for Gender-Critical feminists who claim autogynephilic individuals use the guise of female dress to infiltrate women-only spaces for sexual purposes.

St. Thomas Aquinas (like Rashi) considers cross-sexed clothing a matter of truthfulness. He writes, *"This outward apparel is an indication of man's estate; wherefore excess, deficiency, and mean therein, are preferable to the virtue of truthfulness, which the Philosopher assigns to deeds and words, which are indications of something connected with man's estate"* (*ST* IIa IIae q. 169, a.1, ad. 3). St. Thomas explicitly answered a question about garb during liturgies and concerning dressing below one's status to appear humble or from superstition. St. Thomas directly refers to Deuteronomy twenty-two and states,

> Hence it is in itself sinful for a woman to wear men's clothing or vice versa; especially since this may be a cause of sensuous pleasure and is expressly forbidden in the Law (Deut. xxii) because the Gentiles used to practice this change of attire for the purpose of idolatrous superstition. Nevertheless, this may be done sometimes without sin because of some necessity either to hide oneself from enemies, or through lack of other clothes, or for some similar motive. (*ST* IIa IIae q.169, a. 2, ad. 3)

St. Thomas's first line in this commentary is firmly against cross-dressing, yet, throughout his commentary, he qualifies the precept, claiming one could not be allowed for idolatrous superstition, yet there are exceptions. The allowable reasons range from acceptable deception to not having access to gender-appropriate garb—or other similar motives. Gender dysphoria is not idolatrous superstition, like those participating in the Festival of Cotyttia (Licht 1932, 500). In addition, gender dysphoria is not the same as hiding from enemies or a lack of options. Dressing in female attire can be a source of sexual arousal for some autogynephilic individuals. This arousal, however, is not present at all for androphilic individuals who experience no sexual arousal in opposite-sex clothing (Blanchard, Clemmensen, and Steiner 1987). Instead, androphilic individuals may be using the opposite sex garb for a kind of hiding of one's natal sex or a way of trying to present the truth as they experience it.

The idea that men were convincingly sneaking into areas reserved for women to engage in adulterous affairs may be possible but unlikely on a wide scale during ancient times. The context of Deuteronomy 22 involves purity codes not intended to separate men from women but Jews from non-Jews. A more convincing argument is that Jewish leaders were reacting to the pagan culture surrounding them. At the festival in honor of Cotys, the goddess of sensuality dances with men and women dressed in women's clothing. They passed from ritual to orgies, according to Synesius (Synesius *Synesii Cyrenaei Calvitii encomium*).

Even more relevant is Ctesias, who was related to Annarus, the governor of Babylon, who *"wore the entire dress and ornaments of a woman.... [he] used to come into the room while he was at supper with a hundred and fifty women playing the lyre and singing. And they played and sang all the time that [Annarus] was eating"* (Athenaeus 1927, 530). This tale of Ctesias in the fifth century BCE occurred soon after the compiling of the Book of Deuteronomy. Still, this is common in Rome, Greece, or many other ancient civilizations in that region. The religious and cultural rituals of the ancient world involved dancing with goats (Pan), orgies (Cotys), drunkenness (Dionysus), and otherwise revelrous behavior. The Jewish people's ethical and purity codes intend to keep them from integrating into pagan cultures. The Deuteronomic Code was not written because Jewish men and women were cross-dressing. Instead, these passages intended to keep Jewish people from becoming like pagans, especially in their religious rituals.

The Council Fathers of Nicaea's response to self-made eunuchs is reactionary against the anti-Christian Roman emperors' paganism. In one account by Suetonius (70–120AD), Nero fell in love with a boy who resembled his late wife, so had the boy castrated to preserve his feminine appearance. Nero married Sporus, dressing him as the empress. The pagan culture and abuse of powerful men against defenseless people formed how the church fathers responded to eunuchs. In 342AD, marrying eunuchs became outlawed due to

Christianity's spread throughout the Roman empire (Kuefler 2001, 101–102).

How does the Old Law prohibit eunuchs?

When addressing surgical therapies for transgender individuals, one can interpret Deuteronomy chapter twenty-three, which restricts eunuchs from temple worship. *"No one whose testicles have been crushed or whose penis has been cut off may come into the assembly of the LORD"* (Dt 23:2 NAB). This prohibition against the mutilated, whether self-inflicted or inflicted by another, is not relevant in this passage. The next verse declares, *"No one born of an illicit union may come into the assembly of the LORD, nor any descendant of such even to the tenth generations"* (Dt 23:3 NAB). The Lord holds vengeance against nine generations of innocent people because of the guilt of their ancestors. Still, He has less vengeance against their former oppressors, Egypt, *"Do not abhor the Egyptian: you were a resident alien in his country. Children born to them may come into the assembly of the LORD in the third generation"* (Dt 23:8–9 NAB). The ability to worship the LORD appears strangely prohibitive by modern standards. Therefore, more context is needed to understand these passages as liberatory.

This section of Deuteronomy contains what appears to be strange codes of behavior,

"You shall not sow your vineyard with two different kinds of seed" (Dt 22:9 NAB);

"You shall not plow with an ox, and a donkey harnessed together" (Dt 22:10 NAB);

"You shall not wear cloth made from wool and linen woven together" (Dt 22:11 NAB); and

"You shall put tassels on the four corners of the cloak that you wrap around yourself" (Dt 22:12 NAB).

All these odd laws listed in Deuteronomy 22 and twenty-three are part of the purity codes to keep the chosen people of Israel apart from their pagan neighbors.

How does the prophetic tradition redeem eunuchs?

These purity code laws possess no intrinsic moral value, and all of Israel did not embrace these teachings. The prophet Isaiah preached contrary to the purity code:

> The foreigner joined to the LORD should not say, *"The LORD will surely exclude me from his people"*; Nor should the eunuch say, *"See, I am a dry tree."* For thus says the LORD:

> To the eunuchs who keep my sabbaths, who choose what pleases me, and who hold fast to my covenant, I will give them, in my house and within my walls, a monument and a name. Better than sons and daughters; an eternal name, which shall not be cut off, will I give them.

> And foreigners who join themselves to the LORD, to minister to him. To love the name of the LORD, to become his servants— All who keep the Sabbath without profaning it and hold fast to my covenant. Them I will bring to my holy mountain and make them joyful in my house of prayer; Their burnt offerings and their sacrifices will be acceptable on my altar. For my house shall be called a house of prayer for all peoples. (Is 56:3–7 NAB)

Isaiah preaches that the LORD will accept the foreigners and eunuchs and receive monuments in their name. Isaiah's message is inclusion, calling the Lord's *house a house of prayer for all peoples.* Isaiah's message is not the purity code language of the Sadducees or Pharisees, but the prophets' radical message.

How do the Gospels and Acts address eunuchs?

Jesus takes the message of Isaiah further and calls all His disciples to become like eunuchs if they can accept it. Jesus calls being a eunuch the better way,

> [His] disciples said to him, *"If that is the case of a man with his wife, it is better not to marry."* He answered, *"Not all can accept [this] word, but only those to whom that is granted. Some are incapable of marriage because they were born so; some because they were made so by others; some because they have renounced marriage for the sake of the kingdom of heaven. Whoever can accept this ought to accept it."* (Mt 19:10–12 NAB)

Jesus turns society on its head, where those in the Jewish tradition who were outcasts, excluded from the temple worship, and the assembly of the faithful become the chosen few. To be a man of influence in the ancient world was to be married with many children. Women, children, and eunuchs did not enjoy the same rights as men. Jesus asks his followers to renounce their male privilege and become one of the wretched of the earth. He asks them to be humiliated, being no better than a eunuch—a slave.

This call of the eunuch is not merely the call to celibacy but the inclusion of the natural-born eunuchs. The first-century Jewish language had three terms for natural eunuchs, *aylonith,* the people with underdeveloped genitalia who never appear more feminine than masculine. *Androgynos,* are those who appeared equally male and female with both sets of sex organs and *tumtum*, those whose sex is unclear but becomes apparent in time (J. Hare 2015). Natural eunuchs would be recognized medically as intersex individuals. By extension, if the theory that transgender people possess intersex brains is correct, this title by extension could include gender dysphoric people.

Jesus preaches the complimentary and permanent nature of marriage, yet, he carves a path of holiness for the other, for those born outcastes, made outcastes, or choose to become outcasts for the sake of the kingdom. In Christ, the unclean no longer exist, only the chosen. J. David Hester, Ph.D., notes,

> Jesus heals the blind, the paralyzed, the possessed, the fevered, the leprous, the hemorrhaging, even the dead, in every case restoring them to full societal membership. In the case of the eunuch, however, there is no implication whatsoever of *'illness'* or social *'deformity'* in need of restoration. Instead, the eunuch is held up as the model to follow. (Hester 2005, 38)

[Ethiopian Eunuch, first century]

Jesus's call for social justice and the *love* of all outcastes is especially noted as unique within religious ethics and primarily attributed to Christianity. Where do transgender people fit into the Biblical narrative of the Gospel? Right in the heart of it. Jesus does not call the eunuch to become like the male and female of Genesis, but to choose the *better way* for those who can bear this cross. Jesus calls them to embrace their reproductive disability as a sign of the kingdom. They were not to fit within the societal binary system (although Jesus calls marriage excellent and holy) and servants not of the earthly powers but of the Lord. Further, He calls His own disciples to become eunuchs for the sake of the kingdom.

Finally, in the Acts of the Apostles, St. Philip, guided by an angel, encounters an Ethiopian eunuch in Gaza. The eunuch came to Jerusalem to worship and study the prophet Isaiah when St. Philip ran up to his chariot. According to Deuteronomy 23:2 & 8, being both a eunuch and a foreigner, worshiping in the Temple would be impossible. Fortunately, he read Isaiah instead of Deuteronomy. St. Philip explained to the eunuch what Isaiah had predicted and taught him about Jesus. St. Philip then baptized the eunuch in the river. The apostles performed many miracles of healing throughout the Acts of the Apostles, yet God did not make the eunuchs physically whole again. The eunuch remained a eunuch but now a Christian.

The application of Scripture for transgender people is rich. Transgender people are not abandoned as monstrous but are called to be children of God in their *otherness*. Jesus calls men and women to the sanctity of marriage but creates a path of holiness for non-married people who can live as undivided servants of God. Jesus calls their path a better way. People who follow Jesus occupy a better way of celibacy and still a holy way of marriage. Jesus presents the eunuchs born that way or made that way by others with a difficult challenge. Jesus tells the others to be celibate but acknowledges, *"Not all can accept [this] word, but only those to whom that is granted"* (Mt 19:10 NAB). What about the natural eunuchs and those made so by others? What if they cannot accept this? What does this passage mean for the intersex person? The homosexual? The transgender person? Jesus proposes a challenge for some but a commandment for the other.

On the contrary, St. Thomas Aquinas notes that eunuchs, spiritual or natural-born, are not free from lust. In his commentary on the

Gospel of St. Matthew, St. Thomas reflects, *"Likewise, this [castration] is not useful when done, because such men, even though they do not have the act, still they are not free from concupiscence. Hence, the lust of a eunuch shall devour a young maiden (Sir 20:2)"* (Aquinas, *Commentary on the Gospel of St. Matthew*, 1568). If original unity is made whole again through the sacrament of marriage or the spiritual marriage to Christ. The image of original unity for the natural eunuch comes through St. Paul's image of the Body of Christ.

The body of Christ theology should be both a consolation and a challenge to someone not in the state of married life. Christ Himself established excellent paths and vocations for these people who are transgender, but there are also challenges. Others may enjoy two options, but for the eunuch, they are ordered to a better way and the more difficult one. The eunuch should not be forced to bear this cross alone but should experience the church's support and formation to guide them along their path of perfection. They continue to fall as long as the Christian community is unable to support them. Eunuchs, by their precise nature in the first century, are not solitary people but people part of a community and with clearly defined roles. The church must accept the challenge to interpret the Holy Spirit to create a clear vocation for these modern-day eunuchs.

3.7 SCIENCE & RELIGION

Within this book, the most extensive section is dedicated to medical science rather than to the Scriptures. This approach is intentional since, for transgender people, the Scriptures and Councils of the church are only tangentially related. *Sacra Doctrina* is necessary and enlightens the pastoral approach one must take when addressing the transgender issue. Still, any attempt at applying Sacra Doctrina will only address the strawman version of the issue without medical science. A strawman application is ineffective and insulting to transgender people and would question the astuteness of the church leadership.

Due to notable cases such as Galileo Galilei's condemnation in 1633, people remain skeptical about the Catholic Church's acceptance of science. This presumption that the church is anti-science omits copious amounts of historical evidence to the contrary. Many are familiar with Gregor Mendel, the father of genetics being an Augustinian friar, Nicolaus Copernicus, the father of a heliocentric solar system being an Augustinian canon, and maybe Fr. Georges Lemaître, S.J., the father of the Big Bang Theory. A chapter written by Fr. William Wallace, O.P., titled *Quantification in Sixteenth-Century Natural Philosophy* (found in a festschrift dedicated to Ralph McInerny), examines how the European church brought society to the brink of modern science (Wallace 1999, 11–24).

Does the church listen to leading scientists?

In the present age, the church is also at the forefront of modern science. The Pontifical Academy of Sciences boasts the membership of forty-five Nobel laureates such as Ernest Rutherford, Niels Bohr, Max Planck, Erwin Schrödinger, Otto Hahn, and Charles Hard Townes. Even Stephen Hawking would regularly attend plenary sessions of the academy. Its roots go back to the Academy of Lynxes in 1603 and restored to its ecclesiastical purpose in 1847 as the *Accademia Pontificia dei Nuovi Lincei* by Pope Pius IX, one year into his thirty-one-year papacy. The academy received its current name and home in the Vatican Gardens in 1936 by Pope Pius XI.

Are science and religion at odds?

On November 8, 2012, Benedict XVI told members of the Pontifical Academy of Sciences that dialogue and cooperation between faith and science were urgently needed to build a culture that respects people and the planet. The pontiff proclaimed, *"Without faith and science informing each other, the great questions of humanity leave the domain of reason and truth, and are abandoned to the irrational, to myth, or to indifference, with great damage to humanity itself, to world peace and to our ultimate destiny"* (Benedict XVI 2012). He continued claiming that as people strive to

> unlock the mysteries of man and the universe, I am convinced of the urgent need for continued dialogue and cooperation between the worlds of science and of faith in building a culture of respect for man, for human dignity and freedom, for the future of our human family, and the long-term sustainable development of our planet. (Benedict XVI 2012)

Benedict XVI captures the heart of the Catholic response towards modern science. Science should not try to become a religion, nor should religion seek to take the place of science. Cardinal Avery Dulles, in his recount of John Paul II's 1988 conference on science and religion, wrote, *"Science can purify religion from error and superstition, while religion purifies science from idolatry and false absolutes. Each discipline should, therefore, retain its integrity and yet be open to the insights and discoveries of the other"* (Dulles 2007, 19). We build a society based on respect for human dignity and the planet's long-term sustainability through continued dialogue between science and faith.

How does the church respond to situations where scientific truth contradicts the truth of faith? According to G.K. Chesterton, Siger of Brabant in the thirteenth century claimed,

> The Church must be right theologically, but she can be wrong scientifically. There are two truths; the truth of the natural world, which contradicts the supernatural world. While we are being naturalists, we can suppose that Christianity is all nonsense; but then, when we remember that we are Christians, we must admit that Christianity is true, even if non-sense. (Chesterton 1933, 104)

201

St. Thomas Aquinas revolted against this concept and, in contrast, claimed there can only be one truth approached by two paths. Pope Leo XIII agreed with the Thomistic approach when addressing this question in the 1893 encyclical On the Study of Holy Scripture (*Providentissimus Deus*). Leo XIII argued that science and theology are separate disciplines; therefore, they do not contradict each other if scholars keep their respective areas of expertise. Science classically asks the question: how does something occur? Theology naturally asks the question, why does something occur? The scientist should not view the biblical writers as explaining the visible world, as this had not been their intent.

Through what lens should the church interpret science?

How did Leo XIII get to this radical stance compared to his successor Pius IX who condemned all aspects of modernity in the 1864 appendix, Syllabus of Errors (*Syllabus Errorum*)? In 1879, the Pope introduced the encyclical Of the Eternal Father (*Aeterni Patris*) to reclaim the values of Scholasticism and the works of St. Thomas Aquinas. The Thomistic approach embraced all pagan, Muslim, Judaic, scientific, Scriptural, or philosophical knowledge. Likewise, Leo XIII embraced all truth as a sign to the world that the church is not a superstitious archaic institution but a beacon of light shining in the darkness. Thus, in 1891, the pope opened the Vatican Observatory to discover the truth of the cosmos.

In 1892, the pope with the Dominican Order opened *L'Ecole Biblique* in Jerusalem to critically study the Bible from a historical and archeological perspective. In this move, the church definitively took the stance that she wanted to discover the truth of Scripture and defend the Word of God against those who believed scripture to be a work of fiction detached from history and reality. Thus, Pius IX responded to the modern world by condemning it, while Leo XIII responded to modernity by opening the church's doors and inviting everyone in with faith that all forms of truth will lead to the *Truth*.

John Paul II, in his address to the Pontifical Academy of Sciences on October 22, 1996, quoted his predecessor Leo XIII in his encyclical On the Study of Holy Scripture (*Providentissimus Deus*), *"we know, in fact, that truth cannot contradict truth"* (John Paul II 1996). The truth of scientific knowledge and the truth of religious teaching are epistemologically consistent. There can only be one truth. Leo XIII quoted from St. Augustine: *"And if in these Books I meet anything which seems contrary to truth, I shall not hesitate to conclude either that the text is faulty, or that the translator has not expressed the meaning of the passage, or that I myself do not understand."* (Leo XIII 1893, sec. 21) (Augustine. *Ep. lxxxii.*, i. et crebrius alibi) This fundamental principle is the key to unlocking how the church will address every new scientific revolution.

Many churchmen resisted the newly presented scientific truths upon the dawn of the heliocentric and Darwinian revolutions. At first, discoveries may challenge the church's authority and establish a new cosmology and anthropology. In the present era, the Catholic Church is not still fighting either of those two battles. As early as 1950, in his encyclical On the Human Race (*Humani Generis*), Pius XII wrote that no inherent conflict between Christianity and evolution exists. The Magisterium *"does not forbid that, in conformity with the present state of human sciences and sacred theology, research and discussions, on the part of men experienced in both fields, take place with regard to the doctrine of evolution, in as far as it inquiries into the origin of the human body as coming from pre-existent and living matter"* (Pius XII 1950, sec. 36). The church wisely does not canonize any scientific system. Regardless of how the process occurred, in the end, God created man. Pius XII states, *"the Catholic faith obliges us to hold that souls are immediately created by God"* (Pius XII 1950, sec. 36), how ensoulment occurs is a mystery.

Why does the church need to keep listening to scientists?

With the openness and willingness to embrace the truth expressed by Leo XIII, it is vital to honor the integrity of scientific studies. However, science is not dogmatic or infallible, so it is crucial not to canonize any scientific research or a collection of studies. Scientific studies are like dots on a connect-the-dots game for children. At the beginning of the research, the dots only appear to be a random assortment. Then, several different connections may be made between them, resulting in different images.

Nevertheless, as studies increase and scientists fill the gaps with additional dots, the image becomes more explicit. Eventually, when there are enough data points, even a child realizes the image's nature without wild guessing. In the field of transgender science, we do not possess enough dots. This lack of dots allows for many interpretations of how to unite them into an image correctly. This paper aims to present the scientific and philosophical dots as honestly and thoroughly as possible and then offer a couple of reasonable ways to connect them. As scientists place additional dots, some theories will likely become obsolete. The church could wait and not make any affirmative statements on transgender issues until scientifically litigating the matter. Pastorally the church cannot wait decades before ministering to her sons and daughters suffering from gender dysphoria.

3.8 Concept Review

Chapter three addressed the culture war and its battle over conservative and liberal values while discussing the highly debated cancel culture, which curbs free speech when addressing the transgender issue. This section also raised concerns about the nature of politically correct questions and the allowable scientific study results related to transgender identities. Finally, this section addressed the major transgender social issues promoted by the media, particularly the bathroom laws and sports debates.

The popular book, *How Harry Became Sally* introduces how Catholic cultural circles frequently discuss the transgender issue and how popular culture silences it. This section also reviewed relevant passages of Scripture and how to apply the principles covered under cross-dressing and eunuchs to the transgender issue.

John Paul II's *Theology of the Body* is also utilized to imagine possible vocations for transgender individuals as eunuchs for the sake of the kingdom. Finally, this section ends with the Catholic bridge between conservative and liberal values without engaging in the culture war itself. A living example of a public leader who tries to transcend modern tribalism is Pope Francis, who notably remarked, the job of the Christian is to build bridges, not walls:

> Peace builds bridges, whereas hatred is the builder of walls. You must decide, in life: either I will make bridges, or I will make walls. Walls divide, and hatred grows; when there is division, hatred grows. Bridges unite, and when there is a bridge, hatred can go away because I can hear the other and speak with the other. When you shake the hand of a friend, of a person, you make a human bridge. You make a bridge. Instead, when you strike someone when you insult another person, you build a wall. Hatred always grows with walls. At times, it may happen that you want to make a bridge, and you offer your hand, but the other party does not take it; these are the humiliations that we must suffer in life in order to do good. (Francis 2018)

CHAPTER 4
SEXUAL ABNORMALITIES &
INTERSEX

Although androgynes, whom men also call hermaphrodites, are very rare, yet it is difficult to find periods when they do not occur. In them, the marks of both sexes appear together in such a way that it is uncertain from which they should properly receive their name. However, our established manner of speaking has given them the gender of the better sex, calling them masculine.

— St. Augustine, *The City of God*

Male, female, and intersex persons are all created in the image of God, and all are called to be conformed to the image of Jesus.

— Megan DeFranza, Ph.D., *Sex Difference in Christian Theology*

Two theories underlie the debate regarding the nature of transgender persons: (1) sex is binary, and (2) sex is a spectrum. The binary sex model argues that the different sexes are complementary and necessary for sexual reproduction. This topic is covered extensively *supra* in 2.1. The opposing view claims intersex individuals are examples of the wide range of sex between two binary poles. So, is sex a binary, or is sex a spectrum?

Evolutionary biologist Colin Wright, Ph.D., argues that every six thousand flips of a coin land on edge. This statistical anomaly is expected, yet, one does not conclude the existence of more than two sides to a coin (C. Wright 2020). Intersex is a condition whereby the coin falls on the edge. The intersex condition is not a single condition but an umbrella term describing several conditions ranging from severe and evident to minor and unnoticeable. Intersex people are not a new occurrence, and societies have effectively integrated intersex people into the culture for thousands of years.

Sex is the physical and anatomical characteristic that defines a human being as either male or female. The pediatric community assigns a child male or female using established scientific criteria. Biologist Anne Fausto-Sterling, Ph.D., of Brown University, defines a typical or biological male and female as follows:

> We define the typical male as someone with an XY chromosomal composition and testes located within the scrotal sac. The testes produce sperm which, via the vas deferens, may be transported to the urethra and ejaculated outside the body. Penis length at birth ranges from 2.5 to 4.5 cm; an idealized penis has a completely enclosed urethra, which opens at the top of the glans. During fetal development, the testes produce the Müllerian inhibiting factor, testosterone, and dihydrotestosterone, in which juvenile testicular activity ensures a masculinizing puberty.
>
> The typical female has two X chromosomes, functional ovaries which ensure a feminizing puberty, oviducts connecting to a uterus, cervix and vaginal canal, inner and outer vaginal lips, and a clitoris, which at birth ranges in size from 0.20 to 0.85 cm. (Blackless, Charuvastra, et al. 2000, 152)

The development of a young male or female originates from the genotype of XX or XY from the first moments of conception, so it is typically easy to distinguish between the two sexes using this criterion. The chromosomal approach emerged in 1923 with the discovery of DNA. Sex determination developed further in 1991 with the discovery of the *Sry* gene.

Priest and biologist Fr. Nicanor Austriaco, O.P., who earned a Ph.D. from *Massachusetts Institute of Technology* in microbiology, wrote in *Blackfriars*, *"A male has a Y chromosome with the Sry gene that triggers the development of his testicles, while a female has neither, triggering the development of her ovaries. These gonads then direct sexual differentiation and maturation via the activity of the sex-specific hormones that they produce"* (Austriaco 2013, 702). Unfortunately, some abnormalities make this selection process far more complex in approximately 1.7% of the population who are intersex (Blackless et al., 2000). Intersex, previously called hermaphroditism, is not the same as gender dysphoria or transgender.

Most intersex people can unknowingly live with intersex conditions for decades until finally diagnosed with an intersex condition in adulthood. Some intersex people have the biological distinction of not being clear in one sex or another within their secondary sex organs. Only a minority of intersex disorders produce genitalia of both sexes or, more accurately, ambiguous genitalia. An intersex person might have XX or XY chromosomes, but they might have XXY or XXX or a mosaic of XX and XY cells within a single person. Other intersex people have 46 chromosomes with XX or XY genotypes. Due to the *Sry* gene mutation, both testosterone and estrogen are released into the human fetus, and both sex characteristics develop. In one instance, an individual with XY chromosomes and a normal SRY gene gave birth. (Dumic et al. 2008, 183).

Former Olympian Maria José Martínez-Patiño (1961—), a top Spanish hurdler, believed she was a female and unknowingly had male chromosomes, testes, [1] and no ovaries or uterus. In 1985, after doctors

---

[1] *"Until 1968 female Olympic competitors were often asked to parade naked in front of a board of examiners. Breasts and a vagina were all one needed to certify one's femininity. But many women complained this procedure was degrading. Partly*

conducted a routine chromatin test and determined that the former gymnast was genetically male, she was not allowed to participate in the University Games in Kobe, Japan. (Schaffer and Smith 2000, 138). Nevertheless, Maria presented all the physical characteristics of a female, including her external genitalia, and doctors declared her to be a girl at her birth. Still defending her conviction that she is a woman, Maria announced, *"I knew I was a woman"* (Fausto-Sterling 2000a, 2).

Megan DeFranza, Ph.D. (1975–), explains, *"The Y chromosome does not always determine male identity; production and receptivity to androgens are more influential"* (DeFranza 2019, 93). Complete Androgen Insensitivity Syndrome occurs when the person is genotypically XY but phenotypically with both genitals. All other secondary sex features are feminine, including the brain. If a person is genotypically male and phenotypically primarily female, which would tell more about a person's sex? The document *Male and Female He Created Them* attempts to give advice,

> [I]n cases where a person's sex is not clearly defined, medical professionals can make a therapeutic intervention. In such situations, parents cannot make an arbitrary choice on the issue, let alone society. Instead, medical science should act with purely therapeutic ends and intervene in the least invasive fashion based on objective parameters and with a view to establishing the person's constitutive identity. (*Male and Female He Created Them,* sec. 26)

One should not assume that the genotype is the most important or only relevant factor determining a person's sex. The Aristotelian and Thomistic approach considers the phenotype to be greater than the genotype since action follows *being* not DNA. Therefore, if an individual can become pregnant inside her body, that individual is a female by definition. Medical professionals follow the Aristotelian stance, learning in the 1980s that sex is not interchangeable, and gender expression is rooted in the brain, not the genitals. Consequently, doctors may not be capable of determining the sex of intersex babies

---

because such complaints mounted, the IOC decided to make use of the modern 'scientific' chromosome test" (Fausto-Sterling 2000a, 3).

until further bodily maturation occurs and the child's gender expression unfolds.

In 2005, fifty medical professionals established the *Clinical Guidelines* and *Handbook for Parents*, which advised the wait-and-see approach for intersex children. The current strategy by the 2005 *Clinical Guidelines* and the teachings of the church are aligned. Neither medical nor ecclesiastical teaching is in disagreement in this regard. Therefore, the CCE should be cautious about not overemphasizing language, which states *"the ideas of intersex,"* since this is a biological reality for millions of people. Nominalist gender theorists weaponize intersex to subvert the sex binary, as the church correctly observes. The church must separate those with intersex conditions from those using intersex people as a means to an end (see *infra*-4.1).

This book raises intersex for two reasons: first, it dispels the simplistic view that everyone is born unambiguously male or female. XX or XY chromosomes do not directly determine masculinity and femininity. Genotypes do not strictly determine one's sex, and phenotypes are at times uncertain. Second, this book argues that sex is binary, yet intersex conditions require sensitivity and exceptions to the binary rules surrounding sex. If the presumption XX and XY always determined one's sex were correct, it would mean someone like Maria José Martínez-Patiño is acting out of mental illness or social sexual rebellion, which does not appear to be the situation.

Intersex people who identify entirely as one sex but are genotypically the opposite sex leads to an ambiguous ontology. Among transgender people, the intersex etiology may occur primarily in the brain, a region that can largely remain obscure to doctors. The intersex brain hypothesis, as promoted by many medical professionals, will be discussed *infra* chapters seven and eight. Lastly, Fr. Austriaco explains his understanding of the biological formation of gender identity,

> We simply have to conclude that we cannot make an accurate judgment regarding these individuals' sex/gender. Some reports suggest that core gender identity is consistent with assigned sex in most cases across a wide range of hormonal abnormalities, seemingly regardless of whether sex assignment is as a male or as a female. (Austriaco 2013, 714–715)

Fr. Austriaco's primary conclusion after reviewing sex and gender studies is that medical science is unclear how biology influences gender identity.

[Fr. Nicanor Austriaco, O.P., 1968—]

4.1 Intersex as an Ideology

Since the propagation of *Humanae Vitae* (Of Human Life) in 1968, popes have actively fought against an ideology of sexual liberation—declaring that sex and procreation are inseparable. Since the 1960s, the sexual liberation movement has expanded from reproductive self-determination to separate biological sex from sexual acts and gender. Vocal personalities in the debate include some intersex individuals who advocate that their condition is not only medical but a biological rebuke to the binary sexual ideology.

The founder of the Intersex Society of North America, Cheryl Chase, makes the bold claim that the *"male/female binary is not immutable."* She then makes an even bolder statement that it *"furnishes an opportunity to deploy 'nature' strategically to disrupt heteronormative systems of sex, gender, and sexuality"* (Chase 2006, 301). Cheryl has no qualms about being among the *Hermaphrodites with Attitude*, the name of her chapter in *The Transgender Studies Reader*, 2006. Some gender theorists have added intersex to the LGBTQI rainbow, including Amnesty International (LGBTQI Glossary n.d.). Although some intersex people might appreciate the support, equally as many are uncomfortable politicizing their disability. If biology becomes a tool of ideology, individuals on all sides of the conversation need to differentiate between biology and philosophy. The existence of intersex people is a biological fact; it is nature's way to *"disrupt heteronormative systems of sex, gender, and sexuality"* is a philosophical ideology (Chase 2006, 301).

The church responds to this ideology, claiming it is *"one which, in fact, ignores the suffering of those who have to live situations of sexual indeterminacy"* (*Male and Female He Created Them*, sec. 26), criticizing the activist community for politicizing a group of people with a medical condition for their own political agenda. If intersex people create a concept of ambiguous masculinity and femininity, this is not the fault of people born with Klinefelter's Syndrome, Androgen Insensitivity, or any other disorders. Some intersex individuals support gender theory and sexual liberation, but all intersex individuals do not share such positions.

We are not having an *intersex moment* as Dr. Anderson claims there is a *"transgender moment"* (Anderson 2018a, cover). If an intersex person's sex appears ambiguous, the person, in reality, still has binary sex. An intersex person is never able to both impregnate and become impregnated. An intersex person cannot self-propagate. The intersex person can either become pregnant, making her female, or impregnate, making him a male. Due to a genetic condition, a sterile individual is not a member of a third sex; they are simply sterile members of one of the two sexes. Similarly, if a person had Thalidomide syndrome and was born with a deformed morphology, like a missing or shortened limb, that person does not become a new animal species. People with Thalidomide syndrome are not different species because they have a congenital disability, so why would someone with a sexual congenital disability become a member of a third gender?

Cheryl Chase uses her platform to advocate for an overthrowing of heteronormative values. Still, according to Emi Koyama, founder of the Oregon chapter of Intersex Initiative, *"most people born with intersex conditions do view themselves as a man (or woman) with a birth condition like any other"* (Koyama 2006).

4.2 Biological Sex
Mutability in Lower Species

As a condition of creation's normativity, sex is usually considered immutable and unchangeable. When young Judeo Christians learn the story of Noah's Ark, they learn that all animals are either males or females and that God selects them, two by two. The concept that sex is not necessarily binary in other species may sound like a gender ideology intended to eradicate the concept of sex; however, it is biologically valid and not uncommon in the animal kingdom. As humans differ significantly from lower species, the fact that sex can change within those species is not direct proof that gender or sex can change in humans. Nevertheless, these lower species share common evolutionary ancestors, and their biology may uncover the human etiology of certain sexual anomalies. However, these lower species share common evolutionary ancestors, so their biology may offer clues regarding the origins of certain sexual anomalies in humans.

The reptilian complex is within humans' deep brains; the primary brain functions are the same as when humans were evolutionarily reptiles. In Thomistic terms, this would be the *"sensitive power,"* the faculties of the soul responding to a stimulus, digesting food, showing aggression, defecating, reproducing, et cetera (*ST* Ia q. 78, a. 1). Within these essential functions are also some of the *"evolutionary baggage"* (Wischik 2020). This reptilian carry-over is efficient in providing the framework for essential sensitive functions, but what if elements of reptilian aggression and mating also continue into the homo sapiens?

Fish, amphibians, and reptiles comprise 75.9% of the 66,178 vertebrate species on the planet (The World Conservation Union 2014), and they all lack sex chromosomes. Environmental conditions determine their sex primarily through temperature, which affects the distribution of enzymes and hormone receptors in embryos. Once nature selects the sex for fish and reptiles, it does not typically change within the mature stage of the species (C. Wu 1995).

In some species of amphibians, sex can switch throughout their lifespans. This biological reality is the basis for the crisis in the Jurassic Park series, where frog DNA filled the gaps of missing dinosaur DNA, which allowed the dinosaurs to change sex and mate. Although the movie and books are fictional, the description of amphibian sex mutability is correct. The ability of amphibians to be able to switch sex originates in the hypothalamus. Jiang-Ning Zhou, M.D., and Frank Kruijver, M.D., conducted two crucial studies involving the hypothalamus and its correlation to the transgender brain (*infra-7.2 and 7.3*).

In invertebrates, the hypothalamus is an integral part of the brain for controlling sexual behavior. At the University of California, Deborah Cummings, Ph.D., and Pauline Yahr, Ph.D., identified the site in the male gerbil's brain, which controls their copulatory behavior. The researchers in this study injected female gerbils with testosterone during development, causing the hypothalamus of the gerbil to develop a male nucleus. As a result, their behaviors are observably more like males gerbils (Cummings and Yahr 1984). This study is heavily cited as the first evidence suggesting that brains affect hormones and hormones affect the brain.

Researchers have also discovered how hormonal influences in the womb can affect the behavior of adult mammals. When rodent fetuses develop next to one another in a litter, one fetus's steroid hormones appear to influence the adjacent fetus's neutral and secondary sex structures. (Crews 1994). A female mouse lying in utero between two male mice develops higher testosterone and lower estrogen concentrations when becoming an adult. As a result, the female mouse is less sexually sought after by males and more likely to show aggression towards other females. This study points to the possibility that defective androgen receptors may affect a fetal brain's normal sexual development.

Overemphasizing the relationship between lower species and humans can be imprudent. Humans are not genetically like frogs, gerbils, or mice. However, it is essential to consider that most vertebrate species have varying degrees of sexual mutability. Nature is complex, and one should remain open to the idea that natural variations within human sexual development are inevitable, although rarely advantageous.

4.3 KLINEFELTER'S SYNDROME

This genetic disorder is systemic in individuals with 47 chromosomes rather than the traditional 46. This additional chromosome results in combinations like 47, XXY, and 47, XYY. This genetic defect occurs once in 1,000 births (Cameron 1999, 93). This disorder in men is external male genitalia, small testes, infertility, greater height, poor coordination, lower than average intelligence, and breast growth. It is not uncommon for men with Klinefelter's syndrome to be unaware of it until being assessed for infertility. A 1999 literature review of elective abortion rates found that about 58% of pregnancies in the United States diagnosed with Klinefelter's syndrome were terminated (Mansfield, Hopfer, and Marteau 1999, 808).

Clinic Feature of Klinefelter's syndrom and Turner's syndrome

Tall Structure

Poor Beard Growth

Minor Breast Development

Female Pubic Hair Pattern

Testicular atrophy

Short Structure

Webbed Neck

Shield Chest

Underdeveloped breast and widely spaced nipples

Rudimentary ovaries

Nevi

Figure 4.1 Klinefelter and Turner Syndromes

4.4 TURNER SYNDROME

Turner Syndrome is a genetic disorder whereby the individual is born with 45 total chromosomes rather than the typical 46. The Turner Syndrome karyotype is XO or 45 X. In this situation, all or a section of the second X or Y chromosome is missing. This disorder occurs once every 2,000–3,000 female births in cases where some of the Y chromosomes are absent; there *"is not enough to cause male sexual features"* (Zinn 2016, 540). Features include a short-webbed neck, low-set ears, shorter than average stature, swollen hands and feet at birth, and infertility. These individuals also have a more frequent rate of heart defects, diabetes, and hypothyroidism. Doctors have not identified the cause of this syndrome.

4.5 ANDROGEN INSENSITIVITY SYNDROME: CAIS AND PAIS

Thi s syndrome is less common than Klinefelter and Turner Syndromes, occurring only once in every 13,000 births. Although this syndrome is rare, it is significant because it causes the most classic and recognizable intersex examples. Androgen Insensitivity Syndrome is both a complete (CAIS) and partial disorder (PAIS). This disorder in women affects one of the X chromosomes, which makes women carriers. The phenotypic features include delays in puberty, taller than average height, and less than average body hair for women with this disorder. Since these physical characteristics are an idealized form of a Western woman, this syndrome is not easily recognizable as an intersex abnormality during puberty.

Males, during gestation, become unable to process male hormones (androgens). The entire female genitalia forms with partially or fully undescended testes, a short vagina, and no cervix for a male with CAIS. Although the female genitalia appears normal to medical professionals, the disorder may not reveal itself until puberty. Due to the absence of a womb, puberty does not lead to menstruation; however, secondary female characteristics will develop. The body cannot absorb any testosterone, and some of the unabsorbed testosterone gets converted into estrogen.

Individuals with PAIS are less likely to be passable as cis women. People with PAIS exhibit symptoms ranging from normal male genitalia with infertility to entire exterior female genitalia but with no pubic hair. This range of variation is medically rated on a scale of one to seven, with one being the most masculine features and seven being the most feminine. In a 2002 review of literature, of 14 individuals with PAIS, 77% were satisfied with the sex parents and physicians assigned at birth (Migeon et al. 2002, e31)[2]. Again, like CAIS, this syndrome is only showing phenotypically in men with 46 XY chromosomes.

---

[2] The conclusion is likely correct although the source is unreliable. Doctors. Claude Migeon and John Money are founders of the Gender Identity Clinic which conducted questionably unethical procedures in the 1960s and 1970s.

4.6 ADRENOGENITAL SYNDROME

This condition affects people with XX chromosomes and a cortisol defect, whereby there are no feedback loops. The result is that the adrenal gland keeps making androgens. This syndrome causes male genitalia to form and a masculinized brain. If female hormones become active naturally or through hormone supplements, the person will start to menstruate through the penis (Wischik 2020).

4.7 OVO-TESTES

This disease was formerly called True Hermaphroditism, whereby the child is born with both male and female external genitalia. Internally, the individual typically has one ovary and one testis. This condition accounts for fewer than 5% of intersex cases and only occurs once in every 83,000 births. The most common way this phenomenon occurs is when either two sperms fertilize one ovum when two fertilized ova fuse together or with the *Sry* gene mutation.[3] Embryos are gonadally identical, regardless of genetic sex, until the sixth to the eighth week of gestation, when the *Sry* gene triggers the Anti-Müllerian Hormone (AMH), which stops the female sex organs from forming. Without the *Sry* gene, both sets of sex organs form at the same time.

Countless possible genetic abnormalities cause physical mutations of the reproductive system. Therefore, it is impossible and unnecessary to discuss all intersex mutations to understand that abnormalities exist within the human genotype and phenotype. Physicians estimate that one in every 2,500—4,500 children is born intersex (Hughes 2006, 490). However, Dr. Anne Fausto-Sterling claims a much higher rate of one in 60, using an expansive definition of intersex or disorders of sex development (DSD). These abnormalities are deficiencies in the human genome, but they do not change the person's ontology affected by the deficiency.

---

[3] A DNA-binding protein also called gene-regulatory protein/transcription factor found on the Y chromosome.

4.8 MEDICALIZATION OF INTERSEX

While the medical community pushes forward with a single therapeutic approach involving hormones and surgery, the intersex community is beginning to explore more natural alternatives. With the invention of prenatal testing, parents have chosen to abort more than half of intersex children (Mansfield, Hopfer, and Marteau 1999, 808). The history of intersex people and the pushback of some intersex people to medicalize or abort them is worth exploring.

The original understanding of intersex came from Greek mythology, whereby the gods Hermes and Aphrodite named their offspring Hermaphroditus. Plato interpreted this myth to create his theory of three original sexes found in the *Symposium* (189–193). Early Jewish commentators considered Adam in the original unity a hermaphrodite before the division into *is* (male) and *issa* (female) (Kvam, Schearing, and Ziegler 1999, 77–78). During the medieval period, the Jewish code of law called the *Tosefta* considered hermaphrodites legally male in some instances and female in others. For example, when menstruating, the person must be segregated from society with other women, but at other times was forbidden from being in spaces meant for women only (Fausto-Sterling 2000a, 33).

Gaius Pliny (23–79AD) recalled the emperor Romulus would drown hermaphrodites as *"monsters,"* but in the first century were used as prostitutes in ritualistic and secular enjoyment (Bostock and Riley 1857, 2:136). Throughout history and presently, the social relationship with the individual depended on the ability to pass as one gender. Economic, political influence, and family also significantly affected the possibilities for an intersex person to flourish within society. For Catholic and Orthodox Christians throughout the church's history, religious life or celibacy remained a collectively acceptable vocation used to conceal sexual abnormalities.

German-Swiss doctor Theodore Klebs (1834–1913) depended primarily on the existence of testes to determine whether a person is male or female. Doctors at the time claimed, *"No matter how womanly a patient looked, no matter if she had a vagina, fine and round breasts, a smooth face, and a husband she loved, if she had testes, she would be labeled a male"* (Dreger 1999, 9). After two world wars leaving men maimed by the mid-twentieth century, cosmetic surgery and medical science had reached a tipping point, and medical treatments for children born with ambiguous genitalia became available. Unfortunately, the process of medically realigning sex became disastrous since it was always easier to remove a penis than to add one, which meant all intersex surgeries produced female results regardless of any other factors. This book will address this issue in more depth *infra-5.4.*

Finally, in 1997, Milton Diamond, Ph.D., called for a moratorium on all intersex surgeries until the child's sex was determined later, which was codified by the *American Academy of Pediatrics* in 2000. The *British Association of Pediatric Surgeons* followed suit in 2001. In 2020, the therapeutic response to the intersex condition was straightforward: the best option is to wait until children are old enough to show their sex and, in some cases, is old enough to consent to the surgery. The physical structure of the penis or testes in an intersex child is not enough of a determinant to accurately predict the child's functional sex. If the testes do not produce testosterone or if the person has CAIS or PAIS, then the testosterone will not masculinize the brain or other sex-specific male features. The masculinized or feminized brain is the ultimate determining factor for identifying one's true gender.

Gender advocates like Dr. Fausto-Sterling call for an end of the two-sex system and advocate for five instead in her 1993 article, *The Five Sexes*. Dr. Fausto-Sterling later admitted she had intended to be provocative, but she also wrote with *"tongue firmly in cheek"* (Fausto-Sterling 2000b, 19). Nevertheless, the idea of non-binary sex caught on regardless of her intent. This type of gender theory is precisely about which the document *Male and Female He Created Them* warns. The church document claimed: *"The process of identifying sexual identity is made more difficult by the fictitious contract known as "gender neuter" or "third gender," which has the effect of obscuring the fact that a person's sex is a structural determinant of male or female identity"* (Congregation for Catholic Education 2019, *sec.* 26). Of course, the church and society are sensitive to the struggles of intersex people. However, are there intersex accommodation and sensitivities available if an individual had an intersex brain, or are the intersex sensitivities only available for people with ambiguous genitalia?

Although the *church rejects gender neuter and third gender ideologies, it is difficult for the church to reject the belief that people could be left natural as they are born.* Medical concerns affecting the person's health should be addressed, but should society force children into unnecessary cosmetic surgeries to perpetuate a binary ideology? If a person is born with a distinguishable binary sex, there are vocations for them. If one is not born into explicit binary sex, does a person have to be adopted into one, or can a person be allowed to be left naturally ambiguous? If an intersex person like Tia Pesando (*supra*-3.4) wanted to become a nun, what is the church's response? Or if Tia wanted to be a monk, could *he*? Jesus himself noted that *some are born eunuchs... and others become eunuchs for the sake of the Kingdom of Heaven* (Mt 19: 12). This book will cover this subject in greater depth in chapter eleven.

Dr. DeFranza comments, *"This short history shows how the hermaphrodite began as a legendary creation of the gods, was tolerated at the margins of societies for millennia, only to be surgically eliminated in the last hundred years"* (DeFranza 2015, 57).

4.9 CONCEPT REVIEW

C hapter four introduced the science section of this book by addressing natural sex anomalies. The analysis separates the ideology of sex as a spectrum from the biological realism of the binary sex model. This section presents a medical overview of the forms of intersex disorders as well as a historical review of society's interpretation of intersex people. Intersex is not a single condition but an umbrella term to refer to dozens of conditions across a wide range of phenotypes. For intersex people, the masculinized and feminized brain is primarily the deciding factor determining one's actual sex. For transgender people, the gonads may not be ambiguous, but what if the brain is oppositely feminized or masculinized? What if the intersex part of the person is in the brain and not in the body's visible appendages? In chapter seven, this book will discuss the possibility of an intersex brain.

Lastly, this section suggests that an intersex condition could exist naturally, not as a political ideology threatening the binary system but as a natural eunuch. This rejection may be less motivated by rejecting the binary system and more motivated by a rejection of unnecessary cosmetic surgery, which tends to idolize the body. Dr. DeFranza advocates for Christians to recognize the *imago Dei's* presence in the flesh of the intersex people (DeFranza 2015, 288). If those with intersexed morphologies are encouraged to leave their bodies natural, could the same argument be made if they claim to have an intersex brain? Is the medicalized approach always the best approach for dealing with sexual ambiguity? Ironically, some gender theorists are the ones most rigidly adhering to gender stereotypes, demanding surgery to conform to some idea of what it means to be a man or woman.

CHAPTER 5
TRANSGENDER SCIENCE
BEFORE 1980

It is the fact that falsehood is never so false as when it is very nearly true.

— G.K. Chesterton, *Saint Thomas Aquinas*

My personal feeling is that surgery is not a proper treatment for a psychiatric disorder, and it's clear to me that these patients have severe psychological problems that don't go away following surgery.

— Jon Meyer, M.D., *Sex Reassignment: follow-up*

Studying history is the act of reflecting on God speaking to His people in the world. Awareness of the unfolding events of history links generations and the evolution of human knowledge—those who lack prudence, *memoria*, or memory of the past. When a person does not live through an experience, one must practice *docility* or the ability to be taught. Those who lack memory and docility will lack good counsel and understanding in the present and foresight into the future. Shrewdness keeps people from repeating the same mistakes from the past, but this requires people to study history. For example, approaching the medicalization of transgender people without considering the past centuries is patently imprudent. A prudent person considers all available: history, science, philosophy, and experiences within a range of circumspection to proceed cautiously.

The transgender movement from the late 1800s to the 1980s went through an unprecedented period of unfolding. The movement evolved from taboo and fetishism before the 1950s to pop curiosity in the post-World War II period. Medically treated transsexuals gained social acceptance in the 1960s and early 1970s, only for society to demonize and reject them by the end of the 1970s. Skepticism over the genuineness of sex reassignment surgeries resulted from two false claims being over-emphasized: first, science can cure anything, and second, the patient is the paying customer who determines the therapeutic treatment. By the end of the 1970s, some doctors came to question both modernist ideals.

Throughout this chapter, one must consider if science and philosophy confirm that the body is moldable to match the mind. Also, because the medical community can perform a procedure, how should the ethical framework determine if a procedure should be done? Going by the hypothesis, *what can happen, will happen* is an unhealthy approach to medical science. Instead, this book advocates for the use of the virtue of prudence when applying medical procedures.

5.1 EARLY SCIENCE OF HERMAPHRODITES

Plato in the *Symposium* uses Aristophanes' speech to propose three sexes: the original male (*arren*) sex born of the sun, the female (*thèly*) of the earth, and the third, combining qualities of both the others and called androgynous (*androgynos*), born of the moon. Androgyny, the third sex, combines both male and female features and does not lack a sex (Plato *Symposium*, 189–193). Ancient Greek myths should not be disregard as fairy tales, for Aristotle wrote, *"Even the lover of myth (philomythos) is in a sense a lover of wisdom (philosophos), for myth is composed of wonders"* (Aristotle *Metaphysics*, 982b18–19).

Aristotle differed from Plato, teaching the possibility of only two sexes. Therefore, he wrote, mothers providing either insufficient or excess material while the child developed in the womb caused sexual abnormalities. For sexual determination, Aristotle followed Hippocrates' theory on sex formation in the womb but not a third sex, *"The heat of the male partner during intercourse determined sex. If the male's heat could overwhelm the female's coldness, then a male child would form. In contrast, if the female's coldness was too strong or the male's heat too weak, a female child would be born"* (Hake and O'Connor 2008, 25).

Aelius Galenus (129–210), a second-century Greek physician, continued Aristotle's theory of the heart's heat. Aelius determined the sexes with his theory that the uterus' right side contained male heat and the left side of the uterus controlled female coolness. Sharon Preves, Ph.D., notes, *"Depending upon where in the grid an embryo fell, it could range from entirely male, through various intermediate states, to entirely female"* (Preves 2003, 34). Thus, Aelius is the first written example of sex being considered a spectrum with male and female poles on either side. This theory is not based on myth but rather on an inaccurate understanding of human biology.

Sixteenth-century French surgeon Ambroise Paré (1510–1590), who served kings Henry II, Francis II, Charles IX, and Henry III, is considered by historians to be the father of surgery and modern forensic pathology (Forrai 2006, 447). Ambroise considered the onset of secondary sex characteristics (intersex organs) in pubescent girls to result from girls who jumped and played so much that they raised their body temperature too high. The heat pushed out their female organs (Preves 2003, 34). Until German scientists Schleiden, Virchow, and Bütschli discovered chromosomes in the 1800s, the caloric theory of sex development remained the West's leading theory for explaining intersex people. Although the theory may sound archaic, the caloric theory is accurate for lower species like the Mississippi alligator, whereby the temperature of the incubated eggs determines the sex of the offspring. There is some evidence suggesting that environmental factors may affect mammalian sex determination as well (Chan and Wai-Sum 1981, 9).

5.2 TRANSVESTITISM: 1877–1947

The twentieth century did not treat transgender people favorably. In 1910, *Die Transvestiten,* published by sexologist Magnus Hirschfield, M.D., built on Dr. Richard von Krafft-Ebing, M.D.'s 1886 classic, *Psychopathia Sexualis* (von Krafft-Ebing 1906; reprint).[1] Dr. Hirschfield, unlike Dr. von Krafft-Ebing, differentiates transvestitism from homosexuality (Hirschfeld 2003). The term transsexual may originate from the writings of Dr. Hirschfield. Sexologists Vern Bullough, Ph.D., and Bonnie Bullough, Ph.D. state, *"Hirschfeld in 1910 called one of his patients a psychic transsexual,"* but they give no reference for this claim (Bullough and Bullough 1993, 257). The Nazis destroyed most of Dr. Hirschfeld's research in 1933, so any evidence of Dr. Hirshfield's work with early twentieth-century transsexuals is presumably lost. One of the few accounts of early twentieth-century transsexuals is Ralph Werther, who published under the alias Earl Lind. In the 1918 *Autobiography of an Androgyne,* Ralph describes a club of androgynes called Cercle Hermaphroditos. They meet at Paresis Hall, a brothel and gay bar in New York City that opened in the 1890s (Lind 1975).

In the first quarter of the twentieth century, scientific journals and magazines did not broadly publish transvestism cases outside a few tracts. Seldom would physicians encounter anyone admitting to such a diagnosis. However, by 1930, *Sexology* magazine started to receive letters from transsexual individuals seeking sex reassignment surgeries. Since sex reassignment surgeries were beyond the capability of medical science during the 1930s, editors of the magazine offered no advice to writers of these letters and, in some cases, discouraged their attempts to transition. (Meyerowitz 1998, 166).

Medical technology has improved dramatically in the wake of two world wars, including the ability to perform reconstructive surgery.

---

[1] Dr. Ira Pauly claims this definition is also in von Krafft-Ebing's 1877 *metamorphosis sexualis paranoia,* but I have been unable to find that this book exists. (Pauly 1992).

Simultaneously, in 1949, David Cauldwell, M.D., in *Psychopathia Transsexualis,* used the term transsexualism to identify people who wanted a sex change (Cauldwell 1949, 274). The ability to attempt sex reassignment surgeries, along with public recognition of the disorder, increased the desire for surgeons to attempt these surgeries.

As fate would have it, Harry Benjamin, M.D., became a cornerstone in the transsexual movement by a series of unrelated coincidences. Dr. Benjamin, a native German, escaped to New York at the start of World War I to practice medicine and conduct research on glands, an area of study not yet explored by modern science. During his research on animals, Dr. Benjamin castrated and implanted opposite sex glands to change the sex of the mammal hormonally and socially. Dr. Benjamin used the research conducted by chemists Casimir Funk, Ph.D., and Benjamin Harrow, Ph.D., to isolate androgenic steroids from human urine to create a hormone supplement capable of reversing the effects of aging.[2] Dr. Benjamin put to use his knowledge of hormones and glands over the next decade to treat old age or *geronto-therapy,* a term he coined in 1943 (Schaefer and Wheeler 1995, 75).

---

[2] A technique already discovered 2000 years earlier and recorded by Ovid as *"stuff from a mare in heat"* (Taylor 1996, 213).

5.3 THE AGE OF HARRY BENJAMIN
1948–1975

D
r. Benjamin's life changed in 1948 when he and Alfred Kinsey, Sc.D., stayed at the same San Francisco hotel. While taking sex histories for one of his studies, Dr. Kinsey found an individual who wanted a sex reassignment. Dr. Kinsey referred this young person to Dr. Benjamin, who, as an endocrinologist, may have been able to assess the individual's hormone levels. Dr. Benjamin agreed to meet Van, a twenty-three-year-old MtF individual who claimed to experience life as a girl since two. Once in High School, special accommodations for cross-dressing ceased, and Van stopped attending school. Van remained home doing *"women's work"* and socially presenting like a woman. Van wanted to become a woman, wife, and mother and did not receive sexual excitement from wearing women's clothing. However, Dr. Benjamin tried to find an American surgeon to perform cosmetic operations to feminize Van. Simultaneously, the Attorney General of Wisconsin interpreted this surgery under state law to be a kind of *"mayhem,"*[3] which made sex reassignment surgeries illegal within the United States. Between 1953

---

[3] Mayhem is defined as, *"Every person who unlawfully and maliciously deprives a human being of a member of his body, or disables, disfigures, or renders it useless, or cuts or disables the tongue, or puts out an eye, or slits the nose, ear, or lip, is guilty of mayhem"* (Garner 2019). This begs the question, what is meant by *"unlawful."* Typically, a person who gives consent to be touched is not touched unlawfully. There is a question of whether a transgender person's consent could be viewed as valid or if they are unable to consent under the theory of diminished capacity because of mental illness. This ultimately hinges on whether a person believes this is a mental illness which causes people to think irrationally about their self-image, or is this a matter of the feminine brain in a male body or vice versa?

and 1958, Van, called Susan, repeatedly traveled to Germany for reassignment surgeries, after which time she quietly moved to Canada.

In 1949, Dr. Benjamin again became part of history by treating a married couple who claimed to be opposite genders from their assigned sexes. A California clinic wrote to Dr. Benjamin, *"[B]oth partners became transvestites; the former wife became a man legally and had the marriage annulled[4]. However, the pair still live together in reversed roles; the former wife takes the role of a husband and breadwinner, and the former husband now stays at home and keeps house"* (Ettner 1999, 15). Dr. Benjamin assisted the couple by providing counseling and hormone treatments to manage the dysphoria better. Elmer Belt, M.D., of UCLA medical center, quietly performed the first American sex-reassignment surgery for the MtF individual of this complicated marriage.

Concurrently, as these procedures began, people like Billy Tipon, a famous mid-century jazz musician born a female, held a successful career as a male performer. A decade after Billy Tipon's death, his family revealed he was born a natal female (Kay 1998). Willmer "Little Axe" Broadnax, a notorious gospel singer from the 1940s to 1960s, lived as a man throughout his entire life, only to be revealed after his death that he was born a female (Gettell 2016). Many transgender people stealthily assumed the opposite sex identity during this period, never revealing this truth to the general public.

From the thousands of patients seen by Dr. Benjamin, George Jorgensen became the most famous. George contacted Dr. Benjamin as a young United States G.I. in 1952. The same year, George was referred to Dr. Christian Hamburger in Sweden to remove his penis and testicles and receive a vaginoplasty. Thus, George became Christine Jorgensen—a name selected out of gratitude for her surgeon. The *New York Daily News* banner reported, *"Ex-Gi Becomes Blonde Beauty: Operations Transform Bronx Youth"* (Daily News 1952).

Dr. Benjamin began to give lectures on *Transsexualism and Transvestism as Psycho-Somatic and Somatopsychic Syndromes* in 1953, which shot off a flare for all those suffering from gender dysphoria. Also, in

---

[4] The marriage was legally annulled by a matter of law since both members of the marriage becoming legally men in a time prior to same-sex marriage.

1953, upon Christine's return, she opened a famed nightclub act, which kept her name on the marquee for the next decade. After the celebrity status exposure of Christine Jorgensen, Pandora's box was open, and demand for surgery was high for gender dysphoric individuals seeking assistance. By 1965 Dr. Benjamin treated 307 patients who would become the subjects in his book, *The Transsexual Phenomenon* (Benjamin 1966). Finally, Dr. Benjamin released the flood gates with his national publication, and thousands of patients flooded his clinic. Still, both laws and science were not on their side. A letter from an MtF patient in 1969 indicates that the surgery did not always succeed despite the surgeon's best efforts. The patient wrote:

> My male sexual organs are gone! Dr. _____ performed "in cold blood" on me one of those horrible mutilations. My so-called vagina entrance looks like a ring of empty scrotum. I will have to live, if I have the courage, with this monstrosity. (Ettner 1999, 37)

On June 28, 1969, the tide further shifted for the LGBT community with a Stonewall Inn raid in New York City's West Village. Unlike countless prior incidences of arrest and harassment at LGBT institutions, the customers fought back this time, which led to three days of rioting. In addition to similar ones at Compton's Cafeteria in San Francisco and Cooper's Donuts in Los Angeles, this incident awakened the sleeping giant of queer people around the country. Among the first to participate in this movement were queer men, young prostitutes, drag queens, transvestites (the term used for transgender people), and many other members of the LGB community (Erickson-Schroth and Jacobs 2017, 136). Marsha P. Johnson and Sylvia Rivera, two MtF individuals, have become legends within the queer community for their activism in New York around this time. Together they founded the Street Transvestite Action Revolutionaries (STAR), a group dedicated to helping homeless young drag queens, gay youth, and trans women (Vincent 2020). A social movement was on the rise.

[Virginia Prince, 1912—2009]

Another famous patient of Dr. Benjamin was Virginia Prince (1912–2009), an MtF individual who controversially claimed sex reassignment surgeries could not effectively change one's sex. Virginia Prince claims genital reconstructive surgery was the wrong choice for 90% of those who sought it. Virginia claimed, *"Sex reassignment surgery is a communicable disease,"* attracting the interest of transvestites, seduced by the publicity and the hope the surgery would improve their lives (Prince, 1978, 271). Virginia Prince originated the term *transgenderist* to differentiate between cross-gender individuals, in contrast to transsexuals who underwent surgeries to change sex (not gender). She believed she was dealing with a gender issue and not a sex issue. Therefore trying to change one's sex was missing an essential distinction between the two (Prince 1969, 53), although Virginia received hormones and some feminizing surgeries throughout her life.

While Dr. Benjamin and Christine Jorgensen understood a strong link between one's body and gender, Virginia Prince considered gender psycho-social and disconnected from sex. Virginia advocated for the belief that one's gender can change by merely changing one's role within society. In Virginia's view, gender does not exist in and of itself, nor does gender identity have any bearing on a person's sex. Thus no sex change is necessary since a person's sex does not constitute the problem.

Dr. Benjamin developed the Benjamin Scale (Benjamin 1966), similar to the Kinsey Scale, to show the range of transgender identities in natal males. This scale suggests a range of transgender identities rather than the two clear categories: transgender or cisgender people. The scale ranges from one, a male with no transexual tendencies, to six, a male who principally engages the world as a female. Using the Benjamin Scale, only types five and six would benefit from any medical intervention. Although this scale is no longer in use, having been replaced by the *DSM*, the modern medical science of the previous decade validates the perspective that being transgender is a spectrum. Therefore, while one can argue for medical interventions for treating gender dysphoria, one must acknowledge that not all gender dysphoric individuals experience the dysphoria to the same degree.

Group	Type	Name	Kinsey Scale	Conversion operation
1	I	Transvestite (Pseudo)	0-6	Not considered
1	II	Transvestite (Fetishistic)	0-2	Rejected
1	III	Transvestite (True)	0-2	Rejected, but the idea can be appealing
2	IV	Transexual (Nonsurgical)	1-4	Attractive but not requested or attraction not admitted
3	V	Transexual (Moderate intensity)	4-6	Requested, usually indicated
3	VI	Transexual (High intensity)	6	Urgently requested and usually attained

Figure 5.1 The Benjamin Scale

Despite the shortcomings and legal challenges, patients in the 1960s traveled across the world for surgery, often to Georges Burou, M.D.'s (1910–1987), Clinique du Parc in Casablanca out of desperation (Batty 2004). French gynecologist Dr. Burou was able to operate with discretion inside his private colonial quarters, performing as many as 3,000 surgeries by 1973 (Green 2008, 612). Clinique du Parc became so notorious among the transsexual community that *"going to Casablanca"* became a colloquialism for getting sex reassignment surgery (Goddard 2009, 982).

By 1965, Johns Hopkins medical center became the first North American hospital to offer support for sex reassignment surgeries and do so without the legal charge of mayhem. By 1975, twenty other centers opened, and around 1,000 patients underwent sex reassignment surgeries (Meyerowitz 2002, 217–222). The mainlining of this practice was both a blessing and a curse for the transgender community. Previously, transgender people hid their gender identities, and outside of the spotlight, no one suspected a person of being a transsexual. Their invisibility and small numbers within society became their protection. However, with their own medical center, transgender people became targets of ridicule. In the *Journal of the American Medical Association*, 1978, Melvin Belli, Esq. claims, *"Most gender clinics report that many applicants for surgery are actually sociopaths seeking notoriety, masochistic homosexuals, or borderline psychotics, and not true transsexuals"* (Belli 1978, 2144).

In the case of *Hartin v. Director of the Bureau of Records and Statistics*, the courts opined:

> Surgery for the transsexual is an experimental form of psychotherapy by which mutilating surgery is conducted on a person with the intent of setting his mind at ease, and that, nonetheless, does not change the body cells governing sexuality. In the words of one of the medical members of the Board, *'I would think that it would be unsound if, in fact, there were an encouragement to the broader use of this means of resolving a person's unhappy mental state.'* (Hartin v. Director of the Bureau of Records and Statistics 1973)

Although the court was not going to criminalize the doctors for performing these surgeries, the court made their opinion quite clear; the State did not want to normalize this behavior. The court fundamentally determined these were attempts to cure a mental illness, and the procedure did not prove successful.

The battle over transgender surgeries became a philosophical battle over the Hippocratic Oath and the meaning of therapeutic surgery. If a person believes the surgery is restorative, does that make the treatment therapeutic, or are there objective standards? If a patient has the surgery performed and subsequently commits suicide, is the doctor liable for performing surgeries that are not effectively therapeutic? One can argue that removing healthy organs should not be considered therapeutic in any case. Nevertheless, others argue rhinoplasty does not have an objective therapeutic value, only a subjective personal value, and no one threatens to make rhinoplasty illegal (Ettner 1999, 32).

In addition to legal concerns and the charges from medical professionals that the procedures were quackery, the most significant challenge transgender individuals faced was financing the surgeries. Affluent people with enough money to pay any price were among the first to receive sex-reassignment surgeries. However, this disorder affected people of all economic classes, so Reed Erickson (1917—1992),[5] an FtM individual who inherited a fortune and later became extraordinarily wealthy through real estate investments, founded the Erickson Educational Foundation in 1964 to help fund transsexual research and lower costs.

---

[5] *"Sadly, by the time of his death in 1992 at the age of 74, he had become addicted to illegal drugs and died in Mexico as a fugitive from US drug indictments"* (Devor n.d.).

5.4 THE GENDER IDENTITY CLINIC 1965–1978

D
r. Edgerton became involved in this field when, as Chief plastic surgeon at Johns Hopkins, an individual with a partial sex reassignment surgery requested his services. Through the cosmetic nature of their field of practice, plastic surgeons reconcile changing a person's body to help with emotional self-identification. The Gender Identity Clinic, organized quietly in 1965, was composed of surgeons, endocrinologists, psychologists, psychiatrists, and a single legal expert. This team included Dr. Benjamin, an endocrinologist researcher, John Money, Ph.D., a psychiatric researcher, Claude Migeon, M.D., an endocrinologist, and Dr. Howard Jones, a gynecologist.

In 1969, at the American Association of Plastic Surgeons' annual meeting, Milton Edgerton, M.D., Norman Knorr, M.D., and James Callison, M.D., announced in a paper titled, *The Surgical Treatment of Transsexual Patients: Limitations and Indications*, that they were opening the first transsexual treatment center. Thus, the Gender Identity Clinic at Johns Hopkins became the first full-time center dedicated to treating transsexual people. In addition, the clinic developed criteria for performing sex-reassignment surgeries, which set the bar for other facilities (Edgerton, Knorr, and Callison 1970).

1. The patient must have no ambivalence about the surgery. It cannot be part of a life crisis or a depressed homosexual.

2. The patient must be mentally healthy. The person may not suffer from other forms of mental illness.

3. The patient must be better served by surgery than psychotherapy.

4. The patient must be able to adjust to the new gender role when returning to their normal life.

These four criteria comprised a basic framework for analysis, although not always easily applied. Dr. Edgerton found, *"schizophrenic illness occurred more often in transsexuals than in the general population, and that this was suggestive of an association between the two disorders"* (Edgerton, Knorr, and Callison 1970). A study conducted 30 years after his observation confirmed that schizophrenia was a common condition among transgender people.

Dr. Edgerton also devised a system of pastoral care, which became widely accepted. His instruction to other medical professionals was to accept what the client was expressing. He taught,

> It is not difficult for the surgeon to establish a good relationship with transsexual patients—but to do so, he must deal with the patient as a member of the psychological sex chosen by the patient! To think of a male transsexual as a *"male"* is to completely defeat the working doctor-patient relationship. (Edgerton, Knorr, and Callison 1970, 44)

Although there is a temptation not to concede one's sense of objective reality, the only way to help the patient through their dysphoria would be by first showing respect to their experience and, by doing so, building trust.[6] For example, the Gender Identity Clinic only performed sex-reassignment surgeries on less than 10% of patients who applied (Belli 1978, 2146). Still, they helped treat the other 90% non-surgically by developing a relationship of trust and respect.

---

[6] Pope Francis has taken a similar approach by using a transgender person's personal pronouns. The pontiff's concession on pronouns was not a submission of reality but is a pastoral way to build a relationship of trust and respect.

[John Money, Ph.D., 1921— 2006]

John Money, Ph.D. (1921—2006), as a founding member of The Gender Identity Clinic of Johns Hopkins Medical Center, became one of the leading experts in sex reassignment surgeries. Dr. Money sought to eliminate intersex deformities by performing medical interventions early to give a child an explicit sex. Typically, a doctor can more easily remove a disfigured penis than build one, so surgeons reassigned many intersex and disfigured children as females. Dr. Money operated on the philosophy that gender is a social construct; therefore, if a child is raised as a girl and believes she is a girl, the child will become a woman. In 1955, Dr. Money introduced gender roles as a concept separate from biology (Money 1955, 253).

On the opposite coast, Richard Green, M.D., and Robert Stoller, M.D., from UCLA's Department of Psychology, opened a competing Gender Identity Research Clinic to help gender variant children embrace their birth sex (Stoller 1968). Larry Newman, M.D., a professor of psychology at UCLA and student at the time of the founding of the clinic, claims, *"The goal at UCLA was never to change a child's behavior… but rather to find a way to give them the best chance at happiness in the long term"* (Newman 1976, 685). This clinic operated when gender theorists advanced the idea that gender is a fluid social construction and people can change their gender through socialization. The gender-neutral theory has been debunked, reaffirming the wisdom in their approach of not making sudden life-altering transformations in their young patients' lives. Dr. Newman defends the clinic's stance by pointing out, *"most of the participants of the study who as children said they wanted to be girls grew up to identify as gay men over the next 15 years. Many of those participants became comfortable with their biological sex without therapy"* (Newman 1976, 686).

In 1969, doctors Money and Richard Green joined forces to published *Transsexualism and Sex Reassignment*, to which other members of the medical community responded with disgust. One such psychiatrist wrote:

> Aside from the violation of the primary principle of doing no harm to the patient, and aside from the smug complacency of this dehumanizing gang whose consciences require no sop than doing what the patient wants, I think there is reason to distrust both their descriptions and the very existence of this *"disease"* called *"transsexualism."* (Ettner 1999, 42)

243

Psychoanalyst Charles Socarides, M.D., published a letter from an utterly miserable patient,

> I recently read a paper submitted for publication describing the wretched, hopeless existence of one of these *"women."* Of course, once the mutilation is done, a sober assessment of the results might lead logically to suicide. How could such a patient make an honest statement? In regard to the latter point, this *"disease"* seems to have sprung up in compliance with the *"advances"* in surgical butchery. Whoever heard of it before these surgical geniuses made their expertise known? You may have noticed in the book that the patients keep on trying to get more and more surgery. I suspect the whole thing is an iatrogenic matter that permits the patient to become the collaborator in a disguised, horrible, regressive representation of a sadistic sexual act. (Ettner 1999, 42)

In a more extended response to doctors Money and Green, Dr. Socarides published *A Psychoanalytical Study of the Desires for Sexual Transformation [Transsexualism]: The Plaster-of-Paris Man* (1970), which claimed the transsexual was a sexual pervert who escapes homosexuality and *"fastens to the idea of changing his sex through the psychotic mechanism of denial"* (Socarides 1970, 341) and *"such operations are doomed to ultimate failure because they do not change the basic underlying conflict"* (Socarides 1969, 156).

Dr. Edgerton, one of the founders of the Gender Identity Clinic, defended his clinic and the work of doctors Money and Green. He stated, *"At the moment, I am rather convinced that if I were such a patient, surgery would offer me the only existing realistic hope for happiness. It is far from an ideal solution. I continue to ask these patients if they have had second thoughts about their surgery. They do not. Quite to the contrary, they remain very grateful for the assistance"* (Ettner 1999, 42). Despite Dr. Edgerton's claims, once Paul McHugh, M.D., became the psychiatrist-in-chief of Johns Hopkins in 1975, the practice of sex-reassignment surgeries came under scrutiny.

In 1976, Charles Ihlenfeld, M.D., a colleague of Dr. Benjamin and an advocate for sex reassignment surgeries, became concerned with their approach after administering cross-sex hormones on 500 patients over six years. He concluded,

There is too much unhappiness among people who have the surgery. Too many of them end as suicides. Eighty percent who want to change their sex shouldn't do it. Whatever surgery did, it did not fulfill a basic yearning for something that is difficult to define. This goes along with the idea that we are trying to treat superficially something that is much deeper. (Ihlenfeld 2004, 151)

In 2011, Dr. Ihlenfeld reaffirmed his stance in an interview with Walt Heyer, a former MtF individual who detransitioned. He claimed, *"gender reassignment surgery isn't the answer to alleviate the psychological factors that drive many with the compulsion to change genders"* (Heyer 2018, 147)

5.5 THE END OF THE GENDER
IDENTITY CLINIC 1979

The year 1979 was a pivotal year for people who identify as transgender. Dr. Benjamin launched The Harry Benjamin International Gender Dysphoria Association (HBIGDA)[7]. This association released the first set of Standards of Care for Transsexuals, a twofold protocol designed for medical professionals when treating gender non-conforming patients while also protecting them from malpractice claims. A patient no longer needed to be seen at a gender clinic to have basic standards of care.

By 1979, two thousand people applied for surgical transition at the Johns Hopkins Gender Clinic, and only 24 were allowed, showing the extreme caution taken by the doctors at the Gender Clinic (Erickson-Schroth and Jacobs 2017, 13). Despite the clinic approving few sex reassignment surgeries, Jon Meyer, M.D., the director of the sexual behaviors consultation unit claimed, that the surgery served *"as a palliative measure [but] it does not cure what is essentially a psychiatric disturbance"* (Gender Identity Clinic 1979, 2). Further, *"surgical intervention has done nothing objective beyond what time and psychotherapy can do"* and *"no differences in long-term adjustment between transsexuals who go under the scalpel and those who do not"* (Meyer and Reter 1979, 1010).

In a letter to the editor in the New York Times, 1979, Dr. Meyer placed the final nail in the coffin for Johns Hopkins Gender Identity Clinic. Dr. Meyer stated, *"My personal feeling is that surgery is not a proper treatment for a psychiatric disorder, and it's clear to me that these patients have severe psychological problems that don't go away following surgery"* (Meyer and Reter 1979, 1012).

---

[7] Since 2007 HBIGDA has been renamed, the World Professional Association for Transgender Health (WPATH).

The research conducted by Dr. Meyer was all Dr. McHugh, the chief surgeon at Johns Hopkins, needed to close the Gender Identity Clinic. Dr. McHugh, through his observations, already suspected the treatments were not successful. He experienced,

> That patients several years after surgery were contented with what they had done and that only a few regretted it. But in every other respect, they were little changed in their psychological condition. They had many of the same problems with relationships, work, and emotions as before. The hope that they would emerge now from their emotional difficulties to flourish psychologically had not been fulfilled. We psychiatrists, I thought, would do better to concentrate on trying to fix their minds and not their genitalia. (McHugh 2004)

Dr. McHugh observed that the MtF surgeries did not cure the underlying psychological issues, which led to the surgery in the first place. During his interviews with transsexuals, he found they talked a great deal about sexual experiences and showed little interest in discussing babies, children, or other topics relevant to real women. Among the MtF individuals interviewed, the majority identified as female and found themselves attracted to women. If a natal-born male thinks like a man and relates sexually to the world as a man, how does the medical community justify claiming the person is truly a woman? These are individuals who *desire*[8] to be women, not individuals who are women. Doctors McHugh and Meyer divided transsexualism into two categories, homosexual type and heterosexual type. Dr. McHugh claimed, *"One group consisted of conflicted and guilt-ridden homosexual men who saw a sex-change as a way to resolve their conflicts over homosexuality by allowing them to behave sexually as females with men."*

---

[8] Referring to the *DSM-5*.

[Paul McHugh, M.D. 1931—]

The other group included,

> Mostly older men consisting of heterosexual (and some bisexual) males who found intense sexual arousal in cross-dressing as females. As they had grown older, they had become eager to add more verisimilitude to their costumes and either sought or had suggested to them a surgical transformation that would include breast implants, penile amputation, and pelvic reconstruction to resemble a woman. (McHugh 2004, 3)

The Clark Institute in Toronto and the work of Ray Blanchard, Ph.D., confirmed these conclusions. Taking these observations to their logical conclusion, they are both surprising and controversial. If transgender identities are coping mechanisms for some homosexuals or a surgical response to a fetish, reassignment surgery and hormone treatments would not be appropriate.

At the beginning of Dr. McHugh's article *Surgical Sex: Why we stopped doing sex-change operations* in *First Things,* he recites the Serenity Prayer, *"God, give me the serenity to accept the things I cannot change, the courage to change the things I can, and the wisdom to know the difference"* (McHugh 2004, 3). Dr. McHugh claims sex is not something changeable—our way of thinking can be. On one side, medical professionals claimed psychological treatments were the appropriate response. On the other, transgender activists argue, *"the mind—the sense of self—was [seen as] less malleable than the body"* (Meyerowitz 2002, 99). Transfeminist Rachel Anne Williams states, *"Their body is false. The body is the problem. The body is what is causing the pain and the anguish"* and not their gender identities (R. A. Williams 2019, 168). The statement of Rachel Anne Williams begs the question, how can a healthy body cause pain? How can a healthy body be a problem? How is a healthy body false? The body is following its form.

Sub.#	Age (yrs.)	Toy Choice	Rough Play	Interest in Marriage	Doll Play	Wants to be a Boy	Favorite Activities	Favorite Activities (according to parents)
1	11							
2	10							
3	12							
4	11							
5	6							
6 ♿	10							
7 ♿	9							
8	11							
9	12							
10	7							
11	7							
12	5							
13	7							
14	12							
15 ♂	16							
16 ♂	5							

Figure 5.2 Reiner/Gearhart's follow-up results from questionnaires of Dr. Money's patients 2004

Key: The answers were on a scale of 1-5. 1 being the most typically female response and 5 being the most typically male response.   1 | 2 | 3 | 4 | 5   ♿ individual in a wheelchair, ♂ individual raised male.

Dr. McHugh, with the help of resident psychiatrist of Johns Hopkins, William Reiner, M.D., reevaluated the work of his predecessor. Dr. Money, convinced by his ideology that gender is a social construct, would transition children born intersex to become female. He confidently asserted that the child would psychologically develop as a female if the transition occurred within the first three years of life. Since these deformities would primarily occur in males (XY), Dr. Money would remove the deformed testicles and penis early. As a result, the child would have no natural testosterone growing up, which may hormonally confuse the child's gender.

At the request of Dr. McHugh, Dr. Reiner conducted follow-ups for sixteen children born with cloacal exstrophy, a condition where the penis never fully forms but the testes are intact. The medical field does not consider this condition to be intersex since the person is entirely a male hormonally, and only the structure of the penis is deformed.[9] In this situation, a child in the womb receives testosterone levels for the first stages of development and only becomes testosterone deficient after the surgery to remove the testes. Dr. Money and others believed children are born genderless, and culture combined with post-birth hormones creates gender identity.

In the New England Journal of Medicine in January of 2004 (Reiner and Gearhart 2004). Dr. Reiner released his study's result, which discovered that of the sixteen children born with cloacal exstrophy, only two of those children had parents who refused the treatment to change the young boys into girls. These two children grew up to be young men. Of the fourteen children surgically altered to appear as females, eight rejected the feminine identities given to them, and even without testosterone, grew up to be young men. One additional child experienced sexual ambiguity, but five grew up to be female.

Moreover, *"Only one subject stated that she had never wished to be a boy, and only one subject—who later adopted a male identity—stated a very strong interest in marriage, with interest in marriage being more typical of female responses in childhood"* (Reiner and Gearhart 2004). Dr. McHugh noted, *"All sixteen of these people had interests that were typical of males, such as hunting, ice hockey, karate, and bobsledding"* (McHugh 2004). See figure 5.2 for more examples.

Dr. Money's most infamous case involved David Reimer, a.k.a. John/Joan. In 1966, he *"corrected"* a botched circumcision by removing the penis and turning the young boy into a girl. Drs. Money and Anke Ehrhardt, Ph.D., published this case in a notorious 1972 book, *Man*

---

[9] The penis, although commonly used as the determining physical structure for identifying a physical male, has no masculinizing effect on the brain or any of the other features of the male body since a penis is not gonadal. The penis is a consequence rather than the cause of masculinization.

and Woman, Boy and Girl, in which they claimed this surgery to be successful. For decades, gender theorists have cited this book as proof sex is *just* morphology—something medically alterable, and gender is a social construct. As the *New York Times* reviewer of the book points out, *"This body of work, basic to modern social science, has lent credence to the idea that human beings are almost endlessly malleable"* (Collier 1973). This argument supported the false concept that men and women are the same at birth beyond a cultural difference.

Milton Diamond, Ph.D. (1934—), unconvinced by Dr. Money's conclusions, followed up with "John/Joan," who, in real life, is *"Barbara/David."* In the early years, the twins, *"Barbara" and Brian recalled, Money allegedly made the children participate in "sexual rehearsal play."* During therapy, *"Brenda assumed a position on all fours on his office sofa and made Brian come up behind her on his knees and place his crotch against her buttocks"* (Burkeman and Younge 2004). Dr. Diamond discovered that Brenda realized herself to be a boy between the ages of nine and eleven and, at twelve, rejected her female hormones and attempted suicide. At the age of fourteen, Barbara's dad finally told her why she felt like a boy, and subsequently, *he* began taking testosterone and transitioned to the life of a male. Between fifteen and sixteen, he began receiving phallic reconstruction and, at twenty-five, married a woman and adopted her children (Diamond and Sigmundson 1997, 299–300).

After the release of Dr. Diamond's report, *"John"* later revealed himself to be David Reimer to publicly persuade the medical establishment to stop performing this type of treatment on young boys. In 2002 David's twin brother Brian committed suicide by overdosing on antidepressants. In part, the family blamed Dr. Money for Brian's suicide because of his sexual role-playing activities with his brother as a child. After a period of significant depression himself, David using a shotgun, committed suicide on May 5, 2004, at 38 years old.

Although Dr. Money remained a pediatric and medical psychology professor at Johns Hopkins University from 1951 until he died in 2006, he received around sixty-five honors. He contributed to about 2,000 publications (Ehrhardt 2007). However, Dr. Money's practices and theories are now suspect. His views about gender malleability have been debunked. His sex play with young children would perhaps be criminal by today's legal standards, and his quickness to modify body parts at the Gender Identity Clinic was discredited. As a result, the clinic shut down (Silberner 2006). Janice Raymond, Ph.D., in her 1994 new introduction to *The Transsexual Empire*, suspects one of the key non-public reasons the Gender Identity Clinic shut down was because Dr. Money *"branched out into the realms of child pornography and incest... Money's colleagues were reported to be uneasy with his public statements and writings on incest, and increasingly, over their alliance with him"* (Raymond 1994, Intro).

One must acknowledge how difficult it is for people of one natal sex to be placed in the incorrect gender group. When a person is misgendered socially, the effects are devastating, from social uneasiness to completed suicide. In these cases, boys returned to their chromosomal sex; however, one can imagine how high the anxiety levels would be for someone suffering from a hormonal or neurological condition, which would make them feel as though they are in the wrong body. If they are mentally in the same condition as David Reimer, the consequences will be fatal.

Second, one may note how medical experts are often overconfident in their views of gender-sex ideology. For a decade or more, all experts in the field and the press incorrectly followed certain unproven assumptions to the detriment of their patients. The echo chamber of academia continues to resound their praises long after these ideologies have been discredited because of their tragic outcomes. Even when the mass hysteria of teenage transitioning comes crashing down, there will likely be no negative consequences for the practitioners of ideology. Doctors like Johanna Olson-Kenedy, M.D., who performs double mastectomies on twelve-year-olds, or Norman Spack, M.D., who started the American puberty blocker trend for pre-pubescent youth, are popular and will continue to be popular regardless of the carnage.

[Janice Raymond, Ph.D., 1943—]

5.6 THE TRANSSEXUAL EMPIRE

The year 1979 brought an additional challenge to the transsexual community, which arrived with Dr. Raymond's book, *The Transsexual Empire*. Salve Regina alumna, and former Sister of Mercy, Janice Raymond, wrote, *"Transsexual surgery is the invention of men initially developed for men"* (Raymond 1994, xiv). Dr. Raymond is a second-wave feminist, a movement inspired by Betty Friedan's *Feminine Mystique*, which advocated for abolishing gender roles at work and home. People who adhere to a second-wave feminist ideology have two contrasting concerns regarding claims of transgenderism. First, transsexuality reaffirms rigid stereotypical binary gender roles, contradicting their gender-neutral ideology. Logic dictates, if no difference between men and women exists, one cannot be transsexual. Second is MtF individuals in women-only spaces. Although the presence of all people assigned male at birth within women-only spaces is a problem, autogynephilic individuals are the primary concern since they have bodies and behaviors of biological men and are sexually attracted to and fetishize women.

Dr. Raymond is not alone in her criticism of MtF individuals entering the feminist movement as women. Beth Elliot, a trans folk singer and activist who served on the 1973 West Coast Lesbian Feminist Conference organizing committee was scheduled to perform. The keynote speaker Robin Morgan refused to participate if the event involved the transgender folk singer, claiming Beth was *"an opportunistic, an infiltrator, and a destroyer—with the mentality of a rapist,"* Robin further noted, *"He has a prick! That makes him a man."* (Morgan 1973). Lesbians are particularly sensitive to the presence of autogynephilic (MtF) individuals in their space. Although claiming to be lesbians, autogynephilic people do not resemble nor act like women. This positioning entitles them to women-only spaces designed to keep precisely these fetishistic individuals out.

Dr. Raymond claims women have a healthy outlet to reject the rigid gender stereotypes called feminism. Western society traps men within a system where they can only accept their role in the patriarchy or reject masculinity, but they do so alone. Feminists note that men invented classical femininity. Large breasts, long hair, curvy bodies, soft voices, and other stereotypes were part of the *"construction of man-made femininity"* (Raymond 1994, xv). Naturally, men want to possess those bodies which were artificially their creations anyhow. Dr. Raymond quoted Simone de Beauvoir, *"if [woman] did not exist, men would have invented her. They did invent her. But she exists also apart from their inventiveness."* In Dr.Raymond's own words, she claims, *"Men, of course, invented the feminine, and in this sense, it could be said that all women who conform to this invention are transsexuals, fashioned according to man's image."* (Raymond 1994, 106) Dr. McHugh similarly noted, *"The post-surgical subjects struck me as caricatures of women. They wore high heels, copious makeup, and flamboyant clothing"* (McHugh 2004).

Within the definition of man or woman is a wide range of actions. By rejecting his femininity as a man, he reinforces the rigid stereotypes of what it means to be a man. If a man is sensitive, soft, nurturing, and emotional, he should not become a transwoman but a sensitive, soft, nurturing, and emotional man. The feminist call for men to stop being patriarchal occurs when men stop conforming to constructed masculine norms and become their authentic selves socially. Likewise, women liberate themselves when they stop judging their womanhood on the male-dominated, Victorian ideal of femininity and allow their natural femininity to shine through. Dr. Raymond claims a transsexual is a

> *"Fantastic woman,"* the incarnation of the male fantasy of feeling like a woman trapped in a man's body, the fantasy rendered flesh by a further male medical fantasy of surgically fashioning a male body into a female one. These fantasies are based on the male imagination, not in any female reality. (Raymond 1994, xx)

Dr. Raymond critiqued, by defining transsexualism as a medical condition, individuals do not challenge their personal and social expectations for being a man or woman. Dr. Ramond notes that liberalism's uncritical acceptance of the transgender narrative is vice *"masquerading as sympathy for all oppressed groups"* (Raymond 1994, 110). Societal men do not pay the price to go along with this collective polite delusion, but women. Feminists claim that all public spaces are male-dominated, so the rare private women-only space is not a privilege but a place of final retreat. Dr. Raymond claims society is forcing women to accommodate MtF individuals is part of the *"age-old theme of women nurturing men, providing them with a safe haven, and finally giving them our best energies"* (Raymond 1994, 110).

Transgender individuals confuse identity with desire. Thomas Szasz, M.D., makes similar claims as Dr. Raymond. Dr. Szasz proposes, if poor people wish they were rich, is that *"trans-economical,"* or an old person who desires to be young, a *"trans-chronological,"* or a black person who would like to be white a *"trans-racial?"* (Szasz 1979, 3) Dr. Szasz asks, is not dissatisfaction different than a disease? To want to be something or someone else is not a disease in any other case. The proper response to a person with unachievable desires is therapy or to change the expectations. If a black person desires to be white, it is not the whiteness one desires but the social advantages of being white. One may either bleach one's skin, wear contact lenses, color one's hair, or change the injustice systems.[10] The feminist approach is not to colonize and assimilate minority populations into the power normativity but to make space for diversity.

Part of this dissatisfaction affects everyone, not just transsexuals. The consumerist marketing approach of the capitalistic system aims at making people feel dissatisfied. For example, formal Comments of the American Society of Plastic and Reconstructive Surgeons filed with the FDA in 1982 claimed small breasts are not only a deformity but *"a disease which in most patients results in feelings of inadequacy"* (F. Barringer 1992, c12). In response to their marketing campaign, millions of women rushed to acquire silicone implants to enhance their self-esteem or satisfy men. Thinking anyone's dissatisfaction might be overcome through plastic surgery is like believing dermatologists can solve racism (J. Shapiro 1991, 262).

---

[10] In contrast, presently within certain liberal circles, an advantage exists when claiming to be a member of an oppressed class of people. Rachel Anne Dolezal (1977—) became the Spokane, WA head of the National Association for the Advancement of Colored People (NAACP) claiming to be African American. Rachel was born to white parents

Birthed from Dr. Raymond and her counterparts came Trans Exclusionary Radical Feminists (Terf) or Gender Critical Feminists.[11] Terfs, a term coined in 2008, continues the protest of second-wave feminists who claim autogynephilic men hijack the feminist movement. Although Terfs is a twenty-first-century incarnation, second-wave feminists never stopped stating their opposition to natal males in women-only spaces. The United Kingdom is especially famous for its Terfs, sometimes being referred to as *Terf Island.* Present Terf arguments have not evolved beyond what Dr. Raymond claimed initially in 1979 or Dr. Germaine Greer in *The Female Eunuch* in 1993. Transgender activists frequently use the term Terfs in a pejorative sense to criticize any woman who does not support the rights of MtF individuals as women. As Jamie Raines, Ph.D. (1994—), an FtM progressive YouTuber, asserts, *"You are not a feminist unless you support all women and transwomen are women"* (Raines 2020).

The church can take a back seat in some philosophical battles over gender ideology since Terfs are polemically at the frontlines. However, the church can assist especially with pastoral support, an element not present in radical feminism. For example, Terfs claim that society constantly forces women to coddle men's insecurities, and on this issue, they refuse to be emotionally manipulated out of women-only spaces. Although the stance Terfs take is valid, they do not consider that many gender dysphoric people are deeply hurting and require support, even if not in the form of acquiescence.

---

[11] The discussions held by Gender Critical Feminists are typically on Reddit and Tumbler with some presence on Twitter, if their *transphobia* does not get them banned.

5.7 CONCEPT REVIEW

Chapter five covered the history of the first 100 years of the modern transgender movement, including the medical evolution of terminology and treatments. This section introduced key theorists in the field of sexuality and those who became instrumental in changing the way people thought about transgender people, including its pioneer Dr. Benjamin, the Blonde Bombshell Christine Jorgensen, the infamous Dr. Money, and those who brought on its demise, Drs. Meyer and McHugh. The first hundred years also brought the rise and fall of the first North American gender clinic, which through its shortcomings, taught sex and gender are not as mutable as doctors once thought in the 1960s and 1970s.

The year 1979 birthed three significant changes: the founding of the Harry Benjamin International Gender Dysphoria Association (HBIGDA); the closing of the Gender Identity Clinic; and the publication of *The Transsexual Empire*, which began a feminist movement now called Trans Exclusionary Radical Feminists (Terfs), who politically and philosophically oppose self-proclaimed lesbian transsexuals.

Chapter 6
Blanchard's Typology:
Psychological Etiology
1980–1995

If one more person tells me that all gender is performance, I think I am going to strangle them.
— Julia Serano, Ph.D., *Gender Outlaws: The Next Generation*

I don't feel like a man trapped in a woman's body. I just feel trapped.
— Anonymous, *The Transsexual Empire*

Ray Blanchard received a Ph.D. in psychology from the University of Illinois in 1973. He researched sex drive reduction therapies for sex offenders at the Ontario Correctional Institute until 1980, when he joined the Clarke Institute of Psychiatry[1] in Toronto. His own research, combined with his medical review of the Gender Identity Clinic files, led him to develop what is commonly called *Blanchard's Typology*. Dr. Blanchard has since served on the American Psychiatric Association *DSM-4* Subcommittee on Gender Identity Disorders, and the board subsequently named to the *DSM-5* committee.

Notable at the time, Dr. Blanchard did not doubt anyone's claim of being authentically transgender, a stance out of line with many in the psychiatric community who believe some transgender people are fake or pseudo-transsexuals (Prince 1978, 263). When people claim that Dr. Blanchard considers transgender people fake, transgender activists commonly mean that he does not support the ideology of gender ontology. Blanchard's typology locates gender dysphoria in sexual orientation and paraphilia rather than *being* of the opposite sex. This distinction might mean a gender dysphoric male is a fake woman, but not a fake transsexual. As a clinician, Dr. Blanchard does not waste energy fighting the culture war or antagonizing transgender people. Instead, he uses his typology as a tool to better treat the cause of his patient's dysphoria.

Dr. Blanchard rejected the notion that gender identity is based upon the subjective experience of one's sex and is instead based on a realist approach based on objective observations (C Williams 2012). Dr. Blanchard identified four classes of transgendered people: homosexual, heterosexual, bisexual, and asexual/analloerotic (Blanchard 1985). Despite using a typology to identify transsexualism, Dr. Blanchard advocated for sex reassignment surgery for patients within each of the typologies when psychologically advantageous; hence these categories are not intended to invalidate the gravity of gender dysphoria (Blanchard 2000).

Dr. Blanchard used the terms autogynephilic and androphilic to describe the causes of dysphoria. For autogynephilia, Dr. Blanchard claimed, the etiology was *"a kind of error locating the heterosexual targets in*

---

[1] Now called the Centre for Addiction and Mental Health (College Street site).

the environment" (Blanchard 1991, 246). In androphilia, the cause of the dysphoria is within one's homosexual fantasy to be sexually embraced by a masculine heterosexual man. Only by presenting themselves as stereotypical women do they achieve this fantasy of being received as a natural woman. Although nominalist gender theorists consider one's sexual expression, sexual orientation, and sexual identity entirely independent, these correlations are undeniable. Consequently, Dr. Blanchard's typology considers the link between sexual identity and sexual orientation.

In his 1990 book, *Clinical Management of Gender Identity Disorders in Children and Adults,* Dr. Blanchard introduced the typologies by presenting two precursors to transsexualism—drag queens and transvestitism. Contemporary transgender activists target Dr. Blanchard's concepts since some of his terminologies are now considered politically incorrect.[2] Transgender activists starting in the late1990s began to object strongly to the terminology used by Dr. Blanchard. In particular, groups rejected his classification of *"heterosexual"* and *"homosexual"* type transsexuals since this categorization implies the person's natal sex is the proper sex. In addition, the association of heterosexual type transsexuals with transvestites was strongly opposed.

In 2003 J. Michael Bailey, Ph.D. released *The Man Who Would Be Queen: The Science of Gender-Bending and Transsexualism* (2003). Dr. Bailey, a colleague of Dr. Blanchard, used his typologies and the theories of prominent University of Toronto psychologist and sexologist Kenneth Zucker, Ph.D., who worked with children whose parents identified significant gender-atypical behaviors. Natalie Wynn claims that Dr. Bailey wrote the book using examples from his own experience as a

---

[2] As an example of an outdated theory, Blanchard considered drag queens, *"clearly have a gender identity disturbance of some type"* (Blanchard, Clinical Management 1990). This may have been true in the 1980s when Blanchard wrote his text; however, in the last 10 to 20 years, drag queens have been primarily a means of paid entertainment and fundraising within the LBGT community and there is no connection between the costume and sexual arousal or personal sexual identity. Occasionally a homosexual man attempted drag before coming out as an MtF transsexual, but this is a short-term step and does not represent the majority of drag experiences where transitioning is not considered (O'Brien 2018).

white cis man *titillated* by his perceived sexual perversion of the transsexual prostitutes he encounters (Wynn 2018).

Under outside pressure, Northwestern University launched a formal investigation against Dr. Bailey, the psychology department chair. Still, the university ultimately dropped the claim due to a lack of ethical or academic basis for the complaint. Alice Dreger, Ph.D., captured this episode in her book *Galileo's Middle Finger*,

> Accusations against Bailey were a sham. Dr. Bailey's sworn enemies had used every clever trick in the book—juxtaposing events in misleading ways, ignoring contrary evidence, working the rhetoric, and using anonymity whenever convenient, to make it look as though virtually every trans woman represented in Bailey's book had felt abused by him and had filed a charge. (Dreger 2015, 100)

Dr. Bailey's book kept the conversation about Blanchard's Typology theory alive, although the renewed attention raised his theory to a higher degree of criticism. Some of the critiques of Dr. Blanchard's theories are predominantly complaints against his lack of twenty-first-century political correctness. Other criticisms involved identity politics whereby a cis man would categorize transgender people based on their sexual desires, and others had valid scientific critiques of the science behind the theories.

Modern social critiques seldom consider Dr. Blanchard's proposed etiological foundations to the different forms of transsexualism. Transgender activists usually adhere to the cogito ergo sum argument, which asserts that the only requirement for a person to be a man or woman is that they believe themselves to be male or female. Frank Leavitt, Ph.D., and Jack Berger, M.D., wrote, *"Transsexuals, as a group, vehemently oppose the homosexual transsexual label and its pejorative baggage. As a rule, they are highly invested in a heterosexual lifestyle and repulsed by notions of homosexual intercourse with males. Attention from males often serves to validate their feminine status"* (Leavitt 1990, 500).

Although Dr. Blanchard's work from the 1980s and 1990s may appear insensitive by today's standards, it is necessary not to lose sight of this theory regardless of the terms used. It is also important to remember that Dr. Blanchard wrote these studies over 30 years ago, and the standards for political correctness changed. However, it does not make the theory behind the study invalid. If activists expel every historical text containing some element of political incorrectness, the library would be nearly empty (Ely, Meyerson, and Davidson 2006).

Dr. Blanchard used the medically accepted definitions of his time. For example, Dr. Blanchard used the following definitions: gender dysphoria refers to discontentment between one's biological sex and the desire to possess the body of the opposite sex. A gender dysphoric person also desires to be regarded by others as a member of the opposite sex. Dr. Blanchard defines transsexualism as extreme gender dysphoria persisting without fluctuations for a period of years (Blanchard 1990, 56).

The idea that transsexuality develops as a result of extreme gender dysphoria is currently opposed. The American Psychiatric Association (APA) claims that a person can be a transsexual without gender dysphoria (American Psychiatric Association 2013). Furthermore, some social scientists claim, *"although the associated medical and psychiatric diagnoses of being transgender are important factors for treatment, being transgender is not pathological and, hence, treatment cannot be focused on the diagnosis and eradication of pathology"* (Cashman and Walters 2016, 19). Nevertheless, receiving a life-altering surgery and reversing one's hormones for the rest of one's life while accepting a higher risk of early mortality is not something worth embarking upon if the treatment does not fix a tremendous psychological burden.

It appears improbable for someone to go through the legal and cultural challenges of changing one's sex, all without any real distress. If transitioning is casually chosen, the APA states transitioning is a personal preference. Consequently, insurance or public healthcare would not pay for these treatments since they are not the result of a medical disorder. Insurance does not cover optional cosmetic surgeries. Those who claim to experience early-onset gender dysphoria are not at odds with Dr. Blanchard's conclusions. Gender nominalists claim all people are non-binary and are vehemently opposed to Dr. Blanchard's theory of psychological explanations for these desires.

Dr. Blanchard categorizes transsexual etiologies into autogynephilic (heterosexual) and androphilic (homosexual) transsexuals. Autogynephilic etymologically means *"love of oneself as a woman"* and an androphilic *"man lover."* This division aims to discover the etiology of dysphoria. Dr. Blanchard claims that MtF individuals attracted to women have different causes for their dysphoria than MtF individuals attracted to men or FtM individuals attracted to women. This concept is politically incorrect and contradicts the narrative that sex and gender and sexual orientation are entirely distinct categories sharing no essential overlap.

Blanchard Typology, 1990	Meaning	Characteristics
Autogynephilic (heterosexual)	A biological male who feels like a woman and is attracted to women	Act typical of a normative man shows no early signs to others, dates/marries women, and has children. Transitions around 40 years old.
Bisexual	A biological male who feels like a woman and is attracted to men as far as they make him feel more like a woman	Act typical of a normative man shows no early signs to others, dates/marries women, and has children. The transition averages around 40 years old.
Analloeroic (asexual)	A biological male who feels like a woman and is attracted primarily to the feminine various of himself and not others	Act typical of a normative man, shows no early signs to others, might be a virgin or uninterested in sexually intimate partners. The transition averages around 40 years old.
Androphilic (homosexual)	A biological man or woman who feels like the other sex and is attracted to members of the same biological sex	Acts typical of the norms of the other sex (called *sissie* or *tomboy*), is sexually involved with people of the other sex, is aware of the dysphoria earlier than autogynephilic individuals.

Figure 6.1 Blanchard's Typology 1990 (Blanchard 1990)

6.1 AUTOGYNEPHILIC
HETEROSEXUAL TRANSSEXUALISM3

Through his observations and reading case files, Dr. Blanchard found that the experiences of MtF individuals attracted to women (*gynephilic*) contrasted with androphilic transsexuals. Dr. Blanchard describes autogynephilia: *"In anatomic autogynephilia, the individual is oriented toward the characteristic features of the feminine physique (e.g., breasts), but he attempts, in some way, to locate these features on his own body"* (Blanchard 1991, 247). At the time when Dr. Blanchard published his study, autogynephilic subjects were all natal men. These individuals were typically well adjusted to their male peer groups growing up, naturally enjoyed normal activities for young boys, and did not show overt signs of effeminacy. In early adulthood, they tend to work in male-dominated occupations, and most of these men were married at least once and had children. Many of these individuals, when seeking treatment, are still currently married and would like to remain married to their wives.

When they are not deliberately feminizing their attire, they otherwise present as typical heterosexual men. Autogynephilia is similar to transvestism in the earliest stages. Eighty percent of the autogynephilic MtF individuals claimed to experience sexual arousal when first cross-dressing (Blanchard, Clemmensen and Steiner 1987). Autogynephilic MtF individuals often experience conflict over this identity to fear how their families, children, friends, and professional colleagues may react. Since these individuals convincingly pass as lifelong heterosexual men, those closest to them are shocked when they identify as women. Dr. Blanchard claims the Autogynephilic MtF individual's average age who comes to the Clarke Institute of Psychiatry

---

[3] Many in the Autogynephilic category prefer the term *gynephilic* rather than Blanchard's typology of autogynephilic or heterosexual transsexual. Gynephilic means attracted to women, which states nothing about the principal's gender.

is 39 years of age, which is, on average, 13 years older than androphilic (homosexual) transsexuals who first come to the clinic.

An autogynephilic MtF individual can physically transition to varying degrees of femininity. Autogynephilic individuals seldom receive all the available feminizing surgeries and procedures. Some men will present as women at various times in life. In contrast, others seek breast augmentation or complete transsexual surgery, and others live their lives as men without revealing their secrets. Autogynephilic MtF individuals are more likely to *"vacillate in their resolve to live as women"* than androphilic transsexuals, according to a study by Götz Kockott, M.D., and E.M. Fahrner, Ph.D. (Kockott and Fahrner 1987, 512).

Dr. Blanchard claims many Autogynephilic MtF individuals hope to settle down after the surgery and live ordinary straight female lives. Many individuals even hope to find a heterosexual man to embody the feminine state fully; nevertheless, sex reassignment surgery does not change one's sexual orientation. They continue to be attracted to women as they did before. Autogynephilic MtF individuals desire the fantasy of being feminine more than the reality of being a woman. After surgeries, this sexual attraction to women can lead to shame that she must engage in *"lesbian"* relationships if she wants to be engaged in a meaningful sexual relationship at all (Blanchard 1990, 59).

Until recently, the incidence of FtM autogynephilia was virtually nonexistent. At the time of Dr. Blanchard's writing in 1990, the two women who identified as autogynephilic FtM individuals (meaning they are attracted to men) became involved with exceedingly feminine homosexual men who took on a female role in the relationship. Presently, more FtM individuals might qualify as autogynephilic. Still, since Blanchard's Typology has gone into disfavor, health care statistics on transsexual individuals seldom track sexual orientation as a relevant factor. Consequently, the exact rate of FtM autogynephilia is undetermined. Dr. Blanchard calls this new manifestation autohomoerotic gender dysphoria, where women escape being a female to be intimate with homosexual men. Autohomoerotica is most common among teens and individuals in their early adulthood. According to Drs. Bailey and Blanchard, a young person

Acquires the delusion that s/he is the other sex because s/he is suffering from gross thinking deficiencies. There are little systematic data on this type of gender dysphoria, although clinical mentions of heterosexual women with strong masculine traits, who say that they feel as if they were homosexual men, and who feel strongly attracted to effeminate men go back over 100 years. (Bailey and Blanchard 2017)

Whereas autogynephilic individuals are attracted to the idea of *having* a women's body, autohomoerotic individuals are attracted to the idea of *intimacy* with gay men. Thus, intimacy with others is a secondary characteristic for autogynephilic individuals while primary for autohomoerotic individuals.

To the displeasure of some, Dr. Blanchard boldly links the etiologies of autogynephilia and transvestitism. Dr. Blanchard suggests they are degrees of the same spectrum of transvestite behavior. He wrote,

The various similarities between transvestitism and heterosexual transsexualism (Autogynephilic) suggest that these conditions may be the same disorder. This notion is reinforced by many cases of heterosexual transsexualism (Autogynephilic), which seem to have developed out of transvestitism. (Blanchard 1990, 59)

Although a link between transvestitism and autogynephilia may be possible, this does not mean autogynephilia is *"fake transgenderism."* Virginia Prince suggested autogynephilic individuals are not transgender, while those with androphilia are *"real transgenderism."* Dr. Blanchard's only point for making the distinctions is to help identify the etiological root for transgender identities, which may not be a singular cause. He notes transvestitism does not appear to progress the feelings one has about women's attire, and instead, the feelings remain consistent throughout life. In contrast, for an autogynephilic MtF individual, the attraction begins the same as the transvestite but leads the person wanting to fully embrace a feminine identity as his own (Blanchard 1990, 59).

A classic story of autogynephilia is represented in *The Transsexual Empire* by Dr. Raymond in T.C. Boyle's *The Women's Restaurant*, printed in *Penthouse* (1977). This story echoes the concerns of Rabbi Rashi of the eleventh century, who warned of men dressing as women to invade women-only spaces. Dr. Raymond introduces the story:

The Women's Restaurant (1977)

The story begins by setting the scene in and around Grace & Rubie's Restaurant and is written from the point of view of the voyeuristic narrator. *"It is a women's restaurant. Men are not permitted. What goes on there, precisely, no man knows. I am a man. I am burning to find out."* The narrator then proceeds to caricature Grace and Rubie as butch and femme, as well as to relate his several attempts to gain entrance. After two unsuccessful endeavors, he goes to a department store, buys a pink polyester pantsuit, a bra, pantyhose, and cosmetics with which he makes himself up to pass as a woman. He gains entrance and is able to experience what he has been missing (Raymond 1979, 111).

Here I was, embosomed in the very nave, the very omphalos of furtive femininity—a prize patron of the women's restaurant, a member, privy to its innermost secrets. There they were—women—chewing, drinking, digesting, chatting, giggling, crossing, and uncrossing their legs. Shoes off, feet up. Smoking cigarettes, flashing silverware, tapping time to the music. Women among women. I bathed in their soft chatter, birdsong, the laughter like falling coils of hair. I lit a cigarette and grinned. No more fairybook-hero thoughts of rescuing Rubie—oh no, this was paradise.25 Having drunk six tequila sunrises and a carafe of dinner wine, the male intruder/narrator finds it necessary to relieve himself, but forgets to sit down when he urinates in the rest room, at which point he is discovered by Grace. The story ends with his savoring of the triumph of temporary infiltration and a plan for permanent invasion. I have penetrated the women's restaurant, yes, but in actuality it was little more than a rape. I am not satisfied. The obsession grows in me, pregnant, swelling, insatiable with the first taste of fulfillment. Before I am through, I will drink it to satiety. I have plans. The next time I walk through those curtained doors at Grace & Rubie's there will be no dissimulation. There are surgeons who can assure it. (Boyle 1977, 112)

6.2 AUTOGYNEPHILIC
BISEXUAL TRANSSEXUALISM

D r. Blanchard also addresses bisexual MtF individuals. This group shares the most in common with autogynephilia, growing up without any effeminate features and fitting in with typical male roles. However, Dr. Blanchard claims this type of bisexual orientation *"need not reflect an equal erotic attraction to the male and female physiques and would perhaps be better characterized as pseudobisexuality"* (Blanchard 1990, 67). An androphilic MtF person is attracted to men's bodies and genitalia, the same as heterosexual men are attracted to women's bodies. For a bisexual MtF individual, the sexual arousal comes primarily from fulfilling the cross-dressing fantasy. The MtF person experiences greater arousal in being encountered as a real woman than an actual physical attraction to the man himself. These individuals want to fulfill the fantasy of possessing the feminine but ultimately cannot enjoy the experience since their emotional and psychological sexual attraction is not directed towards other men. They are ultimately heterosexual men engaging in a sexual fantasy.

6.3 AUTOGYNEPHILIC
ANALLOEROTIC TRANSSEXUALISM

Another form of Autogynephilic MtF is analloerotic, derived from the Greek etymology *an-*, *"lacking,"* and *alloerotic*, *"sexual feeling or activity finding its object in another person."* Some people describe analloerotic fixations as asexual transsexualism, which is not the case in most situations. Analloerotic individuals are often not interested in having intercourse with another person, but *"they feel attracted not by the women outside them, but by the woman inside them"* (Hirschfeld 1948, 167). The Clarke Institute of Psychiatry described that around 7 to 8% of MtF individuals might be analloerotic (Blanchard 1990, 63). These individuals, like other autogynephilics, expressed typical boy behavior and did not exhibit signs of effeminacy. Instead, they express a high degree of sexual arousal coming from women's attire. The average age of visiting the clinic for help matches the age of other autogynephilic MtF groups, about fifteen years older than the androphilic transsexuals.

[Androphilic]

6.4 ANDROPHILIC TRANSSEXUALISM

T he final group is the androphilic transsexuals, otherwise called homosexual type transsexuals. This category contains two groups, androphilic MtF individuals and androphilic FtM individuals. Dr. Blanchard claims androphilic transsexualism's etiology must be different from autogynephilic transsexuals. Androphilic transsexualism has an etiology rooted in an extreme form of homosexuality. Dr. Blanchard speculates that MtF and FtM homosexual type transsexuality is an intense expression of homosexuality. He considered the following continuum: heterosexual→bisexual→homosexual → gender-dysphoric homosexual → transsexual homosexual (Blanchard, Clemmensen, and Steiner 1987).[4] Instead of thinking of sexuality on the Kinsey Scale between completely heterosexual and completely homosexual, one can think of the scale between heterosexual and transgender. Steven Greenberg from *The Advocate* described the androphilic scene in gay bars in the 1990s as a,

> Transgression of boundaries [which] actually turns out to be conformity to sex roles once more, with many men flocking to hormones and surgery to attract other men as artifactual, ultrafeminine women... [who] try to become the image of the perfect woman, i.e., the Cindy Crawford-like model, and that disturbing *"prefeminist"* notions of femininity pervade the transgendere community" (Greenberg 1993, 51).

Dr. Blanchard concluded that from the earliest memories, androphilic boys are attracted exclusively to males. Their romantic fantasies are directed at males, and their sexual experiences are predominantly with males. Nonetheless, some may experiment with heterosexual behavior for societal reasons. These individuals are

---

[4] From Dr. Blanchard's 1990 hypothesis, there would be few brain differences between homosexual transsexuals and cis gender homosexual. This hypothesis has not been directly tested yet (Guillamon, Junque and Gómez-Gil 2016, 1634).

predictably maladjusted to being little boys, preferring the company of little girls, girl play, and girl activities according to their culture. As they get older, they often get bullied because of *acting like girls* and showing effeminate features. They show an interest in women's clothing, style, and accessories. They may start showing effeminate gestures and speech patterns.[5] The LadyBoys of Thailand fit into this category.

Dr. Blanchard found that androphilic transsexuality rarely goes away at any point in life. In contrast, autogynephilic transsexuality often remains closeted for extended periods throughout their lives. Only 10% of androphilic transsexuals experience any sexual arousal when cross-dressing. Eighty percent of Autogynephilic MtF individuals self-reported experiencing sexual arousal wearing women's clothing at least some of the time (Blanchard, Clemmensen, and Steiner 1987). During the 1980s, the average age of an androphilic transsexual seeking help at the Clarke Institute of Psychiatry was 24. At the same time, the average age of an autogynephilic MtF seeking help was 39.

FtM individuals outnumber MtF androphilic individuals, according to a study by Dr. Blanchard in 1987 (Blanchard, Clemmensen, and Steiner 1987). Unfortunately, one cannot ascertain the rate of homosexual vs. heterosexual type transsexuals today since medical facilities do not track this metric as a relevant statistic. In cases of FtM transsexuals, they present themselves to be tomboys at an early age, engage principally in boy play, and have young boy peers. Like effeminate boys who do not grow up to become transsexuals, most tomboys do not either. Rarely do tomboys become transsexuals, and the majority are not homosexuals.

In contrast, feminine boys are less likely to grow up to be heterosexual men, although exact statistics are not available. Young tomboys do not typically face the same social stigma as sissies[6] and

---

[5] Dr. Richard Green from UCLA found that of young boys identified by family or doctors as androphilic, *"The majority of feminine boys do, in fact, end up in adulthood as homosexuals, but they are fully content with their male sex and have few, if any, gross cross-gender behavior"* (Green 1987). Effeminate boys seldom become transsexuals naturally and caution should be taken not to preemptively assume a child is transgender based on his effeminacy.

[6] Terminology used by Blanchard in his studies, (Blanchard, Clinical Management 1990).

graduate high school at higher rates than MtF androphilic individuals. FtM individuals seek treatment at the same age as MtF androphilic individuals. Androphilic people do not self-report any experiences of arousal when cross-dressing in men's clothing.

Whether MtF or FtM, the androphilic types share remarkably similar characteristics, patterns, and timeframes for development. Whether heterosexual, bisexual, or analloerotic, the autogynephilic types share similar causes of arousal, similar developmental social traits while growing up, similar ages for seeking treatment, and similar motivations for seeking treatment. Postmodern approaches prefer every distinction on a scale of variation rather than clear black and white differences. Still, Dr. Blanchard's observations point to two distinct principles of causation.

6.5 CRITIQUES AND DEFENSES OF BLANCHARD'S TYPOLOGY

This book could dedicate an entire chapter to Blanchard's critics, but this is not the book's purpose and thus is reduced to one section of chapter six. Dr. Blanchard has been called the *"right-wing darling"* by transgender activist Brynn Tannehill (Tannehill 2019, 139). Dr. Blanchard maintains the biological realist understanding of typical sexuality, claiming, *"Normal sexuality is whatever is related to reproduction...homosexuality would be not normal but benign"* (Blanchard 2013). Dr. Blanchard's views are not politically correct but biologically self-evident. He claims in his own words, *"I'm not one of these guys who goes out of his way to be politically incorrect. But I don't think we should promulgate untruths for the sake of political agendas, even if they are worthwhile political agendas"* (Blanchard 2013).

Julia Serano, Ph.D., has been considered a philosopher who has definitively *"debunked"* the science of autogynephilia (R. A. Williams 2019, 144). Dr. Serano's debunking arguments fall into three camps (Serano 2010b, 180).

Accusations:

1. This typology is based primarily on clinical samples of a case study and not scientific research with controls.

2. If transsexuality is understood as a fetish or an extension of sexual orientation, then sex reassignment surgeries and medications might not be covered by medical insurance.

3. This offends the activist community who follow the ontological approach to gender identification. Dr. Blanchard's theory views gender dysphoria through the lens of desire. Therefore, Dr. Blanchard does not validate the claim that a transgender woman *is* a woman.

Responses:

1. A descriptive exploratory study is an acceptable method for conducting psychological research.

2. Insurance should never determine the outcomes of science.

3. Charles Moser, M.D., a critic of Dr. Blanchard, claims, *"although autogynephilia exists, the theory is flawed…many MTFs readily admit that this construct describes their sexual interest and motivation. Nevertheless, it is not clear how accurately [Blanchard's theory] predicts the behavior, history, and motivation of MTFs in general"* (Moser 2010). This critique captures the essence of postmodernity. Whereby actual MtF real autogynephilic individuals claim his theory accurately describes their lives. Still, the argument might not describe hypothetical people—therefore, the science is invalid. A valid argument would be if statistically significant rates of MtF autogynephilic individuals found the theory falsely categorized their experience. No one is making this claim.

A study by Dr. Bailey and Kiira Triea in 2007 claimed modern professionals should accept the Blanchard theory because it has more explanatory potential than what they call the *"feminine essence narrative."* The idea put forward by some transsexuals is that they are rather uncomplicatedly *"women trapped in men's bodies."* Psychologists initially used the concept of *Anima muliebris in corpore virili inclusa* to describe homosexual men (Ulrichs 1868). Dr. Blanchard explained, *"Transsexuals seized upon this phrase as the only language available for explaining their predicament to themselves and for communicating their feelings to others"* but are aware the concept was not a literal understanding (Blanchard 2000, 4). At present, it is unclear whether or not the activist community takes the statement literally.

Transgender identification may be less consistent today than in the 1980s and early 1990s. In the twentieth century, a transsexual encountered more difficulties than in the twenty-first century. Patients with gender identity disorder would have been desperate and without any other options if they were to come to the Clarke Institute of Psychology in the 1980s. The cases Dr. Blanchard used to create his theory involved these extreme cases.

Today, unifying features among transgender people are more challenging to locate since more people identify as transgender. When the California Assembly Bill (AB2218) authors claim that 27% of youth between the ages of twelve and seventeen are gender non-conforming and maybe transgender, fewer commonalities will exist among the millions within this category (CA 2020). The current grouping of transgender people includes gender dysphoric adults (Dr. Blanchard's sample pool) and gender activists and teenagers who are dysphoric in a general sense. With this *maximal* definition of what it means to be transgender, large groups of young people will be exceptions to Dr. Blanchard's theory which did not include these twenty-first-century categories.

Anne Lawrence, M.D., a self-proclaimed autogynephilic, authored a book defending Dr. Blanchard against accusations like those of Dr. Moser. Dr. Lawrence's book, *Men Trapped in Men's Bodies: Narratives of Autogynephilic Transsexualism* (2012), reveals 249 cases collected between 2009 to 2011, affirming Dr. Blanchard's findings. Although the terminology of autogynephilia might be unpopular within the transgender community, the concepts remain relevant. Unable to reject the theory of autogynephilia, the trans activist community has renamed it a *"cross-sex gender fantasy"* rather than the cause of dysphoria. (Cross Dreamers 2018).

[Anne Lawrence, M.D., 1950—]

6.6 CONCEPT REVIEW

D r. Blanchard's typology was one of the most significant insights in the previous 100 years of transgender science. Dr. Blanchard's theory was not based on ideals or a phenomenology but based on Thomistic realism. His observational approach is reminiscent of Aristotle's *De Generatione Animalium,* whereby he understood his subjects on their terms and with careful observation to create accurate generalizations and assumptions. His theories are not only about how the transsexual individual existed presently but where the causation originated. What is the principle from which the agent derives his character? The action of cross-dressing arises in the nature of a person's being, which he identified as transvestitism and homosexuality. Despite the limitations of any system of classification, grouping individuals is medically helpful. Rather than using the ontological approach, Dr. Blanchard identifies the sources for dysphoria, then applies therapeutic strategies for managing dysphoria. When the causes of desire are distinct, the relief to satisfy the desires will not be the same.

CHAPTER 7
SCIENCE OF THE TRANSGENDER BRAIN 1995–PRESENT

I think how nice it would be to unzip my body from forehead to navel and go on vacation. But there is no escaping it; I'd have to pack myself along.

— Leslie Feinberg, *Journal of a Transsexual*

Personally, I am drawn to the brain-hardwiring hypothesis, not because I believe it has been proven scientifically beyond a doubt, but because it best explains why the thoughts I have had of being female always felt vague and ever present.

— Julia Serano, Ph.D., *Whipping Girl*

In Harvard's blog series, *Dear Mr. President*, Katherine Wu, a graduate student in the Department of Biology and Biomedical Science, published the article *Between the (Gender) Lines: the Science of Transgender Identity* on October 25, 2016. Katherine presents several scientific studies related to probable causes of transgender identities. The overall theme of the studies presented by Katherine is that transgender identification is natural and genetically determined. This section will focus on the scientific evidence that a Harvard scientist and activist considers the most affirming.

In contrast to Katherine, Gender Critical (second-wave), Feminists reject the hypothesis that women and men possess sexually dimorphic brains, making it impossible to develop a transgender brain. Like Paul McHugh, M.D., some laymen in the church echoed this second-wave feminist approach as a means of rejecting the transgender ideology. When battling a relativistic culture, the argument that gender does not exist is more convincing than the argument that sex is the basis of gender and both are immutable.

Dr. McHugh makes a similar claim against the *born this way* ideology, claiming that if everyone is bisexual and sexual orientation is fluid, then homosexuality is purely a choice. Thus, no one is born that way. Although these arguments are logically consistent, this chapter argues that relativism cannot honestly battle relativism. Only light can dispel darkness, and only realism can dispel relativism. This chapter examines both ideologies and reaffirms biological realism, recognizing the fundamental differences between males and females in primates, including *homo sapiens.*

Medical science also indicates that the brains of transgender people are most similar to those of their assigned sex at birth. In addition, according to some research, transgender individuals possess some brain structures similar to people of the opposite sex. If these morphological differences exist, their presence still does not determine if the individual is psychically like a woman (ontologically) or if they only result in the desire to be the opposite sex (concupiscence). This section is vital to help determine any natural biological basis for the claims of a gender dysphoric person having an intersex brain.

7.1 Male and Female Brains

Evolution of Gender

John Searle, D.Phil. (1932–), wrote, *"Mental phenomena, all mental phenomena whether conscious or unconscious, visual or auditory, pains, tickles, itches, thoughts, indeed, all of our mental life, are caused by processes going on in the brain"* (Searle 1984, 18). One cannot overstate the importance of the brain concerning sexual identity. Medical laypeople typically think of the penis and breasts as the essential sex organs, but in effect, the largest sex organ is a person's brain.

In a thought experiment, Rachel Anne Williams creates a hypothetical scenario whereby evil neuroscientists steal Janice's brain and attach it to machines to survive (R. A. Williams 2019, 189). Rachel claims Janice would cease having physical sex without a body except for the brain itself, a sexed organ. This sexing of the brain is a foundational concept for truscum or transmedicalists. The argument would be persuasive if doctors discovered within the skull of a transgender person an opposite-sexed brain. Unfortunately, transgender people retain the bodies of their natal sex, which includes, overwhelmingly, the morphology of their brains. This chapter will examine subtle differences within the brains of people with gender dysphoria. Second-wave feminists argue that male and female brains are nearly identical, but how does one explain transgender people if this is true? If brains are not gendered, is gender dysphoria a delusion or part of a transgender ideology?

Helena Cronin, Ph.D., a Darwinian philosopher at the *Centre for Philosophy of Natural and Social Science* in London, points out the differences in young boys and girls cannot be because of subtle modern patriarchal influences on evolutionary history. In a debate, she claimed, *"Now, 800 million years later, in our species as in all others, these differences pervade what constitutes being male or female, from brains to bodies to behavior"* (Cronin 2005). This evolutionary understanding of human nature and the sexes' formation also relates to Thomistic realism and the link between biology and behavior. St. Thomas defends, *"Gratia non tollit naturam, sed perficit,"* grace does not destroy nature but perfects it (*ST* Ia q.1, a. 8, ad 2).

Catholics do not reject evolution and do not need to embrace intelligent design, which Pope Francis and Pope Benedict XVI rejected. For example, Pope Francis responds to questions about intelligent design, stating, *"When we read about Creation in Genesis, we run the risk of imagining God was a magician, with a magic wand able to do everything. But that is not so…He created human beings and let them develop according to the internal laws that he gave to each one so they would reach their fulfillment"* (Francis 2017). Further, Fr. Benedict Ashley, O.P. also comments on the relationship between evolution and the development of the family and gender:

> Probably evolving humanoids at first had a brain a little bigger than other primates, yet sufficiently better integrated so that they had the beginnings of true language. This new capacity, even in rudimentary form, greatly enhanced humans' ability to survive. These humans now could act socially in hunting, food-sharing, defense, and invention. Natural selection thus favored rapid expansion of the human brain, especially the cerebrum. Humans could then refine their uses of intelligence and speech so as to depend less on strength and instinct, more on their ability to live socially through invented, transmitted, progressive culture. The human family, with its primary bond between parents and children (unique as regards the role of father) and pair bonding between male and female, developed and became the basis of wider social groupings. Therefore, our remarkable human capacities to think, create, and communicate arise from the elaborate development of our central nervous system, which enables us to integrate information received from the environment and live socially in a culture shared with others. (Ashley 1985, 23)

To the chagrin of British feminist Gina Rippon, Ph.D., who advocates that all differences between young boys and girls are learned behavior, Dr. Cronin claims culture, environment, and subtle messages in pink and blue play only a minor role in forming the brains of youth. Is Dr. Cronin correct that evolutionary biology is the basis for gender, or is Dr. Rippon correct that gender is a social construct? The answer to this question has profound effects on understanding transgender people. This book claims that although culture shapes gender, it is important not to overemphasize culture over deep-seated evolutionary biology. Dr. Cronin claims people should trust that nature plays a significant role in gender, considering every other primate brain is sexually dimorphic. What would be the grounds for Dr. Rippon concluding humans are any different?

Brain Organization Theory

Brain Organization Theory (BOT) is the most plausible theory for biologically driven gender differentiation in the brain. This theory states that the same hormones that trigger female and male brain formation during pregnancy determine the neuropathways used in adulthood. Endocrinologists argue, exposure to these hormones during fetal formation influences how one thinks about one's gender (Erickson-Schroth 2014, 99). For instance, BOT explains the way people behave and act. BOT also controls the way people experience their sexuality (e.g., being attracted to the opposite sex). It argues that human brains are naturally sexed at a very early stage of fetal formation. This theory is not without controversy. Rebecca Jordan-Young, Ph.D., notes,

> The extent and nature of physical differences in the brains of human females and males are highly controversial, with some scientists claiming that there are no clear-cut differences, others claiming that there are some subtle average differences, and still, others claiming that the differences are dramatic. (Jordan-Young 2010, 49)

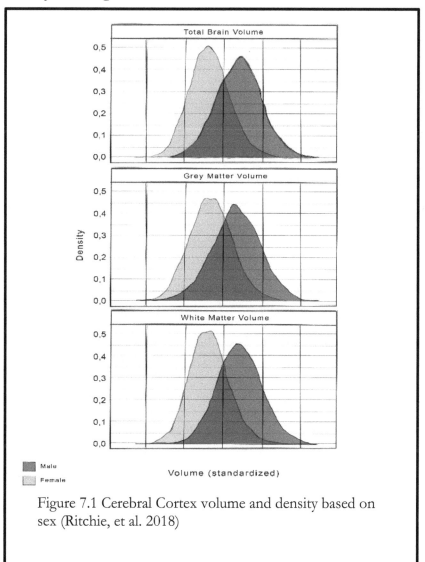

Figure 7.1 Cerebral Cortex volume and density based on sex (Ritchie, et al. 2018)

A 2018 UK Biobank study, the largest of its kind, examined the brains of 2,750 females and 2,466 male participants. The samples were collected using an MRI machine, and the average age of a participant was 61.7 years. The researchers concluded, *"We report evidence on the pattern of sex differences in brain volume, surface area, cortical thickness, white matter microstructure, and functional connectivity between adult males and females in the range between middle—and older-age"* (Ritchie et al. 2018, 2962).

In figure 7.1, the structures of male and female brains are primarily overlapping. The male brains are further to the right than female brains, naturally, because male brains are 8% larger than female brains. One can argue this is due to the larger average size of a male head. However, the male brain also has greater density, which is a feature set apart from size. Regardless of the reason, the male brain is larger, so if volume corresponds to function, men would have a greater function.

It does not follow that men are 8% more intelligent than women.[1] In the graphs above, the male samples demonstrate a wider arch, meaning more significant variation within the category of male brains. In contrast, female brains are more homogenous in size and density. In regards to size and density, no medical science has proven transgender people develop these opposite-sex characteristics. Although the size and density of the brain are the most notable differences between males and females, there is no evidence to suggest psychic differences exist due to these two easily measurable factors.

---

[1] Sperm Whales develop brains six times larger than human brains, yet brain size does not guarantee that they possess six times the functionality of humans. Although larger brain size sometimes contributes to a sign of a more intelligent species, countless examples exist of species with smaller brains which show superior intelligence than species with larger brains. For example, crows are highly intelligent and advanced in multilevel critical thinking skills, yet its brain is a tiny fraction of the size of a cow's brain, a species which does not display multilevel thinking.

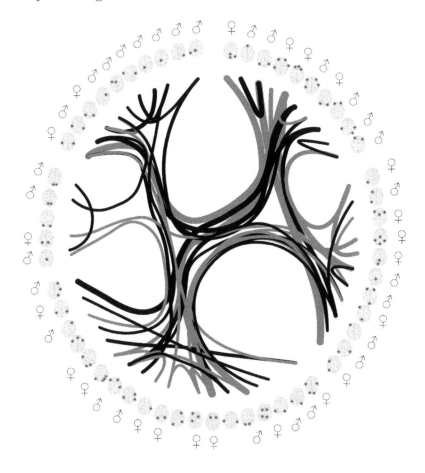

Figure 7.2 Spatial maps for individual connections (Ritchie, et al. 2018)

In figure 7.2, researchers assessed the resting state using an MRI scan of nerve connectivity and weighted degree of nodes. This diagram shows the spatial maps for individual connections. The male and female symbols differentiate the two sexes. The darker colors and thickness of the lines represent the effects of sex on a connections' strength. Five distinct nodes show the different neuron clusters. From this figure, one can detect a great deal of overlap between sexes; yet, differences in weight and volume and the functions also differentiate the sexes.

Brain Matrix

When examining a male versus female brain's biology, it is vital to realize that what is studied is averages. When looking at more than 2,000 male and female brains, specific patterns develop, but this does not tell us about any specific person. For example, during the sixth week of human development, the presence or absence of *Sry* and *Sox9* genes set on course a bifurcation of sexual development. These genes set into motion a series of chain reactions that act like *"a falling chain of molecular dominos, which manifests itself as outward physical changes in the organism"* (Austriaco 2013, 713). These falling chains of molecular dominoes form the sex organs, the gonads, and the brains of the developing child. The exact trajectories are like a butterfly effect. Nothing is random; everything occurs due to predetermined factors related to its environment, but how it unfolds would take a supercomputer to calculate.

In a 2012 Finish study, Annamarja Lamminmäki, M.D., studied forty-eight infants (twenty-two boys, twenty-six girls) by testing testosterone levels in urine from seven postnatal to age 6-month-old children. Dr. Lamminmäki found the levels of testosterone predicted sex-typical behavior in the first six months of life. Dr. Lamminmäki tested 14-month-olds using the Pre-School Activities Inventory (PSAI) and playroom observation of toy choices. The more testosterone exposure early in life, the more stereotypical 'boy' activities they engaged. Low testosterone levels resulted in stereotypically *'girl'* activities (Lamminmäki et al., 2012).

Some women may mirror patterns more common in *male brains,* and men may mirror patterns more common in *female brains.* This finding does not mean the person is homosexual or transgender. Dr. Simon Baron-Cohen, who authored *Essential Differences* (2003), discovered that these general rules about male and female brains apply in most cases. According to PET and MRI scans, one in seven (14%) females and one in five (20%) males possess what is observably a more opposite sexed brain (Gurian and Stevens 2005, 287). What comprises a male or female brain is a combination of hundreds if not thousands of features, some more significant than others. Using statistical averages, scientists can determine that men and women have certain differentiating features. Each individual's brain comprises a mosaic of more male or female traits (Joel, Berman, et al. 2015, 15468). What comprises a male or female brain is a combination of hundreds if not thousands of distinctions.

Figure 7.3 Brain Sex Matrix (Joel, Berman et al. 2015)

These traits are primarily a result of the brain bathed in testosterone or estrogen during the first months of human development. Nevertheless, this practice does not create an entirely male or female brain. As Julia Serano, Ph.D., explains, *"Hormones do not simply act like unilateral on/off switches controlling female/feminine or male/masculine development"* (Serano 2007, 48). Dr. Serano is correct that a sexed brain is not black and white. Instead, all brains are a mosaic of millions of black, white, and grey pieces that unite to create an icon of gender. In this regard, the terms male and female brains are out of context.

A male has a male brain 100% of the time, and a female has a female brain 100% of the time. This language may echo back to the discussion gender theorists have about MtF individuals having female penises. They argue that because *transgender women are women*; therefore, every part of their bodies is female.

In contrast, if a person is a man, the person's totality requires a male brain because men have male brains. Thus, a male with a higher feminization rate in the brain still has a male brain because he is a male. In this regard, Type A and Type B characteristics may be more useful since all brains contain both Types A and B characteristics in various ways. Thus, suggesting traits within the brain that create a male or female brain is biological partialism.

In the *Brain Sex Matrix* shown in figure 7.3, each horizontal line represents a person, and each vertical column represents a trait. [2] Within these seven dominant traits, a matrix of Type A and Type B traits exists (represented with black and grey boxes) within both the male and female categories. A direct correlation between the two sexes exists and the two brain types. The female brain is light grey (more Type A), and the male brain is black (more Type B). The gender mosaic gives way for the understanding of sex and gender as a spectrum. However, if a scientist were to create the brain matrices for every human, one would likely continue to see the same patterns, people

---

[2] A continuous color representation of the degree of femininity (light grey) – masculinity (black) of the seven variables showing the largest sex/gender differences in the Maryland Adolescent Development in Context Study (MADICS) sample. Each horizontal line represents one participant and each column represents a single variable. (Created based on Joel et al., 2015).

falling within these two categories: mostly black on one side, primarily light grey on the other.

Although there is diversity within individuals, there is a quantum gap between the two categories; thus, it is not a spectrum that blends into one another seamlessly. Thus, human identities have a wide range of expressions having neurological and hormonal etiologies, but a wide range does not make gender a spectrum. As an example to prove this point further to the reader, if gender were a spectrum, there would be a much higher rate of female serial killers, mass shooters, and violent criminals. Violent crime rates are binary as a result of gender being binary. Do these studies suggest that since these expressions are naturally occurring, is the unnatural use of surgeries, hormone blockers, and hormone supplements necessary?

Scientists like Dr. Baron-Cohen and Dr. Cronin note that the differences between males and females of the human species are minor compared to other species (Cronin, Rippon, and Baron-Cohen 2016). The differences between male and female brains exist as a fact of biological science. Furthermore, these physical differences in the brain form ways males and females engage with the world. The subtle ways in which men and women act differently affect how society views the genders, successes, and failures, of which many occur on each side. Men occupy most corporate boards and most prison cells; women make less money over a lifetime and live longer lives. These dichotomies, on average, are socially as well as naturally driven.

Environmental effects

Proponents of brain plasticity like Daphna Joel, Ph.D., of Tel Aviv University, often point out how the environment changes a person's brain daily and even hourly. For example, stress can change structures in human brains if it persists for even fifteen minutes (Joel 2012). By the time humans are born, they have already experienced tremendous development and immutability within the brain, having bathed in either testosterone or estrogen for about six months. The next few months up until two years postnatal is another tremendous time of brain development and crystallization. This development never altogether stops but slows down. The brain's pathways become increasingly immutable with time until the early twenties, when the hormones have fully formed the brain and subsequently reverse the order, losing 100,000 brain cells every day.[3]

Although the brain becomes immutable in many functions, the brain still responds to stimuli through the senses and adapts. Reading or doing art changes the brain throughout a human's life and slows neuro-decline. Food, relationships, music, stress, happiness, prayer, practicing a virtuous life (or not) become part of the brain's functions. Creating habits changes the brain, which is why breaking habits takes time and practice and requires not just the intellect. Paul McHugh, M.D., also claims,

> Even if evidence existed that brain studies showed differences, which they do not, it would not tell us whether the brain differences are the cause of transgender identity or a result of identifying and acting upon their own stereotypes about the opposite sex, through what is known as neuroplasticity. (McHugh 2014a, 9)

A male can have an affinity towards things culturally and stereotypically associated with girls. Still, a male is not a girl regardless of desires or behavior as Dr. McHugh states, *"no matter how many of the stereotypes about girls [he] adopts and no matter how deeply [he] believes that affinity for those stereotypes about females transforms [him] into a female"* (McHugh 2014a, 7). Desire does not change material reality. This type of Thomistic realism has been replaced within mainline academia with Spinozism, *sentio ergo sum*—I *feel*, therefore, I *am,* whereby, if one desires to be a woman, one *is* a woman. However, if one desires to be affluent and British, desire alone creates neither of these realities.

Interestingly, Dr. McHugh does not recognize the theory of a sexually dimorphic brain, or at least not to the degree it determines immutable behavior. He then recognizes that actions and choices on the part of the individual can cause dimorphism. Dr. McHugh's theory of the gender-neutral brain may be helpful in his attempt to debunk the theory of a transgender brain. Still, it dismisses 800 million years of evolution and the practical wisdom of parents who recognize the difference between young boys and girls. When Dr. McHugh claims no

---

[3] Every day not only the brain but also the heart, kidneys and liver shrink until there comes a time when the body gets weaker and weaker and one of the essential organs ceases to function. Life eventually comes to an end (Vanier 1997, 141-142).

scientific studies prove the existence of male and female brains, he ignores dozens of studies, some of which are in this chapter. It is essential to be truthful with the evidence rather than win a legal battle using false scientific conclusions.

Differences in brain structures

Below are listed twelve of the many differences found between typical male and female brains. As stated above, the individual male or female brain is a mosaic with millions of combinations. However, a few generalized categories are most significant in their functionality and produce recognizable human activities associated with sex differences. Every person has different mental mosaics, which is why human beings are unique individuals, yet sex is still didactic. Still, individual men and women can be vastly different, partially based on this mosaic and somewhat on the environment.

Dopamine

Males produce more dopamine in their bodies than females, which allows males to react faster. The higher dopamine levels and greater blood flow in the cerebellum are advantageous, but it requires physical movement of the human body to operate effectively (Smith and Wilhelm 2002, 14).

Gray/White Matter

Male brains retain up to seven times more gray matter activity, and female brains possess ten times more white matter activity. Gray matter represents information processing centers in the brain, and white matter represents the networking of–or connections between–these processing centers. Gray matter exists in concentrated nodules, and white matter is more evenly distributed throughout the subcortical (Haier et al. 2005, 322).

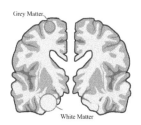

295

Corpus Callosum

Females develop a corpus callosum, the nerve bundles that connect the brain's two hemispheres, up to 25% larger than the corpus callosum found in males (Carter 1998, 40). The more robust connection between the two hemispheres allows females to perform multiple tasks at once. For example, using centers on both hemispheres of the brain helps females advance in verbal skills.

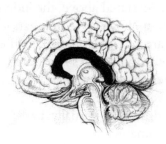

Temporal Lobes

Females create more vital neural connectors in their temporal lobes, allowing females to listen better and distinguish words with peripheral hearing. These neural connectors also help the memory of sensory perception (Blum 1998, 289). Therefore, the male temporal lobe will become more active only during sensory-tactile experiences.

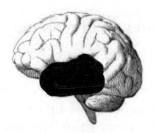

Hippocampus

The male and female hippocampus functions differently, as well. The hippocampus is responsible for memory storage. Males take longer to memorize objects and, in particular, written lists but are more successful in memorizing more items and more complex lists (Baron-Cohen 2003, 178).

Frontal Lobes

Females develop more active frontal lobes, which allow females to be less impulsive when making executive decisions than males. Impulsivity is vital in battle and sports but not the best in academia. The frontal lobes also develop earlier in females compared to males (Caviness 1996, 732). Richard Haier Ph.D., professor of psychology in the Department of Pediatrics, discovered,

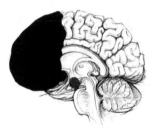

Human evolution has created two different types of brains designed for equally intelligent behavior. Eighty-four percent of gray-matter regions and 86% of white-matter regions involved with intellectual performance in women were found in the brain's frontal lobes, compared to 45% and zero for males, respectively. The gray matter driving male intellectual performance is distributed throughout more of the brain, while female intellectual performance is concentrated in the frontal lobe. (Haier et al. 2005, 320)

Scientists do not understand these differences to mean better or worse outcomes *per se*. Instead, in most cases, the functional differences are interconnected with other functions, even the best scientists can only partially understand.

Cerebellum

Males develop more prominent and active cerebellums, useful in physical activity, balance, and eye-hand coordination. Males also develop a greater flow of blood in the cerebellum, the part of the brain which reacts to stimuli.

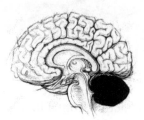

Amygdala

Males possess 10% larger amygdalas, the part of the brain responsible for aggression; however, when dealing with familiar malicious objects and people, the female brain showed *"a sustained amygdala response"* (Andreano, Dickerson, and Feldman-Barrett 2014, 1389). Thus, differences in structures and functionality between male and female brains are evident, although the effects on daily human interactions may vary.

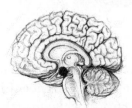

Broca & Wernicke

Females possess more significant development of their Broca and Wernicke areas in the front and temporal lobes. These regions are the principal language centers of the brain. Thus, the female brain has more neural pathways and centers for language than males, which gives females an advantage over verbalizing emotions and experiences (Moir and Jessel 1989, 195).

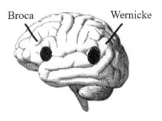

Hormones

Females create more estrogen and oxytocin, while males create more testosterone and vasopressin. Estrogen and oxytocin are critical hormones in the brain for cognitive assessment in Broca and Wernicke regions and aid verbal communication. Testosterone and vasopressin are vital for creating aggression and estimating spatial objects. The female brain's feminine hormones help her communicate while the masculine hormones in the males help them learn through hierarchical competition and aggressive play (Rhoads 2004, 264).

Blood Flow

Male brains better compartmentalize activity to save mental energy; thus, male brains use 15% less blood flow than female brains (Marano 2003, 41). An advantage of this compartmentalization is that males can focus better on a single task for extended periods. Female brains can concentrate better on many activities simultaneously but not the same depth with a single act. If males experience too much stimulation simultaneously, the response is a swelling of the amygdala, which leads to frustration and aggression (Gurian and Stevens 2005, 50). In addition, prolonged frustration will lead to a release of cortisol, which increases adrenaline in males.

Rest State

When males enter the rest state, activity in the brain goes dormant apart from essential functioning centers. When a female enters a rest state, less blood flows to the brain, but many parts of the brain are still functioning at low levels. As a result, men can sit in a boat fishing or waiting in a lookout hunting for prolonged periods with little brain activity. If a woman were to attempt the same actions, her brain would still be functioning at a higher level, and she would be thinking about many things she could be doing. Women would not enjoy idle activities as men do; on the contrary, females can learn and listen even when bored, although absolute boredom is much more painful since their brains do not truly maintain a resting state.

7.2 MALE AND FEMALE HYPOTHALAMUSES: BSTc

Dr. Jiang-Ning Zhou, M.D., from the University of Amsterdam, conducted two notable studies of the hypothalamus in transgender corpses, published in 1995 and with Frank Kruijver, M.D., in 2000. Dr. Zhou and his colleagues were aware that the volume of the central subdivision of the bed nucleus of the stria terminalis (BSTc) is more prominent in men than in women. The BSTc is also an area of the brain that is essential for sexual behavior. Responding to transgender individuals' claims that they felt they had a male or female brain, these researchers placed this theory to the test. Would an MtF individual possess a male BSTc or a female BSTc?

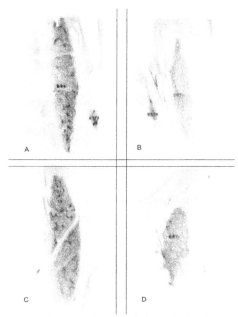

Figure 7.4 Representative sections of the BSTc. A: heterosexual man; B: heterosexual woman; C: homosexual man; D: MtF transsexual (Zhou, et al. 1995)

301

For his 1995 publication in the journal *Nature* (Zhou et al. 1995), Dr. Zhou studied 6 MtF transsexual brains over 11 years and equal numbers of heterosexual men and women and the brains of homosexual men. Dr. Zhou discovered that six BSTc sites in the brains of MtF individuals were more similar in size to that of heterosexual women than to either homosexual or heterosexual men. The study found, *"The BSTc volume in heterosexual men was 44% larger than in heterosexual women. The volume of the BSTc of heterosexual and homosexual men was found not to differ in any statistically significant way ... Although the mean BSTc volume in the transsexuals was even smaller than that in the female group, the difference did not reach statistical significance"* (Zhou et al. 1995, 69).

To better understand this information, the artist rendering in figure 7.4 clarifies the difference between male and female BSTc. The similarity between the BSTc of females and MtF individuals will be more evident after viewing figure 7.4. It is apparent that quadrants A (heterosexual man) and C (homosexual man) are the most similar in BSTc structure and size, while B (heterosexual woman) and D (MtF individual) are most equally paired. The difference in sizes of the BSTc between homosexual and heterosexual men is negligible, given that the sample size of the two groups combined was only twelve individuals. The difference between MtF and heterosexual and homosexual men would not likely vanish with a more extensive study given a 44% difference in size, which is beyond the researcher's margin of error in standard deviation. Figure 7.4 shows one BSTc from each category of individuals, so it is essential to examine all the data collected.

In figure 7.5, the first is heterosexual men (M), the next is homosexual men (HM), followed by heterosexual women (F), and the last category on the right is MtF individuals (MtF). As it is clear when showing the data points for this study, the first two categories of heterosexual and homosexual men are nearly identical in the mean volume of BSTc. It is also clear that the MtF individuals show the lowest volume of BSTc and are closest to the class of heterosexual women. If it was not clear at the beginning of this section, comparing BSTc volumes is not like comparing shoe sizes of men, women, and MtF individuals and finding a correlation. Connecting organ sizes within twelve individuals is not proof of any sex-based essentialism. However, the hypothalamus' BSTc section is a principal center responsible for sexual functioning within the body.

If the study's limitations were not already apparent, the use of six MtF brains is not a large sample size. The larger the sample size, the more conclusive the results would be. However, this study dissects the hypothalamus, dehydrates it, and embalms it in paraffin, making obtaining a larger sample size difficult. This process would first require the subject to be deceased. Another challenge raised in the study is that all the homosexual men, two heterosexual men, and one MtF individual died from complications from AIDS. Since all male and MtF categories included individuals with AIDS and did not appear to place them outside of their category of male BSTc, it does not appear to be a significant factor.

Another complication is that the MtF individuals were not without hormonal and surgical modifications to their bodies. These were transsexual women who wholly or partially transitioned to the other sex using hormones and surgeries. Five of the six MtF individuals were orchiectomized, meaning doctors surgically removed their testicles. The orchiectomization may appear to be an Achilles heel of what otherwise appears like a convincing case study. Dr. Zhou considered this and noted the one MtF individual who was not orchiectomized was statistically in the middle of the other MtF individuals who were orchiectomized. In addition, the researchers located two brains of heterosexual cis men who were orchiectomized due to cancer surgery one and three months before their deaths, and they showed typical male volumes of BSTc. The effects of long-term orchiectomization are not shown in the control group of this study.

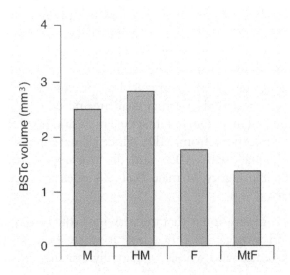

Figure 7.5 Graph of BSTc volumes in the hypothalamous; M: heterosexual men; HM: homosexual men; F: heterosexual women; tF: MtF transsexuals (Zhou, et al. 1995)

In addition to orchiectomization, all the MtF individuals were treated with estrogen. These hormonal manipulations could be another Achilles heel in this case study. Still, again Dr. Zhou considered this and looked at the brain of a cis man who developed a feminizing adrenal tumor, which induced high blood levels of estrogen, who nevertheless retained a very large BSTc. In addition, one of the MtF individuals in the study stopped taking estrogen 15 months before death and another three months before death. Thus, Dr. Zhou suggests fewer reasons to believe there was a correlation between estrogen and BSTc volume.

In an article arguing against Dr. Zhou's conclusion, Hilleke Hulshoff, Ph.D., in the 2006 edition of the *European Journal of Endocrinology,* published *"Changing your sex changes your brain: influences of testosterone and estrogen on adult human brain structure"* (Hulshoff 2006, 108). Dr. Hulshoff's results showed anti-androgen and estrogen treatment decreased brain volumes of eight male-to-female subjects towards female proportions. In comparison, androgen treatment in six female-to-male subjects increased brain and hypothalamus volumes towards male proportions. The average age of transsexual people during this experiment was 35 years. The MRI tests were taken at three different periods: before any hormone treatment, during the hormone treatments, and then again before surgery. The effects of hormones taken while people are still in their twenties may have a different effect on the brain than on people later in life. Besides, stopping hormone treatment for a few months may not change the effects of prolonged exposure to hormones, chiefly if taken while the brain was still forming. Alone, Dr. Zou's 1995 study is essential but far from conclusive.

7.3 SOMATOSTATIN-
EXPRESSING NEURONS

In 2000, Drs. Frank Kruijver and Zhou and other researchers from the University of Amsterdam released a second study in *The Journal of Clinical Endocrinology & Metabolism* (Kruijer et al. 2000), which confirmed the earlier findings. This study now included forty-two brains, of which twenty-six were from the 1995 survey. Instead of just looking at the volume of the BSTc, the research also evaluated the number of somatostatin-expressing neurons (SOM) found in the BSTc. This study included an FtM individual, which was the most significant addition to the study. The study found,

> The number of SOM neurons in the BSTc of heterosexual men was 71% higher than that in heterosexual women, whereas the number of neurons in heterosexual and homosexual men was similar. The BSTc number of neurons was 81% higher in homosexual men than in heterosexual women. The number of neurons in the BSTc of male-to-female transsexuals was similar to that of females. In addition, the neuron number of the [FtM] was clearly in the male range. The number of neurons in [MtF] transsexuals was 40% lower than that found in the heterosexual reference males. (Kruijer et al., 2036)

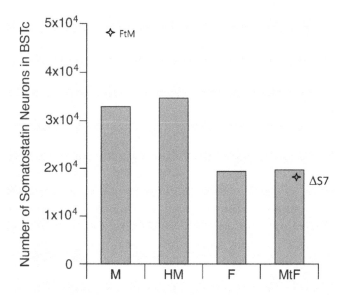

Figure 7.6 SOM Neurons in M: heterosexual men; HM: homosexual men; F: heterosexual women; MtF: MtF transsexuals (Kruijer, et al. 2000, 2036)

This study's results reaffirm the 1995 study, as apparent in figure 7.6 from the 2000 study. Notably, the FtM individual located on the chart as *"FtM"* above the left column of figure 7.6 is not only in the male range of SOM but also at an above-average range for men. Also notable is brain ΔS7, which is located to the very right of the graph. This individual was 84 years old and *"strong cross-dressing identified,"* but was never orchiectomized, sexually reassigned, or treated with CPA (a testosterone blocker) or adult estrogen treatments. Despite not being physically or chemically modified at any time for possessing feelings of having a transgender identity, individual ΔS7 possessed SOM and BSTc levels consistent with MtF individuals and heterosexual women.

This study's shortcomings include that six of seven MtF individuals were the same subjects as the earlier study. The best way to assure this study's accuracy would be by replicating it with more significant numbers. Unfortunately, the number of available MtF brains donated before the year 2000 limited Dr. Kruijver's research. Despite the shortcoming of the small sample size, one finds a high success rate in the consistency of the findings. Only one FtM brain was available, but

SOM levels for this brain fell perfectly within the projected expectations. Also, ΔS7 affirmed, without physical alterations or hormones, that the BSTc and SOM levels for MtF individuals match the studied women.

Dr. Hulshoff responded to this work in his 2006 study out of the University of Utrecht,

[In the studies conducted by Dr. Zhou (1995) and Dr. Kruijver (2000)] All these transsexuals had received cross-sex hormone treatment before their brains were studied. Therefore, the altered size of the bed nucleus of the stria terminalis could have been due to the exposure of cross-sex hormones in adult life. Alternatively, the different sizes of the bed nucleus of the stria terminalis in transsexuals could have been present prior to cross-sex hormone treatment, reflecting (potentially hormonally determined) differences in the development of the (pre-and perinatal) brain, or possibly genetic differences, between transsexuals and non-transsexuals. The aim of our study was to examine the influence of exposure to high levels of cross-sex hormones on brain structures in adulthood. (Hulshoff 2006, 108)

Dr. Hulshoff's critique of doctors Zhou and Kruijver's studies reiterates the same issues the researchers have already raised. The subjects' pool was not ideal in size or scope, yet, given their limitations, the researchers acted with due diligence to mitigate their limiting factors by including additional controls. Since no one tested the six MtF individuals before their surgical and hormonal alterations, it is impossible to ascertain if their BSTc or SOM were typical of their gendered identity. Dr. Kruijver's study is still significant since ΔS7 was never physically or hormonally treated, yet his SOM and BSTc volume were still consistent with cis female controls. In addition, the FtM individual had not received any hormonal treatment before her tests and yet showed SOM and BSTc volumes synonymous with cis men. Dr. Hulshoff's response could explain the six original MtF subjects, but not those added into the 2000 study by Dr. Kruijver.

7.4 PIMOZIDE CURE

In 1996, Basant Puri, M.D., and Iqbal Singh, M.D., released a study called, *"The successful treatment of a gender dysphoric patient with pimozide."* This study found success in treating an androphilic cross-dressing gender dysphoric individual. In addition, the researchers using a daily dose of 2 mg caused the feelings of gender dysphoria to cease.[4] Pimozide is an antipsychotic drug often used to treat people with Tourette Syndrome. However, when doctors reduced the patient's dose to 1 mg after one year, gender dysphoria rapidly returned. Pimozide acts to block the reuptake of dopamine at neuronal receptors, allowing it to circulate in the synapses (Puri and Singh 1996).

The researchers claimed the twenty-three-year-old fulfilled the study's criteria for a monosymptomatic delusion.[5] However, the doctor's conclusion is questionable since the patient was also schizophrenic and violent. Hence, the patient can more accurately be diagnosed as having comorbid conditions. The study claimed that after four years on 2 mg of Pimozide, the patient was free of gender dysphoria, but it is essential to know if the treatment had long-term effects. Since the study's publication, no researchers conducted subsequent follow-ups to know if gender dysphoria has ceased entirely. Researchers have also recognized a single case of exorcism having cured transsexualism (Barlow, Abel, and Blanchard 1977)[6]. Still, single claims of short-term cures are not conclusive evidence of proper treatment.

The Pimozide study is cited as evidence against the surgical and hormonal treatment of gender dysphoric people. Simultaneously, the transgender community rejects this study since they only advocate for

---

[4] Although not his homosexuality

[5] *"An illness characterized by a single delusion that is sustained over a considerable period of time"* (Munro 1980, 34).

[6] Note this is Edward Blanchard and not Ray Blanchard.

procedures to make their bodies match their minds. Most transgender people are adamantly against doctors prescribing antipsychotic medication to gender dysphoric patients to cure the dysphoria (Z. Jones 2016). However, it is essential not to let politics prohibit science, which may cure a disorder. The alternative treatment is major reconstructive surgery and a regimen of hormone blockers and supplements for the rest of a person's life. Those who oppose a medication to relieve gender dysphoria do not recommend a natural and less medically invasive approach but instead a process far more invasive and less natural.

Wellbutrin is designed to help with bipolar disorder, anxiety, and depression. The side effect is that it also helps a person to quit smoking. Many individuals are prescribed this antipsychotic medication to quit smoking, but that does not mean this patient is psychotic. Likewise, transgender people should not reject a drug because of its other applications.

This study may be a fundamental key to understanding gender dysphoria, or it could be a flawed study of a coincidental circumstance. Since this study only involved one subject who was not uncomplicated, it would be necessary for this study to be repeated with a broader subject pool. Regrettably, the study has never been repeated in twenty-five years, although it has been widely cited (Z. Jones 2016).

7.5 IDENTICAL TWINS

Milton Diamond, Ph.D., acknowledged for exposing John Money, Ph.D., in the infamous John/Joan case, conducted the twin study in 2013. His research was directed through the University of Hawaii-Manoa and published in *The International Journal of Transgenderism* and is noted for considering transsexuality *"a form of brain intersex"* (Diamond 2013, 34). This journal article is not to the same standards as doctors Zhou and Kruijver's research through the University of Amsterdam and the peer-reviewed journal, *The Journal of Clinical Endocrinology & Metabolism*. Still, this study is notable since the LGB community reveres Dr. Diamond for his identical twin studies. His most important study proved a higher prevalence of homosexuality in identical twin pairs when one twin self-identified as homosexual. Both twins identifying as homosexual were at a higher rate than expected based on the prevalence of homosexuality in the general population. The results of this study indicate an epigenetic link to homosexuality.

In the transgender study, Dr. Diamond cast his net wide, capturing vast amounts of subject data about monozygotic (identical) and dizygotic (fraternal) twins. He used sources like the Library of Congress Medline and YouTube and internet sources to collect data on twins, of which at least one of the two identified as transgender. Dr. Diamond also placed ads and used the help of colleagues to collect surveys from twins. Examining the data collected from others, he was able to gain information on twenty-seven male and sixteen female twin pairs. Through his surveys, he was able to collect an additional sixty-nine twin pairs. Of identical twins who responded, thirteen out of thirty-nine (33.3%) sets of natal male twins were concordant for transsexual identity. Eight out of thirty-five[7] (22.8%) sets of natal female twins were concordant for transsexual identity. Of fraternal twins, one out of twenty-one natal males had a concordant for transsexual identity. In

---

[7] Incorrectly written as "25" on page 27.

contrast, none of fifteen natal females had a fraternal twin who was concordant for transsexual identity. In total, 110 sets of twins, twenty-two pairs (20%), had both identified as transsexuals.

The rest of Dr. Diamond's article involves the questionnaire about how transgender people were raised, the household's openness to express variant gender identities, and same-sex attraction. Regrettably, of 110 subjects in the twins' study, less than twenty subjects answered each question. The small sample size and the nature of the anecdotal questions mean this section goes on for eight pages and is not the most didactic. Among the fourteen natal males who responded, 71.4% only engaged in sexual relationships with women (autogynephilic). Five of fourteen (35.7%) natal women replied in the affirmative that they thought their parents wished they were born male; however, 79.6% of respondents replied they believed their parents had no preference if they were born a male or female. Thus, no significant correlation appears between parental acceptance of cross-dressing, LGBT lifestyles, or shaming children about their birth sex regardless of the social factors that existed in the homes of these 110 twin pairs. In contrast, one set of twins separated at birth, another at four years old, and a third at 14. Each of these three sets of twins transitioned without the other twin knowing it until years later.

The results of this study suggest a possibility of a genetic element to transgender identification. Suppose transgender identities occur at a rate of about 0.6% of the population, according to a 2016 study from The Williams Institute (Flores et al. 2016). In this case, 20% of twins sharing a transsexual identity is a statistically significant occurrence. It is possible to question the data collection methodology since no current method exists to collect an accurate cross-sample of the twin/transgender population. Nevertheless, as long as Dr. Diamond conducted his research in good faith, there is a reasonable likelihood of obtaining relatively accurate observations with at least 110 subjects. Dr. Diamond claims this may point to a *"neurodevelopmental condition of the brain,"* which links feelings of transgender identity with dimorphic structures.

Intersex is a similar neurodevelopmental condition suggesting transgender people could develop an intersex brain. The theory of an intersex brain and a neurodevelopmental cause continues to be a probable explanation at present. Suppose there are morphological or hormonal causes for dysphoria. In that case, researchers cannot determine if these abnormalities result in the *desire* to be the opposite sex or psychically *being* the opposite sex. A psychological analysis is needed to consider if gender dysphoric people have the psyche of their assumed sex or merely desire to be so.

Dr. Diamond's study also points to an epigenetic approach. If this occurrence were entirely genetic and based on just one gene, identical twins would mirror a 100% similarity in transgender identities between siblings. If instead, the cause was epigenetic, then the presence of the gene must be present, but also any number of other factors would also need to be present beyond pure genetics.

7.6 GRAY MATTER

In 2009, Eileen Luders, Ph.D., and the Laboratory of Neuro Imaging at UCLA published a study in *Neuroimaging* titled, *"Regional gray matter variation in male-to-female transsexualism"* (Luders et al. 2009). Gray and white matter in the brain are two of the differentiators between males and females. There is no indication that the part of the brain associated with sexual identity is in gray matter or white matter, contrary to studies conducted on the hypothalamus, which medical researchers believe is one of the causes of one's sexuality. This study is still significant since brain technology took a quantum step forward between 1995 and 2009. In this study, the researchers used an MRI machine rather than postmortem samples. The samples doctors Zhou and Kruijver used were from natal men who were orchiectomized and took estrogen for decades right up until death or stopping treatment slightly before death. Although doctors Zhou and Kruijver considered this and found control samples to confirm this was not the cause of the low BSTc and SOM volumes in MtF individuals, these shortcomings were still factors that needed to be overcome.[8]

---

[8] Doctors. Zhou and Kruijver found two heterosexual men who were orchiectomized at the end of their lives due to cancer, and their BSTc volumes were typical of other men so this did not appear to be the cause. On the contrary, being orchiectomized in the final years of life rather than decades before death, may simply mean it takes a longer period of time before orchiectomization affects the BSTc volume in the hypothalamus or the combination of estrogen and orchiectomization has a composite effect. The 2000 study again confirms the 1995 study's findings with the sample ΔS7, an individual never orchiectomized or on estrogen; however, this is a sample size of one. It is not an insignificant finding, but a sample size of one cannot be conclusive.

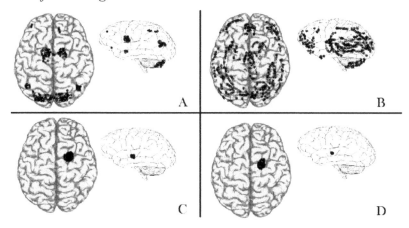

Figure 7.7 SOM Neuron levels in gray matter (Luders, et al. 2009, 907)

Dr. Luder studied twenty-four MtF transsexuals not physically or chemically treated for transgender issues. The subjects were still alive and, thus, did not die from complications. The median age of the subjects was 46.73 years. The study also included sixty controls comprised of thirty cis men and thirty cis women.

In this test, Dr. Luders divided the brain into twenty-two regions and created cluster-specific box plots to evaluate the amount of gray matter within this region. In all but two regions, cis women contain the highest levels of gray matter. In comparison, in two regions, MtF individuals possessed the highest levels of gray matter, and cis men contained no regions in which they possessed the highest level of gray matter. For the twenty regions where cis women had the highest levels of gray matter, MtF individuals retained the lowest amount of gray matter. Still, they were within a reasonable range of being consistent with cis men.

Figure 7.7 shows artist renderings of the brain scan images. Quadrants A and B show women develop more gray matter than MtF individuals and cis men. In C, the reader can observe the brain's putamen region where MtF transsexuals develop more gray matter than cis men. In D, the dark region shows the same putamen region illuminated, meaning the MtF individuals have a higher gray matter volume than cis men. The study clarifies that in quadrant D, MtF individuals have more prominent gray matter than women as well.

315

In the BSTc and SOM studies, researchers found a direct correlation between BSTc/SOM and sexual functioning. Gray matter is neurological material, and the Putamen region of the brain influences degenerative neurological disorders and motor functions. Still, studies do not show a connection between this region and sexual expression or personality. This unknown connection leads to further questions about the function of the Putamen region.

The study results showed the regional gray matter in the brains of MtF individuals more closely patterned cis men than women. MtF individuals showed a larger gray matter volume in the right putamen region than cis men and women. If this study is accurate at face value, this would mean MtF individuals do not develop *women's brains,* but some regions of their brains are not typical of brains belonging to cis people. The study also makes the statement,

> Further research needs to resolve whether the observed distinct features of transsexuals' brains influence their gender identity or possibly are the consequence of being transsexual. Alternately, other variables may be independently affecting both the expression of transsexual identity and the neuroanatomy in transsexuals that led to the observed association between both. (Luders et al. 2009, 907)

Returning to Katherine Wu's[9] Harvard post, *Dear Mr. President,* she states this case as evidence for a transgendered brain's existence. She concluded, *"Several studies confirmed previous findings, showing once more that transgender people appear to be born with brains more similar to the gender with which they identify, rather than the one to which they were assigned"* (K. Wu 2016).[10] Alas, the discussion section of this study does not confirm Katherine's statement. Instead, this study suggests one of three viable options:

1. The putamen section of the brain *"causes"* MtF individuals to be biologically born transgender.

---

[9] Since 2018 she earned a Ph.D. and is a Boston-based science reporter for NOVA Next and senior producer for Story Collider.

[10] On the phrase *"Several studies"* are links to Drs. Luders' and Rametti's research which are addressed.

316

2. If men firmly and earnestly believe they are women, it can change the gray matter volumes in the brain's putamen section.

3. There may well be a different unknown factor affecting both the putamen region of the brain and sexual identity.

The 2016 Guillamon study (Guillamon, Junque, and Gómez-Gil. 2016) confirms that the third option is the most likely conclusion. Evidence from this study finds that MtF and FtM individuals develop brain subgroupings that show standard features not entirely male or female but with similar features among themselves.

7.7 WHITE MATTER MICROSTRUCTURES

In the 2011 *Journal of Psychiatric Research*, Giuseppina Rametti, M.D., and her colleagues at the Universities of Madrid and Barcelona reported they discovered FtM individuals exhibited white matter microstructures more similarly matched patterns found within cis males (Rametti et al. 2011, 203). This study included eighteen FtM individuals, twenty-four cis males, and nineteen cis females. All FtM individuals exhibited early-onset gender non-conformity (before puberty) and were erotically attracted to women, identified as *homosexual type transexuals* (Blanchard, Clemmensen, and Steiner 1987, 139), and evaluated by a psychiatrist using the Spanish version 5.0.0 of the International Neuropsychiatric Interview. Doctors did not hormonally treat these patients before the testing. The researchers used MRI scans to examine fractional anisotropy (FA), a method of determining the brain's fiber tracts by tracking the movement of water molecules. Microfiber tracts in men and women run in different patterns, with men naturally having higher FA values.

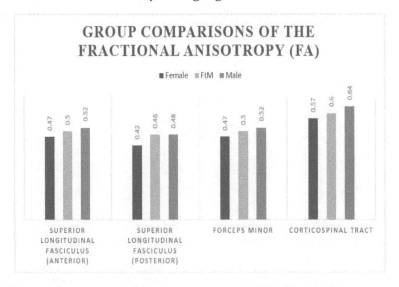

Figure 7.8 Group Comparisons of the fractional anisotropy (FA) in the four fasciculi present sex differences.

When looking at figure 7.8 in this study, one can see the four sections of the brain selected. The FtM individuals express FA values slightly more consistent with cis males in the superior longitudinal fasciculus and the forceps minor. Still, with the standard deviation (STD), their FA values fall right about in the middle between cis men and cis women. In the corticospinal tract, the FA value for FtM individuals falls closer to that of cis women. Still, it might again be directly between FA values of cis men and cis women with the standard deviation. The superior longitudinal fasciculus site is the most interesting since FtM individuals shared the same FA values as cis men, 0.48, and cis women at 0.42, although with the STD, this may not be conclusive. It cannot be discounted that FtM individuals showed the same FA values as cis men in the superior longitudinal fasciculus. Out of the entire brain, the superior longitudinal fasciculus is the only location where this was identical. When considering all the brain regions, only this one section showed similarities for eighteen FtM individuals. This study is not conclusive evidence without replicating this study with larger samples. The paper's results section is mildly shocking in its overreaching claims, inconsistent with the facts presented by her research. She opined,

> In conclusion, our results show that the white matter microstructure pattern in untreated FtM transsexuals is closer to the pattern of subjects who share their gender identity (males) than to those who share their biological sex (females). Our results provide evidence for structural differences in the untreated MtF transsexual's brain. (Rametti et al. 2011, 203)

From this conclusion, one can only assume that Dr. Rametti failed to include additional information that assisted her in coming to this conclusion. In this study, the data she provided shows the four regions she reported on. There was a similar pattern between FtM individuals and cis male brains in the superior longitudinal fasciculus. The FtM individuals showed FA values high for cis women in the other three regions but low for cis men. This conclusion does not confirm the claim, *"the white matter microstructure pattern in untreated FtM transsexuals is closer to the pattern of subjects who share their gender identity."* The most honest conclusion is that there appears to be a link between the FA values of FtM individuals and cis men in the superior longitudinal fasciculus. Still, a study with a broader subject pool would be needed to confirm this. A sample size of eighteen is not large enough to definitively reach this conclusion.

7.8 Intersex-Brain

In a 2016 brain study by Antonio Guillamon, M.D., and colleagues, they discovered homosexual type[11] individuals do not develop typical male or female brains but rather, *"each have their own cerebral phenotype"* (Guillamon, Junque and Gómez-Gil 2016, 1627). This study concludes early-onset homosexual transsexuals, individuals attracted to persons with the same natal sex, develop an intersex condition restricted to the brain. This finding confirms Dr. Diamond's conclusion that an intersex brain can occur. Indirectly, Dr. Guillamon's study also confirms Dr. Blanchard's conclusions that there are different causes of autogynephilia and androphilia. In addition, Dr. Guillamon reaffirms the findings suggested by the brain studies from 1995 and 2000, including doctors Kruijver, Zhou, Pool, Hofman, Gooren, and Swaab, whereby transsexual people possess some brain structures similar to those of the opposite sex, are not a copy of an opposite-sex brain. Dr. Guillamon wrote, *"It is simplistic to say that a female-to-male transgender person is a female trapped in a male body. It's not because they have a male brain but a transsexual brain"* (Russo 2016).

Although every person is a matrix of male and female brain types, MtF and FtM individuals held standard average features separate from the common average features of either cis men or women. For example, on average, MtF individuals are composed of male structures, including similar intracranial volume, gray matter, white matter, and cerebrospinal fluid, but a cortical volume and thickness, unlike either cis men or women. MtF individuals, on average, possess female and male white matter fiber bundles in the right hemisphere. Dr. Guillamon found that the *pars triangularis* (part of the Broca region, used for semantic processing) in homosexual MtF is thicker than heterosexual male controls. In contrast, for homosexuals, it is thinner than in heterosexual males.

---

[11] See Blanchard's Typologies, *supra* chapter 6.

Homosexual-type transsexuals express a feminized *pars triangularis*, while cisgender homosexuals express a demasculinized *pars triangularis*. Dr. Guillamon suggests that if FtM individuals develop *"feminine, defeminized, and masculinized morphological traits,"* [12] MtF individuals develop *"masculine, feminine, and demasculinized traits."* These results demonstrate that these abnormalities are likely neurodevelopmental disorders, as Dr. Diamond suggested (Guillamon, Junque, and Gómez-Gil 2016, 1627).

The research concluded that autogynephilic MtF brains were slightly feminized but not like that of cis women. Furthermore, researchers could not differentiate between an MtF autogynephilic individual and a heterosexual male in the *pars triangularis*. In contrast to androphilic men and women who expressed different brain structures. These findings support the theory stating the cause of transgender identities is rooted in a common ancestor with transvestitism and not etiologically related to homosexual-type transgender identities.

---

[12] The terms masculinization and feminization refer to any change that makes an individual more like typical males or females. While the term demasculinization and defeminization denote any change makes an individual less like a typical male or female.

7.9 CONCEPT REVIEW

Chapter seven is one of the most important in the book since it does a topical review of the studies used to make the most significant claims about transgender science. Katherine Wu made a bold and unwavering claim in a Harvard online journal stating the science was clear. She claimed, *"transgender people appear to be born with brains more similar to the gender with which they identify, rather than the one to which they were assigned"* (K. Wu 2016). Medical researchers found no evidence to validate the old understanding, *Anima muliebris in corpore virili inclusa.*[13] Science is, in fact, clear this is *not* true. Researchers found considerable evidence to show that MtF and FtM individuals possess structures most similar to their natal sex; however, doctors discovered notable examples of structures more in line with their gender identities. Dr. Guillamon and his colleagues uncovered homosexual type MtF individuals and FtM individuals having standard features among brain matrix patterns.

The evidence from these studies points to a neurodevelopmental etiology. The conclusions include an epigenetic creation where a particular gene or combination of genes is necessary and other likely hormonal and environmental factors. These factors introduced in the womb and within the few months following birth are interacting with a child's hormones to create a transgender brain phenotype. In transgender subjects, anomalies within the hypothalamus are significant since this location likely determines sexual identity. It is also associated with the reptilian complex discussed *supra* in section 4.2. Chapter eight will continue this biological understanding of a possible neurodevelopmental etiology.

---

[13] A female psyche confined in a male body (Ulrichs 1868, 140).

Chapter 8
Neurodevelopmental Etiology

Both gender identity disorder and schizophrenia are
neurodevelopmental disorders, and that they may share common
causal mechanisms and risk factors

— Dr. Ravi Rajkumar, M.D.,
Gender Identity Disorder and Schizophrenia

The brain is an organ that can go wrong just like any other.

— Daniel Amen, M.D., *The Minds of Boys*

Chapter eight synthesizes the medical studies surrounding transgender identification, connecting the various elements of the observations found in chapters six and seven. For example, suppose a person only considers one or several brain studies. In that case, the only determination is that some transgender people develop some brain structures different from people within their natal sex. These studies provide interesting facts but do not create causation.

This book attempts to accurately place the data points of medical research so that proper circumspection may *connect the dots*. A proper understanding of the evidence creates a realistic image of transgender brain science. This section seeks to present facts about the body and make connections that will accurately address transgender people's challenges.

This chapter claims that there is a clear neurodevelopmental cause for gender dysphoria. Neurodevelopmental disorders are seldom singular and occur along with numerous indicators like left-handedness, dyslexia, autism, or more insidious illnesses like schizophrenia. These developmental qualities are a result of neuro pathways formed in the brain before or during infancy. An unusual morphology in the hypothalamus caused by natal hormones could cause feelings of gender dysphoria. This explanation is not entirely simple since some neurodevelopmental disorders may cause gender dysphoria as a secondary effect rather than directly. For example, people with autism (ASD) or obsessive-compulsive disorder (OCD) may be more susceptible to suggestions on the internet that changing one's gender will be a path to happiness and wholeness. Also, issues like Body Identity Integrity Disorder (BIID) and Body Dysmorphic Disorder (BDD) may be partially neurodevelopmental and partially social. Eating disorders or cutting, for example, could be BDD, but it often naturally desists into adulthood. If a disorder is neurodevelopmental, it is not clear that it is permanent or not a secondary effect that doctors could treat by addressing the direct cause.

8.1 COMMON
PSYCHOLOGICAL ETIOLOGY

T he 1970s were full of theories about the psychological causes of transgender identification. Followers of Sigmund Freud, M.D., suspected that psychological disturbances occurred within transsexual people's psyche. Leonard Lothstein, Ph.D., proposed, it was a *"pathology in the mother-child relationship and defective object relations"* (Lothstein 1979, 214), an idea repeated in observational studies by (Gilpin, Raza, and Gilpin, 1979); (Moberly 1986); (Ovesey and Person 1976); and (Macvicar 1978). Charles Socarides, M.D., takes psychology a step further in his article, *Transsexualism and Psychosis,* where he claims that *"beneath the desire 'to change sex' may lie serious, if not overwhelming, psychopathology-even of a psychotic nature. Transsexual wishes may arise from oedipal conflict, preoedipal fixation, or schizophrenic processes"* (Socarides 1978, 379).

Another primary theory of the 1980s was the concept that transsexualism was a form of borderline personality disorder. Dr. James Kavanaugh concluded that one possibility for the etiology of transsexualism was the attempt to *"discard bad aggressive features and replace them with a new, idealized perfection"* (Kavanaugh and Volkan 1979, 366). Dr. James Murray claims that transsexual conditions are *"a subgroup of borderline disorders"* (Murray 1985, 454).

The 1990s and 2000s attempted to exonerate transgender people (no longer medically called transsexuals in the DSM-5) from accusations of being mentally ill. In a study by Collier Cole, Ph.D., 435 gender dysphoric individuals using MMPI data reported, *"transsexualism is usually an isolated diagnosis and not part of any general psychopathological disorder"* (Cole et al. 1997, 15). In a Dutch study, researchers compared adolescent psychiatric outpatients with adolescent transsexuals. They concluded, *"the argument that gross psychopathology is a required condition for the development of transsexualism appears indefensible"* (Cohen et al. 1997, 16).

Neurodevelopmental Etiology

Kristina Olson, Ph.D., claimed that there was *"novel evidence of low rates of internalizing psychopathology in your socially transitioned transgender children who are supported in their gender identity"* (Olson et al., 2015, 7). Dr. Olson's study examined seventy-three prepubescent transgender children (ages three to twelve). She determined that there are statistically significant internalizing psychopathology levels within this group. However, within the title of her study and her conclusion, she claims that transgender youth do not experience psychopathology if they are *"supported,"* but her study does not examine supported versus unsupported youth.

The 2000s did not confirm the 1997 reports from Cole et al. and Cohen et al. In 2009, Stephen Levine, M.D., and Anna Solomon found *"90% of these diverse patients had at least one other significant form of psychopathology."* The researchers also warned, *"Gender identity specialists, unlike the media, need to be concerned about the majority of patients, not just the ones who are apparently functioning well in transition"* (Levine and Solomon 2009). A 2014 study showed that 62.7% of gender dysphoric people suffer from other Axis I comorbidity (Azadeh Meybodi 2014, 2).

A 2016 review of literature in the *International Review of Psychiatry*, done by Cecilia Dhejne, M.D., and colleagues, reported a strong correlation between individuals with gender dysphoria and other mental illnesses (Dhejne, Van Vlerken, et al. 2016, 44). Melanie Bechard, M.D., and colleagues found the same results in 2017 when reviewing the files of adolescents (Bechard et al., 2017, 678). California transgender healthcare bill (AB 2218) in August of 2020 stated into the public record, *"Transgender adults are significantly more likely to report having a disability due to a physical, mental, or emotional condition, 60%"* (CA 2020).

Two studies published in 2014 found that conditions including ADHD, autism, affective and anxiety disorders, depression, and schizophrenia occur at significantly higher rates among transgender people. Ravi Rajkumar, M.D.,'s study concluded, *"Both gender identity disorder and schizophrenia are neurodevelopmental disorders and that they may share common causal mechanisms and risk factors"* (Rajkumar 2014).[1] Dr. Rajkumar considered that one to eight of every 1,000 people have

---

[1] Although I was initially skeptical of Dr. Rajkumar's report out of India, the research appears thorough.

Schizophrenia and one in every 10,000 males and one in every 25,000 females suffer from gender dysphoria. He used transgender rates from an Irish study, which is lower than American studies. Using the Williams Institute study, there are 1.4 million Americans who identify in any way as transgender, which would mean four individuals for every 1,000 are self-identified as transgender, a rate much higher than Dr. Rajkumar uses. Using the liberal Williams Institute number with the conservative rate of one person having schizophrenia per 1,000 people, there should be no more than one person per 250,000 people with transgender identities and schizophrenia. Clinics internationally looking at comorbidity find combined schizophrenia and transgender identities rates around 3 to 40% when it should be around 0.0004% using independent variable probability.

If there is not causation, there is undoubtedly a correlation between schizophrenia and transgender identities. Since 3 to 40% is not an indication that most people with gender dysphoria have schizophrenia (or vice versa), one cannot conclude that either disease necessarily causes the other. However, the multifactorial model of causation could include psychosis as a contributing factor. The most plausible explanation is that, like schizophrenia, gender dysphoria is neurodevelopmental. During the early stages of brain development, the factors that caused the brain to form atypically, resulting in schizophrenia, also caused the brain to form atypically concerning sexual identity.

In 2014, John Strang, Psy.D., and colleagues released a report which claimed that transgender identities persist at much higher rates for people who also suffer from Autism Spectrum Disorders (ASD) and Attention Deficit Hyperactivity Disorder (ADHD). Both ASD and ADHD are neurodevelopmental disorders. The study found, *"Participants with ASD were 7.59 times more likely to express gender variance; participants with ADHD were 6.64 times more likely to express gender variance"* (Strang et al., 2014, 1528). Varun Warrier, Ph.D., and Simon Baron-Cohen, Ph.D., recently reported using a sample pool of 641,860 individuals to determine that less than 2% of the general population is autistic while *"between 4.8% and 26% of individuals who present at GD [gender dysphoria] clinics have an autism diagnosis based on several different criteria"* (Warrier et al. 2020). This study examined medical neurodevelopmental disorders causing epilepsy but could not find a correlation between epilepsy and gender dysphoria. Dr. Strang's study confirms a possible common cause for gender dysphoria and some neurodevelopmental disorders, including schizophrenia, ASD, and ADHD.

A 2013 Italian study titled, *Sociodemographic and Clinical Features of Gender Identity Disorder* reported, of 140 transgender individuals, 1.4% were also currently suffering from any psychotic disorder (Fisher et al., 2013). In contrast, an English 2012 report from the Department of Health concluded that 0.4% of the general population suffers from an active psychotic disorder (Kirkbride et al., 2012, 175). The rate of psychotic disorders is higher in communities of people with gender dysphoria than the general population, but most people with gender dysphoria are not otherwise psychotic. Comparing an Italian to a British study suggests a trend but not absolute proof since cultural or sociological factors might account for some variances. There may be some differences in how medical conditions are diagnosed and reported as well.

The United States Department of Health and Human Services found that between 2009 and 2013 that 63,000 children a year were victims of sexual abuse (United States Department of Health and Human Services 2013). The consequences of child rape are significant, leading to multiple layers of mental illness, often about sexuality and identity. Attempting to be sexually unattractive to their predators even after the abuse has stopped is common. Weight gain and a lack of hygiene are defense mechanisms to keep potential predators away. Disgust with one's body and an attempt to disassociate from that body is a defense mechanism.

Detranistion activist Erin Brewer experienced severe sexual trauma as a young girl and developed gender dysphoria. She transitioned to a male but, in her 20s, realized that her sexual trauma was the cause of her dysphoria. With therapy, Erin overcame her dysphoria and now attempts to educate the public about her mistaken identity. She created a children's book, *"Always Erin,"* to teach children and adults that just because one feels dysphoria does not mean that they are in the wrong body. Erin claims that no one is born in the wrong body (Brewer 2021). Sexual abuse and general psychosis cause some individuals to identify as transgender. Still, since most transgender people are not victims of rape or diagnosed with psychosis, this cannot be a singular explanation. Likewise, the cause of gender dysphoria is not singular. Gender dysphoria is a large umbrella used to explain many forms of bodily discontentment.

8.2 HORMONE INDUCED
CEPHALIC DIFFERENTIATION

A nother popular theory in the 1990s was the suspicion that transgender identity relates to hormone-induced cephalic differentiation at some critical gestational stage (Dorner et al. 1991). A consequence of this hormonal differentiation would be some different phenotypical characteristics more commonly shared among transgender people. For example, a 1992 study showed that MtF individuals are three times more likely to be left-handed than cis-gendered individuals (Watson and Coren 1992). A 1996 study showed that FtM individuals were taller than cis women (Ettner, Schaht et al. 1996). In FtM individuals, a *"transversely oriented inframammary ligament extending from the sternum to the lateral margin of the pectoralis major muscle is invariably present in female transsexuals"* (van Straalen, Hage, and Bloemena 1995, 240). Six independent studies have shown a *"higher rate of polycystic ovaries in this population"* (Ettner 1999, 54).

These studies all share a common theme: hormonal variation in the womb appears to affect some transgender people with a cluster of other phenotypic features, in addition to feelings of gender dysphoria. Thus, a hormonal prenatal and early postnatal etiology appears to be one of the best directions for understanding the possible biological origins of gender dysphoria.

Tonya G. White, Ph.D., presented to the *Second International Congress on Sex & Gender Issues* her findings on a potential etiology for gender dysphoria,

> The neural proliferation within the neural tube undergoes a caudal migration ending between weeks 18 to 24. Over half of the neurons and glial cells generated undergo an active pruning process—a programmed cell death known as apoptosis. Genes become activated to prune specific brain cells, and once pruned, they cannot regenerate. Activation of these cellular *"suicide"* genes involves genetic, hormonal, and immunologic factors, although chance may also play a role.
>
> It has been shown that the right hemisphere develops approximately ten days before the left. In most individuals, there is an active pruning on the right hemisphere such that when the left hemisphere develops, it claims dominance. If this active pruning on the right does not occur, and if this involves the motor strop of the brain, the right hemisphere may attain dominance resulting in a left-handed individual. If this process involves the language center, the result may be dyslexia. Since testosterone is involved in cell survival, it can potentially affect [sic] pruning and thus account for the increased rates of dyslexia in boys. If this same process involves the area in the brain wherein lies one's sense of gender identity (see Dr. Zhou, 1995), it could potentially result in discordant gender identity. In some manner, that is poorly understood, within the structural components of the brain, within these connections of neurons and synapses, lies one's core sense of gender self. As with any developmental process, the route taken may be quite different than expected. Neurons, too, can take the *"road less traveled."* (T. White 1997)

During fetal development, neuron pathways form how the brain functions, from right-handedness to dyslexia to issues with gender identity. These pathways have some plasticity, but once the brain crystallizes during the initial stages of the development process, it becomes difficult to change those pathways.

Dr. Baron-Cohen found that brains are sexed as early as one day old, demonstrating the challenges one would have changing one's sex and gender, even if attempts are made early in the child's life (Gurian and Stevens 2005, 287). Could these abnormally traveling neurons be the cause of the unusual shapes within the hypothalamus? Could these neurons also create the anomaly of men using white matter and women using more grey matter? This study adds to the mounting evidence that gender dysphoria is epigenetic and a neurodevelopmental disorder.

8.3 Androgen Receptor
in MtF Individuals

I n 2009, Dr. Lauren Hare published an Australian study in the *Journal of Biological Psychiatry* titled, *"Androgen Receptor Repeat Length Polymorphism Associated with Male-to-Female Transsexualism"* (Hare et al. 2009). If there is a significant androgen receptor gene mutation, an XY individual could be born with female-appearing genitalia. In less extreme cases, a long polymorphic chain would indicate that testosterone was not being received. Thus the male individual was effectively testosterone deficient (although sufficient testosterone was being produced), an occurrence that could prohibit the natural masculinization of the male brain during development.

Dr. Hare repeated a Susanne Henningsson, Ph.D.,'s 2005 study (Henningsson et al. 2005), which claimed to have found a link between a dinucleotide CA polymorphism in the estrogen receptor β (ERβ) gene (Henningsson et al. 2005). Dr. Hare studied 112 MtF individuals and 258 cis males, creating a much larger sample size than Dr. Henningssson's study, which only had twenty-nine MtF individuals. Researchers assessed all the subjects for repeat length polymorphism in the androgen receptor (AR), estrogen receptor beta (ERβ), and CYP19 (aromatase), which converts androgens into estrogen. Although Dr. Hare used the same methodology in the 2009 study, the β (ERβ) gene did not change any positive polymorphic chains, as found in the 2005 study.[2]

Researchers in the 2009 study recognized a significant association between extended androgen receptor (AR) gene polymorphisms and MtF individuals. Longer CAG DNA patterns repeating in the

---

[2] This means that the 2005 study had one of three possible problems, 1. the study was flawed; 2. Swedish transsexuals have different DNA than Australian transsexuals; or 3. with a much larger sample size the anomalies disappeared.

androgen receptor gene led to reduced androgen receptor protein binding. The defects of the androgen receptors affect the body's ability to metabolize testosterone. Longer chains suggest that the androgens are not being processed and turned into testosterone. There was no correlation between MtF individuals and estrogen receptor beta (ERβ) and CYP19 genes. The lack of testosterone flooding the brain during pregnancy may lead to a more feminized brain for the child. Researchers conclude:

> It is possible that a decrease in testosterone levels in the brain during development might result in incomplete masculinization of the brain in male-to-female transsexuals, resulting in a more feminized brain and a female gender identity. (Hare et al. 2009, 95)

Although Dr. Henningsson's study from 2005 was rejected in its claim that the ERβ gene had any effect on the MtF individual's testosterone receptivity, Dr. Hare's study found significant evidence linking the AR gene polymorphism to MtF individuals. This case is notable since it contained a large sample size of 370 individuals, and it found a direct link between MtF individuals and the AR gene.

8.4 POLYMORPHISM OF
ERβ GENE IN FtM INDIVIDUALS

D
r. Henningsson's study misreported the link between the ERβ gene and gender dysphoria in MtF individuals. Still, Dr. Rosa Fernández found convincing evidence which linked polymorphism of the ERβ gene in FtM individuals. Her study in 2014 published the continuation of Dr. Hare's work, titled *"The (CA)n Polymorphism of ERβ Gene is Associated with FtM Transsexualism"* (Fernández 2014) and published in the *Journal of Sexual Medicine*. This study aimed to investigate the possible influence of the sex hormone-related genes: AR (androgen receptor), ERβ (estrogen receptor β), CYP19 (aromatase) in the etiology of FtM individuals. This study used 273 FtM individuals and 371 cis females, making this one of the most extensive studies to date. This study mirrors Dr. Hare's study, except that it studies FtM rather than MtF individuals.

This study showed that FtM individuals differed significantly from cis women concerning the median repeat length polymorphism ERβ, but not the length of AR and CYP19. The consequence of the long polymorphic chains is that estrogen is not being produced, and there is less feminization of the brain. Figure 8.1 demonstrates what would happen if the ERβ signal receptors were not sensitive to receiving the estrogen produced in the system. This figure could also explain Dr. Hare's findings of the AR gene in MtF individuals by exchanging ERβ with AR, estrogen with testosterone, and feminization with masculinization.

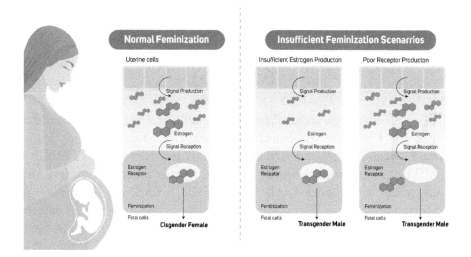

Figure 8.1 Polymorphism of ERβ Gene explained

8.5 BODY INTEGRITY IDENTITY DISORDER/ BODY DYSMORPHIC DISORDER

Medical researcher Antonia Ostgathe and her colleagues at the University of Hamburg in 2014 conducted a pilot study comparing individuals with Body Integrity Identity Disorder (BIID), a neurodevelopmental (biological-genetic) disorder, to individuals with gender dysphoria (Ostgathe, Schnell and Kasten 2014) (Sedda and Bottini 2014). BIID describes a phenomenon in which physically healthy people feel a constant desire for impairment in their bodies. The most common example is a strong desire to amputate a healthy limb (First 2005, 1).

The Body Dysmorphic Disorder (BDD) Foundation describes BIID as,

> The preoccupation is focussed [sic] not on a feeling of defectiveness but on the sufferers' expectation that they would be much more comfortable if one or more limbs or digits were amputated. They do not believe (as in BDD) their limbs to be defective or ugly, nor do they wish cosmetically to alter the limb. BIID is more akin to a Gender Identity Disorder. BIID is not part of BDD. (Body Dysmorphic Disorder Foundation n.d.)

In contrast, BDD is defined as,

> A disabling preoccupation with perceived defects or flaws in appearance. It can affect both men and women and makes sufferers excessively self-conscious. They tend to check their appearance repeatedly and try to camouflage or alter the defects they see, often undergoing needless cosmetic treatments. Onlookers are frequently perplexed because they can see nothing out of the ordinary, but BDD causes devastating distress and interferes substantially with the ability to function socially. (Body Dysmorphic Disorder Foundation n.d.)

The differentiation between BIID and BDD is primarily over one question: is there hatred and obsession over a limb or external feature? If there is indifference towards the body image, it is BIID, and if there is hatred towards the body image, it is BDD. The BDD Foundation considers gender dysphoria to be more akin to BIID, although the study of Antonia Ostgathe suggests otherwise.

Despite the ethical, legal, aesthetic, and cultural prohibition of removing healthy limbs, specific individuals become determined to remove that limb, either through surgery or self-mutilation, even to the point of performing feats, which may become life-threatening. This disorder is not the same as gender dysphoria. An MtF individual may be disgusted by his penis but does not typically self-mutilate to remove his secondary sex organs. A gender dysphoric person would like to be socially, aesthetically, and otherwise perceived as a healthy member of the opposite sex. Antonia's study hypothesized that both disorders' etiology might be similar, but this is not to assimilate the disorders into a single disorder.

The study surveyed twenty-four BIID and nineteen transsexual individuals. Both groups could not rationally explain their desire, but most (75 and 73.7% respectively) attributed it to biological-genetic reasons. *"Regarding the question of body image and body perception, the hypothesis could be proven that both BIID sufferers and transsexuals have a strong feeling that their biological body does not match their mental body image"* (Ostgathe, Schnell, and Kasten 2014, 140). [3] The average age for first realizing that individual was BIID was 10.7 years and transgender, 13 years. When these groups started experimenting with these ideas, BIID individuals started to fake disabilities around 14.82 years, while transsexuals started cross-dressing at the age of 13.46. Finally, there were trivial differences in the intensity of the psychological strain and the restrictions on life quality. [4]

The two groups differ in that BIID individuals do not have negative feelings about the body part, which they would like to have

---

[3] BIID: M=9.08, STD=± 3.23; Gender Dysphoria: M= 9.05, STD=± 2.72; U-value= 216.5; Significance (U-test): p=.757

[4] BIID: M=8.42, STD=± 3.02; Gender Dysphoria: M= 9.63, STD=± 2.34; U-value= 155.5; Significance (U-test): p=.066

removed. For example, there are no negative feelings towards the arm, which they feel should be missing (Blanke et al., 2008). On the contrary, transsexuals strongly dislike and even hate their secondary sex organs (Beier, Bosinski, and Loewit 2005). If confirmed, this realization suggests that gender dysphoric individuals are less like people with BIID and more like individuals with BDD since the impressions about that organ is severe and not indifferent.

Although it has a small sample size, Antonia's pilot study points to the possibility of a common neurodevelopmental cause for BIID, BDD, and gender dysphoria. If there is a common cause, could there also be a standard therapeutic solution? With rare exceptions, BIID and BDD are not cured through plastic surgery to make the body match their identity, but they provide therapy to align the mind with the body. With transgender people, the medical community's solution in most cases is hormone blockers, supplements, and surgery. Unfortunately, the results of the effectiveness of transgender surgeries are inconsistent. Studies have not been done to compare BDD and gender dysphoria, although this study suggests that it would be a fruitful endeavor.

8.6 CONCEPT REVIEW

Multiple studies in chapters seven and eight have established a correlation between neurodevelopmental, mental disorders, and gender dysphoria. These comorbidities strongly suggest that there is a common neurodevelopmental etiology (Dhejne, Van Vlerken, et al. 2016), (Rajkumar 2014), (Strang et al. 2014), and (Fisher et al. 2013). Dr. Diamond also claims to have found an epigenetic link in his Twin Studies, which affirms a biological foundation to the disorder and supports the claim that there is a genetic link combined with hormones, neurotransmitters, and environmental factors.

Chapter eight assessed the studies which hypothesize *how* a neurodevelopmental disorder like this could occur. For example, if a male had a polymorphic AR gene, he would not be receptive to testosterone within regions of the brain, which would be necessary to masculinize those brain structures (Hare et al. 2009, 95). Likewise, if a female had a polymorphic ERβ gene, she would not be receptive to estrogen within regions of her brain, which would be necessary to feminize those brain structures (Fernández 2014, 721). The consequence of an inadequate masculinization or feminization would result in the different brain structures found in chapter seven, including the BSTc and SOM volume and size (Zhou et al. 1995) (Kruijer et al. 2000), the gray matter regions (Luders et al. 2009), the white matter microstructures (Rametti et al. 2011), and the dozens of other regions of dissimilarities found in Dr. Guillamon's 2016 study (Guillamon, Junque and Gómez-Gil 2016).

Finally, this chapter links to various possible treatments by comparing gender dysphoria to similar neurodevelopmental identity disorders, particularly BIID and BDD. Treatments used for these disorders include the use of neurotransmitters and body affirmation therapy. Unfortunately, researchers are not publishing follow-up research on its effectiveness in treating gender dysphoria apart from a sole case where the neurotransmitter Pimozide was used successfully. Although a solitary case does not determine a cure, it suggests that treatments for gender dysphoria and BDD/ BIID may be similarly effective and should be explored medically.

The shortcoming is that no studies demonstrate that any of the biological differences being examined have predictive power. Doctors McHugh and Mayer claim, *"current studies on associations between brain structure and transgender identity are small, methodologically limited, inconclusive, and sometimes contradictory"* (McHugh and Mayer, 2016, 104). However, doctors McHugh and Mayer are correct that these studies are imperfect and inconclusive at times. Nevertheless, one cannot negate that the medical evidence of the previous half-century begins to point in a direction that gives doctors some parameters for understanding the root of transgender identities.

Chapter 9
Dysphoric Youth

A story is told of an old priest, who asked if he had learned anything about human beings in the many years of hearing confessions, first said 'No,' but then, 'Yes. There are no grown-ups.'
— Philippa Foot, Ph.D., *Natural Goodness*

We see no references to transgender children prior to the mid-1990s.
— Tey Meadow, Ph.D., *Child*

In the Times of London, Anglican bishop N.T. Wright wrote a Christian perspective on sex transitioning adolescents, *"This involves denying the goodness, or even the ultimate reality, of the natural world. Nature, however, tends to strike back, with the likely victims, in this case, being vulnerable and impressionable youngsters who, as confused adults, will pay the price for their elders' fashionable fantasies"* (N.T. Wright 2017). Unfortunately, modern Western societies do not have a good record for understanding children's nature and responding appropriately with rational responses. Instead, so-called experts have instituted their theories on children with disastrous effects.

Can people engineer nature?

After WWII, the United States had optimism about experts' ability to engineer the modern world in every way. However, their excitement to make a better world was also naïve and arrogant. The newly shared utopian vision based itself on ideology rather than realism. Jean Vanier, Ph.D., described this period in *The Broken Body,*

> There was the world of the 'fifties and 'sixties. The terrible war with Nazi Germany had ended. People were weary and wanted to build peace; countries long-dominated by colonialism were being liberated; economic expansion seemed to promise the possibility of a good life to be had by all! There were high hopes that poverty and hunger would be banished from the earth and that each human person would find freedom from want and freedom to create their own destiny. (Vanier 1988, 4).

Modern humans believed they were *free to create their own destinies*. So-called experts believed cities would best be served by tearing down old organic neighborhoods and replacing them with modern high-rises and highways to make people happier. The architecture and decoration of schools, churches, and public institutions were once pillars of human creativity and skill, only to be stripped of their beauty to focus on the useful, practical, and *idea* of community. The experts who thought they understood people's minds artificially created a society of utilitarianism, but this society did not create happiness as they hypothesized.

The grandmother sitting on the door stoop could have predicted this disaster, but in a Faustian swoop, she was discarded to a tower which only aims to warehouse the elderly. Children might have shown society how to flourish, but instead, they were pulled from their neighborhood schools and placed into large boxy institutions with regulated curriculums from a central office. The *idea* of children superseded *real* children. Condescending men in corner offices unknowingly designed the institutions of human depression, isolation, and compartmentalization. Karl Marx says capitalism failed us, but unnatural and anti-realist ideologies are not capitalism. Still, self-proclaimed rational, enlightened modern men dictate how societies should operate without consciously experiencing what it is to be a man, woman, an old person, or a child. The belief that man can create himself and that the body is merely raw material to be molded inevitably leads to cosmetic surgeries and hormones to reinvent one's identity. Most adults are prudent enough not to engage in life-altering activities without considering the consequences, but teens are often unable to demonstrate this discipline yet. This chapter examines both gender dysphoric youth and young people who are dysphoric in a general sense but are not specifically gender dysphoric.

9.1 GENDER THEORY FOR YOUTH

I n the last 50 years, Western medicine made significant mistakes in its attempt to construct children into unnatural beings under the false assumption of brain plasticity. They followed ideology rather than realism. This uncommon nonsense, filled with fantasies of false hopes and unattainable dreams. These dystopias will all come crashing down, and society will, with any luck, learn an important lesson, as a generation learned with the failures of John Money, Ph.D., and his concept of sex mutability.

Unfortunately, Dr. Money's failure was not impactful enough for second-wave feminist Gina Rippon, Ph.D., at Aston University. A BBC broadcast announced Dr. Rippon as *"one of the UK's leading experts in brain imaging and neuroscience."* Dr. Rippon claims, *"there is no such thing as a male or female brain type-and instead, the brain is a plastic organ, shaped and moulded [sic] by experiences, in which childhood is key"* (BCC Media Centre 2017). Dr. Rippon is renowned for her gender-neutral ideology in her book *The Gendered Brain* (2019).[1] Feminist author Rachel Cooke in response, proclaimed, *"A neuroscientist's brilliant debunking of the notion of a 'female brain' could do more for gender equality than any number of feminist manifestos"* (Cooke 2019). However, the ideological agenda behind Dr. Rippon's focus is questionably unscientific and more a practice of selecting evidence to prove a point rather than allowing the evidence to dictate the findings. This approach of cherry-picking evidence is similar to the claims of Dr. McHugh, who claimed humans are not sexually dimorphic in an attempt to prove a transgender brain cannot possibly exist; see *supra* 7.1 (McHugh 2014a, 9). No one within the field of primatology doubts primates possess sexually dimorphic brains. (Lindenfors, Nunn, and Barton 2007) (Smaers et al. 2012, 205)

---

[1] Dr. Rippon also has given feminist activist speeches titled *How Neurononsense Keeps Women in Their Place* which focused on how Neuroscience is a philosophy creates gender gaps and oppresses women, the feminist argument against sex essentialism (The Royal Institution 2016).

(Montgomery and Mundy 2013, 906). To claim humans are not sexually dimorphic is to deny humans are like other primates.

Dr. Rippon joined forces with Javid Abdelmoneim, M.D., and the BBC in a documentary *No More Boys and Girls: Can Our Kids Go Gender Free?* The duo attempted for one year to teach and raise children in a gender-free environment. Dr. Abdelmoneim claimed, *"This is about giving children a full development so they can achieve absolutely anything they want"* (BCC Media Centre 2017).

In contrast, social philosopher Michael Gurian makes the case that the education system is failing boys because of the false idea that boys and girls think alike and learn the same way. When looking at the difference between boys and girls, social factors do not reduce the notability of these differences. Boys earn most D's and F's as high as 70% of the time; boys make up 80% of the disciplinary problems. Seventy percent of children with learning disabilities are boys, 80% of the children on Ritalin are boys. Young men are between a year and a year and a half behind most girls in reading and writing skills, 80% of high school dropouts are young men, and men comprise only 44% of the college population (Gurian and Stevens 2005, 22). An epidemic in learning disparity exists within schools, but the inequity is not sexism against girls causing this gap.

Michael Gurian found that boys' and girls' brains work differently. Many boys are left behind in schools because the educational method caters to how females learn. Sitting quietly and listening is how female brains learn. Male brains require bodily movement and activity, something not often practiced outside of gym and recess. Grade school education focuses on sitting quietly, listening, and working alone in one's own head—skills better fit for females. Instead of socially constructing so-called genderless classrooms, modern brain science suggests it would be better to separate passive and active learners so that everyone can access a learning method complementary to their nature. Using the strengths of each sex and following the guidance of nature, children become healthier, happier, and more productive. Using non-realist ideology to fit children into gender-neutral social movements harms children.

The proposed genderless classroom is a further feminization of an already feminine model of grade school teaching. The neutral aspect of the classroom focuses on empowering women and making boys more sensitive. Teachers for decades attempted to make young males sit quietly and do their work, but this is not a natural male skill set. This social experiment will help girls who are already far surpassing their male counterparts, but how will this improve the outcomes for young boys? Boys should be encouraged to be sensitive and nurturing, and girls should be taught how to be leaders and, as Sheryl Sandberg advocates, to *Lean In*, but this does not come from being genderless. Justice comes from recognizing the strengths and weaknesses of each sex and each individual and complements their character with the appropriate challenges to help a child flourish.

Transfeminist activists like Rachel Anne Williams advocate replacing masculine aggression with feminine softness as the predominant leadership style. She writes,

> In my gender utopia, all the *'soft'* characteristics associated with femininity in terms of communication style would be held by everyone. That is, the ideal distribution of aggressive and docile traits would eliminate the aggression entirely and replace it with the softness stereotypical of women. (R. A. Williams 2019, 75)

Although Rachel presents her utopian ideology of a better society, utopias are not for this world. According to Thomists, human flourishing must start with human nature and not the nature of angels or robots.

Hasbro experiences the pressure of creating gender-neutral toys, creating a *"gender-neutral playhouse."* Despite their efforts, little girls used the playhouse for their dolls and playing house, while the boys used it to catapult shopping carts from the roof. Finally, Christina Hoff Sommers, Ph.D., reported, a Hasbro manager came to a startling conclusion: *"boys and girls are different"* (Sommers 2013). Dr. Sommers also reported another toy company attempted an ad with boys playing with a Barbie Dream House and girls playing with guns and gory action figures. These are the utopian dreams of gender nominalists attempting to engineer children socially, but this will never come to fruition since 800 million years of evolution are working against them.

Pope Francis, in a 2015 General Audience, stated,

> I ask myself if the so-called gender theory is not, at the same time,
> an expression of frustration and resignation, which seeks to cancel
> out sexual difference because it no longer knows how to confront
> it … the removal of difference creates a problem, not a solution.
> (Francis 2015b)

Adult's ability to repeat flawed dystopian ideals in every generation must be part of the human condition. No matter how terrible the previous social experiment ends, someone will quickly reframe the ideology as the next great idea 30 years later. Children are not choosing these experiments any more than the child victims of Dr. Money, who had children's genitals removed because of the false belief that gender is a social construction and sex is mutable for the first years of life.

In the United Kingdom, a group of transgender mothers called *Mermaids* goes into classrooms of young children to expose them to the idea that they fall on a gender spectrum. The children decide if they are a boy, girl, or nonbinary. Mermaids introduce the chart with the slogan *"Gender identity is on a spectrum. We all have our own unique identity"* (Owens 2019). Presenting this material to grade school children is bound to confuse what four-year-old child identifies with either G.I. Joe or Barbie? When adults claim 27% of youth twelve to seventeen are, to some degree, transgender (CA 2020), and doctors are willing to start the medicalization of gender non-conforming youth at the age of twelve, society is slipping into another sex/gender dystopia. Transgender activists like Zinnia Jones further advocate for all children being placed on hormone blockers until they consent to male or female puberty. Ideology is replacing realism. Zinnia tweeted,

> If children can't consent to puberty blockers which pause any
> permanent changes even with the relevant professional evaluation,
> how can they consent to the permanent and irreversible changes
> that come with their own puberty with no professional evaluation
> whatsoever? (Z. Jones 2020)

While adults are confused about gender, adolescents are as well. Dr. Vanier witnessed working with the youth, *"In some young people, awareness of the disorder in the world is accentuated by an awareness of their own inner turmoil and darkness. They feel lost, fragile, and confused and suffer from a lack of personal identity… A number of them also feel that their own sexuality is chaotic"* (Vanier 1997, 97–98). As this chapter progresses into the question of transgender children, the recent history of modern medicine's abuse of children based on inaccurate science about brain plasticity and bad philosophy about the nature of sex and gender should remain a vital framing within these questions.

The rates of cosmetic surgeries performed on children manifest the chaos described by Dr. Vanier. Cosmetic surgeries on youth 13 to 19 years comprise 4% of all cosmetic surgeries, including 228,797 surgeries in data from 2017 (American Society of Plastic Surgeons 2018). Of the total cosmetic surgeries conducted in 2017, surgeons performed 92% of these surgeries on females.[2] Teenage girls are significantly affected by impossible beauty standards presented not only by the mainline media but through social media use on their phones. In addition, dysphoria often causes obsessions with perfection. Might some of this gender confusion in youth be a type of gender dysmorphia?

---

[2] No data is available to show the sex breakdown of specific age groups.

[Jean Vanier, Ph.D., 1928—2019]

9.2 GENDER DYSPHORIA IN YOUTH

I n *Understanding Gender Identities*, James Beilby, Ph.D., and Paul Eddy, Ph.D., claim,

> In many sectors of our culture, the debate is not whether parents should support the transitioning of a gender dysphoric child, but rather how—that is, what the nature and timing of that support should look like. (Beilby and Eddy 2019, 34)

Medical professionals also report that referrals for gender dysphoric youth are up tenfold in the last six years (D. A. Jones 2019, 4). In 2007, the youth went to the only youth gender clinic in the country, while in 2021, parents can choose from over fifty (Stahl 2021). Based on what they think the experience is like to be the opposite sex, gender dysphoric children believe they are the opposite sex. WPATH guidelines require youth under 18 years old to receive parental consent and therapy before receiving cross-sex hormones. The feelings of dysphoria also must persist for at least six months. Unfortunately, doctors do not always follow these fundamental requirements. Clinical psychologist at *Boston Children's Hospital,* Laura Edwards-Leeper, Ph.D., helped hundreds of youth transition their genders.

In a *60 Minutes* interview with Lesley Stahl, Dr. Edwards-Leeper raised concerns about transitioning youth. Lesley asked, *"Do you have conversations with your colleagues about this whole area of accepting what young people are saying too readily?"* to which Dr. Edwards-Leeper replied

> Yes. Everyone is very scared to speak up because we're afraid of not being seen as being affirming or being supportive of these young people or doing something to hurt the trans community. But even some of the providers are trans themselves and share these concerns. (Stahl 2021)

YouTuber Blaire White also recounts a conversation she had with one of her surgeons, who had hundreds of patients. He claimed nearly every patient suffered from gender dysphoria a few years ago. Presently, most young females coming in consider themselves non-binary and are not suffering from gender dysphoria. Due to his attempted pushback, he is earning a label of being transphobic. The doctor's caution is not an attempt to be anti-transgender. Still, he recognizes that most transitioning regret comes from young non-binary youth who did not accept the permanency and extent of this transition. When dissatisfaction sets in, the youth are unaware that these procedures are not entirely reversible. This doctor considered leaving the field of gender transitioning since his work is increasingly doing more harm than good (B. White 2021b).

Actor Mario Lopez in June of 2019, in *The Candice Owen Show* interview, made the statement that he thought parents labeling their three-year-old child transgender definitively is *dangerous*. Lopez said,

> I would say if you come from a place of love, you really can't go wrong. But at the same time, if you're three years old, you say you're feeling a certain way, or you think you're a boy or a girl, whatever the case may be, I just think it's dangerous as a parent to make that determination then, *'Okay, you're gonna be a boy or a girl'*…I just think of the repercussions later on. (Lopez 2019)

The media's backlash clarified what narratives were politically acceptable, and Lopez had crossed a line by claiming it was dangerous to accept a three-year-old's fantasy as reality.

The Gay & Lesbian Alliance Against Defamation (GLAAD) responded to Lopez, who had supported GLAAD events in the past claiming, *"Medical and psychological experts, and parents of children who are transgender, have long discredited the ideas that @MarioLopezExtra shared. The real dangerous action is when someone with a public platform uses bad science to speak against a vulnerable group of children (GLAAD 2019)."* Curiously, what claims did Mario make, which GLAAD believes medical and psychological experts long discredited?

This new stance of the *cogito ergo sum* epistemology is being applied with even greater scope since the theory no longer required the *cogito* statement to be from the mind of a rational human being who had reached the age of reason (see *Supra*, chapter 2.7). Instead, any *cogito* statement of any person, regardless of mental capacity, must be automatically believed. Paul McHugh, M.D., disagrees with GLAAD's assessment claiming, *"Most young boys and girls who come seeking sex-reassignment are utterly different from [Caitlyn] Jenner. They have no erotic interest in driving their quest. Rather, they come with psychosocial issues—conflicts over the prospects, expectations, and roles that they sense are attached to their given sex—and presume that sex-reassignment will ease or resolve them"* (McHugh 2015).

In a 2016 study by Mark Yarhouse, a Christian parent of a transgender youth reflected,

> I didn't know [he was] transgender, but around the age of three, I knew he was different. Being transgender wasn't on my radar, but being gay would have been. There were some things [transgender daughter] did that I thought were gay but then other things that were the exact opposite. It was kind of confusing. (Yarhouse et al., 2016, 202)

For parents in this political climate, how do they decide for a child the best approach if they observe gender confusion or if the child claims to be a person of the opposite sex? One distinction would be the age of the minor since sixteen-year-old children are different from three-year-old children. Also, if the signs of gender dysphoria were consistent since early childhood, doctors should consider this situation differently than if the youth experiences late-onset gender dysphoria. Of course, the minor's age would not be a sufficient distinction for Dr. Olson-Kennedy from UCLA or critics of Mario Lopez, but it would be the practical wisdom (*phronesis*) one should use.

Before the twenty-first century, most instances of transgenderism were noticeable in gender dysphoric males as early as two to four years of age (Shrier 2021). Traditionally, early-onset gender dysphoric youth would reconcile their gender identities by early adulthood, most of whom became homosexual. These individuals as adults represent 0.01% of the population or one in 10,000. The second population of transgender people is late-onset gender dysphoria which occurs primarily in teenage girls (70%). Before 2007, no scientific literature on the topic existed, and transitioning rates were exceedingly rare (Shrier 2021).

In 2016, FtMs comprised only 46% of all sex reassignment surgeries in the United States, and by 2017, double mastectomies comprised 70% (American Society of Plastic Surgeons. 2017b). Currently, this group is the largest group of transgender people. Like with anorexia, bulimia, and cutting, teenage girls suffer the most from social contagions. The condition should reasonably affect one in 10,000 people; in some small girls schools, as many as 30% of the seventh-grade class identify as transgender (Shrier 2021).

In a Brighton school of 1,600 students, 40 children between eleven and sixteen said they did not identify with their natal sex, while 36 more said they were *gender fluid* (Reynolds 2018). In addition, teenage girls in Gen Z are notably withdrawn from the in-person social interaction of previous generations: going to the mall, rock-n-bowling, participating in social clubs, and competing in group athletics is declining. Instead, teenage girls judge their worth based on the number of likes they receive on social media. At the same time, their reflexive disposition causes them to obsess over what other people think about them.

Youth with Autism Spectrum Disorder are more susceptible to going down this rabbit hole and convincing themselves that transitioning is the solution to their identity crisis (Strang et al. 2014, 1528). Autism rates for gender dysphoric youth are as high as 26% (Warrier 2020). Online activities consume the time not spent with in-person interactions with peers. Transitioning stories of FtM youth on YouTube and trans support groups on Reddit offer an appealing solution to their feelings of not fitting in. Story after story of individuals claiming they were miserable and hated their bodies until they transitioned offers hope for girls who were generally dysphoric about life.

Differentiating between early-onset and late-onset gender dysphoria is essential when addressing the transgender issue since their etiology is entirely different. If the cause of the desire is some form of a neurodevelopmental intersex brain or, in contrast, misdirected feelings of social inadequacy, the response cannot be the same. Significantly, when addressing both groups to be gentle and understanding, both groups are legitimately suffering but in different ways. The latter group is not pretending to be dysphoric—they are dysphoric; yet, the dysphoria will naturally pass in adulthood with no medical interventions.

What are the consequences of unsupported youth?

Although youth may encounter two forms of teenage gender dysphoria, an unsupported transgender youth may experience some overlapping effects. Transgender youth suffer from many of the same disorders as transgender adults. Transgender youth engage in a higher risk activity, including tobacco use and substance abuse. They are also susceptible to sexually transmitted infections, including HIV (Joint Commission 2011). Transgender youth suffer similar internalizing psychopathology rates, including depression, anxiety, stress, and suicidality (Transgender Law Center 2015). A 2014 Center for Disease Control (CDC) report found similar results. The report claimed youths with unsure gender identities face significantly higher rates of victimization, insufficient school attendance, increased substance use, as well as increased suicidal tendencies and depression (Center for Disease Control and Prevention 2014). The consequences of these stressors lead to increased prostitution levels and, as a result, high rates of HIV/AIDS (Chapin Hall 2018).

One Christian mother in a study on the parents of transgender children responded: *"Hopefully no more kids have to suffer. Kids shouldn't have to suffer or lose their families or even feel like they've lost their family's support and love just because of their sexuality"* (Yarhouse et al., 2016, 199). The data on unsupported transgender youth validate this mother's concern. Two studies found that lifetime engagement in prostitution for MtF adult individuals ranges from 37.8% (Forbes, Clark, and Diep 2016) to 67% (Wilson et al., 2009). A 2008 meta-analysis of twenty-five studies found that 27.3% of MtF individuals engaging in prostitution also were HIV positive (Operario, Soma, and Underhill 2008). Wilson also found that 35% of MtF youth engaged in prostitution or *survival sex* within the previous three months of being interviewed (Wilson et al., 2009). Homeless youth with substance addictions are more likely to turn to prostitution and riskier sex to survive. Why are youth becoming homeless? Why are they resorting to survival sex? Why are they engaging in riskier behavior? The obvious answer is that the family's support system is breaking down, and the youth is deciding to deal with dysphoria in their own ways.

[Rachel Anne Williams]

Where will youth find their support?

Pope Francis, in his 2020 encyclical, Fraternity and Social Friendship (*Fratelli Tutti*), addressed the issue of the sexual exploitation of youth and human trafficking, stating,

> Such is the magnitude of these situations and their toll in innocent lives, that we must avoid every temptation to fall into a declarationist nominalism that would assuage our consciences. We need to ensure that our institutions are truly effective in the struggle against all these scourges. (Francis 2020)

Society does not find ways to support LGBT youth actively. One example is the pornography industry's exploitation of at-risk youth. Pornography sites report transgender pornography to be one of the most viewed categories. The pornography website *RedTube* reported that men are 455% more likely to search for transgender porn than sex categories with biological women (Redtube 2016). Men interested in women with penises is a paraphilia recognized as *gynandromorphophilia*. One MtF individual wrote,

> When straight men consume too much cis porn, they become bored and may be drawn to the novelty and stigma of trans porn. This is why so many straight men might hook up with trans women but do not bring them to Thanksgiving dinner. (R. A. Williams 2019, 23)

More explicitly, Rachel Anne Williams wrote, *"Straight men will f— ck us, but not love us"* (R. A. Williams 2019, 22). The fetishism directed towards transgender people tends to be greater than the fetishism within the transgender community. When transgender youth enter the adult world of sex, they enter as a hypersexualized object of desire, which is quickly discarded or destroyed after being used. Transgender youth cannot be left unsupported by family and church to figure out how to become a young adult while left in the hands of unloving strangers and predators.

A New York City study found that 50% of MtF African Americans and Latinas were HIV positive (Erickson-Schroth and Jacobs 2017, 51). In a separate article, Wilson claims many of the younger MtF sex workers enter the field through their relationships with older MtF sex workers (Wilson et al., 2012). These relationships result in the arrest of 67% of ethnic minority MtF individuals and an incarceration rate of

37% (Garofalo et al., 2006). Wilson found that 52% of MtF individuals report a lifetime involvement with the correctional system (Wilson et al., 2009). In addition, ethnic minority MtF youth reported an 18% homelessness rate, and 46% claimed they had difficulty finding a safe space to sleep (Garofalo et al., 2006). Transgender youth face challenging obstacles: the lack of support from adults who do not seek the child's best interest. At risk, youth are often the target of exploitation or the victims of neglect. Kate Bornstein, in *Gender Outlaw*, explains the complexity of the transgender community:

> **Post-operative transsexuals** (those transsexuals who've had genital surgery and live fully in the role of another gender) look down on: **Pre-operative transsexuals** (those who are living full or part-time in another gender, but who've not yet had their genital surgery) who, in turn, look down on: **Transgenders** (people living in another gender identity, but who have little or no intention of having genital surgery) who can't abide: **She-Males** (a she-male friend of mine described herself as *"tits, big hair, lots of make-up, and a dick."*) who snub the: **Drag Queens** (gay men who on occasion dress in varying parodies of women) who laugh about the: **Out Transvestites** (usually heterosexual men who dress as they think women dress, and who are out in the open about doing that) who pity the: **Closet Cases** (transvestites who hide their cross-dressing) who mock the **Post-op transsexuals**. (Bornstein 1995, 67-68)

The transgender community has only become more divided since 1995, when Kate Bornstein explained the complex reality of the transgender community. Transgender YouTuber Blaire White described a situation in the 2010s when she figured out her gender dysphoria as a late teen. Blaire went to a transgender support group to seek advice from older transgender people with experience in gender dysphoria. Instead, Blaire found a roundtable of non-binary activists who claimed she was part of the problem for trying to conform to the gender binary model and she was already a woman by stating she was a woman (B. White 20201b). Between gender activists with an agenda, distrust among members of the same community, and predators within these social circles, transgender youth do not have a safe space to discern their feelings and receive grounded psychological counsel based on realist philosophy and medical research.

The youth then turn to strangers for love and attention but are only further exploited. Rachel Anne Williams presents another scenario in *Transgressive*:

> A straight cis male is horny, watching trans porn. He gets so horny that he wants to find a trans girl to fulfill his fantasy. He goes on Craigslist and finds someone. He has sex with her, cums, and then has a sudden feeling of disgust, his sense of being a straight man now threatened because he possibly got off on her having a dick or was disgusted by the idea that he "just f —cked a dude." He gets enraged and defensive, "panics," and then assaults and/or murders the trans woman for having the audacity to be herself. I am not making up this scenario at all. It is taken from real life, often involving trans women of color, sex workers, the marginalized…
> (R. A. Williams 2019, 23–24)

Does the church take a position to support transgender youth? Yes, the church cannot leave transgender or LGBT youth to the secular society to discover their vocation in the world. If LGBT youth do not realize their place within the Catholic cosmology, they will be left to find themselves within nihilistic consumerism, which eats itself.

The church is called to change the hearts of those who persecute marginalized people. Notably, the church must also consider her part in creating a hostile environment for LGBT youth. The church never preaches Catholics should commit acts of violence towards transgender people. Still, does the tone of its preaching sometimes *"other"* people, making it easier or even justified when violence is committed against them? Archbishop Robert Carlson wrote,

> What the Catechism says about our treatment of those who experience same-sex attraction applies with equal force to our treatment of those who are uncomfortable with their biological sex, and those who identify as transgendered. The Church rejects unjust discrimination and every sign of unjust discrimination against them.[3] (Carlson 2020, 11)

---

[3] *CCC*, 2358

Is non-discrimination enough, or can Catholics do more to protect their most vulnerable brothers and sisters? Archbishop Carlson teaches more on this matter under the topic of charity *infra* in section 11.1.

9.3 Early Onset Gender Dysphoria

T he *DSM-5* has specific criteria for Gender Dysphoric children. If children show at least six of the below criteria, they can receive the diagnosis of gender dysphoria:

1. An intense want to be the opposite gender or persistence that he is the opposite gender (or a different gender other than the one he was born as).

2. Boys who were born as males have a prevalence toward cross-dressing or wearing clothing that is seemingly more feminine. Girls who were born as females prefer dressing in what would be considered men's clothing and are powerfully opposed to dressing in regular female apparel.

3. When it comes to creative play or making up games, the child has the desire to be in the other gender's role.

4. The child would rather play with the toys or be included in the activities that are usually deemed appropriate for the opposite sex.

5. He chooses to play with children of the opposite sex.

6. Boys will refuse to play with toys that are considered those that are usual for boys. Girls will rebuff games and toys that are generally meant for females.

7. The child will have an intense dismay with the sexual parts of his body.

8. He wants the primary/secondary sex features that are equal to the experienced gender.

9. The child has extreme anxiety and stress, as well as problems with functioning in social circles, school and other situations.

These criteria would apply to gender dysphoric children, many tomboys, sissies, gender non-conforming youth, and many homosexual youth. However, these criteria are also very dissimilar from the experiences of autogynephilic youth who, when left alone, engage in childhoods typical of other children of their natal sex. Therefore, this *DSM's* diagnosis only applies to androphilic youth.

Early-onset gender dysphoria is consistent with Dr. Blanchard's homosexual type transsexual. They identify more with the opposite sex from an early age. When five-year-old children begin to wear opposite-sex clothing or tell their parents they are of the other sex, these examples are often highly publicized. Young children expressing gender dysphoria did not likely learn this behavior, but rather it is coming from something innate. If a child states these claims or picks opposite gender clothing for a short phase without encouragement, this is not disconcerting since children go through phases. However, when children persist in making these claims for years, it is possible they are not following their imaginations but rather are responding to dysphoria's deeper feelings.

Archbishop Carlson of St. Louis wrote in *Compassion and Challenge*,

> I make this special appeal to parents and friends: when someone you love is unhappy with their biological sex, listen! Keep the channels of communication open. We can sympathize with their feelings without capitulating to their desires. It's important not to leave them feeling alone. (Carlson 2020, 11)

Biological and psychological factors may contribute to feelings of gender dysphoria, anxiety, depression, and low self-esteem. Consequently, a gentle approach might be helpful for a young person. Some experts claim that as high as 94% of *"transgender kids"* cease to identify as transgender as they reach their twenties (Brooks 2018). Debra Soh, Ph.D., in a literature review of eleven studies, found a 90% desisting rate by puberty (Soh 2020, 93). In a sample pool collected from several studies[4], the results showed that of 246 children with gender dysphoria, 207 (84%) remitted after puberty (Steensma, McGuire, et al. 2013, 582). Thomas Steensma, Ph.D., also conducted follow-up studies of 127 adolescents under the age of 12 years. Only

---

[4] Bakwin 1968; Davenport 1986; Drummond et al. 2008; Green 1987; Factors Associated with Desistence and Persistence of Childhood Gender Dysphoria 99 Kosky 1987; Lebovitz 1972; Money and Ruso 1979; Wallien and CohenKettenis 2008; Zucker and Bradley 1995; Zuger 1984/

forty-seven reported they were still transgender by 15, which would mean 63% desisting. Notably, twenty-four adolescents failed to respond, resulting in a high loss to follow-up, suggesting they may have desisted, but this cannot be conclusively stated (Steensma, McGuire, et al. 2013, 583). Critics of Dr. Steensma's study claim the rates of desisting are lower than 63% (Cantor 2017) (Tannehill 2016).

Researchers should define the terms of long-term follow-ups to include early adulthood. Long-term transgender studies that do not include early adulthood are inherently flawed. Puberty does not finish feminizing and masculinizing the brain for most teens in Tanner Stage 4. A follow-up study conducted until the youth reached 25 years would be more accurate as a predictor of long-term happiness than ending the study at 15 years. The rate of desisting will likely increase when the adolescents reach full maturity. Unfortunately, researchers failed to conduct or publish follow-up studies of these older ages.

In response to Dr. Steensma's report, Julia Temple-Newhook, Ph.D., wrote a critical review claiming his study was flawed. First, Dr. Temple-Newhook suggests the researchers may misclassify prepubescent children in studies. Counting gender non-conforming youth as transgender youth creates inaccurate results (Temple Newhook et al. 2018, 3). Second, Dr. Temple-Newhook also claimed the survey was theoretically flawed because his principles assume sex is binary and sexual identity should be stable (Temple Newhook et al. 2018, 5). Lastly, Dr. Temple-Newhook opined that this study does not respect children's autonomy and harms transgender people (Temple Newhook et al. 2018, 7–8).

Dr. Steensma and Peggy Cohen-Kettenis, Ph.D., defended their 2013 report, claiming, among other defenses, the study only presented two different sets of studies with two different rates of desisting (63% and 84.7% by 15 years old). They claimed this report did not attempt to give a definitive answer to the question of desisting (Steensma and Cohen-Kettenis 2018, 225). However, these rates are low since the study did not continue into adulthood. High rates of desisting provide reasons not to treat minors with hormones or surgeries immediately. Since Dr. Steensma's studies are so widely accepted, they are used to justify putting youth on hormone blockers. He responded

The explosive increase in requests for transgender care simply requires a new investigation. Around 2010, for example, around 150 to 200 transgender people were seen every year in the Amsterdam UMC. Now there are 775, with a two-year waiting list on top of that. Research into that small group of people from before 2013 may not apply to the large group that is here now. And here the help of other countries is also needed. *We conduct structural research in the Netherlands. But the rest of the world is blindly adopting our research.'* (Tetelepta 2021)

A Dutch study conducted by Annelou de Vries, M.D., adds a caveat to the desisting rates. When seventy early-onset gender-dysphoric youth between the ages of twelve and sixteen were given the hormone blocker gonadotropin-releasing hormone analogues (GnRHa), the behavioral and emotional problems and depressive symptoms decreased, while general functioning improved significantly during puberty suppression (de Vries et al., 2011). The study found that anxiety levels, gender dysphoria, and body satisfaction did not change while taking puberty blockers. Dr. de Vries warned in the journal *Pediatrics* that the Dutch system requires youth to begin evaluations at a very young age and, through frequent follow-ups, showed improved psychological functioning. No data is available on youth who did not participate in early tracking. Dr. de Vries noted,

This raises the question whether the positive outcomes of early medical interventions also apply to adolescents who more recently present in overwhelming large numbers for transgender care, including those that come at an older age, possibly without a childhood history of GI [gender incongruence]. (de Vries 2020)

The study subjects were also not part of a long-term follow-up to determine the lasting effects of puberty blockers. Yet, notably, none of the seventy subjects stopped taking the puberty blockers, and all started cross-sex hormone treatment, the first step of actual gender reassignment.

The BBC reported a 2015 Tavistock study founding "after a year on puberty blockers, there was a significant increase found in those answering the statement 'I deliberately try to hurt or kill myself'" (Cohen and Barnes 2019). The medicalized approach is controversial since this method does not appear to solve the underlying problems.

Yet, once young people begin transitioning, they continue either because they are content with the changes or hope future treatment may better relieve the dysphoria. Reasonably, one can question if medical professionals ever encourage young people to cease if the treatments are not helping or if the advice is always to go further.

The combinations of studies suggest (1) doctors are misdiagnosing many children with gender dysphoric who are not, which contributes to the high rate of desisting, (2) if a child is not placed on puberty blockers, they possess a much greater chance of desisting from gender dysphoria. This is because the hormone blockers are either relieving some barriers from truly gender dysphoric young people or ceasing the adolescent brain's masculinization and feminization, causing temporary gender dysphoria to persist permanently. Gary E. Butler, M.D.,[5] doctor of pediatrics and adolescent medicine and endocrinology at the University College Hospital London, wrote, "Early puberty blockade may fix the dysphoria and not permit the development of a fluid, non-binary gender expression" [or cisgender expression] (G. Butler 2017, 181). Of these two options, both are possible depending on the developmental stage of the individual. The second option is less popular but consistent with the biology of human development.

Infants use 60% of their energy building their brains, which quadrupled in size by the time they reach six years, at which time, the brain is 90% formed into that of a mature adult. The brain goes through its next stage of development by puberty, when *apoptosis* continues pruning unused areas, molding the gray and white matter, and crystalizing its changes. The effects of sex hormones flooding the brain during puberty and environmental influences during puberty might play a significant role in causing gender dysphoria to desist. Gray and white matter are among the substantial differentiating factors between male and female brains. They go through a considerable transformation during puberty. In this context, doctors would be

---

[5] He was given the European Society for Paediatric Endocrinology Outstanding Clinician Award in 2020 as a result of his clinical expertise and significant national and international developments in the clinical practice of paediatric endocrinology. This is the highest award for a clinical doctor in this field (G. Butler n.d.).

premature to predict how a child's brain will fully develop when puberty is still making changes.

In 2009, Norman Spack, M.D., co-authored the new Endocrine Society Guidelines, which recommended using GnRH analogues (hormone blockers) in prepubertal, Tanner Stage 2[6] children, and lifetime use of sex-changing hormones (Ruttimann 2013). Tanner Stage 2 includes ages eight to fifteen in females and ten to fifteen in males, a period of tremendous hormonal influence on the body. The purpose of blocking hormones in Stage 2 is to prevent the body from masculinizing and feminizing, but the brain is part of the body. If the body is not sexually mature and in the process of developing, stopping the development means the young person will not receive a flood of testosterone or estrogen to the brain.

Dr. Spack, when speaking at the Endocrine Society's annual meeting, said they are not treating transgender kids soon enough. At Boston Children's Hospital, where Dr. Spack practices, he advocates starting puberty blockers earlier than the Society guidelines under sixteen. "The best age for boys, he says, is 12–14 years, while they are at Tanner Stage 2 and have a testicular volume of 4–6 cc; girls should come in younger, at age 10–12 years, with Tanner Stage 2 breast development" (Ruttimann 2013). However, a contradiction arises when a boy allegedly struggling with having a masculinized brain takes GnRH to stop testosterone production at a crucial period of sexing the body. The assumption is that no amount of testosterone or estrogen during sexual development will change the sex structures in the brain. Providing medical evidence would be helpful if this is the claim since many people with early-onset gender dysphoria desist when hormone blockers and cross-sex hormones are not involved in the treatments.

As an illustration, by the time puberty is complete, the dominos all fell and revealed the person as a crystalized adult. In contrast, hormone blockers in teenagers are like stopping the *falling chain of molecular dominos,* as Fr. Nicanor Austriaco, O.P., described in section 7.1. When doctors artificially pause the chain reaction, the substance becomes inert, and the completed adult waiting to emerge remains frozen. Thus, halting puberty is like pulling the caterpillar out of the cocoon. The

---

[6] See Figure 2.2

virtues cultivated during the anticipatory seasons of Advent and Lent would be helpful for people who are not satisfied during the transition. Waiting and anticipation are skills lost in an age of instant gratification.

Antonio Guillamon, M.D.,'s study in 2016 suggests a reason a person's brain may continually develop sexually during puberty:

> In these cases, hormones at puberty might act in two ways. One would be directly on the brain, affecting cortical development, and the other would be to guide the development of the secondary sex characteristics that would, in turn, be perceived as congruent because of the brain changes that take place at this age. (Guillamon, Junque, and Gómez-Gil 2016, 1637)

The teenage years form many parts of the body, but the human brain is not fully mature until the mid to late twenties. Transgender activists like Brynn Tannehill claim, *"Doctors are prescribing drugs which block the onset of puberty to give the child's brain time to mature and to see how their gender identity solidifies"* (Tannehill 2019, 89). However, blocking testosterone and estrogen from forming the sexual identities of youth prevents the brain from maturing. The brain does not mature with time but through hormones interacting with the brain's structures. The emotional centers of the brain are some of the last areas to crystalize. With the current technology, doctors cannot possibly determine with any degree of certainty if a child were to persist with gender dysphoria until puberty finishes. For most people, gender identity crystallized long before this point; however, how this affects people with early-onset gender dysphoria is unknown. Might the additional years of testosterone or estrogen produce an effect? The answer is unknown by the medical community, but the high rates of desisting suggest a connection. The brain will continue forming throughout an entire person's life, but the immediate changes and development will conclude by 30 years within all parts of the brain.

[Brynn Tanehill]

Three Parenting Approaches

When approaching children with early-onset gender dysphoria, doctors Beilby and Eddy propose three possible responses (Beilby and Eddy 2019, 36–38):

1. Gender Realignment
2. Gender Affirmation
3. Watchful Waiting

Gender Realignment

The most controversial approach is Gender Realignment, whereby the parents encourage the child to participate in gender-conforming activities and behaviors. This approach can range from gentle and understanding to abusive. The stories of a blue-collar father catching his son trying on his mother's shoes and getting a beating to *straighten him out* or some variation of this narrative are what people typically think about when hearing this theory. Harry Benjamin, M.D., described gender realignment treatments in his 1966 book *The Transsexual Phenomenon,*

> The transvestitic patient is given an emetic drug. As soon as nausea develops, he has to view slides of himself dressed as a woman, prepared beforehand. At the same time, he has to listen to tape recordings describing in detail the mode and technique of *'dressing.'* This form of treatment continues until vomiting occurs or acute illness prevents continuation. (Benjamin 1966, 52)

This extreme case of gender realignment therapy is horrifying, yet, this meme is not the only way to conduct this approach.

In a David Ruben interview of conservative podcaster and author Ben Shapiro, Esq, Ben reveals his two-and-a-half-year-old son was wearing his sister's sparkly shoes. Ben told him he could not wear those because they are *"girl shoes."* Ben instead purchased cowboy boots for his son, which his son loves and will now not take off. Ben explained, *"When he's two and a half, I am the guy that gets to instill the system which will lead to his greatest happiness"* (B. Shapiro 2018).

This approach is not a matter of scaring the cross-gender feelings out of a child, but as one advocate of this method proclaims, to *"speed up the fading of the cross-gender identity which will typically happen in any case"*

(Meyer-Bahlburg 2002, 361). For this theory, modern approaches to behavior therapy include psychodynamic therapies and parent training (Bonfatto and Crasnow 2018, 29). The goals of these treatments are:

1. Reduction in social ostracism
2. Treatment of underlying psychopathology
3. Treatment of the underlying distress
4. Prevention of transsexualism in adulthood (Zucker 2007, 699)

Parents who are sensitive to their child's feelings might be afraid of this model for fear of being perceived by the child or others as transphobic. However, the high rate of 84% of children desisting from gender dysphoria (by fifteen years old) who first are diagnosed early should be reason enough to delay making hormonal and surgical changes to the child (Steensma, McGuire, et al. 2013, 582). As a compromise, parents often believe the hormone treatments do not create long-term effects since they can be stopped, unlike surgery. One of the most common hormone blockers is Lupron, a drug created to castrate sex offenders chemically (Shrier 2021). The FDA disapproves of Lupron to halt healthy puberty, so the long-term effects are unknown.

The *Endocrine Society* is often quoted for stating that puberty blockers are *"fully reversible,"* but the side effects have not been mentioned in the same report. These include future infertility, weakening of the bones, hypertension, unknown effects on brain development, and the unknown effects of a prolonged delay of puberty in adolescents (Hembree et al., 2017, 3874). With no studies on the effects of puberty blockers on the brain or their long-term effects, doctors cannot confidently state these treatments are *"fully reversible."* *The Ethicists from the National Catholic Bioethics Center* concluded,

> The use of puberty-blocking hormones in children with gender dysphoria is particularly dangerous since this intervention radically disrupts the normal sequence of physical and psychological development that occurs during adolescence. One cannot simply 'reverse' what has been done if the individual should change his or her mind. (The Ethicists from the National Catholic Bioethics Center 2016, 600)

Hormone blocking may produce a more permanent effect than many parents realize. For example, suppose a female has gender dysphoria during puberty. Possibly, the last massive rush of estrogen to the brain during these formative years is needed to complete the feminization of the brain. If estrogen is blocked, this may artificially make permanent gender dysphoria.

The body, including the brain, is not formed until twenty-five years of age or shortly after. In addition to disrupting puberty, hormone treatment may sterilize a person. When doctors prescribe hormone blockers and replacement pills to teenagers after only one visit, minors make a significant life decision. Researchers found, *"they or their parents are consenting to lifelong infertility"* (Russo 2016, 35). For this reason, Archbishop Carlson claims, *"On the topic of Pubertal Blockade: I'm not a medical expert, and I can't cover every conceivable medical and pastoral scenario. But the basic approach of the Catholic tradition is and must be a presumption against this intervention"* (Carlson 2020, 11).

In a 1990s follow-up study, researchers concluded: *"subjects who completed [gender realignment]treatments improved about twice as much as those who did not complete the treatment"* and *"treatment focused on gender behavior was found to significantly improve gender identity"* (Rekers, Kilgus, and Rosen 1990, 137 &130). The gender realignment approach was the primary technique for dealing with gender dysphoria throughout the twentieth century, and this approach did not eliminate transgender identities. Too forcefully trying to discontinue a child's natural behavior would also be problematic since gender only becomes less mutable. By the time the treatment begins, the process may be too late to make any substantial change in the child's mind. By puberty, over 95% of the brain crystallizes. How much does the final 5% contribute to gender identity? The effects of this 5% are completely unknown and unresearched.

As learned by the failures of Dr. Money, changing the gender identity in the brain would be too late by the time the child is born. Some transfeminists like Rachel Anne Williams claim that the first 10 to 20 years of life will not determine if they will remain in their assigned gender. Rachel Anne Williams believes the human mind is not destined to function according to a particular gender, and the human will can change the mind. However, why would she not become cisgender if gender identity were a matter of free will? The only reasonable answer remaining is that Rachel is transgender because of an ideological choice. She writes, *"Biology isn't destiny, and experience isn't destiny. Nothing is destiny. We all contain within ourselves the capacity to change greatly"* (R. A.

Williams 2019, 102). The best medical research to date would disagree with the nominalist approach. Male and female brains are dimorphic, like all other primates. Although these differences may be minor compared to other species, their effects are significant enough to cause significant psychic distress for those whose misalignment is present.

In the previous century, homosexuality was illegal, and conversion therapy was standard for homosexual people. Despite this, conversion therapies did not cure any significant number of homosexual people of their tendencies. Sexologist Dr. Soh claims, *"conversion therapy is unethical because it does not work"* (Soh 2021). The echoes of conversion therapies reverberate in the ears of activists today when considering gender realignment. A difference between gender dysphoria and homosexuality is that homosexuality never desists, while 80% of gender dysphoric youth naturally desists. Despite the difference, twenty states in the United States banned conversion therapy which can include transgender treatments which do not affirm the patients assumed gender. More extreme laws exist in Canada. As a result, no harm is done by using gender realignment therapies if any of 80% of future desisters are helped along the way to relieve their dysphoria easier and faster. For the 20% of children with persistent gender dysphoria, refraining from gender realignment therapies would be necessary since this method will not work. Trying to force their position too strongly breaks down the relationship between the child and parents, school, therapist, et cetera.

A 2015 study showed that LGBT youth who grew up in a religious context had higher rates of suicide than other LGBT young adults (Gibbs and Goldbach 2015, 472). The forceful realignment of gender, particularly with religious backing, only exacerbates the problems rather than alleviates the issues. The church does not want to make a difficult situation worse by forcing practices that do not fully appreciate the complexities of gender dysphoria.

Gender Affirmation

The gender affirmation approach created by Colt Keo-Meier, Ph.D., and Diane Ehrensaft, Ph.D., is the most politically correct currently. The Gender Affirmative Model contained contributions from twenty authors and was published by the American Psychological Association (APA). Doctors Keo-Meier and Ehrensaft write in the introduction, *"Every day we learn more and see how much more we have to learn about helping our children discover and fortify their true gender selves"* (Keo-Meier and Ehrensaft 2018, 5). This approach attempts to affirm the child's sense of gender identity by changing the individual's clothing, hairstyle, name, pronouns, and ways of addressing the child. In addition, Dr. Keo-Meier writes in correspondence with Brynn Tannehill, *"The gender affirmative model supports identity exploration and development without an a priori goal of any particular gender identity or expression"* continuing, *"[Practitioners] do not push children in any direction, rather, they listen to children"* (Tannehill 2019, 92).

Prior to medical treatment, the child endures no permanent changes. If the male child wants to wear a dress or engage in stereotypical female activities or be called a girl, adults will support him in that activity. This approach can be as gentle as allowing a young boy to play with a baby doll as a toy or experiment with female clothing. However, this approach can also be as aggressive as the mother in the documentary, *Transhood,* announcing that her four-year-old son Phoenix would like to be called a girl and use she/her pronouns (Liese 2020). Shortly afterward, Phoenix asserted he is a little boy and was not transgender.

Prominent universities are teaching future teachers to introduce concepts of being transgender to young children. *For example, the Educator's Playbook* put out by the *University of Pennsylvania's Graduate School of Education* claims, *"Asking students of all ages what name and pronouns they would like you to use is a great first step"* (Cross n.d.). The reports of gender affirmation being pushed on children by parents, doctors, and teachers are too numerous to cite in this passage. Pushing gender affirmation on young children without persisting or consistent expressions of gender dysphoria is part of the agenda of nominalist gender theory activists and not a compassionate response to dysphoric youth.

Johanna Olson-Kennedy, M.D., the medical director of The Center for Transyouth Health and Development at UCLA, claims youth *"can really benefit from not going through the wrong puberty"* and *"It is much easier if we can halt their puberty early on in the process… then put them through the right puberty"* (Olson-Kennedy 2014). However, the aim of stopping puberty as early as possible to prevent the pain of the *wrong* puberty may lead to a hasty diagnosis and an inaccurate treatment. As shown in *infra-*

10.4, Dr. Olson-Kennedy not only promotes hormone-blockers for youth and encourages double mastectomies for FtM children as young as 12 years old. Dr. Olson-Kennedy, marrying Aydin, an FtM individual who transitioned after 30 years of living as a female (Brown 2015), boasts intimate knowledge on this topic. Still, her experience may influence her outlook on early-onset gender dysphoria.

One of the social factors which pressure parents into this model is the fear of teenage suicide. The issue of suicide is both an area of concern and a guilt tool used by teens to force their desired treatment. Lisa Littman, M.D., (*infra*-9.4) found websites used by trans youth taught techniques to ensure parents would agree to allow them to transition out of fear of self-harm (Littman 2018).

The American Academy of Pediatrics fully embraces the gender affirmation approach while providing protocols for helping a child transition (American Academy of Pediatrics Committee on Adolescence 2013). Dr. Ehrensaft, supporting the American Academy of Pediatrics' decision, writes, *"In this country, we've grown up in a culture where for so long—and [this belief] still exists—people felt that you had to cure someone who didn't conform to expectations of gender."* The doctor continues, *"When children are supported—and that means accepted—they will do beautifully"* (Jordan 2018). Some advocates of this theory claim no preemptive treatment for children who are only going through a phase will occur since the protocols require the dysphoria to be *"insistent, persistent, and consistent"* (Hidalgo et al., 2013, 286).

During training, Dr. Ehrensaft does not seek to go slowly with these procedures, announcing that *"tweens and young teens undergoing these treatments are not developmentally mature enough to comprehend the full magnitude of irreversible sterilization"* (Ehrensaft 2021). Yet, this does not mean Dr. Ehrensaft is against transitioning. Instead, she explained in the same training to clinicians and parents that the child should not be overburdened with *'TMI'*—too much information. Dr. Ehrensaft goes as far as recommending what she considers irreversible sterilizing hormone blockers to children who are in Tanner Stage 2 (eight to nine years of age) (Ehrensaft 2021).

Dr. Littman's study of parents' experiences of gender dysphoric youth found that doctors were not determining if the dysphoria was *insistent, persistent, and consistent.* Instead, they drew their conclusions without speaking with the parents or doing a physical or psychological examination. Doctors offer hormone blockers and hormones to 23.8% of the youth after the first visit (Littman 2018, 25).

One youth detransitioner named Garrett, in a *60 Minutes* interview with Lesley Stahl, stated, *"I didn't get enough pushback on transitioning"* (Stahl 2021). After two visits to a gender specialist, he had received estrogen, and within three months, he received an orchiectomy. Garrett then received a breast augmentation. Garrett claimed. *"And about a week afterward, I wanted to, like, actually kill myself. Like, I had a plan, and I was gonna do it, but I just kept thinking about, like, my family to stop myself. It kind of felt like how am I ever going to feel normal again, like other guys now?"* (Stahl 2021)

> Many stories from parents are online:
>
> The pediatrician/*'gender specialist'* did not return calls or emails from the primary care physician who requested to talk with her about my son's medical history before she saw and treated him. She disregarded all the historical information provided by the family and primary care physician. [She] did not verify any information provided by my son at his first visit even after being provided with multiple other historical sources which differed significantly from his story. (Littman 2018, 26)

The lack of medical due diligence in the treatment of youth is alarming. In an attempt to *"believe the victim"* in every case, this social slogan became evidence enough for a significant and life-changing transformation in children without any medically verified proof of having a disorder. The gender affirmation approach is celebrated by people who are culturally and politically gender non-conforming. As one advocate claims, this approach moves experience from pathology to pride (Silverberg 2013, 1).

Watchful Waiting

The most prudent response for helping children cope with gender dysphoria is called watchful waiting or the Dutch protocol, the *"current standard of care worldwide"* (Laidlaw, Cretella, and Donovan 2019, 75). Watchful waiting is a blending of gender realignment and gender affirmation. In this therapeutic style, the parents remain neutral regarding their gender identity, not actively discouraging or advocating for sex reassignment. Instead, the goal is to support the people involved in the situation in the healthiest way possible, concerning everyone's feelings and open communication. However, according to proponents of the gender affirmation subgroup, this approach is dangerous since the parent's inaction will only *"prolong the child's experience of dysphoria"* (Murchison 2016).

The current *Standards of Care* written by the *World Professional Association for Transgender Health* (WPATH), using a study by Thomas Steensma, Ph.D., and Peggy Cohen-Kettenis, Ph.D., claim *"A change back to the original gender role can be highly distressing and even result in the postponement of this second social transition on the child's part"* (Steensma, Cohen-Kettenis and de Vries 2011) (The World Professional Association for Transgender Health 2012). In addition, Dr. Steensman found *"Childhood social transitions were important predictors of persistence, especially among natal boys"* (Steensma, McGuire, et al. 2013, 582). Therefore, early social transitioning should be avoided using the WPATH guidelines to prevent youth's additional stressors from maintaining transgender identities founded on embarrassment and fear.

Kenneth Zucker, Ph.D., from the Child, Youth, and Family Gender Identity Clinic in Toronto, was a proponent of a combination approach that included gender realignment therapies and watchful waiting for the youngest patients. Dr. Zucker claims that learning techniques for coping with dysphoria would be in the young child's best interest for a few years while the child was still developing. Unfortunately, in 2015 Dr. Zucker was fired, and the clinic closed after pressure from transgender activists who only believe in the gender affirmation model, regardless of the child's age. Dr. Zucker believed surgeries and hormones helped some individuals cope with gender dysphoria. Still, as the director of a program for children and youth, he advocated for a much longer waiting period before rushing into permanent life-long decisions for children too young to understand the implications of the treatments (Singal 2016).

One transgender Christian advised in an interpretative phenomenological analysis conducted by Mark Yarhouse, Ph.D., and Dara Houp, Psy.D., *"Be more loving. Follow a child's lead."* At the same time, another participant recommended, *"Don't condemn and judge a child in their innocence because it scares you or you don't understand. Instead, seek help from other people, don't be afraid to admit that you don't know"* (Yarhouse and Houp 2016, 59). The watchful waiting approach contains humility not to claim expertise when the experts are unsure about the origins and best treatments for this condition. This approach allows a child's nature to unfold naturally without rushing to solidify what is still undetermined.

In the present moment, adults are examining children's activities through the hyper-sensitive lens of identity (Hayward 2021). Whatever a child does, adults are trying to interpret behavior in terms of being. Sometimes a little boy wears a princess crown; other times, a little girl likes cowboy boots. Children playing with gender makes them normal human children who are playful and imaginative. Adults in Western societies are obsessed with identity politics, but this is not related to the personhood of children. The Dutch Protocol is less about children figuring out their identities and more about the adults getting out of the way and allowing a child to develop naturally.

[Lisa Littman, M.D.]

9.4 LATE-ONSET GENDER DYSPHORIA

Late-onset gender dysphoria is a new occurrence that was practically unheard of two decades ago. Marcus Evans, Ph.D., former governor of Tavistock, points out that when teenagers self-diagnose with a single psychological cause and a single solution, it gives doctors a reason to be concerned (Evans 2020). Psychological issues are seldom ascribed to a single cause and always have variable depths of healing. The proper way to understand dysphoria is to consider family dynamics, mental health, comorbidities, social groups, and other avenues. Doctors found that many young people who went to Tavistock experienced complex situations, including broken family life, autism, eating disorders, and other challenges.

Medical experts like doctors Blanchard, Bailey, and Soh predict this sudden burst of gender dysphoric teens who never expressed signs of gender dysphoria in their early development may be infected with a social contagion. The elements of this contagion include:

1. Feelings of dysphoria resulting from puberty in a sexualized culture.

2. The desire to receive attention when they may have felt unseen and unheard

3. Overprotective parents who want to prevent their child from experiencing pain, even the natural pain which comes from the angst of puberty

4. Nominalist gender theorists are rewriting the narrative of intersex and transgender people to eliminate any biological realism or sexual morality. They use the cultural guilt of society being homophobic to justify their gender relativism.

Once teenage girls start to develop breasts, they become sexual objects for their peers and adult men. The society focused on pornography and stories of sex trafficking minors, mixed with impossible standards of beauty created with social media filters creates dysphoria. No woman, especially a teenage girl, wants to menstruate. Puberty is embarrassing and difficult for a teenage girl who is also developing breasts and transitioning to womanhood socially. The desire to exchange this reality for a boy's or a person with no gender appears on the surface liberating, particularly if a young female is also questioning her same-sex attractions.

American society is also dealing with overparenting and underparenting. Increasingly, parents are allowing technology to entertain their children from an early age. The occurrence of children watching videos on their phones in restaurants while their parents are also on their phones is not uncommon. Children are invisible to their parents so long as they are quiet and not creating any issues. Coming out as transgender immediately shifts attention onto them. Often, this identification is a cry for parental attention.

At the same time, parents are over parenting. If a child is momentarily unhappy, many parents resort to handing them a phone or giving them what they like. As a result, children are not learning the skills of deferred satisfaction. Furthermore, parents overprotect their children. Healthy children need independence to explore outside with their friends, fall and scrape a knee, break bones, become broken-hearted, embarrassed at school, and the list goes on. Getting hurt is part of living. A teen spending every hour outside of school quietly playing on the computer may appear safe, but the youth is not experiencing healthy development. Using hormone blockers to save the child the pain of puberty is an extension of this trend of parents to keep their children safe at all costs. Children know that saying *"I don't feel safe"* will get them whatever they like, but they usually mean *"I don't feel comfortable."* Puberty is uncomfortable.

Gender theorists capitalize on this moment of homosexual acceptance to mainline their ideology. As laws create protections for homosexual people, these same laws indirectly included transgender people (in the broadest sense of the term) under the same umbrella. If two homosexual adults decide to marry under the law, the danger to the commonweal is minimal. Even if youth come out as lesbian, gay, or bisexual, the truth of their orientation will eventually settle. Many young people who *come out* realize their fantasies are a phase, while others persist. Nothing is permanent about sexual fantasies. Still, human attractions, desires, and multilayers of sexuality are more complicated within heterosexual Christian marriage than some Catholics are willing to admit. This book will not go any further into this topic.

In contrast to *sexuality*, when a teen comes out as transgender (identity) and desires to be put on hormone blockers and receive cross-sex hormones, permanent changes are set into motion. Although gender dysphoria may be a phase, the effects may not be as transient. The consequences on the social fabric of society are whatever one claims to be by self-identification, one *is,* and society must recognize them as such. To question this narrative is to erase that person's existence and be considered a hate crime in some jurisdictions.

Rapid-Onset Gender Dysphoria (ROGD) is the newest development in the transgender phenomenon. Dr. Littman from Brown University first published this theory in a report titled, *"Rapid-onset gender dysphoria in adolescents and young adults: A study of parental reports"* (Littman 2018). Gender dysphoria is defined as *"an individual's persistent discomfort with their biological sex or assigned gender"* (Zucker, Lawrence, and Kreukels 2016, 218). Dr. Littman's study creates a new term, ROGD, a specific form of gender dysphoria. Dr. Littman suggests teenage children, particularly females, *"who suddenly start manifesting symptoms of gender dysphoria and self-identifying as transgender simultaneously with other children in their peer group."* This diagnosis proposes a sociological as well as a psychological and biological aspect to dysphoria.

This study finds surprising results about teens who typically had not manifested any signs of early-onset gender dysphoria. Until the 1990s, the issue of transgender youth was relatively rare. No reported cases of late-onset adolescent gender dysphoria occurred before this period. In the late 2010s, teens never having exhibited gender dysphoria are, at 15 years, *coming out* as transgender. Most of the teens reporting this late-onset gender dysphoria are females who had begun puberty several years earlier without any indication of this dysphoria until suddenly, halfway through puberty, the dysphoria appeared.

The transgender healthcare bill (AB 2218) stated that 27%, or 796,000, of youth twelve to 17 years of age in California are viewed as gender nonconforming by their peers at sc0hool (CA 2020). So why is this statistic an element of a transgender healthcare bill unless the lawmakers linked 27% of California youth with transgender healthcare?

Referrals from 13 to 16 years old comprise 77.6% of all transgender youth referrals. Thus, an 81% drop in referrals between the ages of sixteen and seventeen occurs. The trend among teens to *"come out"* as transgender may concern parents, but a more significant concern should be that society is rushing to make permanent transitions when statistics show an 81% natural decline as the youth exit teenage years (see figure 9.1).

Dr. Littman's research and results triggered the transgender activist community because her conclusions suggest a societal cause for transgender identities. Brown University is an ivy league institution famous for being very socially progressive around sexuality and gender expression. The outcry against Dr. Littman's study resulted in Brown University removing the announcement and link to the study on their website. The protests also led to a second review of the study's methodology from *PLoS One* and the article being taken down from their website for seven months while under review. Finally, *PLoS One* returned the study to the website under the title, *"Parent reports of adolescents and young adults perceived to show signs of a rapid onset of gender dysphoria."* The republication was the same study but with a new name and narrower distinctions and discussions but unchanged in its assessment.

Dr. Littman studied adolescents and young adults (AYA) who identified as gender dysphoric to their families. Dr. Littman surveyed 256 parents about their children's behavior. Of the parents surveyed, their children were predominantly natal females (82.8%) with an average age of 16.4 years. Additional statistics are found in Figure 9.2.

The *coming out* process for youth does not relieve stress but appears instead to begin a downward decline. Some suggest that nonsupportive families and communities cause the physical decline of youth after they come out; however, the surveyed parents responded 85.9% favorably to same-sex marriage. In addition, 88.2% believed *"that transgender people deserve the same rights and protections as others."* Also, 7.8% claimed they *"Don't know,"* with only 3.1% of parents responding they did not believe in equal rights and protections for transgender people. Criticism from the transgender activist community had claimed Dr.

Littman's sources[7] for getting the parents for the surveys were biasedly conservative and transphobic. However, unless most 255 parents were lying, the sourcing cannot contribute to an overwhelming conservative bias since the parents' perspective on social issues was generally liberal, according to the surveys.

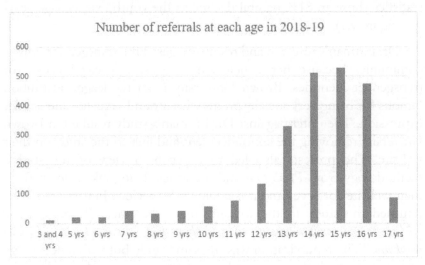

Figure 9.1 Number of Referrals 2018-2019 (Gilligan 2019)

Dr. Littman describes a coming-out process she suggests might be more intricately connected with a sexual liberation or identity trend than biologically driven. Before 2012, no research studies were conducted about adolescent females with gender dysphoria. Late adolescent gender dysphoria was typically the result of early-onset gender dysphoria presenting for care during adolescence. Social factors related to self-identification may influence the transgender individual. Young people may find information online or through friends who might not correctly diagnose the cause of their angst.

Transgender advocate Blaire White claimed hundreds, if not thousands, of detransitioners, reach out to her and claim they went down an online rabbit hole *"they just got way too deep into trans (online) communities"* (B. White 2021a). If someone is already not happy with themselves (a typical teenage problem), coming across online

---

[7] 4thwavenow.com, transgendertrend.com, youthtranscriticalprofessionals.com, and snowball sampling techniques

communities where people reinvent themselves can be attractive to some people.

With its rapid onset, this new occurrence worried parents who, although supporting same-sex marriage and transgender rights, were concerned that their children, who had never shown any indication of gender dysphoria, suddenly *came out* as transgender. Coming out further worried parents when some side effects included separation from their families and non-transgender friends. There was a decline in activities and academics. At the same time, a high level of social media, using belittling talk about anyone who was not transgender, and using a language that did not appear to be their own.

41%   Claimed non-heterosexual orientation first

62.5% Diagnosed with at least one mental health disorder or neurodevelopmental disability prior to *"coming out"*

36.8% The of majority friendship group trans-identified

47.2% A mental health decline since *"coming out"*

86.7% Parents reported a substantial increase in social media/internet use and/or started hanging out in friend groups where one or multiple youth identify as trans

Figure 9.2 Dr. Littman's Results of 2018 AYA Study (Littman 2018)

Dr. Littman found many coaching aids to teach youth what to say to be prescribed hormone supplements and obtain surgeries they desired on transgender websites. Parents discovered their children repeating scripts to medical professionals. Parents suspected these scripts did not reflect their child's experience, but the youth would use them to ensure they would be diagnosed as gender dysphoric and be prescribed hormone supplements. A website's recommendation to youth to suggest that if they did not transition, the parent's hesitancy would lead to suicide. This trump card would often scare most parents into consenting to treatment since they prefer a transgender child to a dead one. Dr. Soh points out.

> This is how unknowing parents, who only want to make life easier for their son or daughter, have become prime targets of a campaign that has weaponized science and medicine and taken vulnerable children as prisoners. A related form of emotional blackmail involves constantly referencing the suicide statistic. (Soh 2020, 232)

Online transgender resources are as varied as the rest of the internet. One online resource titled *Am I Transgender?* (AmITransgender.net), and upon clicking on the link, the only thing written on the page is *"Yes."* After a moment, five website links appear on the page. None of these links point to medical resources but only to blogs focusing on a personal gender theory, whereby anyone could claim to be transgender and must invent themselves. As a link on the site claims, *"a human being does not possess any inherent identity or value and must create these things for themselves"* (r/asktransgender 2015). Another link pointed to *"8 signs and symptoms of indirect gender dysphoria,"* which states:

1. Continual difficulty with simply getting through the day

2. A sense of misalignment, disconnect, or estrangement from your own emotions

3. A feeling of just going through the motions in everyday life, as if you're always reading from a script

4. A seeming pointlessness to your life and no sense of any real meaning or ultimate purpose

5. Knowing you're somehow different from everyone else and wishing you could be normal like them

6. A notable escalation in the severity (of emotions) of these symptoms during puberty

7. Attempting to fix this on your own through various coping mechanisms

8. Substantial resolution of these symptoms in a very obvious way upon transitioning, particularly upon initiating HRT (Z. Jones 2013)

Other than the last symptom, what Zinnia Jones describes is puberty. If any confused teenagers read this list, they might conclude they are transgender, and transitioning may be the solution. However,

Zinnia also claims, *"Transitioning won't solve all your problems, it can only treat or improve gender dysphoria as well as associated depression, anxiety, dissociation, stress, poor body image, eating disorders, sexual dysfunction, social difficulties, substance abuse, self-harm, suicidality"* (Z. Jones 2021). The hope transgender activists promise youth by transitioning is dangerous, dishonest, and contrary to medical science. Zinna, with 23,700 Twitter followers, is a trans role model for many young girls who idolize her.

Teenage girls are significantly affected by impossible beauty standards presented not only by the traditional media but through social media use on their phones. One study found,

> Snapchat Dysmorphia is now a condition affecting the youth. Several plastic surgeons have shared their experiences whereby they encountered requests sounding similar to what a "filtered" Snapchat picture would look like, with one plastic surgeon even having a patient who actually produced a "filtered" image. There are several red flags to look out for in such patients, and proper management in those cases should include counseling and not plastic surgery. (Ramphul and Mejias 2018)

The stresses of an unrealistic expectation of how one appears, leads to self-destructive outcomes, particularly for young girls. Snapchat Dysmorphia applies primarily to youth but can affect adults to a lesser degree. This phenomenon also plays a significant factor within the transgender community. Within transgender groups online, MtF individuals often post images of themselves using filters to not only change their gender but to make themselves 30 years younger. The text associated with these posts suggests that this will be their new self once their hormones and surgeries are complete. These people experience unrealistic expectations.

Renee Engeln, Ph.D., author of *Beauty Sick: How the Cultural Obsession with Appearance Hurts Girls and Women,* writes about the adverse effects of filters on Instagram and Snapchat, claiming, *"There's an issue with losing perspective on what you actually look like, and it's not something we talk about much"* (Brucculieri 2018). Suppose people post enough pictures of themselves using these artificial filters and receive enough positive attention because of them. In that case, one can easily understand why they experience dysmorphia when they see themselves in the mirror. These feelings of inadequacy are dysmorphia brought on by a false sense of how one appears. The reliance on cosmetic surgery to make the body match one's inner sense of being is often impossible and unhealthy. In cases of Snapchat Dysmorphia, the medical community recognizes these desires as *red flags* but is this categorically different from teenage youth experiencing gender dysphoria? Could transgender desires be a body dysmorphia?

Dr. Littman recalls an account from a parent who stated, *"A 14-year-old natal female and three of her natal female friends were taking group lessons together with a very popular coach. The coach came out as transgender, and, within one year, all four students announced they were also transgender"* (Littman 2018, 16). All four 14 to 15-year-old girls being biologically predisposed as transgender and happening to be on the same tennis team as a coach who was also transgender is challenging to believe.

Some critics of Dr. Littman claim young people congregating with other people like themselves is typical and expected (R. Watson 2019). However, suppose a parent never experiences any signs their daughter was transgender, and suddenly all her peer group comes out as transgender. Dr. Soh reported, *"For about 40% of these adolescents, more than half of their friend groups had also come out as transgender. This is more than seventy times the prevalence of transgender adults in the general population"* (Soh 2020, 108). Suspicion foresees a possible sociological cause rather than a biological one.

Youth imitating their peer group is not unthinkable since each generation of youth engages in an identity fad, which they eventually reject. The *goth* movement of the late 1990s and 2000s was one of those passing identity fads. Following *goths* was *emo* and now transgender, non-binary, gender non-conforming, et cetera. In addition, the teenage years are a time of discontentment, an element necessary for psychological maturity. If children did not become discontent with action figures and dolls, they would never ask the more important life questions leading them to a more profound existence. Thus, existential crises are a necessary and vital part of life.

Grace Lidinsky Smith, a twenty-year-old female, got caught up in transitioning stories online. She claimed when talking with Lesley Stahl, *"When I saw them being so happy and excited about this wonderful transformation process to become their true selves, I asked myself, have I considered that this could be my situation too?... I was thinking it would make me free"* (Stahl 2021). Grace was prescribed testosterone by signing a consent form and was given very little guidance. Within four months, she received a double mastectomy, and within one year of the start of the process, she had already detransitioned. Grace now claims doctors did not follow the WPATH's guidelines. She also claims that she had not received adequate therapy before beginning her transition, nor had she experienced over six months of gender dysphoria.

In the British case of *Keira Bell vs. Tavistock and Portman NHS Trust* (2020), Keira Bell sued the National Health Care System at twenty-three years of age, claiming doctors transitioned her to male without following proper cautionary guidelines. At 16, Keira, a natural tomboy, was enticed by online forums about transitioning. After three one-hour appointments, doctors put Keira on hormone blockers. Keira now claims, *"I should have been challenged on the proposals or the claims that I was making for myself,"* she said. *"And I think that would have made a big difference as well. If I was just challenged on the things I was saying"* (Holt 2020). Consequently, the High Court ruled that children under 16 were unlikely to give informed consent to receive puberty-blocking drugs. The High Court also found that the use of hormone blockers produced *"no overall improvement in mood or psychological wellbeing using standardized psychological measures"* (Quincy Bell and Mrs. A v. The Tavistock and Portman NHS Foundation Trust 2020, 73).

Although she never received opposite-sex hormones, a young FtMtF detransitioner, Charlie Evans began her transition to male at fifteen years. She now runs *The Detransition Advocacy Network* in the UK. Charlie claims five commonalities exist among the members of her network. First, they are overwhelmingly female; second, most were lesbian or bisexual; third, many were autistic; fourth, most were under twenty-five years of age; finally, comorbidity with eating disorders, anxiety, and depression were common. In a BBC interview, she claimed that young lesbians are being misdiagnosed with gender dysphoria and put on a medical pathway when they are gay. When asked what would help those young people, she answered, *they need longer therapy periods and help with other mental health issues* (BBC Newsnight 2019).

During the same broadcast, psychotherapist James Caspian, after working with transgender people for a decade, found similar trends with detransitioners. First, he found the popularity of transgender activists on social media consumed the questioning teen. Second, he found young females wanting to escape the pressures and expectations of being female or even trying to undo the trauma of past sexual abuse experienced as a woman. (BBC Newsnight 2019).

After a while, recognizing the difference between early-onset gender dysphoria and dysphoric teenagers who are dealing with issues of sexual orientation becomes easier. In the case of homosexuality, the family often recognizes their child is homosexual before *coming out.* Yet, in Dr. Littman's survey, only 2.4% of parents thought their children were correct in their assessment that they were transgender. The disconnection between the parents' experiences and the medical community's approach is significant, considering many healthcare professionals do not listen to the parents' view and prescribe hormone blockers and hormone supplements after the first visit, without any psychological or medical evaluations (Littman 2018, 18).

Some doctors publicly state, *"puberty blockers buy time until the adolescent is cognitively mature enough to decide whether to acquiesce to the puberty concordant with their natal sex or to proceed with cross-sex hormonal therapy that will bring their identities more in line with their bodies"* (Cashman and Walters 2016, 21) (Edwards- Leeper and Spack, 2012) (Reardon 2016). In contrast, Dr. Soh questions, *"when the majority of experts are too afraid to publicly criticize gender affirmative therapies, parents cannot trust that their child is being given a proper diagnosis"* (Soh 2020, 95).

Is Gender Dysphoria related to Body Dysmorphic Disorder?

About 1.7% to 2.9% of the U.S. population is diagnosed with BDD (Phillips n.d.). Anorexia takes the life of 20% of people who suffer from this form of BDD (Grant and Phillips 2004, 123) (Mirasol n.d.). No matter how difficult the condition of anorexia may be, nothing about the fantasy changes the person's biological reality is dangerously underweight. For the medical community to treat anorexic people as overweight would be malpractice since the body must be treated in reality and not how the patient perceives themselves to be. However, the anorexic person's mental state must be addressed since the dysphoria the person experiences is real but different from a condition affecting the body. Likewise, those suffering from gender dysphoria remain male or female.

Cosmetic modifications cannot change this physical reality, and like with anorexia, the mental state must be addressed. As found in England's National Healthcare System statistics, eating disorders like BDD are highest in the fifteen to nineteen age group, decreasing every subsequent year (C. Stewart 2020) (see figure 9.3). Eating disorders cease over time, either with the help of medical professionals or with self-care and maturity. One million males and eight million females in America suffer from eating disorders (Philadelphia Fight Community Health Centers 2019). Teenage girls are highly susceptible to body image disorders, with 50% of American female youth claiming they use unhealthy means for controlling their weight (Philadelphia Fight Community Health Centers 2019). Yet when society addresses transgender youth, they assume the young person's identity is more accurate than the physical reality.

An indication that ROGD may be associated with BDD or similar social disorders is the rate at which adult heterosexual women are *not* transitioning. Many middle-aged women responded that they felt dysphoric when they were young but outgrew these feelings and are now concerned about the youth making permanent life decisions during puberty (Hayward 2021). Early-onset gender dysphoria, typically, if not exclusively, is androphilic (homosexual type). A statistically significant group of autogynephilic MtF individuals transition later in life. Where are the heterosexual type FtM individuals transitioning later in life? They do not exist. These trends suggest that many homosexual/bisexual girls opt-out of womanhood to become *heterosexual* men. These statistics are not an indication of a neurodevelopmentally driven gender dysphoria but rather a social movement.

The way of treating people with body dysmorphia is by cognitive behavior therapy and antidepressants but never surgery. Therapists also use Exposure and Response Prevention, Acceptance and Commitment Therapy, and Cognitive Therapy, and Dialectical Behavior Therapy combined with medications. The medications are Selective Serotonin Reuptake Inhibitors,[8] which enhance natural serotonin activity and treat major depressive disorders and anxiety conditions. These findings

---

[8] Examples of these medications include Lexapro, Prozac, Paxil, and Zoloft.

suggest the Pimozide finding by Basant Puri, M.D., and Iqbal Singh, M.D., in 1996, may well be correct since both Serotonin and Dopamine are neurotransmitters, and similar medications might treat both gender dysphoria and BDD. In addition, both Serotonin and Dopamine are important neurotransmitters for treating depression and anxiety; both are related to feelings of dysphoria.

The therapeutic approach for treating body dysmorphia includes mindfulness-based *Cognitive Behavioral Therapy*, which *"teaches people to identify, understand, and change negative thinking patterns and behaviors. Patients are taught problem-solving skills during therapy lessons and then instructed to practice them on their own time to build positive habits"* (Intrusive Thoughts n.d.). Contemporary medical communities treat transgender issues by prescribing a lifetime of hormones and performing major surgeries. Even if they can reduce dysphoria, these treatments significantly increase the rate of tumors, heart disease, and other life-threatening illnesses (Dhejne, Lichtenstein, et al. 2011, 5). For example, estrogen therapy includes a 20-fold increased risk of thromboembolic disease, hyperprolactinemia, and gall stone development (van Kesteren, Asscheman, Megans, and Gooren, 1997). The medicalized treatment plan is what the transgender community is primarily requesting. Still, serious medical concerns arise, considering if the medicalized treatment plan is the best option or if alternative treatments may be healthier and more effective.

Body dysmorphia treatments appear preferable to transgender surgeries since body dysmorphic individuals will no longer need medications. In contrast, transgender people need to be on hormones for the rest of their lives, and these hormones potentially create life-threatening side effects. Unfortunately, no studies on treating gender dysmorphia with body dysmorphia treatments are being published. Still, therapy dealing with body image may offer some relief, mainly if a person were young and reacting towards their bodies like many youths with eating disorders do. This treatment might benefit youth too young to transition but could still benefit from some psychological relief.

Can the hormones make the dysphoria permanent?

Hilleke Hulshoff, Ph.D., raises a medical concern about changing one's hormones to change the brain structures, particularly in young people whose brains are still forming (Hulshoff 2006). The belief that giving adolescents hormone blockers and opposite-sex hormones is okay because they are not a permanent change is incorrect. One thirty-one-year-old YouTuber, transitioning from MtF for five months on female hormones, pointed out her own changes (Wynn 2018). She claimed her sex drive stopped and shifted to a female sex drive, which was noticeably different. She also recognized a greater desire for intimacy rather than ejaculation and attraction to men, which was not previously prevalent.

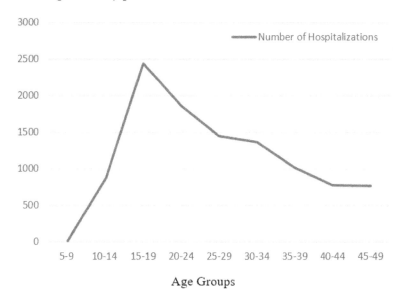

Figure 9.3 Hospital admissions involving a diagnosis of anorexia nervosa in England in 2019/20, by age.

If Dr. Hulshoff correctly asserts chemical changes in the body can lead to a change in the brain structures, taking opposite sex hormones may cause a greater sense of dysphoria than experienced before. Sociological etiology may create biological causation for feelings of gender dysphoria. Youth needs time to figure out who they are as adults. Adding hormones to an already confused teen is a questionable ethical decision in the medical community. Dr. Littman does not make assertions beyond her study's scope, but its consequence suggests practical concerns for any parent of a self-identifying trans-youth.

General Dysphoria in Teenage Youth

Dr. Littman's report confirms what many parents and adults worry about with this new escalation of transgender youth *coming out*. In 2018, the Human Rights Campaign released the *"largest-of-its-kind survey ever"* of LGBT youth to date, with 12,005 participants (Human Rights Campaign 2018).[9] Upon looking at the limited results which the Human Rights Campaign released, they unintentionally confirmed Dr. Littman's theory of ROGD. First, this study shows that LGBTQ youth are incredibly stressed. Unfortunately, no control group was conducted to determine how much more stress LGBTQ youth experience than heterosexual youth. Professor of psychology, Robert Leahy, Ph.D., reported, "The average high school kid today has the same level of anxiety as the average psychiatric patient in the early 1950's" (Leahy 2008). High levels of stress are endemic among typical youth and understandably even higher among dysphoric youth. Dysphoria is a state of unease or generalized dissatisfaction with life, so youth are already dysphoric without any gender identity issues. A transfeminist activist wrote in her memoirs,

> Dysphoria is everywhere we look in American society. Take, for example, the toxic beauty culture that women everywhere are forced to take part in. Part of this culture involves the media promoting images of beautiful, highly photoshopped models representing unattainable ideals, often whitewashed with the assumption that lighter-skinned = better; small waist and big tits= better; long, fine hair (also known as white hair) = better, and so on. (R. A. Williams 2019, 60)

Young men likewise encounter unrealistic expectations of having bodies like Marvel superheroes. Rachel Anne Williams observed that if a young man takes care of his appearance too much, his classmates call

---

[9] The Human Rights Campaign and the University of Connecticut who conducted the study refuse to release the data or a scientific version of this study. UCONN refers all inquiries to the HRC who is only willing to release cherry picked propaganda fact sheets. Despite their lack of academic honesty and transparency, their statistics reveal deep seated unhappiness.

him gay, while if he is too much of a slob, he is also undesirable. She calls dysphoria a *"symptom of modern society"* (R. A. Williams 2019, 62). A study in 2021 found that from 28,000 surveys, 60% of millennials making over $100,000 per year claim to be living "paycheck to paycheck" (PYMNTS 2021). Yet, affluence and comfort have not decreased anxiety and stress for the younger generations. Stress and victimhood are universal, regardless of objective reality.

The more unusual the self-assessed dysphoria, the more stress the young person experiences. Non-conforming and non-binary youth experience the highest levels of stress, according to the Human Rights Campaign study (see figure 9.4). The idea that a child is highly stressed when they possess no sense of their own identity appears obvious. The most interesting correlation is between Cis Girl and MtF youth, where that the MtF youth had a stress level of 85% compared to cis girls at 86%. How can an MtF youth hold statistically the same significant stress as a non-transgender girl?

The correlation shows cis boys (79%) and MtF youth (85%) are more intricately linked than cis girls (86%) and FtM youth (90%). The idea that a school-aged boy dressing as a girl (85%) would suffer from lower stress than a girl dressing as a boy (90%) does not appear to make practical sense. Culturally, the social pressure is far easier for a female appearing more masculine than for a male to be more feminine. One study showed, *"children assigned males at birth, compared to children assigned as females at birth, were victimized more at school for gender nonconforming behavior"* (Cashman and Walters 2016, 12).

The term tomboy might not be flattering, but it does not have the degree of negative connotation as the term sissy. These findings point to the likely possibility that MtF youth function mentally more like boys and FtM youth function more like girls. Youth, who feel like they are in the wrong body, is not confirmed objectively using biological or psychological metrics. People may believe they are in the wrong body, but neither their bodies nor minds work to confirm these feelings. These results affirm the *DSM-5* assessment gender dysphoria is not men and women in the wrong bodies but rather the *desire* to be of the opposite sex.

In a study of transgender FtM youth, Johanna Olson-Kennedy, M.D., found considerable distress over the existence of breasts. The most common dysphoria was the claim, *"I worry that people are looking at my chest (57%), I avoid going to the beach / or swimming in public places because of my chest"* (41%), and *"I avoid using locker rooms because of my chest"* (53%) (Olson-Kennedy 2018, 433).

In a separate study reported in *Phenomenology & Practice*, Marianne Clark found that women experience high anxiety levels in locker rooms. As stated by an adult cis woman named Jennifer, *"I'm never very comfortable in the changing room, sharing that much of myself with strangers"* (M. Clark 2011, 62). In general, women experience stress over their chests, especially in vulnerable situations like wearing a bathing suit or undressing in a locker room. When females are experiencing puberty, and amongst other pubescent females in a social space like a school locker room, this anxiety is heightened. The surprising data in Dr. Olson-Kennedy's study is that *only* 53% of pubescent female youth claim they avoid locker rooms because of their chests. Thus, doctors offering pubescent girls who are uncomfortable with their developing breasts an opportunity to remove them is precarious. Body anxiety during puberty is perhaps one of the most natural and shared human experiences. Eliminating the effects of puberty to avoid anxiety and stress is a new level of anti-realism.

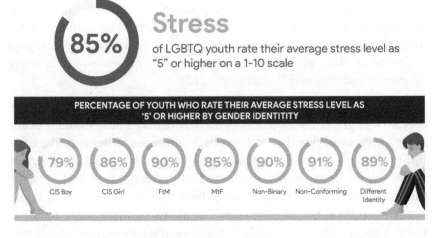

Figure 9.4 Data from the Human Rights Campaign 2018 Study

9.6 CONCEPT REVIEW

Chapter nine addressed three critical issues in the theory of transgender children, the perpetual attempt of psychiatric professionals to recreate society by forcing children into ideologies rather than using observable realism. First, rather than considering children to be natural, creative, playful, *and* a result of 800 million years of evolution, adults consider children rational and their brains highly plastic, neither of which is true.

The modern attempt at a genderless society, starting with genderless schools, ignores the natural differences between young boys and girls and how each experiences a separate way of learning and approaching the world. In the next breath, secular society rushes to the opposite extreme, children are born into the wrong bodies. Both extremes miss the natural approach. The medical evidence shows, and the church teaches two truths can exist simultaneously:

1. There are small/moderate but real biological differences between males and females; *and*

2. There is tremendous diversity within what it means to be a person of either sex.

Rather than society capitalizing on these two incarnations of the human person, theorists try to negate the existence of sex or, on the other extreme, force sex into a narrow stereotype which few people match. The result is mass confusion for both parents and youth.

Gender theorists combined youth with early-onset gender dysphoria and gender non-conforming youth to create a class of transgender children. Fortunately, not all gender non-conforming youth suffer from a neurodevelopmental disorder requiring a medicalized solution during their teenage years. Medical professionals following gender-neutral ideologies are quick to adapt to the reality of the child's mind. These medical professionals reject the concept that gender is rooted in one's sex and natural biology. The most prudent approach for addressing gender dysphoria is the Watchful Waiting technique, although activist groups convinced the medical community to embrace the Gender Affirmation approach.

Late-onset gender dysphoria, unlike any other form of gender dysphoria in adults or children, appears to be affected by a separate societal etiology. Teens with genuine persisting gender dysphoria must exist since adults with gender dysphoria were once adolescents. Yet, coming out as transgender without any previous indicators as a late teen is a new occurrence. This sudden spike of youth claiming gender dysphoria when no earlier indications were present is alarming for parents. Gender theorists demand that parents and institutions affirm a child's sexual identity without questioning the veracity of the claims. Society should reject this disturbing trend. When Pope Francis speaks about gender theory, he refers to this type of ideology, which fights the normativity of creation and is inconsistent with medical evidence.

CHAPTER 10
THE RESPONSE

Whereas God always forgives, and man sometimes forgives, nature never forgives—when one thwarts nature, nature rebukes, retaliates, strikes back.

— Anonymous, *Psychic Wholeness and Healing*

Psychotherapy unrelated to either religion or metaphysics tends to produce an *"anxiously fostered middle-class tranquility, poisoned by its triteness."*

—Erich Przywara, *Kierkegaard's Secret*

Teenagers watching transgender YouTubers may have a fantasy of what it is like to be transgender, while the lived experience is often less than desirable. One of the greatest hopes for people is to be loved and accepted. A scientific adviser to Match.com found that 80% of LGBTQ individuals of the 1,000 surveyed were looking for a relationship involving commitment (Bonos 2016), and 48% of younger LGBTQ singles said they wanted children (Ennis 2016). If transgender people receive hormone supplements and surgeries, their other desires to have their own children may become impossible. These are difficult decisions for any person to make, especially for teenagers who may not consider their decisions' long-term effects. Prudence is a consequence of experience and learning: two things teenagers lack due to their age.

A 2016 survey found that 44% of LGB individuals would not consider dating a transgender person (Ennis 2016). Another study found that only 12% of heterosexuals claimed they were open to dating a transgender person, while 65% claimed they would never consider it (adamandeve.com 2016). Those most likely to accept a transgender person are from the kink and BDSM communities (Tannehill 2019, 46).

Brynn Tannehill, a self-professed *'leading trans activist,'* wrote in her book *Everything You Ever Wanted to Know About Trans** about her own experience dating. She shared, *"From a transgender person's perspective, though, it can be disconcerting and dehumanizing to be treated more like a rare Pokémon that needs to be caught to complete someone's collection"* (Tannehill 2019, 57). Avery Edison similarly noted that while being a transgender person on Tinder, she felt like *"just an item to check off someone's sexual bucket list"* (Edison 2014). A forty-three-year-old autogynephilic individual in an interview expressed her frustration,

> *At this rate, I do not hold out much hope for finding my love. I've tried all the dating sites with not much success. I do actually feel at this point that it is highly likely I will live out my remaining days alone despite being 'amazing' as my friends describe me. What I feel is amazingly lonely.* (Tannehill 2019, 58)

The social dimensions of being transgender are challenging under the best circumstances. However, even if society were more accepting of gender variations, physical, sexual attraction originates at such a subconscious level. Therefore, one's animal instinct of attraction will not be significantly affected by political correctness.

Meredith Talusan wrote in an article, *Why Can't My Famous Gender Nonconforming Friends Get Laid?*

> Alok and Jacob's features haven't been softened by hormones, and they have visible body hair that marks them as more obviously trans, so they have a much harder time. Nonbinary femmes like them are too masc for the straights, too femme for the gays, and too out for nearly everyone else. (Talusan 2017)

People's sexual attractions genuinely confounded Meredith, Alok,[1] and Jacob. Straight men were not interested in unshaven, entirely obviously biological men. A natal male may have a woman's feminine identity (gender), but the other person encounters a male body in the phenomenon (sex) even if surgically altered. The ability of transgender individuals to flourish becomes hindered by the nature of physical attraction and the complexity of relationships.

If a person approaches the more critical life questions about their transgender identity, one may easily be led astray by pop culture and ideological fantasies. The church needs a Thomistic realist method for approaching this grave issue which does not include labeling all transgender people as delusional or part of a nominalist ideology. In the other extreme, if the church gives an unqualified blessing encouraging individuals to proceed in whatever way they *desire*, the church will pave the way for self-destruction. This chapter proposes a heuristic that will *stop*, *listen*, and *decide* how to pastorally support transgender brothers and sisters while using the best medical evidence available.

---

[1] More was written about Alok Vaid-Menon, *supra section 3.2.*

10.1 PROPOSED HEURISTIC

B r. Jacques Maritain, P.F.J., reflected on people during the 1960s in a time after the Second Vatican Council and amid political and cultural upheaval when he wrote in *The Peasant of the Garonne,*

> I know very well that too many people live in despair, that there are too many with pent-up anxieties, that far from being a life of delightful love and mutual gentleness, marriage too often means mutual solitude and daily apprehensions. That too many situations call not only for pity but for a new attitude on the part of those who have to judge of them. I think that the Church, who is, at last, submitting these problems as a whole to a thorough study, can never be too attentive in enlightening the human being about them, nor too merciful to him in his distress. (Maritain 1968, 55)

In his reflections about modern times, Br. Maritain laments the church's lack of rigor, challenge, and seriousness when dealing with complex moral issues. The rejection of fasting, penance, and the devil was not merely about these elements of the faith; they are indicative of a more significant rejection of the severe spiritual transformation which the Gospel challenges Christians to accept. The church should be abundantly merciful while respecting transgender people enough to speak frankly about their condition. The church must be willing to challenge people about their desires in a culture that preaches the *normativity of desire.*

Not everyone in the modern church will be happy with this Thomistic-based response to the transgender issue. In the *National Catholic Reporter,* Fr. Dan Horan, O.F.M., rejected the strict neo-Thomistic approach to transgender people. He wrote, *"It's one thing to admire a centuries-old idea for its own sake, it's another thing to deploy that idea as a means to dehumanize and dismiss whole populations of people"* (Horan 2020). In contrast to Fr. Horan's perception, Neo-Thomism is not a methodology that dismisses whole populations. Instead, it is a methodology taking the human condition seriously enough to give transgender people a thoughtful 500-page pastoral response.

Neo-Thomism does not take the cheap moral approach, claiming all humans are sinners and in need of salvation, so who is anyone to judge? People in authority must listen to good counsel and make proper judgments. These judgments ought to derive from the best science and philosophy available. The suffering, despair, and solitude people experience in the modern world are profound. Religious people should not trivialize the suffering experienced by people with gender dysphoria if they want to welcome them into the body of the church. Br. Maritain calls for the church to be serious about remaining faithful to the Gospel's enlightening power while reminding the church to remain equally merciful. When considering the shortcomings of the current medicalization of people with transgender identities, the church can take steps to alleviate this suffering.

This book proposes the use of a heuristic pastoral model. The word heuristic comes from Greek, which means *"serving to find out or discover."* Heuristic models have three sets of building blocks: *search, stopping,* and *decision* (Gigerenzer 1999, 129). Heuristics follow the virtue of Prudence, which has three steps: receiving good counsel (*consultandum*), judgment (*judicium*), and command (*electio*). Pope Francis, in his apostolic exhortation, The Joy of Love (*Amoris Laetitia*), proposes a similar heuristic: *meeting* with love and tenderness, *accompanying* in truth, patience, and mercy, and *proclaiming* the demands of the Kingdom of God. (Francis 2016, sec. 60). The three steps are to *meet, accompany,* and *proclaim.*

Searching sets out the scope of the discovery. In searching, the pastor finds those lost and meets them on his way back to the Father. The next step is stopping, which determines when enough information is gathered. One gathers information from the source of creation but also from accompanying those on the journey. Christ's incarnational life pushes believers out of their ideologies and off their *ivory couches* (Amos 6:4) to walk with people. As Pope Francis notably preached, *"I ask you: be shepherds, with the 'odour of the sheep'"* (Francis 2013b). Lastly, the decision or proclamation determines how to reach an outcome. The proclamation is a challenge to live in the truth of the Gospel. The proclamation comforts the afflicted and afflicts the comfortable. A heuristic structure creates a framing for approaching an issue.

An *availability heuristic* is an assumption based on a few examples which readily come to mind. A few firsthand experiences, online or in fictional movies, can easily confirm the belief that transgender people are mentally ill older men in dresses. The representational image remains when not representing the whole. If one uses a *base-rate-heuristic*, one considers the probability of creating assumptions. Base-rate-heuristics consider what is true of most transgender people. Knowing the truth about biology, psychology, sociology, and general theories about transgender people will help the church better use a base-rate-heuristic, based on realism rather than a representative or availability heuristic, which relies on emotions, stereotypes, and a non-cognitive epistemology.

Christians attempting to assist a gender dysphoric person must incorporate heuristics as well as a personal approach. Although heuristics are rational, when assisting a person struggling with a disorder, the person must be addressed individually and not as a statistic. Still, within a pastoral setting, the healing approach is not reinvented in every situation. As an example, every Alcoholics Anonymous counselor does not reinvent the process for overcoming alcoholism. For people suffering from addiction, a Twelve-Step Program (a heuristic) is helpful. Some of the steps require thoughtful consideration, like making amends, while others become part of *habitus* for daily living.

When considering the process for responding to children experiencing gender dysphoria, a particular heuristic is needed. This heuristic is intended for people in authority and not for strangers with opinions about other people's children. Christians are not in a position to judge the dysphoria experienced by people over whom they have no authority. If this young person is a niece, nephew, friend of the family, or in a similar relationship, the best approach is to listen, offer good counsel *if it is asked for*, pray for them, and outwardly show them your love. Parents, Godparents, teachers, judges, and public officials should use this heuristic when treating children who have gender dysphoria. The heuristic is as follows:

1. **Early-Onset Gender Dysphoria (birth—puberty)**

   a. **Good Counsel**—The evidence-based approach suggests that 63 to 84% of these children will desist by adulthood, so a wait-and-see approach is most appropriate.

b. **Judgment**—Only under scarce medical circumstances should hormone blockers or cross-sex hormones be given to anyone whose brain has not finished developing to Tanner Stage 5.

c. **Command**—The advice of Archbishop Robert Carlson is to *"Listen! Keep the channels of communication open. We can sympathize with their feelings without capitulating to their desires. It's important not to leave them feeling alone."* (Carlson 2020, 11)

2. **Late-Onset Gender Dysphoria (puberty—early adulthood)**

   a. **Good Counsel**—Possibly a latent diagnosis of early-onset gender dysphoria, although Dr. Littman's study suggests ROGD is a likely possible cause for dysphoria.

   b. **Judgment**—Parents should inform themselves about this condition, obtain an understanding of the experience of transgender people, demonstrate shrewd judgment, and trust their instincts. Consider if this is a latent diagnosis of early-onset gender dysphoria or ROGD. Also, follow advice for 1.b above.

   c. **Command**—The advice of Archbishop Robert Carlson is the same for late-onset gender dysphoria, *"Listen! Keep the channels of communication open. We can sympathize with their feelings without capitulating to their desires. It's important not to leave them feeling alone."* (Carlson 2020, 11)

Below is a proposed heuristic approach for adult transgender people using principles found in *Male and Female He Created Them*.

A. **Good Counsel**—Medical professionals should make the proper medical determinations

   When a person's sex is not clearly defined, medical professionals can make a therapeutic intervention. In such situations, parents cannot make an arbitrary choice on the issue, let alone society. (*Male and Female He Created Them, sec. 26*)

B. **Judgment**—The treatment should aim to restore the natural order

> Man and woman are *created,* which is to say, *willed* by God: on the one hand, in perfect equality as human persons; on the other, in their respective beings as man and woman. Man and woman are both with one and the same dignity *'in the image of God.'* (*CCC,* 369)

C. **Judgment**—The treatment should be the least invasive possible

> Instead, *medical science* should act with purely therapeutic ends and intervene in the least invasive fashion, on the basis of objective parameters and with a view to establishing the person's constitutive identity. (*Male and Female He Created Them, sec. 26*)

D. **Command**— There must be patience and acceptance of oneself, especially when born *'imperfectly.'* Penultimate happiness is a consequence of moral luck and moral virtues. Of the two, the only one man controls his virtues.

> Nature does not make mistakes and does nothing idly (Aristotle *Generation of Animals,* 5,8,788b20)

E. **Command**—Due to the world's fallen nature, the redemption of the body will not occur until the resurrection. Therefore, man depends on God's grace and salvation for his ultimate happiness.

> *Redemption* means, in fact, a *"new creation,"* as it were, it means *taking up all that is created* to express in creation the fullness of justice, equity, and holiness planned for it by God and to express that fullness above all in man, created male and female *"in the image of God."* (John Paul II 2006, sec. 99.7)

Steps two and three are judgments based on the wisdom of step one. To repeat a concept raised in chapter one, making judgments about one another is not the place of equals within society. In his explanation of commutative justice, St. Thomas points out that people only make judgments when they have the proper authority to execute the judgments (*ST* IIa–IIae q.60, a. 2). For a neighbor to execute judgment on his equal is a usurpation and a perverse and unjust judgment (*ST* IIa–IIae q.60, a. 6). As Jesus taught, *"Judge not lest ye be judged"* (Mt 7: 1). In juxtaposition, parents, teachers, pastors, judges, and leaders of the commonweal must make proper judgments based on their responsibility as a people with proper authority. People also have authority over themselves, so transgender people could voluntarily apply this heuristic to themselves.

Suppose a doctor or medical professional does not set goals to use the least invasive means and restore the natural order? Consequently, they may not be the appropriate medical professional from a philosophical perspective. A doctor should make judgments based on professionally researched medical science. Ideally, a practitioner would be a person of faith who embraces the values behind the entire heuristic.

The remainder of this book will focus on these five goals. The first three objectives are determined medically, with substantial deference to the medical community to treat a medical condition. This section does not deal with gender theory or an ideological battle between the church and sexual liberators. Gender theorists already occupy most of the public dialogue, allowing little common ground for fruitful discussion. Nominalist gender theorists are addressed thoroughly in chapters two and three.

The first three philosophical steps to addressing the transgender issue require consideration: Who is man? Pope Leo XIII accepts modern sciences' insights with confidence that *truth cannot contradict truth* (Leo XIII 1893, 23). In the encyclical Of the Eternal Father (*Aeterni Patris*), Leo XIII claims the proper lens to understand the modern world is not René Descartes, Immanuel Kant, and David Hume but St. Thomas Aquinas. Leo XIII ordained Thomistic realism, teleology, theology, and philosophy as the lens through which Catholics interpret secular culture. The church trusts the medical community, but she also challenges the scientific world to become comfortable with Thomistic language and concepts. This book dedicates chapters ten and eleven to creating an educated approach to the transgender issue using Thomistic Christian anthropology.

10.2 Step 1: Medical Professionals

Good Counsel—Medical professionals should make the proper medical determinations

> When a person's sex is not clearly defined, medical professionals can make a therapeutic intervention. In such situations, parents cannot make an arbitrary choice on the issue, let alone society. *(Male and Female He Created Them, sec. 26)*

Archbishop Robert Carlson in June of 2020 made the request, "I ask Catholic hospitals, physicians, and counselors to use their expertise, fidelity, and creativity to discover and follow paths that can help, paths that are in accord with a genuine Catholic understanding of the person" (Carlson 2020, 11). The transgender problem is not primarily a theological issue but rather a medical issue needing moral and theological guidance. Raising the issue of a moral problem can be received unintentionally in the wrong manner. W.E.B. Du Bois asked, *"How does it feel to be a problem?"* (Du Bois 1969) The reader must not turn those who suffer from a problem into the problem itself. Within Thomistic philosophy and theology, temptations arise to see transgender people *as* a moral problem instead of people *dealing* with a medical problem. Importantly, gender dysphoric and gender non-conforming people are the patients, not the disease or disorder.

Transgender people are often their own fiercest critics, so that a tender approach may be the most appropriate. Sandra Bartky, Ph.D., writes, *"The psychologically oppressed become their own oppressors; they come to exercise harsh dominion over their own self-esteem"* (Bartky 1990, 22). The sense that one is responsible for one's own brokenness is only compounded when one is described not only as psychologically damaged but also as morally damaged. Although the church never seeks to create moral damage by stigmatizing a person with any medical condition, the church also believes preaching a false hope for the sake of being agreeable violates the call to follow Jesus. He is *"the way, the truth, and the life"* (Jn 14:6). Those seeking truth must listen to the medical community and respond correctly using sound philosophical and theological reasoning.

Is the etiology for gender dysphoria understood?

Upon considering the claims that the morphology in the brain causes transgender identities, the preponderance of evidence only leads to further uncertainty. Aruna Saraswat, M.D., of Tufts Medical Center, concludes in her research for the cause of transgender identities that the exact mechanism causing people to be transgender is unknown at this time. Nevertheless, Dr. Saraswat states, *"there is strong support in the literature for a biological basis of gender identity"* (Saraswat, Weinand and Safer 2015, 199). Thus, medical evidence suggests something is different within some transgender people's brains; beyond this, one can only speculate.

Can men be born with female brains? Or a woman born with a male brain? Or are gender dysphoria and transgender identities a matter of desire rather than ontology? Following a literature review, Paul McHugh, M.D., and Lawrence Mayer, M.D., concluded that these answers are unknown. They stated, *"Human sexuality and gender are incredibly complicated, a lot of what's presented as 'fact' has no sturdy basis in scientific research, and we really ought to study the entire subject more rigorously"* (Last 2017).

Human development is not a simple flawless practice creating consistent results in one generation from the next. Human genes determine a great deal about the accidental properties of a person, perhaps affecting gender identity. A prudential use of circumspection narrows the scope for what is biologically possible. The range of outcomes based on human genes is limited. A pregnant mother who uses illicit drugs may kill the child within her or cause the child to be born with many developmental problems, but the chemicals in her system can never form a child with three heads, ten arms, wings, and leaves. Room for genetic variation is possible, but not unlimited variation.

The genes instruct the child's formation, the volume of hormones interacting with the body and brain. These hormones develop different pathways that will determine a child's features, like genetic dominos. The nourishment and hormones introduced to the child through the umbilical cord will also determine how the body develops. For example, suppose a mother is under high stress during specific periods of development. In that case, cortisol from stress may more significantly affect a child during some periods of pregnancy over others. Might certain gene combinations and environmental factors in the womb create an intersex brain? Is this hypothesis within the realm of possibility, or is this only science-fiction? The medical evidence covered in chapters seven and eight suggests a partially intersex brain is within the realm of possibilities.

[Fr. Benedict Ashley, O.P., 1915— 2013]

The combination of the genotype, hormones, the mother's chemistry, and the environment in the womb will affect how children develop before they are born. Fr. Benedict Ashley, O.P. explains:

> As the body grows from a single cell by some forty-five series of cell divisions, there is a differentiation into diverse types of cells to form bone, muscle, nerves, skin, and blood, each in its proper quantity, shape, and position. Each newly differentiated group of cells influences variations of still newer types. While this goes on, the basic vital functions of the whole organism must be maintained. The business of living cannot wait till the final structure is complete. (Ashley 1985, 28)

These developments of the human form are extremely complicated since every part of the body is interconnected at a molecular level. As a result, variations and mutations frequently occur during human development. In about every 50,000 to one million duplications, *"a gene is affected by an influx of high-energy radiation or other accident occurring during duplication or assemblage in the chromosome"* (Stebbins 1966, 30).

Despite multiple possible causes for brain abnormalities, a gender dysphoric person is never diagnosed based on genetic, hormonal, or brain testing but on the patient's feelings and desires. Rachel Anne Williams admitted in her own musings, *"I don't know what I am. And it does not matter. But what I do know are my desires"* (R. A. Williams 2019, 193). Rachel went on to list ten *desires* related to being perceived as a woman. The *DSM-5* identifies gender dysphoria as a type of psychological desire.

If a person has a physical disorder, the doctor performs tests on the body. If a person has a psychological imbalance, the doctor considers a person's feelings, thoughts, motivations, and fears. After the evaluation, the doctor may prescribe medications and provide therapy. The doctor tries to realign the psyche. Gender dysphoria is the only condition where the medical profession follows the patient's feelings and desires then acts as if the problem were in the body rather than in the psyche. With gender dysphoria, the doctor does not treat the dysphoria; instead, the doctor creates a hormonal imbalance and removes healthy tissue. Sex reassignment surgery is patently unlike the rest of modern medicine and psychology. They violate their principles in this one situation, with inconclusive evidence to validate this approach.

412

Do the current treatments for
gender dysphoria relieve the dysphoria?

A medical diagnosis of gender dysphoria and transgender identification at the clinical level is based entirely upon a patient describing their feelings about the dysphoria. Anna Hutchinson, D.Clin.Psych., of the United Kingdom's NHS Gender and Identity Development Services (GIDS) determined that something was going wrong after five years. She claimed patients were incredibly sure and clear of what they wanted, but she determined *"what they need is not what they want"* (BBC Newsnight 2019). Dr. Hutchinson claims that what many detransitioners needed was prolonged therapy and not sex reassignment surgery. No shortcut exists for curing unhappiness. Gender dysphoria seldom exists without comorbidity, which needs addressing first, or at least synchronous with the gender identity treatments.

There are no medications or surgeries which can undo gender dysphoria or the feelings of transgender identification. However, Mohammad Hassan Murad, M.D., of the Mayo Clinic, reported: *"Very low-quality evidence suggests that sex reassignment that includes hormonal interventions in individuals with GID likely improves gender dysphoria, psychological functioning and comorbidities, sexual function and overall quality of life."* (Murad et al. 2010).

The Hayes Directory[2] awarded its lowest score, indicating statistically insignificant improvements for transgender people using hormone and surgical treatments. The scientific research is *"too sparse, and the studies [that exist are] too limited to suggest conclusions"* (Hayes 2014, 4). To advocate for the use of cross-hormone supplements, one would first need to show evidence that they medically provide a solution. In contrast, the Hayes Directory concluded the studies *"were inconsistent with respect to a relationship between hormone therapy and general psychological health, substance abuse, suicide attempts, and sexual function and satisfaction,"* concluding, *"Differences between treated and untreated study participants were very small or of unknown magnitude"* (Hayes 2014, 3).

---

[2] The Hayes Rating is an industry benchmark for evaluating the strength of evidence for the use of various medical practices and technologies.

In a Swedish report from 2019, Richard Bränström, Ph.D., and John Pachankis, Ph.D., claimed *"Years since initiating hormone treatment was not significantly related to the likelihood of mental health treatment"* (Bränström and Pachankis 2020, 727). However, this study found no statistical improvements for gender incongruent patients receiving hormone treatments for mental health outcomes.

The Swedish report claims, compared with the general population, *"individuals with a gender incongruence diagnosis were about six times as likely to have had a mood and anxiety disorder health care visit, more than three times as likely to have received prescriptions for antidepressants and anxiolytics, and more than six times as likely to have been hospitalized after a suicide attempt"* (Bränström and Pachankis 2020, 727).

The Bränström and Pachankis study controversially claimed that mental health outcomes increased for transgender patients after sex reassignment surgeries. The study presented this information in figure 10.1. This chart shows promising results of the medicalized approach to addressing gender dysphoria. The mood and anxiety disorders decrease, and the suicide rate disappears. Helping people implement psychological realities into physical false facsimiles is, as Michelle Cretella, M.D., claims, *"not merely emotionally distressing but also life-threatening"* (Cretella 2016, 51). A dead person cannot respond to surveys. When the doctor who is such a significant person in the life of transgender people attempt a follow-up, would their silence be unlikely unless the patient experienced dissatisfaction or fatality? Unfortunately, this information may be too promising to be true since the study does not consider the loss to follow-up with patients who died. In addition, counting failed suicide attempts which result in hospitalization without counting completed suicide attempts which result in death, misses an essential piece of data.

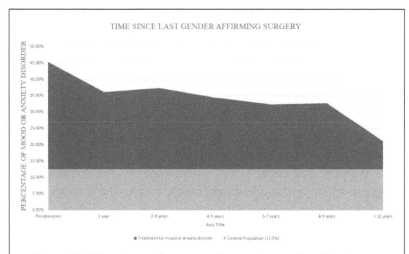

Figure 10.1 Prevalence of treatment for mood or anxiety disorders (health care visit or antidepressant or anxiolytic prescription) and hospitalization after suicide attempt in 2015 among individuals with a gender incongruence diagnosis, by number of years since last gender-affirming surgery.

This study considers Swedish patients who received medical care between 2005 and 2015 but only included patients alive on December 31, 2014, which would exclude anyone from the study who had died for any reason. Swedish studies are notable since they typically have a low loss to follow-up since researchers use the statistical data from the National Patient Register and the Prescribed Drug Register. Even with access to the national database, the correct application of the data is essential. Dr. Cecelia Dhejne found a 2.7% mortality rate from completed suicide attempts (Dhejne, Lichtenstein, et al. 2011, 5). After a suicide attempt, the zero long-term *hospitalization rate* is not as successful if the suicide *mortality* rate is 19 times higher than the national average. This study does not examine short-term hospitalization stays or attempted suicide, which did not lead to hospitalization. The timing for creating the baseline for depression, anxiety, and suicide hospitalization is notably the time right before a patient receives surgery. Before surgery is a period of elevated stress and not a steady baseline.

Colleagues in the field of psychiatry reviewed the methodology of the Bränström and Pachankis study resulting in a reversal of the study's conclusion about the positive outcomes from sex reassignment surgeries (Van Mol et al. 2020). The Editor-in-Chief of the *American Journal of Psychiatry* responded to the article after receiving peer reviews, *"the results demonstrated no advantage of surgery in relation to subsequent mood or anxiety disorder-related health care visits or prescriptions or hospitalizations following suicide attempts in that comparison"* (Kalin 2020, 734). Thus, the ultimate conclusion is that not enough evidence has been found to suggest an increased health outcome due to cross-sex hormones or sex reassignment surgeries. Despite this reversal, the gender activists frequently reference the Bränström study as proof that sex reassignment surgery improves mental health outcomes for transgender people.

Notwithstanding the shortcomings of sex reassignment surgeries, nearly every significant medical and psychiatric professional association officially supports access to sex reassignment surgeries (Lambda Legal 2018). *The American Medical Association Resolution* states, *"Health experts in Gender Identity Dysphoria, including WPATH, have rejected the myth that such treatments are 'cosmetic' or 'experimental' and have recognized that these treatments can provide safe and effective treatment for a serious health condition"* (American Medical Association House of Delegates 2016). Paradoxically, the medical community supports reassignment surgeries in most situations, while the medical research only points to poor outcomes or inconclusive data. No one has developed a perfect treatment for this disorder, yet the American Medical Association coronates the surgical and hormonal treatments.

Fortunately, children allowed to go through puberty without puberty blockers and cross-sex hormones cease identifying with the opposite sex 70 to 98% of the time for males and 50 to 88% for females (*DSM-5,* 455). What has changed in the high percentage of children whose gender dysphoria goes away? Has the child changed socially, psychologically, or anatomically? The answer to all these changes is yes. There may be a single cause for childhood gender dysphoria, or it might be a combination of many causes working together to create the dysphoria.

Unfortunately, the medical community does not have a clear solution for the remaining minority who persist with gender dysphoria.

Instead, doctors have resorted to providing hormone blockers, hormones, and cosmetic surgeries to mask dysphoria. Paul McHugh, M.D., claims sex reassignment surgeries do *"not address the root issues causing clinical distress and makes it harder for the mind to accept reality"* (McHugh 2014a, 19). One does not need to ask the ethical question of whether one *ought to* participate in sex reassignment surgeries as a treatment for gender dysphoria if they cannot first be found to be medically effective.

What is the problem with high loss to follow-up?

In 2014, a Swedish study found that 2.2% of individuals who received the sex reassignment surgeries submitted applications for reversal between 1960 and 2010, which consisted of fifteen of 681 patients (Dhejne, Öberg et al. 2014, 1540). In a review of seventy follow-up studies conducted between 1965 and 1995, Abraham. Kuiper, Ph.D., and Peggy Cohen-Kettenis, Ph.D., from the University of Medicine in Amsterdam, claimed that over 75% reported feeling happier, liberated, and more at ease in their bodies. Only 2% of MtF patients expressed regrets or attempted suicide preoperatively and 0.5% postoperatively (Kuiper and Cohen-Kettenis 1995). In another study, 6% of postoperative patients reported regretting their surgery (van de Grift et al. 2018, 138).

Despite these reported satisfaction rates, there are over 19,000 members of detransitioning support groups (Stahl 2021). Therefore, satisfaction is not easy to determine. According to Dr. Cohen-Kettenis, *"In our opinion, an evaluation of SRS [sex reassignment surgery] can be made only based on subjective data because SRS is intended to solve a problem that cannot be determined objectively"* (Kuiper and Cohen-Kettenis 1988, 441).

Medical professionals have difficulty determining if a patient's follow-up is accurate when asked about regret. According to cognitive dissonance theory, an individual will experience psychologically inconsistent (dissonant) thoughts (cognitions) when reflecting upon previous decisions (Sigall 2017). Within a healthy mind, cognitive dissonance causes a person to battle over two extreme fears, first, *"I am a person who makes good decisions"* and second, *"I am not smart, and I make bad and hasty decisions."* To compensate for this fear, people try to convince themselves and others that they made the right decision. For example, when people buy a car and try to convince everyone, they should also buy a new car. Thus, when a doctor asks patients if they experience regret, the answer may be an overcompensation for cognitive dissonance. For example, in John/Joan's case (*supra-5.5*), the family reported positive results for twelve years until David attempted suicide, and the family allowed him to become a boy once again.

A 2014 study in the United Kingdom found that 83% of people who received plastic surgery claimed they would not repeat their decision if they had the opportunity. Ally Taft, M.D., a partner of the Medical Accident Group, reflected in her experience working with patients,

> We understand that some people feel that cosmetic surgery could change their life and give them the confidence they're perhaps lacking, but we hope the results of this study show that just because you're not happy with your body now doesn't mean you'll necessarily be happy with it once you pay a lot of money to get it changed. (Medical Accident Group 2014)

Studies determine regret for sex reassignment surgeries being less than one percent is inconsistent with data on other similar procedures, which questions the validity of studies when there is also a high loss to follow-up.

A German study of European statistics in 2018 found positive results. 73.9% of transsexual people surveyed post-operatively claimed greater satisfaction in life (Hess et al. 2018, 2). The study reached out to 610 MtF individuals who had received sex reassignment surgeries between 1995 and 2015 from the University Hospital of Essen. Of the 610 people who had received the surgeries, only 156 responded, and subsequently, only 75% of those individuals reported satisfaction, which is 117 people. Six hundred ten people received sex reassignments surgeries, and only 117 people responded positively about these results—21%. That is a high loss of follow-up, which skews the results to favor people's opinions who are more enthusiastic about their results. Instead of a 75% satisfaction rate claimed by NBC (Guillen 2018), one might readily argue a 79% dissatisfaction rate like MtFtM detransitioner Walt Heyer, who included this conclusion in his 2018 book *Trans Life Survivors* (Heyer 2018, 142). The truth is between these two extremes. Walt Heyer claims the low participation in the university study, which performed the surgery, indicates more dissatisfaction than satisfaction.

The Response

Some of the people surveyed had only received the surgeries three years prior, which is not an accurate gauge of long-term satisfaction since a honeymoon period occurs immediately following sex reassignment surgeries (Cuypere et al. 2006, 126). Detransitioning and high dissatisfaction rates also suggest patients' *"pre-treatment beliefs about an ideal post-treatment life may sometimes go unrealized"* (McHugh and Mayer 2016, 108).

In the *60 Minutes* interview with Lesley Stahl, Daisy Chadra, a detransitioning young adult, stated, *"After every step that you take, every milestone, feels like a million bucks. When I got top surgery, I was elated. When I changed my name, I was elated. But when everything that I had set out to do was done, I still felt incomplete"* (Stahl 2021). Daisy's feelings of dissatisfaction are not unique among transgender youth. The search for wholeness in externals and the resulting buyer's remorse is part of the human condition.

The *Aggressive Research Intelligence Facility* from the University of Birmingham reported on the United Kingdom's *National Health Services'* findings of sex reassignment surgeries' long-term results. Reviewing over 100 follow-up studies of postoperative transsexuals, the researchers concluded

> That none of the studies provide conclusive evidence that gender reassignment is beneficial for patients. It found that most research was poorly designed, which skewed the results in favour of physically changing sex. There was no evaluation of whether other treatments, such as long-term counseling, might help transsexuals or whether their gender confusion might lessen over time. (Batty 2004)

The researchers acknowledged that the studies which lasted several years should report inconclusive results *"because the researchers lost track of at least half of the participants."* If subjects did not participate or finish participating in the study, the researcher did not include them. This decision skews the results of the study.

Chris Hyde, Ph.D., director of the Aggressive Research Intelligence Facility, responded to the loss to follow-up problems. He wrote. *"While no doubt great care is taken to ensure that appropriate patients undergo gender reassignment, there's still a large number of people who have the surgery but remain traumatized- often to the point of committing suicide"* (Batty 2004). Between loss to follow-up and cognitive dissonance, rating long-term satisfaction and health outcome rates are, at best, a subjective survey of willing participants and, at worse, wildly inaccurate.

What are the health outcomes for people who received SRS?

A 2015 American study found that 92% of transgender individuals reported attempting suicide before twenty-five (James et al., 2016). A separate survey of high school-age students showed suicide attempts at 6.4% of heterosexuals and 29.4% of gay, lesbian, and bisexuals (Center for Disease Control 2016, Table 27). Proponents of transgender surgeries claim this is due to the social stresses of being transgender in an anti-transgender accepting society. These social stresses may contribute to some cases, but exceedingly liberal and sexually inclusive cultures like Sweden found similar results. With 92% suicide attempt rates, defining any treatment as successful is challenging.

Homosexuals, as an example, are also sexually atypical, yet their suicide rates were a tiny fraction compared with people with transgender identities. Suicide rates of transgender people are similar to people with dissociative identity disorders—around 70% (American Psychiatric Association 2018). The treatment for dissociative identity disorder, according to the American Psychiatric Association, involves psychotherapy. *"Therapy can help people gain control over the dissociative process and symptoms. The goal of therapy is to help integrate the different elements of identity… medication may help treat related conditions or symptoms, such as the use of antidepressants to treat symptoms of depression"* (American Psychiatric Association 2018).

In 2016, the Obama administration considered whether Medicare and Medicaid Services would cover sex reassignment surgeries. As a progressive president in the last term of his eight-year presidency, he had lots of discretion to mandate the sex reassignment coverage; however, his administration denied the initiative based on a thorough investigation into the studies available at the time. The memo recommended

Based on a thorough review of the clinical evidence available at this time, there is not enough evidence to determine whether gender reassignment surgery improves health outcomes for Medicare beneficiaries with gender dysphoria. There were conflicting (inconsistent) study results—of the best-designed studies, some reported benefits, while others reported harms. The evidence's quality and strength were low due to the mostly observational study designs with no comparison groups, potential confounding, and small sample sizes. Many studies that reported positive outcomes were exploratory type studies (case-series and case-control) with no confirmatory follow-up. (Jensen, Chin, et al. 2016a)

The Obama administration's final decision in August of 2016 was a refusal of Medicare and Medicaid to cover sex reassignment surgery based on the poor outcomes reported by medical studies. The 2011 Swedish study heavily influenced this decision by showing a 19.1 times higher suicide rate than the general public and no clear evidence to show the treatments are not part of the cause of the suicides.

The study identified increased mortality and psychiatric hospitalization compared to the matched controls. The mortality was primarily due to completed suicides (19.1-fold greater than in control Swedes), but death due to neoplasm and cardiovascular disease was increased 2 to 2.5 times as well. We note that mortality from this patient population did not become apparent until after 10 years. The risk for psychiatric hospitalization was 2.8 times greater than in controls even after adjustment for prior psychiatric disease (18%). The risk for attempted suicide was greater in male-to-female patients regardless of the gender of the control. Further, we cannot exclude therapeutic interventions as a cause of the observed excess morbidity and mortality. (Jensen, Chin, et al. 2016a, 245–2460)

In a 2011 follow-up study in Sweden, researchers found elevated morbidity rates for postoperative transsexuals than the control group of people of the same age. This study does not compare morbidity rates of transgender people who receive sex reassignment surgeries to transgender people who did not receive sex reassignment surgeries. Therefore, one cannot claim sex reassignment surgeries caused increased morbidity. This study is particularly noteworthy due to the high number of deaths by suicide and psychiatric hospitalization for non-gender identity disorder-related issues compared to the general population (Dhejne, Lichtenstein, et al., 2011, 5). These results suggest, if improvements within the life of medically transitioned transgender individuals exist, the results were still poor and cannot be considered an effective treatment. Without these treatments, the outcomes cannot be significantly any worse than these already terrible outcomes.

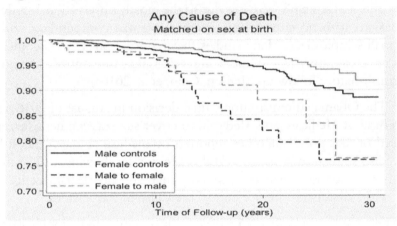

Figure 10.2 Long-term follow-up of transsexual persons undergoing sex reassignment surgery: cohort study in Sweden (Dhejne, Lichtenstein, et al. 2011, 5)

This study shows significantly worse outcomes than any other study. One reason for these adverse outcomes is that this study has no subjective element, eliminating cognitive dissonance. This study has no loss to follow-up because it does not follow up with willing participants; instead, the researchers use the national databases to look at the objective evidence of suicide rates, hospitalizations, and rates of neoplasms, and other health outcomes. This subject pool comprises more than the low rate of those who responded or people one year after transitioning. This study includes everyone over 30 years old. This study shows that the more people included in the study, the longer the study lasts, the worse the outcomes for transgender individuals with hormone replacement and sex reassignment surgeries.

This report is heavily quoted because suicide in postoperative patients is 19 times higher than in general. In figure 10.2, the dashed lines are postoperative transsexual individuals. The solid lines are a control group of people matched by age and sex. Although both groups start simultaneously on the chart, the transsexual grouping immediately shows a rapid loss of lifespan. In 30 years, 25% of the people who received the sex reassignment surgery had died, while over 90% of people of the same sex and age who had not received sex reassignment surgeries were alive.

In figure 10.3, the categorization for the types of death is revealing. In addition to the suicide and hospitalization rates, the number of deaths from tumors (neoplasm) is also four times higher than the control group. Transsexuals who participate in hormone-blocking and hormone replacement have a greater chance of developing tumor growth due to taking Estrogen (Knight and McDonald 2013, 18). Estrogen treatments also lead to potentially deadly blood clots that start in the leg and move to the lungs (pulmonary embolism). Both estrogen and testosterone can severely impact cholesterol and triglyceride levels. Seemingly unrelated health outcomes are worse for transgender individuals. For example, the rate of diabetes in transgender individuals is 25.9%, while LGB individuals have diabetes at a 13.7% rate. Also, 40% of transgender people are diagnosed as obese, while 24.6% of cisgender people are obese (Erickson-Schroth and Jacobs 2017, 52).

	Outcome incident rate per 1000 person-years 1973-2003	Controls
Any death	7.3	2.5
Death by suicide	2.7	.1
Death by cardiovascular disease	2.4	1.1
Death by neoplasm (cancer)	2.2	1.0
Any psychiatric hospitalization*	19.0	4.2
Substance misuse	5.9	1.8
Suicide attempt	7.9	1.0
*Hospitalization for gender identity disorder not included		

Figure 10.3 Morbidity Rates (Dhejne, Lichtenstein, et al. 2011, 5)

The results of these studies reveal an important insight. If the medical treatments correctly treated gender dysphoria, a significant reduction in the life span results from the sex reassignment surgeries and hormones. Furthermore, hormone treatments are not safe. A person may identify as a man, but if a person is hormonally a woman and uses hormone blockers and androgen supplements, this will cause havoc on her body, which was not designed to handle testosterone at the levels natural for men. According to Dr. Cretella, *"these medications arrest bone growth, decrease bone accretion, prevent the sex-steroid dependent organization and maturation of the adolescent brain, and inhibit fertility"* (Cretella 2016, 53). The other side-effects of testosterone therapy *"include the development of polycythemia, dyslipidemia, increased cardiovascular risk, and endometrial hyperplasia"* (Seal 2017, 212). In addition to the physical dangers of hormone treatment, another finding in the 2011 Dhejne report was that patients' mental instability did not subside with the sex reassignment surgeries. Hospitalization for mental health issues was 4.5 times greater than the general population ten to 15 years after the surgery. Also, suicide attempts were 7.9 times higher, substance abuse is 3.3 times higher, and crime involvement was twice as high as people who did not receive sex reassignment surgeries. Forty-one percent of transgender people report attempting suicide compared to 1.6% of the general population, with rates rising to 55% for those who lost a job due to bias (Grant et al., 2011).

The social pressures on transgender people are also much higher than the general population, with 51% claiming they were harassed/bullied in school, and 64% are victims of sexual assault (Tanis 2016). Transgender people of color report a 56% suicide attempt rate (Haas, Rodgers, and Herman 2014). Also, 57% of family members of transgender people refuse to speak to them, and 69% experience homelessness (Haas, Rodgers, and Herman 2014). A Toronto study showed that 57% of transgender youth ages sixteen to twenty-four would attempt suicide if they were in a *"somewhat to not at all supportive"* home. The transgender youth from a *"very supportive"* family only attempted suicide at a 4% rate (Travers, Bauer, and Pyne 2012).

These high rates of despair, violence, and helplessness, which lead to suicide attempts, are shocking, and a proper response is necessary. However deficient the medicalized therapeutic option may be, the church must support transgender people. A supportive family is one of the most critical factors in the well-being of a transgender person; therefore, the church must show support for transgender people's families and encourage them to keep the lines of communication open. Compassion is necessary, and transgender people must be made aware they are loved, and this disorder is not their fault.

What do gender realist experts say?

The most extreme gender activists will encourage transitioning regardless of the adverse health outcomes or the patient's age. So what do moderates or conservative activists recommend? When considering the advice of experts like Kenneth Zucker, Ray Blanchard, J. Michael Bailey, Anne Lawrence, Debra Zoh, and Abigail Shrier (among others), their opinions are relatively consistent. They claim some people with early-onset gender dysphoria benefit tremendously from a medical approach to help socially transition to their gender identity. These professionals are fully aware of the risks of transitioning, but their experience with gender dysphoria has convinced them that this is the best approach for some people.

Professor of Moral Theology at Saint Vincent de Paul Regional Seminary in Denver, Colorado, E. Christian Brugger, D.Phil., similarly claims transgender sex reassignment surgeries should be allowed in a minimal capacity. He argues that medical professionals must be reasonably convinced that a specific patient *"could never find psychological peace aside from the surgery, that is, it would have to be a last resort"* (Brugger 2016, 15). All of the above experts agree that society should accommodate adults who suffer from life-long gender dysphoria. The same experts also agree that some youth may have lifelong persisting gender dysphoria, while most teenage youths are experiencing a social contagion. This advice of medical professionals who hold principles of gender realism should carry a great deal of influence on this heuristic.

Does the medical community have any other options?

Harry Benjamin, M.D., in *The Transsexual Phenomenon,* deduced from his 20 years of experience, *"Psychotherapy with the aim of curing transsexualism so that the patient will accept himself as a man, it must be repeated here, is a useless undertaking with presently available methods. The mind of the transsexual cannot be changed in its gender orientation"* (Benjamin 1966, 54). Dr. Benjamin's conclusion has been the dominant theory for the previous half-century, though the medical profession has advanced substantially in the same amount of time. Dr. Benjamin concluded,

> *Since it is evident, therefore, that the mind of the transsexual cannot be adjusted to the body, it is logical and justifiable to attempt the opposite, to adjust the body to the mind. If such a thought is rejected, we would be faced with a therapeutic nihilism to which I could never subscribe because of the experiences I have had with patients who have undoubtedly been salvaged or at least distinctly helped by their conversions. (Benjamin 1966, 54)*

Dr. Benjamin's conclusions are not particularly optimistic and can undoubtedly be improved with a more holistic approach.

In addressing the first step of this heuristic, substantial deference is given to the medical community and its ability to offer effective treatments. Medical doctors Anna Terruwe, M.D., and Conrad Baars, M.D., in their book *Psychic Wholeness and Healing*, state that regarding people of faith trying to conduct psychological treatments,

> [N]o one should proceed on his own neither in the matter of diagnosing one's own illness nor in applying our therapeutic directives. Of even greater danger, especially in Charismatic Renewal and Pentecostal circles, is the popular practice of *"inner healing"* by minimally qualified persons. They may possess the necessary faith and goodwill towards their neurotic brothers and sisters in Christ, but too many are either similarly affected without realizing it or lack the professional knowledge necessary to effectively help severely afflicted neurotic patients short of rarely occurring instantaneous cure. (Terruwe and Baars 1981, 111)

Highly regarded Dutch Catholic scientists, doctors Terruwe and Baars warned pastors and well-intentioned Christians that medical laypeople should not be the ones to diagnose or offer medical therapeutic treatments without the supervision of a medical professional. Psychiatric professionals do not always correctly treat the multi-layers of psychosexual development. 16,000 youth have been placed into religious-based conversion therapies before eighteen, and 698,000 people participated in conversion therapy for being LGBT (Mallory, Brown and Conron 2019). The Williams Institute found that LGBT individuals who underwent religious counseling were more likely than those who received no therapy to commit suicide (Meyer, Teylan, and Schwartz 2014).

When conversion therapy bans are put into effect, as found in a minority of states, clergy who the state has not licensed as mental health professionals and are exempt from these bans. Doctors Terruwe and Baars could not stress strongly enough that religious people must use self-restraint and not overstep their expertise and engage in practices that hurt the person already struggling. The document *Male and Female He Created Them* echoes this advice in claiming medical professionals *can make a therapeutic intervention.* Holy Scripture also affirms this stance in the Book of Sirach.

> *God makes the doctors and enlightens the doctor's mind:*
>
> *Make friends with the doctor, for he is essential to you; God has also established him in his profession. From God, the doctor has wisdom, and from the king, he receives sustenance. Knowledge makes the doctor distinguished and gives access to those in authority.* (Sir 38 1-3 NAB)
>
> *God makes the pharmacists and herbs to make medications:*
>
> *God makes the earth yield healing herbs which the prudent should not neglect; He endows people with knowledge to glory in his mighty works, through which the doctor eases pain, and the druggist prepares his medicines. Thus, God's work continues without ceasing in its efficacy on the surface of the earth.* (Sir 38: 4, 6-8 NAB)
>
> *Ben Sira advises his son if he is sick:*
>
> *My son, when you are ill, do not delay, but pray to God, for it is he who heals. Flee wickedness and purify your hands; cleanse your heart of every sin. Offer your sweet-smelling oblation and memorial, a generous offering according to your means. Then give the doctor his place lest he leaves; you need him too, for there are times when recovery is in his hands. He, too, prays to God that his diagnosis may be correct, and his treatment brings about a cure.* (Sir 38: 9–15 NAB)

The advice of Yeshua ben Sirach from 2200 years ago is similar to religious advice, which is provided today. First, pray, confess your sins, go to the sacrifice,[3] and finally rely on a doctor, particularly one who prays to God for proper diagnosis and treatment.

Doctors Terruwe and Baars advocate for the use of *"a Christian psychiatrist, preferably, but not necessarily, one who is accustomed to praying with his patients."* They also advise using *"[one which] has the full approval of his spiritual director, [since] he can shed any doubts which otherwise would have impeded, if not made impossible, the healing process"* (Terruwe and Baars 1981,

---

[3] For Catholics, this is the Holy Sacrifice of the Mass.

112–113). If medical professionals agree sex reassignment surgeries were the best approach for an individual, this decision is not without conditions.

British MtF transgender (Transmedicalist) activist India Willoughby suffered from gender dysphoria for her entire life, stating something similar to Dr. Brugger. She claims, *"I don't want people to transition either. It is a last resort. It is a really hard life. Anyone who wants to transition thinking it's going to be a bed of roses is wrong"* (Willoughby 2019).

Dr. Brugger goes further, *"They would have to be truthful that what's going on is not a sex change or a gender change, but a gravely disfiguring surgical procedure aimed at realizing whatever psychic stability is possible in this life"* (Brugger 2016, 15). Dr. Brugger's approach might be a more thought-out answer to which Pope Francis alluded to when in an off-the-cuff interview, he said, *"Tendencies, hormonal imbalance, have and caused so many problems… we must be attentive. Not to say that it's all the same, but in each case, welcome, accompany, study, discern, and integrate. This is what Jesus would do today"* (San Martín 2016).

[India Willoughby, 1965—]

10.3 STEP 2: RESTORING
THE NATURAL ORDER

Judgment—The treatment should aim to restore the natural order

> Man and woman are *created*, which is to say, *willed* by God: on the
> one hand, in perfect equality as human persons; on the other, in
> their respective beings as man and woman. Man and woman are
> both with one and the same dignity *'in the image of God.'* (*CCC*, 369)

A lthough this heuristic has shown substantial deference to the
medical community, the heuristic is not without concern that
doctors might violate the church's moral stance and become
engaged in gender ideology. Suppose a doctor does not participate in
gender affirmation. Their refusal may be considered conversion
therapy, which is illegal and considered a hate crime in twenty states.
The refusal of doctors to go along with unreservedly transitioning the
patient may lead to clinicians losing their license to practice medicine.
The stakes are high for medical professionals. In *Matters of Life and
Death*, pediatrician John Wyatt, M.D., used the image of restoring
nature to be more like an art restorationist rather than Lego's
advertisement; *the only limitation is your own imagination*. Doctors should
be like restorers, returning a piece of art to its original glory.
Unfortunately, the doctors today are becoming more like Lego
advertisements than the art restorers.

In the early *Standards of Care* established by Harry Benjamin, M.D.,
a person preparing to transition was required to live as a member of
the opposite sex for one year before hormonal or surgical
interventions. During the trial period, the patient needed to show that
if the transitioning were permitted, the transition would make them
'normal,' meaning they better fit into the binary system (Erickson-
Schroth and Jacobs 2017, 27).

Since WPATH's 2012 Standards of Care release, the requirement
for treatments to better place an individual into a particular gender has

been eliminated. Although the church prefers to follow the advice of medical science, she cannot when medicine branches into ideology rather than natural realism. First, one must consider the metaphysical question of how these medical procedures affect the totality of the individual. Second, how do these medical interventions restore the original creation with its unique and unrepeatable beauty?

Can healthy organs be medically mutilated for the sake of totality?

Pope Pius XII, in his address to the delegates attending the *Fifth International Congress of Psychotherapy and Clinical Psychology* in 1953, warned,

> *With still less reason, can psychotherapy counsel a patient to commit material sin on the ground that it will be without subjective guilt? Such counsel would also be erroneous if this action were regarded as necessary for the patient's psychic easing and thus part of the treatment. One may never counsel a conscious action which would be a deformation and not an image of the divine perfection"* (Pius XII 1953b, sec. 39).

The pope's comment is to the psychological association. The deformation away from the image of divine perfection is not a physical deformation but a moral one. However, the advice would hold true for any deformation away from the totality of divine perfection. Therefore, doctors must reject any deformation, although identifying which physical transformations may be allowed for *"psychic easing"* is unclear. One cannot forget when Pius XII also claimed that the morality of cosmetic surgery *"depends on the specific circumstances of each case"* (Pentin 2010).

A half a year later, Pius XII addressed the Congress of the International Society of Urology, creating three-fold criteria of totality for justifying a procedure that results in anatomic or functional mutilation:

1. The retention or function of a particular organ within the whole organism is causing severe damage or constitutes a threat to the totality of the person;

2. The damage or threat cannot be avoided, or even notably diminished, except by mutilation in question and whose efficacy is well-assured; and

3. One must reasonably expect that the positive effect will compensate for the negative effect. (Pius XII 1953a)

In the 2016 journal Health Care Ethics USA, Becket Gremmels, Ph.D., evaluated transgender issues using Pius XII's criteria. Dr. Gremmel recalls a case presented by Pius XII, whereby a man needed his testicles removed to slow prostate cancer, which accelerates in the presence of testosterone. Although the testicles of this man were not diseased or pathological, their presence accelerated pathology in another part of the body. Thus Pius XII claimed it was acceptable to remove the testicles of the man, consequently sterilizing him. However, in prostate cancer, removing the healthy testicles to extend one's life is not the same as removing testicles to improve one's mental state (Gremmels 2016, 7).

Pius XII taught *"to ensure his existence, or to avoid, and, naturally, to repair grave and lasting damage that could not otherwise be prevented or repaired"* (Pius XII 1952). Removing sex organs to relieve a mental state will sterilize the individuals, preventing them from having a natural family. This action asks if the surgery improves the person's condition in life and maintains health for the totality of the body.

Suppose doctors performed medical procedures to ease the psyche of a gender dysphoric person. For people suffering from early-onset gender dysphoria into adulthood, socially transitioning may be the only way to ease the dysphoria. Moreover, to socially transition, some medical procedures may be helpful for others to perceive that person as a member of that gender. Nevertheless, Dr. Brugger claims that Catholic medical professionals are obligated "to do what they could to ensure *their participation would not contribute to culturally flawed attitudes about these important areas*" (Brugger 2016, 16). Thus, Catholic medical professionals can engage in gender dysphoric treatments established by the medical community, but they cannot appear to promote what Pope Francis calls *"gender theory."*

What does the totality of a sexed person mean?

The church maintains a complementarity of the sexes with male and female expression, masculine and feminine. Although some Christians accentuate these differences to create a caricature of the image of man or woman, the Catholic Church does not take this radical approach. Pope Francis in The Joy of Love (*Amoris Laetitia*) sec.286 warns against the false dichotomy of the wide variation of the sexes and how it may confuse the youth further since most people do not entirely conform to these stereotypes. As stated numerous times throughout this book, *"Each of the two sexes is an image of the power and tenderness of God, with equal dignity though in a different way"* (*CCC*, 2205).

The previous century's medical science suggests various ways people experience sexual orientation, gender, and what it means to be a man or woman. These expressions may have hormonal and neurological foundations, but the fluidity of gender opens the possibility of different ways to live out each vocation. For example, Elle Palmer, an FtMtF individual, began transitioning to a male in her mid-teens to only return to a female at nineteen. The advice she offers now is, *"I would tell myself, I don't have to be a certain way to be a woman. You can dress however you want, you can wear makeup, or you don't have to wear makeup. You don't have to change yourself"* (B. White 2020).

Elle learned that not all accidental qualities of her gender are essential properties of being a man or woman. Aristotle taught this same approach based on the theory of *kind essentialism*. For example, a fire engine might not essentially be red, but it must accomplish specific functions in its design, or the object is no longer a fire engine. If in its design, the object does not have hoses, ladders, wheels, locomotion, speed, et cetera, the substance lacks efficient causality. The term *"in its design"* is vital to the definition of *kind essentialism* because a broken fire engine is still a fire engine.

In an analogous way, how does one determine if a transgender person is a male or female? First, one must look at the material present or the efficient cause (the pieces of the fire engine) and their finality or final cause (a vehicle used to put out fires). Next, if we look at the morphology of a person's body and examine its parts, we can determine bone density, muscle mass, bone structures, organ size, organs present or absent, hormones, and brain structures. From this determination, we ask, what is the final cause of these parts working together. With most cisgender people, these parts work in unison towards the finality of reproduction and family life.

For intersex people, a conflict occurs within the body between the physical components. For example, if the body's male structures do not absorb testosterone, the body and brain become demasculinized. Intersex is a physical ambiguity, so one approaches the question of *quiddity* with caution. If intersex brains are possible, the totality of the person's sex is less evident to the naked eye. If a person is a *"broken"* male, the person is still a male, like a fire engine with a broken axle. For an intersex or transgender person, the *quiddity* might not be answered by the medical community.

Why are specific gender theories so skeptical of biological realism?

Charlotte Witt, Ph.D., does not accept this type of *kind essentialism*. As seen by liberated women, this concept of kind essentialism is threatening and limiting. If one says women is a type of classification, the category must possess a particular type of nature. The practitioners of essentialism are only one step away from telling women *how* they must live out their nature. Still, as an Aristotelian realist, she claims one cannot deny that women encounter the world differently from men. She asserted, when asking everyday people if they believed they would be the same person if they were the opposite sex, everyone says *"no"* (Witt 2011, XI). Thus, the experience which non-philosophers/ non-feminists express publicly is that gender matters. Dr. Witt explores the meaning behind the idea that gender matters. What matters? The chromosomes, the sex organs, the hormones, how one sees oneself, or the social roles?

This topic also remains relevant for gender non-conforming people. Gender non-conforming may be a term used by gender theorists to fight patriarchy. Gender non-conforming might be used to truthfully address the range of expressions of masculinity and femininity within a culture. These two poles of entirely masculine and fully feminine may be the fountainheads of human expression, but individual people are never wholly examples of either. Men and women fall across a spectrum, an idea that should be embraced since a world of Marlboro men and Barbie dolls are not the ideal images of human complementarity.

The Second-wave feminists focus on men and women, encompassing the same masculine and feminine elements—claiming essentially no differences between the two. Groups like *Mermaids* first teach children a stereotypical definition of being male or female. Second, they suggest some children are born into the wrong sex based on their rigid gender stereotypes of G.I. Joe and Barbie. Third, if children are not the opposite sex, they must be non-binary. The shaming of feminine males or masculine females confuses young people and may push some to seek sex reassignment surgery.

Laura Erickson-Schroth, M.D., and Laura Jacobs, LCSW-R in *"You're in the Wrong Bathroom!"* compared Barbie and Ken images in the transgender community as well. The most visible transgender icons are Caitlyn Jenner, Janet Mock, and Chaz Bono. They *"appear to emulate classic expressions of gender, wearing designer clothes and jet setting from mansion to elite hotel to television shows or award appearances in limos"* (Erickson-Schroth and Jacobs 2017, 11). Media gives people outside of the transgender community the impression that transgender people are generally privileged and craving attention. According to fourth-wave feminists, the average transgender person falls on the same ranges of masculinity and femininity as everybody else. No link between gender identity and gender expression exists. There is no one way to be a transgender male or female any more than there is to be a cisgender male or female. This wide range of identities may also point to the concept that gender does not exist and the conversation about transgender becomes irrelevant. Under this ideology, every person is their own gender.

Second-wave feminists are less dangerous to children than fourth-wave, but still, the best way would follow the normativity of biological realism. Allowing a natural state of non-conformity is not dangerous if one is acting according to an authentic self-expression. The meaning behind being a male or female can be broad. Fr. Ashley admitted, *"Even masculinity and femininity turns out to be largely cultural rather than genetic"* (Ashley 1985, 20).

Many MtF transactivists affirmed what Pope Francis means by gender confusion based on false dichotomies. Kate Bornstein, an MtF individual, confessed in *Gender Outlaw,*

> I've no idea what *'a woman'* feels like. I never did feel like a girl or a woman; rather, it was my unshakable conviction that I was not a boy or a man. It was the absence of a feeling, rather than its presence, that convinced me to change my gender. (Bornstein 1995, 24).

In *Transgressive,* Rachel Anne Williams admits, *"My body cannot be reduced to a single category…It confuses those who cannot see the body for what it is: a field of potential"* (R. A. Williams 2019, 121). Dr. Laura Erickson-Schroth, and Laura Jacobs, wrote that some people *"come to their trans identity out of an ongoing exploration of gender and that their understanding of themselves have been influenced by culture and gender norms"* (Erickson-Schroth and Jacobs 2019, 30).

The wide range of personal expression as individuals may be conforming to socially constructed gender norms, or they may be resisting them politically or merely out of their own personal preferences. These individuals would not be against the principle that gender is individual and whatever they want their expression to be. However, gender does not stand for anything objective or universal under the new postmodern understanding of the term gender, and therefore, means nothing. If gender is a meaningless term, the church's response can be the utter rejection of the term altogether. The church can use sex instead of gender since sex results from genetics, hormones, morphology, and other objective medical criteria. In addition, sex relates to reproduction, the complementarity of male and female, and the topics related to sexual morality. Men's and women's restrooms are merely male and female restrooms. If that becomes too controversial, they can simplify the signs further, *"innie"* and *"outie."*

Using common-sense

The classical unification of sex and gender is quite different from the postmodernist perspective. The classical approach to sex is heavily intertwined with causality and teleology, which uses the philosophies of Aristotle and St. Thomas Aquinas. Transgender identities are a breakdown of what St. Thomas would define as *common sense*. St. Thomas writes, *"Sensus enim communis es quaedam potentia, ad quam terminantur immuntationes omnium sensuum"* (Aquinas *Commentary on Aristotle's De Anima II.*, lect.13). Using the Bossuet translation, *"This faculty of the soul which organizes sense impressions so that one unified object is formed from everything received by the senses is called common sense"* (Bossuet 1900, I no. 4, 46). Common sense for St. Thomas means the culmination of the combined impression for all the senses.

Applying the common sense test to the transgender issue, one must look at the person's physical and social characteristics to determine *quiddity*. Social characteristics may support transgender identification; however, this claim of being the opposite gender could not be a personalized gender identity based on desires. Sexual identity must include primarily physicality and, secondarily, gender expression. To use an old cliché, *if it looks like a duck, swims like a duck, and quacks like a duck, it is probably a duck.*

Does causality create differences between gender theorists and Aristotelians?

Each sex is also a property of being a human being. A predicate applies to all instances of the subject term, an example being a person's race. Regardless of a person's occupation, location, or culture, a person's race is consistent. Conversely, the subject term is predicated on all cases of the predicate. For example, to be a person of a certain race requires a unique DNA passed on by biological parents who are members of that race. Consequently, sex is also a property since a human being is predicated on one having a biological sex, and sex is predicated on having a material being. Sex only occurs when something exists with which the sex can be unified.

The properties of sex are contained within its Aristotelian principles of causality. Causality refers to a relationship between the source of action, the effect, and its consequence. In his work, *Physics*, Aristotle defined four causes: formal, material, efficient, and final, each answering *"why"* in a different mode of existence (Aristotle *Physics*, 194b 20–35).

1. The Efficient Cause (motive): the parents who provided the material and form for the offspring. Aristotle writes that an efficient or agent cause is the *"primary source of the change or coming to rest."*

2. The Material Cause: the mother's nourishment in the womb and food while the child develops. Aristotle defines a material cause as *"that out of which a thing comes to be and persists."*

3. The Formal Cause (Logos): the process whereby a zygote becomes an entire adult human being. Aristotle writes that a formal cause is *"the form or archetype, that is, the statement of the essence."*

4. The Final Cause: the end to which the process leads. In natural terms, remarkably like the *Logos*. Aristotle defines the final cause as *"in the sense of end or that for the sake of which a thing is done."* For Aquinas, this leads to the *imago Dei,* the participation in the divine life.

The most important of the four causes for gender theorists, who are often materialists, is the efficient cause. For Thomists, the final cause is the most important since this mode includes beatitude and grace. The teleological end of man is the answer to *quiddity*. Man is born for beatitude. Beatitude is not one of the many human options humanity can choose, but the *raison d'être*. This language allows discussion of transgender issues since all material beings are a combination of form and matter. Gender theorists are typically dualists who use a model whereby form is separable from matter so a person with a male body (matter) could have a female spirit (form). The Aristotelian model does not allow for this dualism since matter cannot exist without form, and form cannot exist without matter.

Matter always follows the form. The reader should not think of form like a Jell-O mold, giving shape to an amorphous substance. Form would be more synonymous with a blueprint for a house (immaterially), one of the Neo-Aristotelians' famous examples (Aristotle *Metaphysics*, vii 17, 1041b28–30). Shingles, boards, windows, doors, et cetera. all have forms and substances *eo ipso* (in and of themselves). Nevertheless, they become objects greater than the sum of their parts when constructed in a certain way: they become a house. The form or blueprint, taken from potentiality into actuality, is the creation of the house. To understand how something is differentiated as a house, a church, an office building, or a pile of materials at The Home Depot, one must understand causality since materially (efficiently), they are all the same.

Is someone a male or female? Sex differentiation, too, depends on the form and matter. If a person has a female form, a particular matter follows, i.e., a womb, breasts, abundance of estrogen, female structures in the brain, et cetera. If all these elements are not present, some combination must be; otherwise, one cannot be a female by any definition. At a micro level, both males and females have an identical efficient cause: cells. The final cause is needed to unite the cells in a way that creates man or woman. At an even more micro level, all beings materially are electrons, protons, and neutrons. What determines a t-rex from a mountain from a train is its form. Without the formal cause, one could not differentiate between the R.M.S. Titanic, the iceberg, the North Atlantic Ocean, or the passengers.

Aristotle, in his explanation of the final cause, provides the following account:

> Anaxagoras asserts that the possession of hands makes the human being the most intelligent of animals. However, surely the reasonable point of view is that he is the most intelligent animal that he has got hands. Hands are an instrument, and Nature, like a sensible human being, always assigns an organ to the animal that can use it. (Aristotle *Parts of Animals*, 4, 687a10)

A male has a certain physicality because he can best use that form, while a female has a different physicality because she can best use that form. Substance follows form. What should be determined by what the substance is and what it becomes is identified as its *Logos*. Michael Nolan, Ph.D., uses the example of fine mushrooms and how they are evaluated based on their taste and qualities, and not in turn based upon what dung pile they grew on (M. Nolan 1995, 243). Found within the biology of the individual is the *Logos*. An infant girl will become a woman and never a man, horse, or any other being. As a person never gets younger with age, the path of life for a person is expressed causally through the *Logos*. This debate over the importance of the *Logos* is not new. As an example, the abortion debate is often over this issue of *logos*. Pro-abortion activists only consider the material (the cells) and efficient cause (the mother). At the same time, pro-life advocates accept the importance of the material and efficient causes and focus upon the formal (personhood) and final (sanctifying) causes.

Is Thomism helpful in this situation?

Although Aristotle helps gain insights into the transgender issue, St. Thomas's Christian anthropology adds additional levels of clarity to the subject.[4] Fr. Dan Horan, O.F.M., criticizes modern neo-Thomists claiming, *"Today theologians ought to be given the latitude to follow a contemporary version of Aquinas's methodology, taking the best resources from the received theological tradition but also the informed insights of experts in various fields of human knowledge"* (Horan 2020). Fr. Horan claims that using the *Summa Theologica* as the correct and only approach to gender theory is problematic if the Thomistic methodology rather than the Thomistic conclusions are not used. This attack on Neo-Thomism is a strawman argument frequently used to disregard Neo-Thomism and sometimes Neo-Scholasticism altogether in exchange for a non-cognitive form of epistemology.

Neo-Thomism is an academically and pastorally rigorous process to lead people to the truth when difficult. Like a mother who learns how to cook healthy vegetables excellently for her picky children, Neo-Thomists prepare multi-layered dishes, not because nuance is easy, but because the results feed the body. The Neo-Thomist focuses on the normativity of creation. The human person's final cause may provide an obstacle to the *"do what you like"* modern mentality but following the creator's design will lead the transgender person to greater liberation.

John Finley, Ph.D., (1976–), a contemporary Neo-Thomist, attempts in his article *The Metaphysics of Gender: A Thomistic Approach*, to reclaim the concepts of sex and gender, which became the intellectual property of gender theorists. In the subjects of gender and sex, gender theorists seek to deconstruct sex and advance sexual liberation. Using Aristotle and St. Thomas, Dr. Finley yokes the concept of gender to sex and anchors both to biology. This unity falls within *uniessentialism* (see *supra-2.4*).

As Dr. Witt claimed, non-cognitivist feminists prefer the Lockean theory of essence, which discounts all these categorizations as arbitrary.

---

[4] . In the *Vanity of Dogmatizing,* 1661 Joseph Glanvill wrote that "Thomas [is] but Aristotle Sainted," a collection of "steril, [sic] unsatisfying Verbosities" (Glanvill 1661, 151). To this, G.K. Chesterton retorted, "St. Thomas did not reconcile Christ to Aristotle; he reconciled Aristotle to Christ" (Chesterton 1933, 14).

Dr. Finley maintains the normative biological understanding of sex and gender, claiming,

> *I here use the term 'gender' to refer to the natural, sexual structures and capacities in virtue of which humans have been traditionally referred to as male or female. Although the field of gender studies has often invoked the 'sex/gender' distinction, I do not intend my use of the term 'gender' to coincide with this distinction's notion of gender as subjectively or culturally constituted personal identity, distinct from a biological structure.* (Finley 2015, 586)

Dr. Finley continues the Aristotelian ontology of *hylomorphism*[5]: the force uniting the form and matter. St. Thomas uses different terminology for these two natures: body (*corpore*) and soul (*anima*). Using metaphysics, Dr. Finley determines that the principle of the composite human person originates primarily from the soul. In The Splendor of the Truth (*Veritatis splendor*), John Paul II affirms the teaching of the Council of Vienna by stating *"the rational soul is essentially the form of the body"* continuing, *"the spiritual and immortal soul is the principle of unity of the human being, whereby it exists as a whole—corpore et anima unus [body and soul]—as a person"* (John Paul II 1993, sec. 48).

Is sex better understood as essence or an accident?

Elliott Louis Bedford, Ph.D., and Jason T. Eberl, Ph.D., argue that claiming sex reassignment surgery cures individuals with gender dysphoria denies at least one of the following tenets of Thomistic *hylomorphism*:

1. The soul is simple and not comprised of parts (e.g., the part informing the brain is female while that informing the genitals is male), and

2. an organ of a live human being is typically developed (even those atypically developed) and functional is not properly informed by a human soul. (Bedford and Eberl 2016, 26–27)

---

[5] Every physical object is matter and form or if a man, *"a composite of soul and body"* (*Contra Gent.,* II. 55, *ad Omnis enim.*). This doctrine has been dubbed *"hylomorphism"*, from the Greek words for matter (*hulê*) and form (*eidos* or *morphê*). *Form unifies the substrate, transforming mere potentiality into actuality.* Without the form substance cannot exist.

Doctors Bedford and Eberl conclude that sex reassignment surgeries result in an *"ontological dis-integrity."* Sex for St. Thomas is both an accident and a property. Sex is classified as an *inseparable accident*. Separable and inseparable accidents can only be principles of an individual and not the species, while proper accidents apply to the principles of the species (Field 1984, 208). A separable accident could be a person's weight, which can go up or down without changing the agent's ontology.

An inseparable accident is not essential to its ontology, but the being cannot exist without it. Self-evidently, male or female sex is not essential to the human person's ontology since all human beings cannot possess both sexes. Human beings are not two separate substances. Therefore, the universal person does not possess a singular sex, but individuals are accidentally attached to one sex or the other. Dr. Finley argues, *"Thomas's account holds that gender is an inseparable accident following from matter, though only present when a "special form"–an animal form–is present...Thomas gives two reasons for assigning gender's origin to matter rather than to form. One reason is grounded in the difference in the activity of the two genders; the other reason is grounded in their shared essence, or species"* (Finley 2015, 226).[6]

Dr. Finley proceeds to show how the creation of sex flows from an inseparable accident of the soul, arguing, *"The presence of an organ indicates a particular configuration of matter for the sake of one of the soul's powers, which in turn flows from the essence of the soul."* Continuing, *"The soul itself arranges material structures as organs so that they might fittingly serve as means through which the soul's various powers can operate effectively"* (Finley 2015, 596 –597).

---

[6] Both Aristotle and Aquinas mistakenly conclude that sex is an accident of matter, since it is not simply the deficiency of matter which produces the female, but the intended form of each sex. The ancient understanding that paternity provided the form while maternity the matter is biologically incorrect. The combination of the semen and ovum through complementarity, equally provide for both the form and materiality of the offspring.

Beauty is the truth of nature,
or should nature be altered?

St. Thomas considers *Integritas, Consonantia,* and *Claritas* the essential attributes of holy doctors (*ST* Ia q. 39, a. 8). This comparison between Jesus—the Son, and exemplified in these three attributes, is beauty. Man is to become like the Son through the *imago Dei* by imitating the virtues of Christ. *Integritas* is wholeness or perfection, which is to be what one needs to be most fully oneself. To be impaired is *"by the very fact ugly."* Fr. Travis Stephens claims sex reassignment surgeries, as an attempt to unite sex and gender identity, are *"not only immoral because they render the patient sterile, but also because they reject the God-given personhood that is manifest through one's sexuality"* (Stephens 2016, 2). Fr. Stephen asserts that the medicalization of transgender people is a rejection of the *imago Dei*.

Consonantia is proportionality or harmony, which should correspond to a metaphysical ideal. Lastly, one is to express *claritas,* brightness, or clarity— *"whence things are called beautiful, which have a bright color."* *Claritas* radiates intelligibility from its inner being and impresses this presence on the mind of the perceiver.

In the *Symposium,* Plato calls the beauty of the body the shadow of the beauty of the spirit (Plato *Symposium,* 209). Fr. Ashley agrees with this imagery, noting, *"This expressiveness is most clearly seen when physical beauty is not merely in static appearance but comes from the dynamism of the figure... [T]he body is the expression, the voice, the glory of the spirit"* (Ashley 1985, 333).

For example, a human person's beauty is when their body is an expression of the interior life's creativity and passions. A person is the most beautiful dancing, painting, singing, praying, cooking, or any other action where a person is being fully human in practice. A woman sitting in a cubicle doing work only as a means to a paycheck will not exude beauty as much as the same woman who is praying, laughing, or being creative. Another example was St. Mother Teresa of Calcutta, who was not objectively a physically beautiful woman. Still, because of her radiating inner beauty put into action, she became a beautiful woman.

St. Thomas connects beauty to Jesus within the Trinitarian model since beauty is rightly expressed materially. The body is clothed in part to protect from the elements; however, at a primordial level found in Genesis 3:21[7], the covering of man and woman was modesty (*ST* IIa–IIae q.169, a. 1). A body reveals to another the self, and *"this intimacy cannot be something merely casual but has deep significance"* (Ashley 1985, 333).

For transsexuals, *integritas* are of particular difficulty since one's identity is brokenness and disorder at the heart of one's identity. Although this may appear contentious, recognizing dysphoria as a type of disorder, the statement merely states the obvious. The anxiety is rooted in a lack of *integritas.*

Transsexual people lack *claritas* since they must mask their biological realities to reflect a different pneumenal (gender) identity. The transsexuals attempt surgeries and hormones to gain *claritas,* so they are like still water, which appears bright, clear, and honest from the surface to the objects below. Unfortunately, the medicalized approach to transsexuality is like a prism intended to distort and create an optical illusion of the intended reality. Prisms may create beautiful rainbows, but they do not show the truth on the other side of the glass piece.

---

[7] The Lord God made tunics of skins for the man and his wife and clothed them.

10.4 STEP 3: LEAST INVASIVE TREATMENT

Judgment—The treatment should be the least invasive possible

> Instead, *medical science* should act with purely therapeutic ends and intervene in the least invasive fashion, on the basis of objective parameters and with a view to establishing the person's constitutive identity. (*Male and Female He Created Them, sec. 26*)

The document *Male and Female He Created Them* requested doctors attempt to cure gender dysphoria by the least invasive means. This approach connects with the second step, to restore the individual to wholeness in the most natural way. The least invasive means is typically the most natural way. This step should be self-evident, but the current medicalized approach to the human body as a moldable object of unlimited potential contradicts nature itself as good, beautiful, and trustworthy. Therefore, Archbishop Carlson asked doctors to find faithful and creative healing paths for transgender individuals (Carlson 2020, 11). Psychological treatment, antidepressants, or natal sex hormone treatments would be preferable to major surgeries and a lifetime of hormone blockers and supplements.

How much is psychic easing healthy?

Church leaders cannot determine the scope of treatment for gender dysphoria based on their lack of expertise in the field of medicine. Instead, the church sets out ethical principles to guide healing processes and create parameters that cannot be crossed. A common belief among faithful Catholics is that sex reassignment surgery may never be an option. The Magisterium has not addressed this definitively. Further, plastic surgery used *for psychic easing* has been praised by Pius XII while he warns of the dangers of vanity (Pentin 2010). The church also has no Magisterial teaching on the 313,000

American women who received breast enhancements in 2018. It would be difficult to definitively declare that psychic easing for transgender people should be condemned when breast enhancements have not been.

The Catechism condemns *amputations, mutilations, and sterilizations* of healthy organs for non-therapeutic reasons in section 2297. The *Enchiridion Symbolorum* quoted in the *CCC*, 2297, gives further insight into bodily integrity, *"Except when performed for strictly therapeutic medical reasons, directly intended amputations, mutilations, and sterilizations performed on innocent persons are against the moral law"* (Denzinger and Schönmetzer 1965, sec. 3722). This text is in a section titled *"Respect for Bodily Integrity,"* but the other topics in section 2297 are kidnapping, terrorism, and torture. Sex reassignment surgery is not thematically like the other intentions for performing *amputations, mutilations,* and *sterilizations.* Thus

., some may argue that this section of the Catechism should not apply to transgender people. Still, this passage is insightful since it discourages surgeries except for *therapeutic medical reasons.*

Carol Bayley, Ph.D., Vice President of Ethics & Justice Education at Dignity Health,[8] wrote in *Health Care Ethics USA, "In the case of bottom surgery that will sterilize the person, I believe that we can use the rule of double effect in a similar way... Sterilization, then, is a side effect of correcting what amounts to a birth defect. It is an unintended but foreseen consequence."* (Bayley 2016, 4). If one can determine a person has an intersex brain, to what degree does sex reassignment surgery correct what Dr. Byley calls a *"birth defect?"*

Steven Jensen, Ph.D., writes, *"Aquinas himself is unequivocal: an action takes its order and moral species from what is intended."* He also warns about using intentions *"constructed in the clouds"* rather than *"tools or materials, the actual causes in the world around us"* (S. Jensen 2010, 4 & 6). Intentions must be grounded in a reality of what is physically possible—an idea based on Thomistic realism. Claiming double effect is too easy when dealing with any bioethical situation without seriously considering the action itself.

In its section on the respect for the life of the body, the Catechism addresses a principle behind modifying the body through surgery when

---

[8] Composed of 859 Catholic hospitals, clinics, and care centers in the south west United States.

stating, *"If morality requires respect for the life of the body, it does not make it an absolute value. It rejects a neo-pagan notion that tends to promote the cult of the body, to sacrifice everything for its sake, to idolize physical perfection "* (*CCC*, 2289). The idolizing of the body may be a relevant point of inquiry for anyone affected philosophically by the materialist culture. The high level of eating disorders and body image issues teenage girls face results from the culture's idolization of the body. Society should not blame the young girls for these feelings of inadequacy, but rather the institutions of the culture, which presents an unrealistic image of feminine beauty.

For the typical transgender person suffering from gender dysphoria, the idolization of beauty is not the central focus. Researchers have found that people with gender dysphoria have a strong dislike of their bodies. People with transgender feelings do not aim for perfection but to "pass" as people of their perceived sex and receive some psychic easing. Some transgender people may seek additional surgeries out of the fear they are not passing or out of the same general obsessions about appearances. All people share these insecurities, but this would not be a unique attribute of transgender people. One concern may be transgender people putting too much emphasis on the body over virtue or friendship, which might be identified as idolatry of the body.

Are there different possible treatments depending on the type of gender dysphoria?

The exact reason transgender people request sex reassignment surgery is to ease their mental anguish caused by a misalignment of their feelings of self-identification and external appearance. The surgery is not intended for reasons of eroticism or vanity but to experience normality and peace. The therapeutic reason is psychological easing rather than physical since modern medical science cannot change a person's sex. No surgery can change a person's chromosomes, hormone production, bone structures, and the ability to reproduce as a person of the opposite sex. The concrete realism behind the *reasons* hinges on the medical professional's determination. Do these surgeries have a therapeutic psychological reason, or are these only false hopes constructed in the clouds?

For autogynephilic individuals, the person typically is attracted to women and has convincingly been a masculine man for his life, making a physical transition challenging physically, psychologically, culturally, and religiously. The etiology of autogynephilia may be rooted in transvestitism, so some eroticism may exist when presenting as a woman. Aiming for dysphoric relief for some autogynephilic individuals can result from wearing feminine underclothing while keeping the individual's social structures intact. The use of feminine lingerie is a compromise, but since transitioning sex is not medically possible, all the available options are compromises. The option which is the least invasive physically and socially are the better options.

Clothing is not the issue for homosexual-type transsexuals (androphilic), so wearing opposite-sex underwear is unlikely to relieve the dysphoria. For these individuals, the dysphoria for adults is least likely to go away on its own. These individuals are naturally gender non-conforming before becoming transsexual people. Not all gender non-conforming people medically transition their sex. Suppose a natal woman can find contentment in being a more stereotypically masculine female. A natal male can find contentment in displaying more feminine features without undergoing hormonal or surgical procedures. This option is the least invasive.

Is surgery necessary?

Unknown to the public, Billy Tipon and Willmer "Little Axe" Broadnax from *supra*-5.3 lived their entire lives as men with no hormone or surgical treatments. Transgender YouTuber Blaire White experiences dysphoria over being perceived as male in public. So she has transitioned hormonally and has surgically feminized her face and chest to be more feminine. Blaire has not chosen to be orchiectomized since her penis is not public and, therefore, not part of her dysphoria (B. White 2019a). Just because a medicalized approach is available does not require a rush to treat every gender dysphoric individual surgically.

In contrast to Blaire, transfeminist Rachel Anne Williams has acted surgically without discerning the cause of her dysphoria. Rachel claims, *"I am a tranny. A transwoman. A trans person. A non-binary trans femme. Whatever. I don't even know what I am"* (R. A. Williams 2019, 34). Rachel advocates away from a rigid binary system. She now considers herself agnostic about gender. Rachel embraces a laissez-faire model of exploring gender while also acknowledging, *"My body is now inextricably linked with the pharmaceutical-medical-industrial complex"* (R. A. Williams

2019, 121). Those within the transgender movement who consider transgender identities healthy and natural need to consider their assertion that they need surgery to be naturally themselves.

Most of the time, young people with early-onset gender dysphoria will desist on their own. Therefore, the wait-and-see approach is the most effective and least invasive. For late-onset gender dysphoria, many youths are likely following a trend, and the wait-and-see approach is best. In both situations with youth, doctors should avoid prescribing hormone blockers since they may stop the young brain from masculinizing or feminizing while it is still forming. However, if the dysphoria continues, the options to transition will still be available in their twenties or thirties. The anxiety over those few years of dysphoria, although significant, may not be as traumatic as the permanent effects of transitioning followed by detransitioning.

The best option is not to rush the transition, with the current understanding of the human brain's development and the high desisting rate. Although a person can receive electrolysis later in life, one cannot regain puberty. Socially detransitioning is difficult. When one comes out as transgender, there are Pride parades to walk in. Societies give transitioners special treatment at school, and several support groups are available in person and online. The major corporations and media outlets call transgender people brave for being transgender. When a person detransitions, one may experience shame among family and friends for having been wrong. If a person has an online community, they are not supportive of their new identity as a cis person. Transgender people perceive detransitioners as a threat to the transgender narrative, and activists attempt to silence their voices.

[Blaire White, 1993—]

The church may want to establish a pastoral plan for detransitioning adults. However, since so many detransitioners experience shame and are fearful their actions will harm other transgender people, the focus should not include politicizing their detransition. In addition, many of these young people have been away from the church throughout their transgender journey, so attracting them back will also be challenging.

Are doctors using the least invasive treatments currently?

Johanna Olson-Kennedy M.D., the medical director of The Center for Transyouth Health and Development at UCLA, has conducted a study on 94 FtM youth with a range of thirteen to twenty-four years of age. Half of these youths were below the age of eighteen. The study followed the outcomes of this group of youth having double mastectomies. Dr. Olson-Kennedy concludes that the results show a high level of success in providing relief for transgender youth. Ninety-four percent of youth reported the mastectomy was extremely important, and 67 of 68 subjects reported no regret. In her report, Dr. Olson-Kennedy stated, *"Self-reported regret was near 0"* (Olson-Kennedy et al. 2018, 431).

Unfortunately, like many of these studies on patient satisfaction, these results are less than accurate. The follow-up studies ended one to five years past the surgery. Considering two of the subjects were only thirteen years of age at the time of the surgery, a one to five-year follow-up study may not accurately reflect these surgeries' long-term outcomes. Of the 94 youth who received mastectomies, two postsurgical youth refused the survey, and doctors could not contact twenty-four (26%). The high loss to follow-up significantly skews the results away from a 100% satisfaction rate. The results are that 71% reported no regret during the one to five-year period, a result far from the near 100% satisfaction rate reported by Dr. Olson-Kennedy. A 29% dissatisfaction rate may be too bold of a statement to claim. Still, like with other transgender surgeries, if patients were delighted with the results, they would be unlikely to ignore or refuse to answer the researchers responsible for the surgery.

Another concern about this study is not just the results but the ethics of the methodology. Forty-nine percent of the subjects in this study were under eighteen, and 25% were under fifteen years old. Is performing double mastectomies on healthy children ethical? In addition, fifty-two youth were ineligible to participate in this study because they did not develop enough chest tissue *"as a result of being either prepubertal or having taken puberty-blocking medications early in development"* (Olson-Kennedy et al. 2018, 434).

Dr. Olson-Kennedy has reportedly claimed, if later in life these youth decide they would like breasts, her advice is, *"If you want breasts at a later point in your life, you can go and get them"* (Robins 2018). This approach of mutilating children's bodies to find out if the change will be helpful appears unethical. Dr. Olson-Kennedy's belief that if youth change their minds, they can just add them back is a disturbing trend away from the sanctity and totality of the youth human body. In Oregon, 15-year-old girls can obtain double mastectomies without parental consent using their Oregon Healthcare Insurance, a policy praised by *Basic Rights Oregon* and *TransActive Gender Center* (Basic Rights Oregon 2016).

If feeling transgender is natural, is a medicalized approach necessary?

Not all people receive the moral luck to meet the expectations of society naturally. According to numerous follow-up studies, medical transitioning is not a physically or mentally healthy option for many transgender people. When describing a transgender utopia, Rachel Anne Williams claims, *"In a perfect world, being trans would be like having freckles, just another thing that makes us unique individuals"* (R. A. Williams 2019, 109). The difference between freckles and a transgender identity is that one can be naturally left alone when one has freckles. Unfortunately, many transgender people request surgeries, pharmaceuticals, and upwards of $100,000 in medical treatments to feel like themselves. In a real transgender utopia, people would be able to rejoice in their natural masculinity and femininity (as Mr. Fred Rogers sings) *just the way you are.* If being transgender meant being gender non-conforming, one could compare the condition to freckles. If a person can find contentment without the medicalized approach, it is the least invasive physically, most natural, and healthiest. The method for finding happiness when in a difficult situation will be addressed in steps four and five.

Covenants

The least invasive treatment is not only biological but social. What healing processes are the least damaging socially? Notably, one must consider how these medical transformations will affect one's covenantal relationships. If a man is autogynephilic and has entered into the sacrament of marriage with a woman, his first responsibility is to his wife rather than his personal desires. If this man has also begotten children, he owes his children an obligation beyond his own fantasies. Only 7% of marriages survive when a spouse sexually reassigns their gender (Tannehill 2019, 51). If a Catholic man must choose between fidelity to his family or his own desires and inclinations, he has a covenantal vow to choose his family as his primary commitment. St. Paul wrote, *"Husbands, love your wives, even as Christ loved the church and handed himself over for her"* (Ep 5:25 NAB). A parent has a responsibility to be a father or mother to their children. They are the primary examples of being a man or woman within a child's life. An innate desire to express the opposite gender does not remove these covenantal responsibilities. A parent can be truthful with children about their own personal struggles at the appropriate age, without leaving the family to pursue one's own self-interests.

Suppose a person is androphilic, either MtF or FtM, and sacramentally married. *Canon Law* recognizes the possibility of the *"incapacity to assume the essential obligations of marriage"* (*Canon Law,* sec. 1095, 3) [9] if homosexual tendencies make the essential duties of marriage impossible to fulfill. Particularly if the individual has begotten children, making every effort to fulfill the obligations of the sacramental covenant is important before rushing to terminate the marriage. The presence of a transgender identity is not a license to disregard the covenant of marriage and the care for one's family.

The original unity is again established through the covenantal co-creative act of reproduction, where the two become one flesh. The *imago Dei* which humanity shares in is not simply Christological but Trinitarian. Likewise, Fr. Donald Keefe, S.J. suggests the Trinity is

---

[9] The psychological problem must be so severe that it makes it humanly impossible, not merely difficult, to take on the essential obligations of marriage. This impossibility can be caused by a mental illness, a psychological disorder, a severe addiction, or a strong homosexual inclination.

imaged in creation most clearly in covenantal marriage—husband, wife, and their mutual vow (Keefe 1999, 108). This moment of communion is challenging for transgender people since the unity of the two sexes becomes impossible after disfiguring the sex organs during sex reassignment surgeries. Further, sterilization adds a further breakdown of the union between spouses.

MtF individuals abandoning their wives has become so widespread that they have created their own term: trans widows. The website *TransWidowsVoices.com* began documenting the stories of wives of autogynephilic individuals whose husbands left them behind. Meanwhile, society celebrates their bravery for coming out without considering the families left behind.

10.5 Concept Review

Chapter ten bridges the gap between the medical understanding of gender dysphoria and a pastoral response. Doctors cannot locate a biological etiology or a specific combination of genes. Nevertheless, a connection between gender dysphoria and neurodevelopmental disorders is possible for those with early-onset gender dysphoria. Without absolute certainty about this phenomenon's biology, these people exist, and their suffering appears to be significant, given the rate of suicide and mortality rates. This phenomenon also occurs globally and is prevalent in conservative and religious communities at the same rate as liberal and *'sexually liberated'* communities.

The current medical treatment for people with this disorder is insufficient, and more convincing plastic surgeries will only better mask the real problems behind this disorder. Fighting one's own biological nature never succeeds since the body's equilibrium is necessary for healthy functioning. Hormone blockers and opposite-sex hormones lead to many new health disorders, including heart disease and cancers. In contrast, no medical treatment can effectively change a person's sex; some medical treatments help mask gender dysphoria. The masking is a lifelong commitment to fighting against one's own natural body. Although gender dysphoria may have a biological cause, the consequence is primarily a mode of thinking and feeling rather than being. Learning to cope with these thoughts and feelings spiritually and therapeutically is better than the artificial approach.

CHAPTER 11
VIRTUES AND GRACE

Everything ideal has a natural basis, and everything natural an ideal development.

— George Santayana, Ph.D., *The Life of Reason*

Simply to wish for a good end does not suffice; we intentionally pursue the end even as the end draws us towards itself.

— Fr. Romanus Cessario, O.P., *Introduction to Moral Theology*

11.1 STEP 4: VIRTUES

Command— There must be patience and acceptance of oneself, especially when born *'imperfectly.'* Penultimate happiness is a consequence of moral luck and moral virtues. Of the two, the only one man controls his virtues.

> Nature does not make mistakes and does nothing idly (Aristotle *Generation of Animals,* 5,8,788b20)

St. Thomas defines virtue as *"a good quality of mind, by which one lives righteously, of which no one can make bad use, which God works in us without us"* (*ST* Ia–IIae, q. 55, a. 4). According to St. Thomas, infused virtues are part of new life in Christ, whereby the effects of sin remain, but the virtues, which God gives freely, overcome the concupiscence of sin. The efficient cause of infused virtue is God, while man's practice of habitus develops acquired virtue. There are four cardinal virtues within the family of classical virtues: prudence, justice, fortitude, and temperance. All the cardinal virtues are moral virtues apart from prudence, which is an intellectual virtue. *"Intellectual virtues,"* according to Fr. Cessario, have *"no ability to shape an overall good moral character, though they do make a person smart and, perhaps, even wise"* (Cessario 2002, 70). St. Thomas claims moral virtues can exist without the intellectual virtues of science, wisdom, and art—but not prudence (*ST* Ia–IIae q. 58, a. 4).

Although Aristotle and his contemporaries established the cardinal virtues, St. Thomas added the three theological virtues: faith, hope, and love. The theological virtues are a particularly Christian dimension to this heuristic. The reader could adapt this process for secular use by excluding faith, hope, and love; however, without theological virtues, the moral virtues are incomplete. For example, being faithful in marriage is a virtue, while being faithful in marriage out of love for one's spouse is even better. For another example, religion is the virtue of giving God what is due, while giving God His due filled with faith, hope, and love is the glory of virtue.

The Christian understanding of virtue is rooted in personhood. St. Augustine wrote in his reflection on Psalm 83, *"Christ is the one who in this life gives us the virtues; and, in the place of all the virtues necessary in this valley of tears, he will give us one virtue only, himself"* (Augustine, *Enarrationes in Psalmos*, Ps. 83, 11). Jesus is the embodiment of virtue, which he gives to us freely. Consequently, virtues are never a list of dos and don'ts. Virtue is freedom and not repression. Instead, virtues are the correct ordering of inclinations and appetites, so the Christian's mind is united with the mind of Christ. Fr. Cessario summarizes, *"by reason of his or her conformity to Christ, the Christian believer enjoys the power to achieve a rectified emotional life"*[1] (Cessario 2002, 189). A rectified emotional life is heresy for noncognitivist Humians[2] who believe knowledge originates in their feelings: *sentio ergo sum* (*see supra-2.7*).

The classical understanding of happiness or human flourishing in Greek is *eudaimonia* and, in Latin, *beatitudo*. For Aristotle, *eudemonia* is connected to the human good *"in conformity with excellence,"* otherwise called virtue (Aristotle *NE* 1098a 16–17). However, *Eudaimonia* is also connected with external goods such as being born a citizen or non-citizen, losing friends or family, loss of property in old age. These otherwise circumstances are considered moral luck. Thus, one can choose a virtuous life to flourish, yet one does not control moral luck.

---

[1] *ST* Ia-IIae q. 60, a. 1
[2] Followers of David Hume

[Fr. Romanus Cessario, O.P., 1944—]

Virtue in a Thomistic understanding is fundamentally different from Aristotelian ethics since Christian virtue is founded in a relationship with Christ. Sr. Mary Angelica Neenan, O.P., wrote, *"True freedom is the ability to choose what is truly good. If God helps us do that, then He is helping us become more free—not obstructing our freedom"* (Neenan 2017, 34–35). Virtue is not primarily an external act but an internal one. St. Thomas wrote that charity is a kind of friendship with God (*ST* Ia–IIae q. 65, a. 5). Fr. Livio Melina (1952–) wrote, *"The heart of virtues is love"* (Melina 2001, 54). For the gender dysphoric Christian, the *Sacra Doctrina* and the call to a virtuous life is not a cold invitation to follow a series of commands; instead, life is an invitation to enter into a relationship. Jesus taught his disciples, *"You are my friends if you do what I command you…I have called you friends"* (Jn 15:14–15).

From an Aristotelian perspective, Alasdair MacIntyre, Ph.D., asks the questions (1) Who am I? (2) What behavior will lead me to be what I ought to become? (3) What kind of community can help me achieve this goal? Fr. Livio Melina, using Thomism, claims this schema must be updated and reformulated to answer only two questions: *"(1) Who do I genuinely want to be? And, if the ultimately adequate answer is given to me in the encounter with Christ, in the church, it then follows: (2) How ought I to live in order to realize communion in love?"* (Melina 2001, 24). These are the questions relevant to the Christian transgender community. The question is not how one feels or how one currently interprets their own identity. The question is, *who do you genuinely want to be?* An answer is never a man or a woman. The question is far more profound than one's sex. The answer is: I want to be loved. I want to be accepted. I want to be in communion. I want to be understood. I want peace. The next question is, does God also want this for me, and how is this best achieved?

Holocaust survivor, psychologist, and author Viktor Frankl, M.D., (1905–1997) in *Man's Search for Meaning* proposed that there is more to life than seeking happiness, and instead, claims people desire meaning. Likewise, logotherapy focuses a person within an existential vacuum to seek meaning in life. Dr. Frankl proposes that one finds meaning in life in the following way:

1. One may find experiences of joy within their present situation;
2. One must attempt to make a positive difference in the world; and

3. Finally, one must have the right attitude, be optimistic about changing the things that can be changed and accept those things that cannot be changed.

Dr. Frankl observed that whether someone retained their identity within a concentration camp corresponded to their ability to find meaning in life. Phycologists Roy Baumeister, Ph.D., and Kathleen Vohs, Ph.D., in an article *Recent Empirical Findings on Meaning and How it Differs from Happiness*, wrote Dr. Frankl's *"theory far extended the psychoanalytic view of human nature."* Dr. Frankl's perspective was anti-materialistic and considered the Aristotelian understanding of causality. He wrote, *"Instead of being mere packs of nerve cells sustaining life by following animal impulses, humans seek to understand their place in the universe and the broader, deeper significance of their activities"* (Baumeister and Vohs 2013, 87). Healthy psychology begins with an understanding of teleology. Thus, for individuals experiencing dysphoria, the first goal in finding satisfaction in life is finding meaning rather than pursuing happiness or comfort. According to doctors Baumeister and Vohs' study, subjects reported an easy life, health, wealth, and being served, establishing happiness in the present moment. In contrast, meaningfulness was related to one's long-term life vision and, consequently, a result of serving and sacrificing for the sake of others.

Studies of childbearing uncovered similar results, claiming parents experience more significant anxiety, depression, and marriage dissatisfaction than spouses without children (Kahneman et al., 2004). However, a separate study found that parents with independent adult children experience greater life satisfaction and fewer signs of depression (Becker, Kirchmaier, and Trautmann 2019). Repeated studies show that having children reduces immediate happiness but increases one's meaningfulness. Having meaning in life is a greater motivation for individuals than happiness. Doctors MacIntyre and Frankl similarly acknowledge that a consistent cosmology creates meaning out of suffering and helps people find peace within their state of life.

Although having a clear cosmology generally relieves stress, studies have found that faith-based counseling for LGBT Christians has only increased the rate of suicides (Meyer, Teylan, and Schwartz 2014) (Gibbs and Goldbach 2015). In theory, being part of a Christian cosmology should reduce dysphoria and suffering, but this is not the experience of many people. The incongruence between theory and practice begs whether Christian communities and faith-based counselors correctly apply Christian principles when addressing LGBT youth? Are these experts engaging in semi-Christian gender ideology rather than Thomistic realism? This chapter proposes that the way to bring healing without increasing stress and depression is to cultivate a life of virtue. The following eight sections will go deeper into cultivating each virtue while experiencing feelings of gender dysphoria.

I. Faith

Summa Theologica IIa–IIae q. 1–16

Therefore, since we have been justified by faith, we have peace with God through our Lord Jesus Christ

— Romans 5:1

St. Thomas calls faith the First Truth. Faith opens the mind to other knowledge since virtue is rooted in what Pseudo-Dionysius calls simple and everlasting truth (Pseudo- Dionysius *Divine Nom.*, vii). To understand how *simple and everlasting truth* appears, one can turn to St. Augustine's commentary on creation in *De Genesi ad litteram*,[3] where he considers the morning and evening knowledge possessed by the angels. St. Thomas offers commentary on this passage in *prima pars* question 58,

> I answer that The expression *"morning"* and *"evening"* knowledge was devised by Augustine; who interprets the six days wherein God made all things, not as ordinary days measured by the solar circuit, since the sun was only made on the fourth day... their knowledge of the primordial being of things is called morning knowledge, and this is according to things as they exist in the Word. But their knowledge of the very being of the thing created, as it stands in its own nature, is termed evening knowledge; because the beginning of things flows from the Word. (*ST* Ia q. 58, a. 6)

This view of the primordial knowledge proceeding from the Word in the morning has strong echoes of what would be defined in the

---

[3] Book IV, chap. 22, 31.

nineteenth century as the Immaculate Conception. A being which is *"when everything appears in the 'perfect image'–forms a basic feature of the dynamism of Christian living"* (Cessario 2002). The evening knowledge is of created reality as truth exists in its own nature, in other words, as it truly is in the material world. For Jesus and the Virgin Mary, this is the same reality, but for the rest of humanity, the morning's perfect image is corrupted by original sin when it takes flesh in the evening. Transgender people especially know this fallen nature since dysphoria is at the heart of the fall.

A 2013 Pew Study discovered that 17% of transgender people consider religion, including Christianity, a *"very serious"* part of their lives (Bautista, Mountain, and Mackenzie-Reynolds 2014, 63). A 2017 study showed that *"religious affiliation is a significant predictor of LGBT individuals' happiness"* (Barringer and Gay 2017, 75). The call to be part of the church is hindered but not eliminated by being transgender since being transgender and having faith are not mutually exclusive.

Someone identifying as transgender affects the faith life of that person, their friends, and family. A parent of a transgender youth noted in one study, *"As far as in my life, I'm a much different person [since her child transitioned]. I'm more accepting, more loving, and not as judgmental. The love that Christ has put in my heart for the GLBT community is huge. I also have a righteous anger towards the church"* (Yarhouse et al., 2016, 198). There are two possible explanations for this mother's newfound openness. First, like Simon of Cyrene, can one possibly discover Christ under the burden of helping another carry the cross? Second, do some who find Christ also get angry at the system which crucified him? Yes, but Christ did not build awareness about the Roman Empire's politics or trivial Jewish infighting. Instead, Jesus creates a path through the Via Dolorosa, cutting through the heart of political and religious power, liberating His own through faith. On the other side, perhaps the mother is not encountering Christ but moving towards relativism. The *anything-goes* mentality can be another way of dealing with moral judgments, stating that if you do not judge my failings, I will not judge your failings. In other words, *I'm okay—you're okay.*

In addition to determining if one is encountering Christ or moving towards relativism, the reader must also consider the difference between authentic faith and fondness towards the idea of God. Faith is achieved in a two-fold manner according to St. Thomas; first, the apostles, prophets, or preachers propose the belief. The second step is the believer's ascent, which comes from *"God moving man inwardly by grace"* (*ST* IIa–IIae q.6, a. 1). Knowledge is not enough, whether intellectual, acquired through preaching, or witnessing a miracle since some will see or hear and believe, while others will not. Faith begins with the grace of God and is perfected by the grace of God. St. Thomas also taught, "And so the moving of reason is not sufficient to direct us to our ultimate and supernatural end without the prompting and moving of the Holy Spirit from above" (*ST* Ia–IIae q. 68, a. 2). Therefore, faith constitutes the perfection of the human intellect.

Bishop of Riez and abbot of St. Lérins, St. Faustus (405–495) compared faith to a nuptial covenant, *"What wedding can this be but the joyful marriage of Man's salvation, a marriage celebrated by confessing the Trinity and by faith in the resurrection"* (Faustus *Sermo 5*, De Epiphania 2). This wedding imagery unites with the concupiscence of holiness, which draws all believers toward God. Fr. Cessario calls this desire *pondus amoris*— *"the weight of divine love that enables the saints to penetrate the hidden mysteries of divine truth"* (Cessario 2002, 23). Espousal love with God is essential for all Christians and is one of Christ's primary images with the church. Peculiarly, Christ calls the eunuchs of Matthew 19 into a deeper union of espousal love since they forgo natural marriage. However, some who are natural eunuchs or made so by others may not want this espousal vocation and prefer the natural sacramental marriage of husband and wife. Even for those *"who cannot accept it,"* the invitation to follow Him in a particular way and with a unique vocation remains.

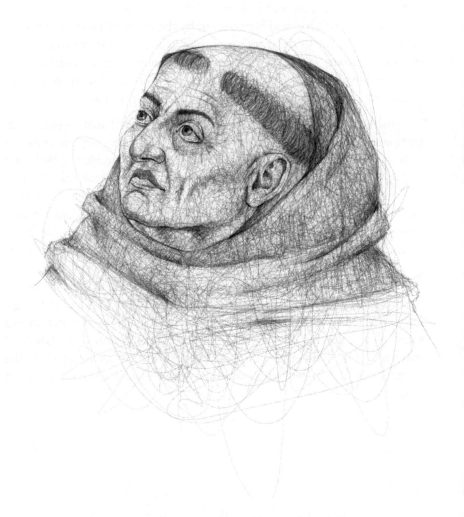

[St. Thomas Aquinas, O.P., 1225—1274]

Vocations are set upon each individual by the creator and are not always consistent with one's feelings and desires. The question is not *"what do I want"* but *"who is God calling me to become?"* Their biology limits women from becoming husbands, priests, and bishops. Their biology limits men from becoming wives, mothers, and religious sisters. Their biology restricts people with severe handicaps from entering the priesthood and religious life. Her biology limits a female peacock from having a beautiful array of colors in her tail feathers. A male black widow spider is limited in his lifespan after finding a spouse. Only a few female ants will be queens within an ant colony, and drones are driven from the nest after they mate. One can complain that life is not fair because of its limitations, but God creates each according to creation's normativity. Within each state of life, God calls each one to holiness and espousal love. Genesis 2:18 states, *"it is not good for man to be alone,"* and for a Christian, man is never alone if he or she consents to the call of espousal love. This love is not a second option but rather *the better way that penetrates the hidden mysteries of divine truth.*

To enter this espousal love is not consenting to an emotional sensation that passes. Espousal love is sacrificial love. Seventeenth-century Dominican friar John of St. Thomas compares this beatitude of mourning with espousal love. He writes,

> To have a perfect union with God and experience his immense goodness requires stripping oneself of creaturely things and possessing a knowledge of their poverty, humiliation, and bitterness; such considerations, furthermore, lead us to cling more closely to God, whom we come to know better as we distance ourselves from creatures. (St. Thomas 1885, a 4, n. 57)

The *kenosis* of vices and false pride while clinging to the bridegroom is another description of espousal love. Faith does not normalize disability or solve health problems, but having faith solves the problem of identity. For a Christian called into espousal love with Jesus, the question of who one is can be confidently answered—beloved.

II. Hope

Summa Theologica IIa–IIae q.17–22

And hope does not disappoint because the love of God has been poured out into our hearts through the Holy Spirit that has been given to us.

— Romans 5:5

The Catechism defines hope as *"the confident expectation of divine blessing and the beatific vision of God; it is also the fear of offending God's love and incurring punishment"* (*CCC,* 2090). According to the Catechism, which mirrors the *Summa Theologica,* hope seeks to acquire friendship with God and is concerned with harming the relationship. St. Thomas writes, *"God's love pours out and creates the goodness in things"* (*ST* Ia q. 20, a. 2). This *exitus-reditus* is at the heart of why man hopes. God creates humanity for himself, and his ultimate destiny is a return to the source. Dr. Josef Pieper authored a book titled *Hope,* which taught, *"Hope, like love, is one of the very simple, primordial dispositions of the living person. In hope, man reaches 'with restless heart,' with confidence and patient expectation toward the arduous 'not yet' of fulfillment, whether natural or supernatural"* (Pieper 1986, 27). This patient expectation described by Dr. Pieper is looking toward the future; hope is the attainment of something not yet acquired.

In an article on Karol Wojtyla and sex reassignment surgery in *The National Catholic Bioethics Quarterly,* Jacob Harrison, Ph.D., wrote, *"The full realization of the human person as body and soul will be fulfilled at the resurrection, further advancing the anthropological idea of body-soul unity"* (Harrison 2017, 297). Thus, for a person with a transgender identity, like all fellow humans, bodily satisfaction is not for this world. Instead,

God prepares wholeness for the saved at the bodily resurrection in the eschaton.

Lawfully a person must hope in God as one's final cause. St. Thomas states one can "lawfully hope in a man or a creature as being the secondary and instrumental agent through whom one is helped to obtain any goods that are ordained to happiness" (*ST* IIa–IIae q.17, a. 4). Now on the vice contrary to hope, despair comes from inordinate appetites. St. Thomas wrote, "every appetitive movement which is conformed to a true intellect, is good in itself, while every appetitive movement which is conformed to a false intellect is evil in itself and sinful" (*ST* IIa–IIae q. 20, a. 1). Hope based on appetites is rooted in false intellect and knowledge, which leads to disorder and pain. One's thinking matters since imprudent counsel creates an impossible chasm when trying to reach one's proper end. When a person has a transgender identity or is experiencing gender dysphoria, having the proper hope in the final and efficient causes is necessary to achieve happiness in this life and the next.

Those individuals suffering from gender dysphoria are suffering from concupiscence rather than rejoicing in the virtue of hope. The emotional appetites associated with concupiscence are love, desire, joy, hatred, aversion, and sadness. The former are simple goods while the latter are simple evils. Although the term used in the *DSM-5* was *desire*, the extent of the dysphoria goes far beyond simple emotions of desire and is instead a strong emotion of desire. St. Thomas claims, *"No virtue is called desire because desire does not imply any present clinging or spiritual contact with God himself"* (Aquinas *Quaestio disputata de spe*, a.1, ad 6). These strong emotions of disgust about one's sex could be better-called irascibility. The emotions of irascibility are an emotional hope, which, if achieved, leads to joy and, if not, turns to despair. The emotions associated with the future evil are courage, fear, and anger when the danger is present. Transgender ideology is about desire, but even more about the emotion of hope. A transgender person may have a fervent hope that changing one's sex will give a person joy, peace, and love.

Unfortunately, if this process does not lead to joy, false hope can lead to despair, which may explain the high rates of depression, anxiety, and suicide. The ability to change one's sex is not biologically possible; therefore, as a human endeavor, if one's desire is dependent on this impossible result, despair is inevitable. On the other hand, the results are possible if the person desires to appear socially like a person of the other sex. E. Christian Brugger, Ph.D., claims *"to counsel, perform or accept for oneself any surgery believing or asserting that what's happening is that a person is changing ('reassigning') his biological sex would always be contrary to the truth and therefore always impermissible"* (Brugger 2016, 15). Therefore, pastorally one should be realistic about the limitations of medical science and only express the truth, even when unpopular, since encouraging a gender dysphoric person to have false hope will be a setup for inevitable despair.

The National Catholic Bioethics Center's Brief Statement on Transgenderism parallels the sentiments of Dr. Bruggers, claiming:

> Hormonal interventions, to block the body's sex-specific hormones or provide the sex-specific hormones of the opposite sex, likewise alter nothing of a person's innate sexual identity ... So-called sex reassignment surgeries of any kind, designed to give the body an appearance with more of the culturally expected qualities of the opposite sex, also cannot modify the true sexual identity of the person, who was created, male or female. Directly intending to transition one's given bodily sex into a *"new"* one (even though this may be perceived as the *"real"* and "true" one) means intending to alter what is unalterable, to establish a false identity in place of one's true identity, and so to deny and contradict one's own authentic human existence as a male or female body-soul unity. Such an action cannot be consonant with the good of the whole person. (The Ethicists of The National Catholic Bioethics Center 2016, 600-601)

This statement reaffirms the Catholic principles of teleology, Thomistic realism, and truth. Cosmetic surgery and the appearance of one gender or another cannot change one's sex. The appearance may better mirror how one feels or identifies, but appearances cannot change a person's essence.

The church is not Buddhist in its rejection of all desire or of the emotion of hope. From a Christian perspective, one needs desires and hopes in the proper ordering and aimed at the proper ends. Fr. Cessario states, *"[T]he virtues of hope shape the proper emotional response that a person should demonstrate when faced with some future, difficult, but attainable good"* (Cessario 2002, 36). Therefore, hoping possesses moral perfection since hope aims for virtuous activity. The virtue of hope places reason into the emotion to establish the proper order.

As a virtue, hope is united with beatitude—a personal intimacy with God. Theological hope is not for worldly things but instead for eternal union with God's blessedness. Fr. Cessario describes the virtue, *"hope seeks God for the hoper, that is, the loving embrace of God's goodness for me"* (Cessario 2002, 38). When the hope of man is perfect blessedness, all other desires become ordered. Rightly one desires God's blessedness since God is the formal cause of man and his teleological end. Since Jesus is the incarnation and not just spirit, hope for temporal goods which lead to beatitude is virtuous. Proximate desires which lead to beatitude are not a contradiction so long as the desires are in the proper order.

The emotions of gender dysphoria relate to the emotional form of hope rather than the theological virtue. One can theologically hope for the Lord to change one's sex; however, this asks for a miracle. God changing one's sex would violate the Thomistic principle that grace does not destroy nature but perfects nature. The church has no known cases of God changing a person's sex for any reason. God could have saved St. Joan of Arc by such a miracle, yet God did not grant this miracle. Transgender desires are connected to an emotional concupiscence[4] rather than the vice held in contrast to the theological virtue of hope. Yet, these movements are intricately linked (*ST* Ia–IIae q.30).

The emotion of hope can be satisfied by magnanimity since the fulfillment of the desire can be accomplished through human efforts. A magnanimous person can reach his or her desires and obtain joy. Magnanimity is illuminated in more depth under its proper cardinal virtue, fortitude. If human effort cannot accomplish the person's desires and only by God's will and achieve this desire, the hope is theological. St. Thomas wrote, *"When it is a case, then, of hoping for something as possible to us precisely through God's help, such hope, by reason of its very reliance upon God, reaches God himself"* (*ST* IIa–IIae q.17, a. 1). The

---

[4] Pope St. John Paul II considers "sensuality and emotionalism furnish so to speak, 'raw material for love'" (Wojtyla, 1981, 159). In the *Theology of the Body*, he uses the term concupiscence 340 times, but these are manifested in three different forms, concupiscence of the *flesh, the eye,* and *the pride of life* (John Paul II, 2006, sec. 26.1).

function of a theological virtue compared to concupiscence is that the former unites the believer with God.

The theological virtue of hope is an essential virtue for a transgender person. St. Thomas writes that due to the lack of original justice, every human person experiences appetitive movements that incline them towards disordered behavior (*ST* III q.69, a. 3). The Catechism teaches, *"Certain temporal consequences of sin remain in the baptized, such as suffering, illness, death, and such frailties inherent in life as weaknesses of character, and so on, as well as an inclination to sin that Tradition, calls concupiscence"* (*CCC*, 1264). The solution for all Christians who suffer from desires is beatitude. As a church, one does not have to carry their cross alone, for as St. Paul claims, *"Bear one another's burdens, and in this way, you will fulfill the law of Christ"* (Gal 6:20).

If no peace is achieved through the virtue of hope, the practice of hope is still not in vain. Believing that by having hope, everything in this life will be easy is the wrong attitude. St. Augustine wrote, *"There are two things that kill the soul, despair and false hope"* (Augustine, *Sermo 87*, chap. 8). Søren Kierkegaard dedicated the book, *The Sickness Unto Death*, 1849 to the concept that the only suffering which matters is spiritual despair, which kills the soul. Absolute despair arises not from disappointment about material loss but from believing God's grace is not enough to save the sinner. This lack of hope rejects the covenant Jesus creates in His flesh and thus constitutes a sinful posture of despair.

The actual sin which creates a living hell or may damn one to eternal hell is despair. Feelings rooted in gender dysphoria may lead one to despair. Yet, regardless of a person's status in life, the virtue of hope remains. The devil's voice, through the vice of presumption, tells the person, (1) you do not need the grace of God, or conversely, (2) God will not provide for *your* salvation, and *your* pain is eternal. Both extreme beliefs are lies effectively exclude people from embracing the authentic gift of hope.

III. Charity
Summa Theologica IIa–IIae q. 23–46

> So, faith, hope, love remain, these three; but the greatest of these is love.
>
> — 1 Corinthians 13:13

Charity is the *queen of all virtues* since she perfects and appropriately orders the powers of the human appetite. Virtue aims the human will to love that which is worthy of love. The only thing worthy of loving is He who is eternal—God alone. Therefore, the heart of all virtues is *caritas*. St. Thomas wrote, *"Charity comes into the definition of all the virtues, not because it is essentially identical with them, but because somehow they all depend on charity"* (*ST* IIa–IIae q.23, a. 4, ad. 1).

St. Augustine in *De doctrina christiana* wrote, *"There are four kinds of things a man must love, one is above him, namely God; another is himself; third is close by him, namely his neighbor; and the fourth is beneath him, namely his own body"* (Augustine *De doctrina christiana*, I, 23). St. Thomas repeats this Augustinian hierarchy of love in *Summa Theologica* IIa–IIae q. 26, a. 1–13. An immense amount has been written about all these loves, but this section will be limited to how they can be part of gender dysphoric people's healing process.

The Mayo Clinic affirms love as a means of coping with gender dysphoria. The clinic stresses the importance of charity towards God, self, and neighbor as a pathway for healing. In addition, they promote maintaining your mental health, seeking out support groups, prioritizing self-care, meditating or praying, and getting involved/volunteering (The Mayo Clinic n.d.). For individuals with early-onset gender dysphoria, following these guidelines will probably not heal the dysphoria, but they may provide some psychic easing. This advice is beneficial for youth with late-onset gender dysphoria since any activity requires them to get off of social media. Focusing on in-person socialization and community service is helpful for dysphoric youth.

Love of God

Fr. Melina speculates on the reason why all virtues depend on charity, *"Without charity, the other virtues are still true, but incomplete,"* he continued, *"Charity, Thomistically understood as friendship with Christ, is 'the form of the virtues'"* (Melina 2001, 55, 58). No matter what is done, that which is done without charity can never be complete. For a transgender person seeking healing, regardless of the medical approaches taken or not taken, healing starts with Christological *caritas* as the entrance into the *communio* of beatitude.

St. Thomas writes, *"Caritas is not any kind of love of God, but the love of God by which he is loved as the object of beatitude on which we are bent by faith and hope"* (*ST* Ia–IIae q. 65, a. 1). This *beatitudinis objectum* (object of beatitude) is the proper and formal object of love. The love of God is the only pure love because one loves the greatest goodness personified. This love of God is not (*adoratio*) worship, but the love of benevolence (*amor benevolentiae*), otherwise called friendship. Jesus explains this mystery, *"I do not call you servants any longer, because the servant does not know what the master is doing; but I have called you friends"* (Jn 15:15). St Thomas further states that God *"by sharing happiness with us"* is upon which the beatific *"friendship is based"* (*ST* IIa–IIae q. 23, a.1). God is man's principal friend and the reason for the other loves. Fr. Cessario calls God the *"First Friend for every member in the communicatio of charity"* (Cessario 2002, 76).

[Thomas Cardinal Cajetan, O.P., 1469—1534]

Cardinal Thomas Cajetan, O.P. (149–1534), in his examination of conscious writes, *"evil is a sort of thing that makes it impossible for sinners to love themselves"* (Cajetan *Commentary on Summa Theologiae*, q.25, a.1). If one suffers from any type of self-loathing, the first step towards healing is to clear one's conscience. For a Catholic man or woman, this is achieved through the sacrament of reconciliation and prayer. For people with gender dysphoria, the first step is to regain the *imago Dei* and reestablish a friendship with God. Having gender dysphoria does not mean transgender people are unique enemies of God. Instead, for a gender dysphoric person, like all Christians seeking healing, the first step begins with friendship with God—without this, no other love or virtue is possible.

Love of Self

St. Thomas challenges Christians to love themselves correctly according to the Gospel. He writes, *"so our love for ourselves is the model and root of friendship; for our friendship for others consists precisely in the fact that our attitude to them is the same as to ourselves"* (*ST* IIa–IIae q. 25, a. 4). The love of oneself is the root and model of how a person can love another. This call to love oneself poses a challenge if a person does not love oneself. Aristotle wrote, *"friendly feelings towards others flow from a person's own feelings towards himself or herself"* (Aristotle *NE,* ix, 4). Fr. Cessario writes, *"When we love ourselves in charity, we love ourselves as befriended by God, for charity numbers us among his true friends"* (Cessario 2002, 78).

Archbishop Carlson of St. Louis warns in his 2020 pastoral letter, "Gender ideology asks us to conflate compassion and compromise. It says, in effect: 'If you were compassionate you would let me have my way'" (Carlson 2020, 8). According to the archbishop, freedom does not come from doing whatever one feels but instead comes from a disciplined and focused life. For example, a musician who has received training and practice is freer to create music than someone who has never had a lesson. To love oneself is to discipline oneself and to create boundaries.

People also need to be flexible and forgiving with themselves. Like Pope Francis, Archbishop Carlson states that because one has predetermined sex, this does not mean rigid cultural gender stereotypes constrain a child. Instead, Archbishop Carlson warns, "How we live our masculine and feminine identity is certainly diverse, and there needs to be room for that. There's a wide variety of personalities, and they don't always fit gender stereotypes" (Carlson 2020, 4). Loving oneself gives one the confidence of nonconformity within the culture. The greatest saints loved God, themselves, and their neighbor enough to conform their lives to Christ and not the stereotypes of how one ought to live. Loving oneself is seeing oneself with the eyes of God.

Love of Neighbor

Transgender icon Laverne Cox stated at *Creating Change*, the National Conference on LGBT Equality, hosted by the National Gay and Lesbian Task Force, *"Loving trans people is a truly revolutionary act"* (Ford 2014). Authentic love is the key to supporting transgender people, a concept agreed upon by progressives and conservatives alike. Jesus claims, *"those who say 'I love God,' and hate their brother, are liars'; for those who do not love a brother whom they have seen, cannot love God whom they have not seen"* (1 Jn 4: 20 NAB).

Love of neighbor is not for his or her own sake but because of the person's relationship with God. Fr. Cessario writes, *"Charity goes out to the neighbor, both angels, and men, who either participate in or are called to participate in the fellowship of God's love (communicatio beatitudinis)"* (Cessario 2002, 77). This love goes out from the self to the other in two separate ways, either as the love of God's friend or love of God's object as a thing. If people are a friend of God's, they seek to enter this *communio*. The *communio* is the family of God.

The love of God's objects is also important, which includes the rest of the created world. Loving the environment, animals, or anything natural is clearly God's object that Christians respect and love out of love for the one who owns them. Fr. Cessario, in the description of God's things, includes the sinner. He claims, *"This last category includes the sinner who de facto is not a friend of God. Hell represents the state of a person permanently excluded from incorporation into divine friendship, reduced as it were to a 'thing'"* (Cajetan *Commentary on Summa Theologiae*, q. 25, a. 1).

[Laverne Cox, 1972—]

Although the Christian cannot love the damned in hell, the Christian is called to love the sinner since, until the final judgment, he or she still may become God's friend. Thus, charity requires the Christian to love the sinner, promoting goodness, and seeking to return the sinner to participate in the mystery of Christ's love. Nothing and no one can escape the love of God, and the God of the faithful Christian is recognized through this virtue of charity. Fr. Cessario adds to this idea, *"Hatred, for instance, stands opposed to the very act of love; acedia and jealousy check the joy of loving; discord and schism thwart the peace that charity produces; and finally, offensiveness and scandal hinder the good that fraternal correction seeks to promote"* (Cessario 2002, 92).

In *The Brothers Karamazov* (1880), Father Zosima, a famous Russian monk, spoke to Madame Khokhlakov about becoming convinced of God, overcoming her crisis of faith, and finding meaning in life. She expected the monk to tell her she needed to pray for more hours or accept more harsh penance. Instead, Fr. Zosima advised,

> By the experience of active love. Strive to love your neighbor actively and indefatigably. In as far as you advance in love, you will grow surer of the reality of God and of the immortality of your soul. If you attain perfect self-forgetfulness in the love of your neighbor, then you will believe without a doubt, and no doubt can possibly enter your soul. This has been tried. This is certain. (Dostoevsky 2018, 64)

A virtuous person lives for charity. In this gift of love, one experiences Christ dwelling within. One is open to a *"radical welcoming of another"* (Melina 2001, 55). Charity does not exist in an abstract reality but is the realism of concrete practice, which leads to true friendship, modeled on the Trinitarian *communio*. Although the love of neighbors may not be a cure for gender dysphoria, focusing on others through love and service as a means to love and serve God means less time and energy dedicated to focusing on one's own dysphoria.

Christians do not find themselves looking in the mirror or navel dwelling, but they find themselves when they are an outward gift to others. St. Basil the Great, in his reflections on monastic life, claimed, *"If you live alone, whose feet will you wash... one who is alone will always fail to act out one of the many dimensions of charity"* (Basil, *The Long Rules*, Q. 7).

Thus, the early church's faith was *praxis* and *theoria*—deeds of charity, as well as worship and prayer.

The love of a neighbor is not jealous. True friendship rejoices in another person's beatitude with God. The Dominican mystic Fr. John Tauler, O.P. (1300–1361), wrote in a sermon,

> If I love God, I love St. Paul's rapture more in him than in me. And still, through a charity, that ecstasy also belongs to me. Charity does not suffer from sadness because it is not the first to experience something good. Rather it recognizes only the exultation that comes from knowing simply that one is before God and that only by his gracious gift that lasts forever, not only am I a glorious person, but also unique, singular, and privileged. (Tauler 1910, 438)

This mystic's vision of the relationship between *beatitudo* and *communio* is vital for those with gender dysphoria. One falls into envy easily, especially in the twenty-first century, because of social media. With snapshots of people's lives on display with filters to eliminate physical imperfections. Creative cropping shows a perception that every moment of a person's life is interesting, perfect, and inspiring, leaving many people to experience emptiness, coveting the life of those online.

Fr. Tauler preached in the fourteenth century that Christians should not envy the supernatural grace St. Paul received. St. Paul received grace not for his own sake but as a gift to evangelize the gentile world. Charity allows the Christian to be thankful rather than envious of the gifts given to St. Paul. He also preached that each friend of God is *glorious, unique, singular,* and *privileged.* Some gender dysphoric people may find some peace in the diversity of the Christian family. While some people have gifts of masculinity or femininity, others are blessed with natural physical beauty, and most people are insecure about their appearance. In addition, some people are brilliant, while others are not. Envying what others have is natural, but through the virtue of charity, jealousy can be overcome, and joy can be found in seeing God's love fulfilled in others.

Love of Body

St Augustine preached the love of one's own body. This love is the last of the loves, but it is one of the most important for gender dysphoric people. Fr. Cessario reflecting on the hierarchy, wrote, *"The Christian should love the neighbor more than his or her own body, although one is required to sacrifice one's natural life only for the benefit of another's eternal salvation"* (Cessario 2002, 86). Thus, the true love of self leads to the love of one's own body, both as a gift from God and the dwelling place of God.

Archbishop Carlson offers pastoral support for those dealing with gender identity issues. He wrote,

> If you're uncomfortable with your biological sex, or if you consider yourself as having a gender identity at odds with your biological sex, here's the first thing I want you to know: God loves you. He loves you right where you are. He has a plan for you. (Carlson 2020, 3)

Understanding one's body teleologically helps give meaning to one's existence. Teleology is not a celebration of existence but a journey towards one's creator. Jesus himself manifests this truth in his body; he reveals God's plan for *our* bodies. The archbishop connects the gift of our bodies to the Eucharist in writing, *"The complementarity of men's and women's bodies is made to serve that gift, and allows us to give life. When we integrate that truth into our lives we become living symbols of the Eucharist"* (Carlson 2020, 4).

For the gender dysphoric person, this love is perhaps the most difficult. In a 2005 study, medical researchers discovered through surveys that transsexuals strongly dislike hatred when viewing their secondary sex organs (Beier, Bosinski, and Loewit 2005). This hatred for the body is contrary to this unselfish love that flows from God. If one is called to show charity even for the sinner who hates God, how much more should a person love the body of the friend of God?

If this love of one's body is not easy, *The Story of a Soul* by St. Thérèse of Lisieux may illuminate how Christian charity works in *praxis*:

> There is in the Community a Sister who has the faculty of displeasing me in everything, in her ways, her words, her character,

everything seems very disagreeable to me. And still, she is a holy religious who must be very pleasing to God. Not wishing to give into the natural antipathy I was experiencing, I told myself that charity must not consist in feelings but in works; then I set myself to doing for this Sister what I would do for the person I loved the most. Each time I met her, I prayed to God for her, offering Him all her virtues and merits. I felt this was pleasing to Jesus, for there is no artist who doesn't love to receive praises for his works, and Jesus, the Artist of souls, is happy when we don't stop at the exterior but, penetrating into the inner sanctuary where he chooses to dwell, we admire its beauty. I wasn't content simply with praying very much for the Sister who gave me so many struggles, but I took care to render her all the services possible, and when I was tempted to answer her back in a disagreeable manner, I was content with giving her my most friendly smile, and with changing the subject of the conversation, for the Imitation says: *"It is better to leave each one in his own position than to enter into arguments."*

Frequently, when I was not at recreation and had occasion to work with this Sister, I used to run away like a deserter whenever my struggles became too violent. As she was absolutely unaware of my feelings for her, never did she suspect the motives for my conduct, and she remained convinced that her character was very pleasing to me. One day at recreation, she asked in almost these words: *"Would you tell me, Sister Thérèse of the Child Jesus, what attracts you so much to me; every time you look at me, I see you smile?"* Ah! What attracted me was Jesus hidden in the depths of her soul; Jesus, who makes sweet what is most bitter. I answered that I was smiling because I was happy to see her (it is understood that I did not add that this was from a spiritual standpoint). (Thérèse *The Story of a Soul*, 222– 223)

The diary entry of St. Thérèse offers helpful insight into how to approach friends of God who are *very disagreeable.* Suppose a gender dysphoric Christian could imitate the practices of St. Thérèse when dealing with one's own feelings of disagreeableness towards his or her own body. In case, one may find a path for showing charity towards oneself. Smile at yourself. Pray for oneself when experiencing dysphoria—recalling this body is created specially by God and is a one-of-a-kind gift given to the beloved. The dysphoria may make a person uncomfortable, but a Christian cannot dislike something to the point of hate. In a psychological study by Klaus Beier, M.D., a high rate of transgender people felt intense emotions of hatred when considering their secondary sex organs (Beier, Bosinski, and Loewit 2005).

"Charity," according to Fr. Cessario, *"breaks down all barriers, of nationality, of race, of class, of culture, but it also transcends the more profound, ontological barrier between the orders of creation"* (Cessario 2002, 82). Charity is the forgiveness of one's own brokenness and accepts the brokenness of others. Loneliness can appear as a form of suffering, an inner dissatisfaction—a restlessness of heart. Yet, loneliness is part of being a human being. Love is not a quick fix, but charity is the mutual vulnerability and openness to receiving love in one's broken state. From the self-awareness of one's own brokenness comes the opportunity for profound empathy and charity.

Jean Vanier, Ph.D., in *Becoming Human*, examines this concept of being in one's own body. He claims one *becomes* human by beginning a journey of courage to forgive and be forgiven, where a person is not living the delusion of false hurts but in freedom. In a reflection on Ezekiel's dream, where the people said, *"Our bones are dry, we have no hope. All is over for us."* The prophet Ezekiel responded, *"O my people, now I am going to open your graves. I will bring you up from your graves... I will put my Spirit in you, and you will live"* (Ez 37: 11–14).

IV. Prudence
Summa Theologica IIa–IIae q.47–56

A prudent man foresees the evil, and hides himself: but the simple pass on, and are punished.

— Proverbs 22: 3

The Catechism describes prudence as the virtue *"that disposes of practical reason to discern our true good in every circumstance and to choose the right means of achieving it"* (*CCC*, 1806). Prudence is the *mother of all* virtues since she puts all other virtues in their proper order. All other virtues are dependent upon prudence to achieve their proper ends. Prudence is based on the Greek term *phronēsis* or practical wisdom. In the *Phaedrus,* Plato likened *phronoia*, or wisdom, to an image of a charioteer who directs horses' wild nature (Plato *Phaedrus*, 254e). The appetites are pulling the individual in various directions, yet, for the charioteer to arrive at the destination, one must guide the horses to work together and follow the path set out by prudence. Likewise, concupiscence may drive a person to seek happiness under a different gender identity. While grasping at identity may feel like a three-horse chariot rushing a person in different directions, prudence keeps a gender dysphoric individual balanced and focused on the final end, which is beatitudo.

Prudence is not an end but the means by which all virtues achieve their proper ends. Aristotle called prudence *"right reason applied to action"* (Aristotle, *NE*. vi, 5), a line echoed by St. Thomas. The transgender dilemma is both a question of right ends, namely justice, and right actions to achieve an end, namely prudence. St. Augustine taught prudence was *"a love that discerns"* (Augustine *De moribus*, I, 15, 25). This quote from St. Augustine is aptly applied in this situation since acting prudent is the most loving way to achieve an end goal.

St. Isidore of Seville claims *prudens* derived its name from *porro videns*, *"looking ahead"* (Isidore *Etym.*, prudens). When a gender dysphoric person, particularly a gender dysphoric youth, is contemplating their path forward, foresight is one of the most important virtues one could implement. Foresight includes considering the long-term health effect of the medicalized approach to gender dysphoria. Foresight also considers the sterility created by the medical transformation. These health and relationship considerations alone call into question the possibility of foreseeable happiness in the future decades of a person's life. Therefore, the physical, social, and spiritual lasting consequences of a medicalized approach to self-fulfillment should be decided slowly, discerningly, and with good counsel.

Prudence is composed of eight integral parts, which are component elements for virtue. As a house is composed of walls, a floor, and a roof, prudence is composed of *memoria* (memory), *intelligentia* (understanding), *docilitas* (docility or teachableness), *sollertia* (sagacity or shrewdness), *ratio* (reason), *providentia* (foresight), *circumspectione* (circumspection), and *cautione (caution)*. Memory is a part of prudence that focuses on experiences resulting from *many memories* (ST IIa–IIae 49, a. 1). Memories help a person understand what is true in most cases based on his or her own experience.

Understanding similarly denotes the *"right estimate about some final principle, which is taken as self-evident"* (ST IIa–IIae 49, a. 2). Prudence uses experiences from the past and understanding in the present to inform the person on how to reach their final end. Understanding is affected by one's beliefs about gender theory or the meaning of male and female. For a person dealing with gender dysphoria, memory and understanding might direct a person to consider themselves fit for transsexual surgeries based on their subjective experiences. Many transgender people recall early memories of feeling gender dysphoria and a strong intuition that one is the wrong sex. One may understand oneself to be either a male or female. Within the current political climate, these two components are enough to recommend sex reassignment surgeries. However, this recommendation would be premature when considering six additional integral parts of prudence.

Docility and shrewdness are also essential parts of prudence since they accept wisdom from outside themselves. Docility is one's ability to be taught by others since it is impossible to consider first-hand all particular matters in an infinite way. St. Thomas recommends listening to the advice of *"old folks who have acquired a sane understanding of the ends in practical matters"* (ST IIa–IIae 49, a. 3). Part of docility is listening to the advice of the ancients and the Magisterium of the church, which has practical wisdom about the human person and human psychology which extends beyond the modern period.

Along with docility is shrewdness or sagacity, which is the proper estimate or opinion of the counsel one has received. A shrewd person does not believe everything they are told but instead has the disposition to acquire the correct estimate. Prudence is an intellectual virtue, whereby one asks, does that make sense? For example, several teenage girls identify as FtM within a single classroom. A moderately shrewd person considers this a social trend for these several girls within a brief period, or is this a medical condition that has defied statistics? In Lisa Littman, M.D.,'s study, the parents of teenagers who identified as transgender exercised shrewdness when doubting their children's condition. Shrewdness alone does not make a person prudent, but she is an integral part of prudence.

Reason, foresight, circumspection, and caution are integral parts of prudence aptly applied to the transgender issue. Reason takes into consideration memory, understanding, docility, and shrewdness and applies reason to them. Reason does not only consider one thing but all things which might give way to foresight. Foresight is a particular part of prudence since she is within the definition of prudence. Foresight considers how one may achieve one's end and avoid the perils along the way.

[Prudence]

Circumspection is also necessary epistemologically since she correctly identifies what is possible. If a person believed he was a pony earnestly, is within the realm of possibilities one would consider? Circumspection draws the lines around what is worth considering. St Thomas notes, *"Though the number of possible circumstances be infinite, the number of actual circumstances is not"* (*ST* IIa–IIae q. 49, a. 7, ad. 1). Prudence asks a person to consider a man in a woman's body or vice versa, which exists within the realm of possibilities? Some lines cannot be crossed within the cogito ergo sum argument of the essence of being for all but the most extreme postmodernists. Lastly, caution is an integral part of prudence which aims to avoid or minimize the harm caused by one's actions. Prudence needs caution to grasp the good and avoid evil.

The potential parts of prudence are also vital since they are virtues that give prudence its potency. Prudence, an intellectual virtue, plays a critical role in the cognitive stages of the human act. Prudence has three steps: deliberation (*consultandum*), judgment (*judicium*), and command (*electio*). Each of these steps requires additional effort as they advance and thus requires secondary virtues of prudence. The particular strengths of *habitus* needed to carry out these stages are *euboulia* (disposition for receiving good counsel), *synesis* (judiciousness), and *gnome* (Perspicacity).

Deliberation requires *euboulia* to integrate docility with shrewdness and to consider all of the available options. *Euboulia* is the virtue of receiving good counsel. Fr. Cessario noted, *"Aquinas maintains that the wayfarer who lives according to the gift of Counsel especially imitates the saints in heaven who remain in a state of a simple turning toward God – simplex conversion ad Deum"* (*ST* IIa–IIae q. 52, a. 3, ad. 3) (Cessario 2002, 125). Whereas Aristotle considers prudence an intellectual *capacity to take good counsel* (Aristotle *NE,* VI. 5), St. Thomas regards prudence as applying the *right reasoning to action* (*ST* IIa–IIae q. 47, a. 2) and characterizes *euboulia,* the capacity to take good counsel as a potential part of prudence. Good counsel is consequently the gift associated with prudence.

When considering proper judgment, the application of prudence requires *synesis, "judging well according to common law"* and gnome, which *"denotes a certain acuteness in judgment"* (*ST* IIa–IIae, q. 51, a. 3–4). *Synesis* is helpful in common knowledge, as when a doctor delivers a healthy baby. *Gnome* is a special virtue that is necessary to have a higher virtue of discriminating judgment. *Gnome* makes it possible to apply superior principles, such as equity moderating and interpreting the norms, to obtain fairer results when confronted with unique situations. *Gnome* is needed in cases that do not obey the general rules. *Gnome* judges according to some higher principles—which may be likened to divine providence. St. Thomas states a moral act must not just follow common rules but divine providence using the virtue of *gnome*,

> Sometimes, however, something should be done outside the common rules of behavior... we must judge [some] cases in light of some higher principle beyond the common rules of behavior used in the judgments of the virtue of synesis. Corresponding to those higher principles is a higher virtue of judgment called gnome, which implies a certain comprehensive discernment in judging. (*ST* IIa–IIae, q. 51, a. 4; *S. Jensen Translation*)

St. Thomas uses congenital disabilities as an analogy since typical births would be *synesis,* and congenital disabilities are like *gnome*—which occurs but is not anticipated. A person does not expect to utilize the special virtue of *gnome* any more than when conceiving a child, a mother expects to deliver a child with a congenital disability. St. Thomas writes,

> Thus, monstrous births of animals are beside the order of the active seminal force, and yet they come under the order of a higher principle, namely, of a heavenly body, or higher still, of Divine Providence. Hence by considering the active seminal force, one could not pronounce a sure judgment on such monstrosities, and yet this is possible if we consider Divine Providence. (ST IIa–IIae, q. 51, a. 4)

Although this analogy is only meant as an example of an unexpected divine providence, the analogy unexpectedly illuminates the transgender issue. Suppose a boy like Ben Shapiro's son decides to wear sparkly shoes as addressed *supra* in 9.3. The virtue of *synesis* can be applied to prudential judgment, and one can decide to correct the child to help him adjust to American culture, where boys do not wear sparkly shoes. In the situation when a gender dysphoric youth who has experienced early-onset gender dysphoria persistently and consistently until his or her mid-20s is seeking assistance, the special virtue of *gnome* could apply. *Gnome* is synonymous with congenital disabilities, an event that occurs naturally but not typically. This moral exception does not mean one should rush to embrace a medical approach. One must consider what was presented in chapter ten; however, this is a unique case, and a special kind of prudence—farsightedness is required, which would not be necessary for most circumstances. One cannot treat all cases whereby a person is experiencing gender dysphoria alike. Which prudent approach to this person would point him or her towards God and *beatitudo*? St. Augustine instructs, *"prudence is love choosing wisely between the helpful and the harmful"* (Augustine *De moribus*, I, 15). What is most helpful through the judgments of *synesis* and *gnome*.

Lastly, the reader must crucially consider imprudence and sham prudence concerning the transgender issue. Precipitousness or undue haste obstructs the ability to receive good counsel (*euboulia*) and is a sign of imprudence. Precipitousness also leads a person to become an *inconsiderate* person who does not consider wise people's advice accurately or for Magisterium. Acting quickly and alone, one can be deceived by their own craftiness and self-deception. Fr. Cessario about Nietzsche reflects, *"[T]he penchant in the modern era [is] for people to turn false before themselves, to serve as their own self-executioners. Those unable to love themselves properly are most tempted to fall victim to sham prudence. Since spiritual orphans lack the conviction about their self-worth, they experience difficulty in being honest about how they pursue even their worthwhile goals"* (Cessario 2002, 121).

Modern people face the problem not that they are daft, but rather too cunning, but without the prudence and good counsel for proper moral deliberation. Sham prudence exists in two ways: first by wrong reason, followed by the wrong action. If the premise is false, the vice may appear valid on the face but incorrect in reality. This is the prudence of the flesh, which seeks a worldly end rather than a spiritual end. Being solicitous about temporal matters beyond what is necessary can lead one to fall into the prudence of the flesh. A person who believes being the opposite gender will be the cause of their ultimate happiness is not prudent but under the sham of the prudence of the flesh. A person can also follow sham prudence by using fictitious or counterfeit means to a proper or improper end. If a person uses guile or fraud to achieve their end, it is through the sin of craftiness (*astutiae*).

Monstrous Births

To call transgender people a monstrous birth would be inaccurate since each person possesses the *imago Dei,* and no man is a monster. However, many transgender people feel as if they are monsters. Rachel Anne Williams describes her feelings, *"My gender is monstrous. It cannot be reconciled with the old transsexual narrative of a woman trapped in a man's body. I am a monster trapped in a non-monstrous body... I stick myself with needles filled with bioidentical hormones to break out of the prison cell that is my body. I am experimenting on my own body not because I am in the 'wrong body' but because I aim to see just how far my body can change"* (R. A. Williams 2019, 121). The explanation given by Rachel Anne Williams is precisely the fear Catholics have of the transgender movement; this is potentially a gender experiment too often framed as a civil rights issue. Catholics believe that the cause of the birth abnormality is not sin or evil in a moral sense, but as St. Thomas explains, *one can understand the matter in light of divine providence.* The self-made monster created by gender ideology is a Frankenstein's creation that abhors the natural order and cannot be accepted by Christian people who believe in the world's ordained creation.

V. Justice
Summa Theologica II-II 57–122

But strive first for the Kingdom of God and His justice.
— St. Matthew 6: 33

In contrast to some modern understandings of social justice, the Catholic interpretation of justice is a *"moral virtue that consists in the constant and firm will to give their due to God and neighbor"* (*CCC*, 1807). Justice is composed of two integral parts: do good and avoid evil (*ST* IIa–IIae q. 79, a. 1). All one must do to be just is not to omit to do good and avoid transgressions against the upright. Nine potential parts of justice strengthen one to do good and decline from evil better.

The supportive parts of justice are religion, piety, observance, gratitude, vengeance, truthfulness (*veritas*), friendliness, liberality, and *epikeia* (equity). Religion, piety, and observance aim to give what is due to particular persons, while truthfulness, gratitude, and vengeance are virtues that support the participation of communal life. Gratitude acknowledges benefaction, while vengeance controls the forms of retribution allowed for harm done to oneself or others within the community. Liberality is generosity and openness, while friendliness brings joy and harmony within communal living.

Religion as a virtue is a foreign concept, even for most practicing Christians. Modern Western culture considers religion to be an institutionalization of a faith. In contrast, St. Thomas defines religion as rendering God the absolute honor is His due and *"Implies a relationship to God"* (*ST* IIa–IIae q. 81, a. 1). The virtue of religion is a *habitus* of the will *"that shapes a person to render carefully and permanently to God the supreme honor that is his due"* (Cessario 2002, 149). The justice, which man owes to God, is his *actus essendi,* the act of his own existence.

Christians can never pay this debt by religious observance. St. Thomas explains, *"Because he possesses perfect glory to which creatures can add nothing, we do not give honor and reverence to God for his own sake, but rather for our own sake, because when we do so, our mind is subjected to him and in this our perfection consists"* (*ST* IIa–IIae q. 81, a. 7). The living of a life of properly ordered virtues is freedom. Their Mover perfectly moves all other creatures. Human beings acting in an ordered way requires an act of the will, freely given to all people by the first mover, who is God.

For people with gender dysphoria, the focus may be on survival rather than human perfection; yet, Jesus and the church challenge the faithful to seek perfection, not by one's own works, but by allowing Christ's virtues to work in them. Why follow the natural order and give each his or her due? Because justice leads to freedom and happiness. The more one rebels against justice, the greater the disorder and disease.

It is easy to find examples of religious people focused on ceremonies and titles and not on giving God his due, but this is a lesser form of the virtue of religion. True religion aims at giving thanks to God for the goodness he has provided to humanity. In his commentary to the *Summa Theologica,* Cardinal Cajetan responded, one can call religious whosoever occupies himself with ceremonies, sacrifices, and things of the sort. Still, the saints are those who devote their whole being to God (Cajetan *Commentary on Summa Theologiae,* q. 81, a. 7). One who aims to give to God, which is due, gives devotion and prayer internally and adoration, sacrifice, oblations, and tithes externally.

Lumen Gentium (Light of the Nations) challenges every Christian to consecrate something to God by means of a vow (LG 6). Every proper religious sacrifice and vow, offered in love and prudence, serves the giver's perfection and happiness. For each believer, including people who are transgender, the question is, what can you offer to God in sacrifice. Within the hierarchy of gifts, external belongings are least significant, followed by gifts of one body, and most importantly, the gift of one's will or *actus essendi.* Every challenge in life is an opportunity to offer oneself to God further and thus to become genuinely free. St. Augustine wrote, *"what is given to God is added to the giver"* (Augustine *Epistola,* 127).

Cardinal Cajetan describes the virtue of piety as a gift which *"illumines the just believer to embrace every person, and indeed everything, as a child or possession of the heavenly Father- "ut filios et res Patris"* (Cajetan *Commentary on Summa Theologiae*, q. 101). Piety within the Catholic understanding is grace detached from morality, but an infused virtue allows a person to approach the people and objects in the proper order. Piety is compared to the Beatitude, *"Blessed are the meek, for they will inherit the earth"* (Mt. 5: 5). This meekness is not weakness but inner strength and self-control. The virtue of piety is an essential virtue for people with gender dysphoria.

To experience one's own body as *ut filios Patris,* the Father's son (or daughter), places one's perspective not within one's own subjectivity but within the divine reality. This virtue requires simplicity of heart, but the fruit of the virtue is illumination to witness the created world through the eyes of God. If a person could look into the mirror and see what God sees when looking at His beloved child, *"hating"* what is looking back in the mirror would be impossible. The person in the mirror is the *imago Dei.*

In modern cultural philosophy, the highest ideal is self-expression. For a Christian, the highest ideal is to show fitting gratitude towards God since he is *"the principle of all our goods"* (*ST* IIa–IIae q. 106, a. 1). If one considers one's body a gift from God, perhaps the body can be used however one likes. A present does not come with conditions. However, if one's body and life are like the talent found in Jesus' Parable of the Talents (Mt. 25: 14 –30), when the master will return, seeing what was done with the borrowed coins, within the *exitus-reditus,* the person should return differently from how they left upon returning the soul to God. A debt of gratitude is a moral debt required by virtue, and not responding in a proper way is ingratitude and injustice. The question for each person, including transgender people, is, what is proper gratitude for the gifts you have been given? God gives every person specific bodies and souls, but seldom is a person satisfied. If people were generally gracious with their gifts, cosmetic surgery would not be a multi-billion-dollar industry. This ingratitude of society is not unique to transgender people; instead, they are in line with modernity.

Truthfulness is a key issue within the transgender issue. St. Thomas writes that a moral debt exists insofar as, *"out of equity, one man owes another a manifestation of the truth."* The saint further states, *"it would be impossible for men to live together, unless they believed one another, as declaring the truth one to another"* (*ST* IIa–IIae q. 109, a. 3; ad. 1). In this regard, the transgender person is attempting to show his brethren the truth of his essence. In contrast, one may consider the transgender identity a lie and a deception to his brethren. This virtue hinges on the truth of transgender science and our philosophical anthropology.

Epieikeia is another important Thomistic concept found under the virtue of Justice and is similar to *gnome*. This virtue found in Aristotle's *Nicomachean Ethics* 5.10 makes it possible to rectify injustices by applying the law equally in all cases. In *The Thomist*, Ana Marta González, Ph.D., expanded on the necessity of *epieikeia* to ensure that justice imprudently applied does not become injustice. She explains, *"Gnome, which is the virtue that perfects the judgment prior to the precept of prudence in those matters that are not covered by the general rule, is also a virtue necessary to exercise epieikeia"* (González 1999, 236). St. Thomas calls *epieikeia* a virtue despite others calling her an unlawful vice (*ST* IIa–IIae q. 120, a. 1). The battle over equality versus equity continues today.

Knowing when to follow the law and when to abandon the law of legal justice for a higher prudent application of justice is necessary. The church also may consider *epieikeia* in addition to *gnome* when attempting to help transgender people. The church may seek to establish a heuristic of judgment or *"a simple procedure that helps find adequate, though often imperfect, answers to difficult questions"* (Kahneman 2011, 98). Transgender people are in a similar fallen state as all Christians. In certain medical, psychological, and social situations, the suffering of transgender people is more complex, and the pastoral response should reflect the complexity with careful *epieikeia and gnome*. John Paul II, on the centennial of Leo XIII's encyclical Of the Eternal Father (*Aeterni Patris*), preached on the value of Thomistic realism in pastoral situations, *"we are not dealing here with man in the 'abstract,' but with the real, 'concrete,' 'historical' man. We are dealing with each individual, since each one is included in the mystery of Redemption, and through this mystery, Christ has united himself with each one forever"* (John Paul II 1991, chap. 6, no, 53). Using the fullness of the virtues helps to support people with gender dysphoria.

VI. Fortitude
Summa Theologica IIa–IIae q. 123–140

She clothes herself with fortitude and fortifies her arms with strength.

— Proverbs 31: 17

"Fortitude is the moral virtue that ensures firmness in difficulties and constancy in the pursuit of the good. It strengthens the resolve to resist temptation and to overcome obstacles in the moral life" (*CCC,* 1808). For people with gender dysphoria, creating a *habitus* of fortitude will be necessary for placing the emotions in their proper order. The virtues put reason into emotion. Emotional obstacles need to be overcome, but unlike the Stoics, Christians do so through grace and the virtues' activity using the passions to participate in psychic healing adequately.

In section two, *Hope:* the issues of concupiscence and irascibility were raised to contrast the theological virtue of hope with the feelings of hope and desire. Section two emphasized that the virtue of hope is only fulfilled with *beatitudo* and *communio.* In contrast, magnanimity and the integral parts of fortitude fulfill the emotion of hope. Nevertheless, St. Thomas, in his reflection on the appetites, does not discard this type of hope as meaningless emotions. Instead, the saint writes, *"the irascible or the concupiscible power can be the seat of human virtue, for in so far as each participates in reason, it is a principle of a human act"* (*ST* Ia–IIae q. 56, a. 4).

If reason informs the appetites, emotions become the authentic starting point toward something moral. Reason, informed by faith, illuminates the mind towards uprightness through the infused intellectual virtue of prudence. Fr. Cessario writes, *"Unruly emotions pose the most serious threat to maintaining a watchful prudence"* (Cessario 2002, 162). The resolute desires experienced in gender dysphoria are part of the *unruly emotions*, of which the Thomistic solution is to illuminate the feelings with reason and truth.

Fortitude strengthens the Christian to place the emotions in their proper order, but knowing the correct order is also a virtue. St. Thomas's realism contrasts with Platonism, Cartesianism, and Stoicism since he does not believe that action automatically follows knowledge. In keeping with the ghost within the machine understanding of the human person, the Cartesians believe the body simply acts as the intellect desires. St. Thomas includes emotions in his anthropological realism. St. Thomas interprets the *passions animae* to be morally neutral in themselves. The action following the emotion can be judged by virtue of prudence. No agreed-upon moral code exists in the modern Cartesian epoch whereby a person can judge the emotion's efficacy. The problem of relativism and non-cognitivism, as addressed *supra* in chapter three, becomes a dilemma under the virtue of fortitude since it is not clear towards what end courage should aim. Cardinal Cajetan wrote that fortitude remains ordered to humanize the sense appetites towards bringing the appetites into conformity with the rational good (Cajetan *Commentary on Summa Theologiae*, q. 123, a. 1,2). Fortitude is a moral virtue bringing the agent towards a finality, yet without a final goal, it is passion without a cause.

Fortitude is composed of four potential parts for virtue. The parts are magnanimity, magnificence, patience, and perseverance. The first two virtues are virtues of enterprise since they send the Christian outward. Magnanimity is the pursuit of honorable actions. St. Thomas describes magnificence as something which *"denotes the doing of something great"* (*ST* IIa–IIae q. 134, a. 2). These virtues help the Christian conquer the sin of pusillanimity or smallness of spirit, which convinces the persons that evil exists everywhere and trying to overcome obstacles in life is too difficult, so trying should not be attempted. This vice causes a person to be suspicious about all goods and leads to anxiety.

Another vice that affects people in Western culture is *mollite* or effeminacy, whereby *"a man is accustomed to enjoy pleasures"* and *"it is difficult for him to endure the lack of them"* (*ST* IIa–IIae q. 138, a. 1, ad. 1). Finally, one has an underlying belief that if something is uncomfortable or complex, it must be wrong. The fear of uncomfortable situations is an extreme perversion of egotistical hedonism. The modern man sits on the couch scrolling through social media on his mobile device while playing video games and smoking pot to avoid pain. The man is consuming processed instant foods that never rot and drinks endless large cups of high fructose corn syrup. The man receives government checks and has every material need met but has no desire to live.

In contrast, fortitude creates an *insatiable desire* for the works of justice (*ST* IIa–IIae q. 139, a. 2). Sloth is a capital vice that encourages the agent to abandon fortitude. Dealing with gender confusion or having a deep-seated existential crisis is challenging. However, something can be overcome through the exercise of fortitude, which directs the appetites to the right reason. People are looking for easy answers to complex issues, but the big questions of life require fortitude. For those with gender dysphoria, virtues will not remove the medical condition, but having the habitus of magnanimity or bigness of spirit stretches a person beyond the limitations of gender identity.

The last two potential virtues support the Christian in enduring one's vocation. Patience guards the Christian against succumbing to affliction, and perseverance helps the Christian to persist over extended periods of difficulty. This struggle of sloth also encourages people to seek easy and quick solutions to complex problems. Rather than addressing underlying existential challenges that require patience and perseverance, man seeks an immediate answer. For example, in response to an unwanted pregnancy, the quick response of the culture is abortion. However, adoption can be a lifesaving option for the child and healthier for the mother with more patience.

With gender dysphoria, some people later in life have suffered from the disorder and have shown patience and perseverance for decades. However, in the case of ROGD from chapter nine, young people who abruptly claim gender dysphoria seek permanent and life-altering procedures without exercising the virtues of patience and perseverance to see if these feelings would persist. The wise option according to prudence would be to practice the virtue of patience. The virtue of patience is primarily for overcoming the emotion of sorrow in the face of suffering. Patience is a virtue that keeps people from killing themselves from sadness and despair. Patience becomes a special virtue in light of the high rates of self-harm and suicide among transgender people.

Transgender activists may point to the *"coming out"* process as magnanimous since bravery does what is difficult. However, one must be watchful of mock courage—which is vice in sheep's clothing. These vices are presumption, ambition, and vainglory. Fr. Cessario describes mock courage as, *"When someone is ignorant of a danger involved, too optimistic about the nature of the danger, overly confident concerning his abilities, moved by untoward emotions of anger or depression, or is overly motivated by bounty-seeking"* (Cessario 2002, 168). These people perform brave acts that are not fortuitous. Jumping at emotions is not sufficient grounds for being brave. Instead, fortitude is bravery in collaboration with charity and prudence. Cognitively figuring out every situation is not always necessary. Instead, *"sometimes the recta ratio agibilium—the truth about what to do here and now —flows directly from well-ordered and fully developed sense passions"* (Cessario 2002, 164). A virtuous person, one with a virtuous *habitus*, will naturally do what is moral.

The Holy Spirit provides the virtue needed. As St. Thomas wrote, *"perform [virtual acts of justice] with an insatiable longing which represents a 'hunger and thirst for righteousness'"* (*ST* IIa–IIae q. 139, a. 2). The Holy Spirit supplies the virtue of fortitude for *instinctus* or the grace *"directs believers to the right course of action towards building up the Church"* (Cessario 2002, 174). The virtues are to direct people towards holiness and not towards their own relativism. Do what the Lord commands, and He will provide grace and virtue.

VII. Temperance
Summa Theologica IIa–IIae q. 141–169

Do not follow your desires but restrain your appetites.

— Sirach 18: 30

St. Thomas directs the virtue of temperance towards two subjects: food and sex. These two areas are not of direct concern for gender dysphoric people; however, the methodology and grace for overcoming these natural desires may be helpful for people experiencing innate feelings of cross-sex identities. Temperance is a virtue used to moderate the concupiscible appetite. The Catechism defines temperance as *"a moral virtue that moderates the attraction of pleasures and provides balance in the use of created goods… The temperate person directs the sensitive appetites toward what is good and maintains a healthy discretion"* (*CCC,* 1809).

Appetites are biological needs and inclinations. St. Thomas explains that appetites must be able to be satisfied, stating, *"By nature, each thing is bent on what fits it. And so human beings naturally crave an enjoyment that matches them"* (*ST* IIa–IIae q. 141, a. 1, ad 1). Temperance, paired with prudence, would warn the person with gender dysphoria that the desire cannot be accomplished since changing one's sex is not medically possible. If an appetite desires an object which is harmful to the desirer, a moral disorder exists. The disordered appetite can be expressed in two ways: (1) the appetites can act against the reasonable order of virtue, wanting too much or too little natural good. And (2) wanting something frustrates the Creator's design for human well-being (Congregation for the Doctrine of the Faith 1986, 7). When the gender dysphoric person has an appetite to be of the opposite sex, this desire is expressed in the latter description—frustrating the Creator's design for human totality since the appetite is impossible to achieve.

"The virtue of temperance is engaged first with emotions of desire and pleasure about goods of sense, and then as well with emotions of grief arising from their absence" (*ST* IIa–IIae q. 141, a. 3). For people with gender dysphoria, these senses are not food, sex, or physical pleasure but internal senses, specifically imagination. Therefore, the subjective parts of abstinence, sobriety, chastity, and sexual abstinence are not needed to curb these desires. However, they are beneficial virtues to practice as a Christian for other reasons.

The potential parts of continence, clemency, and modesty with the expression of humility are relevant. *"Humility crowns the life of Christian love, even as it provides the first steps for beginning the life of charity"* (Cessario 2002, 195). The humble person trusts the Lord. The virtue of humility allows for an openness to God's grace. The beatitude of St. John the Baptist is, *"I must decrease so that He may increase"* (Jn 3:30). Humility, a part of temperance, seeks to moderate the appetites by placing one's own will secondary to God's will. Cardinal Cajetan's commentary on humility from the *Summa Theologica* taught the humble person to consider himself *ut indignus*—as unworthy. Still, the humble person is also enduringly conscious that everything he receives comes from God (Cajetan *Commentary on Summa Theologiae*, q. 161).

For a person suffering from gender dysphoria, the individual is not *per se* deficient in humility, temperance, or any other virtue. The intention in introducing these virtues is not to label a group of people morally deficient, especially if gender dysphoric people are suffering from a medical disorder outside of their control. Yet, through *beatitudo, communio,* and the virtuous life, happiness and healing are possible.

If the desire is emotional and based on impulse, the desire is based on the concupiscible appetite. St. Augustine, by analogy, explains concupiscence in his writings on St. John's *Bread of Life* discourse. He writes, *"You have only to show a leafy branch to a sheep, and it is drawn to it. If you show nuts to a boy, he is drawn to them. He runs to them because he is drawn, drawn by love, drawn without any physical compulsion, drawn by a chain attached to his heart"* (Augustine, *Tractate* 26). The emotional draw carries no virtue or vice within the feelings; therefore, emotions are a simple concupiscence.

Step four in this heuristic focuses on the applied virtues a person can practice to alleviate dysphoria. For example, a persistent theme of concupiscence or a *"strong desire"* is apparent in the diagnosis of gender dysphoria in the *DSM-5*:

1. A strong desire to be rid of one's primary and/or secondary sex characteristics

2. A strong desire for the primary and/or secondary sex characteristics of the other gender

3. A strong desire to be of the other gender

4. A strong desire to be treated as the other gender

5. A strong conviction that one has the typical feelings and reactions of the other gender

The concept of desire is not always reconcilable with virtue. St. James wrote, *"[E]ach person is tempted when he is lured and enticed by his own desire. Then desire conceives and brings forth sin, and when sin reaches maturity it gives birth to death"* (Jm 1:15 NAB). The Catechism also warns that *"Etymologically, 'concupiscence' can refer to any intense form of human desire. Christian theology has given it a particular meaning: the movement of the sensitive appetite contrary to the operation of the human reason"* (*CCC*, 2515). The mythical Cupid shares etymology with con*cupis*cence. If Cupid hits a man with his arrow, he becomes passionately lustful. The *passions* make a man *passive,* and the emotions take control of his intellect and will. The apostle St. Paul identifies concupiscence with the rebellion of the 'flesh' against the 'spirit' (Gal 5: 16, 17, 24; Eph 2: 3). The response from a moral theologian for a person whose suffering originates with a strong desire would be to counteract concupiscence with the virtue of temperance.

Concupiscence has two kinds: emotional and sinful. When addressing concupiscence rooted in a medical etiology, one cannot reduce these feelings to the sin of lust since these desires are involuntary. This disorder may be a *rebellion of the flesh* as St. Paul describes, but this rebellion would be man's fallen state rather than a particular voluntary sin. Obsessive-Compulsive Disorder, Autism, and Body Dysmorphic Disorder/ Body Identity Integrity Disorder are all *rebellions of the flesh* since the body is at odds with the soul in the form of desire. In some cases, these are neurodevelopmental disorders with physical and hormonal etiologies. These conditions require both spiritual and medical therapeutic responses. Paul McHugh, M.D., remarked,

> The transgendered suffer a disorder of *'assumption'* like those in other disorders familiar to psychiatrists. Other kinds of disordered assumptions are held by those who suffer from anorexia and bulimia nervosa, where the assumption that departs from physical reality is the belief by the dangerously thin that they are overweight. (McHugh 2014b)

The concupiscence which lacks voluntariness would have to be emotional concupiscence rather than lust. Fr. Cessario cautioned, *"[C]onsiderations obviously merit careful attention, especially when it comes to evaluating particular actions of those persons who are judged to be in some state of psychological distress, it must also be remembered that emotional upset of this kind does not constitute a desirable state for human beings"* (Cessario 2001, 112–113). Some of these disorders can be overcome entirely with therapies, like Body Dysmorphic Disorders. In contrast, others like Autism are only partially treatable using selective serotonin reuptake inhibitors (SSRIs) to minimize the effects.

A proper pastoral response to someone with gender dysphoria is recognizing that although the individual is suffering from concupiscence or irascibility, no culpability occurs. St. Thomas uses the word *malum* (evil) to signify *"the undesirable absence or defect of a good that is due,"* then distinguishes the difference between *malum poenae* (evil suffered) and *malum culpae* (evil fault) (*ST* Ia q. 14, a. 10). For people who suffer from gender dysphoria, one is dealing with *malum poenae*. Archbishop Carlson raises the imagery of Jesus drawing near those experiencing *malum poenae* or participating in *malum culpae*. Jesus reaches out to not only those who choose to sin but to the leper, a person with paralysis, a woman with a fever, a woman with a hemorrhage, two blind men, and many others with conditions they did not choose (Matt 8–9). The archbishop recognizes gender dysphoria is *"a condition people experience, which is not the same as a sin, and a condition most people experience as not freely chosen"* (Carlson 2020, 3).

Jesus himself makes this distinction in the Gospel of St. John with the man born blind. His disciples asked him, *"Rabbi, who sinned, this man or his parents, that he was born blind?"* Jesus answered, *"Neither he nor his parents sinned; it is so that the works of God might be made visible through him"* (Jn 9:2–3 NAB). The disciples were asking Jesus, is this man guilty of *malum culpae* or his parents, but Jesus responds neither: the man is suffering from *malum poenae*. Evil is a parasite on the natural good. St. Thomas taught that the defect of a good exists as part of transforming the man born blind to the man re-created whole. God uses all things to manifest His glory. The person with *malum poenae,* the man born blind, receives a divine vocation. Up until the moment Jesus appeared to him, he could not have understood the reality of his disability. Brian Brock, Ph.D. in his interpretation of *The City of God XXII.19,* interprets St. Augustine to suggest *"some disabled people, like the martyrs while getting functionally healed, will retain the marks of their glorious roles as divine witnesses in the Resurrection"* (Augustine's *Hierarchies* 2012, 74) (Brock 2012, 97).

As discussed in chapter three, this concupiscence is involuntary. This form of concupiscence is not the sin of lust, as St. Augustine discusses in *The Confessions.* Instead, it is the Thomistic understanding of concupiscence as a robust innate desire. The Catechism states concupiscence is a *"movement of the sensitive appetite contrary to the operation of the human reason"* (*CCC,* 2515). Although this is *contrary to the operation of human reason,* the desire itself is not evil. Fr. Cessario describes,

> Concupiscence signifies willing a good to oneself, the desire of what is good for the subject, a wanting that is not necessarily disordered, for it is implanted in us by the author of nature and continues under the reign of grace. By loving this way, we seek for ourselves some authentic good. (Cessario 2002, 42)

Fr. Cessario refers to concupiscence's appetite rather than a specific concupiscible disordered desire in this passage.

Under the Thomistic approach, a healthy person has appetites subordinated to reason, contrary to David Hume's perspective, where reason is the slave of the emotions. This is a type of weaponized empathy whereby emotion subjects reason to itself. Drs. Terruwe and Baars write, *"it is the nature of the emotional life to be subject to reason, and, therefore, it must naturally desist in its operation when reason has judged the concrete object of its inclination not to be a universal good"* (Terruwe and Baars 1981, 26)—taking the idea from ST Ia-IIae q. 74, a. 3,.ad. 1. *"The appetite is subject to reason."*[5] The solution to this dilemma, according to Drs. Terruwe and Baars cannot be by repression of emotions. They claim,

---

[5] *Appetitus sensitives natus est obedire rationi*

"Medically speaking, it is a proven fact that repressed emotions cannot be controlled by reason and will" (Terruwe and Baars 1981, 39). Repression will only lead to more profound neurosis. Every emotion and every repressed emotion has *"a psychic component which is accompanied necessarily by a somatic component"* (Terruwe and Baars 1981, 18), or as St Thomas calls *transmutatio corporalis* (*ST* Ia–IIae q. 22, a.3).

In *Love & Responsibility*, Cardinal Karol Wojtyla sometimes promotes the Thomist view that concupiscence is not being sinful in itself. He claimed concupiscence is only sinful when the desire becomes the *"deliberate conscious self-commitment of the will to the promptings of the body, which conflict with objective truth."* The real challenge is *"emotional subjectivism"* (Wojtyla 1981, 163–164). Is the object of desire based on an ontological reality or based on personal feelings?

The Thomistic approach is to allow the emotions to be purified in the light of reason. Besides, repression of one emotion begins a chain of further repressions. The doctors claim, *"every subsequent repression requires less effort, as is true in the acquisition of any habit"* (Terruwe and Baars 1981, 52). The way to break the cycle of repression and neurosis is to create emotional maturity. A person needs the safety to allow his or her emotions to be judged by reason. As people let go of neuroses, they experience the freedom to let go of other neuroses. Fr. Cessario writes about emotional maturity, *"only the loved person can accept discipline as a means to grow closer to the source of love"* (Cessario 2002, 58). St. Bernard of Clairvaux presents a reasonable balance, *"Fear of God's judgment, apart from hope, casts us down into the pit of despair, while indiscreet hope, unmixed with a reasonable fear, engenders hurtful security"* (Bernard, *Sermo in Cantica*, 6).

Gender theorists also advocate for the liberation of sexuality from repression, which is why many are quick to embrace transgender identities and a medicalized approach to transformation. Unfortunately, the twentieth and twenty-first centuries have not proven that this sexual liberation removes sexual neuroses successfully. During a period of secularity, situational ethics, and moral relativism, the common person has never been as sexually free as in modern society. Despite this, neuroses are as prevalent as before with stress and anxiety about one's body. Drs Terruwe and Baars propose that *emotional maturity* is the key. They wrote that healing begins with two steps: *"first, the repressed emotion must be brought into consciousness, and second, the patient must be taught how to deal with the emotions in a rational manner"* (Terruwe and Baars 1981, 90). Psychiatrist Dr. Claude Wischik also made this claim in 2020, stating sexual maturity is necessary for healthy sexual interactions, and repression will never accomplish this (Wischik 2020). Dr. Viktor Frankl made similar claims about freedom, stating that freedom is not the last word. He wrote, *"I recommend that the Statue of Liberty on the East Coast be supplemented by a Statue of Responsibility on the West Coast"* (Frankl 2007, 536).

Emotional healing and maturity will be essential for the healing of a transgender person; not by possessing the virtue of temperance, all dysphoria will vanish. When discerning spiritual support for a person with gender dysphoria, the goal is not to replace medical advice from trained medical professionals with prayer or *"inner healing"* guided by well-meaning but untrained faith leaders. This principle was already explained in step one. With disorders like schizophrenia or cancer, feeling better is not a cure but does return a quality of life and help the healing process. With disorders like gender dysphoria, depression, or anxiety, a chemical cause may arise for these occurrences, but the feelings of peace and contentment are a cure. Suppose starting the day by attending Mass, reading Holy Scripture, or redirecting one's energy towards a Christian identity rather than a sex-based one allows a person a few hours of peace. In that case, the therapy has *"worked."* Repressing *fear* and *desires* can never lead to healing (Terruwe and Baars 1981, 91); instead, this fear can be relieved by hope, and energy could be directed in other more rational directions.

The more energy dedicated to establishing a Christian identity is less energy dedicated to sex-based identity. Transfeminist activist Rachel Anne Williams, who does not identify as a Christian, affirms this identity approach by claiming, *"My primary identity is that of a 'philosopher.' Before 'woman,' I am a philosopher. Before 'trans,' I am a philosopher. Being a philosopher is more predictive of my behavior and thorough than any other trait. It's fundamental to who I am and how I operate"* (R. A. Williams 2019, 73). Unfortunately, Rachel Anne Williams's philosophy is sophistry rather than realism, leading her deeper into the chaos of fruitless ideology. For a Christian person who has a transgender identity, the Christian identity should supersede the transgender identity since the Christian identity is rooted in reason. By correctly ordering the identities, greater inner peace is possible.

VIII. Mercy
Summa Theologica II-II 30

I desire mercy and not sacrifice.
— St. Matthew 9:13

Although Archbishop Carlson gives a challenge to individuals with transgender identities, he offers an even greater challenge to the church to show mercy:

> Very simply: these are our brothers and sisters. They have been subjected to violence and harassment, which is a violation of their human dignity. We, for our part, must protect them, welcome them into our hearts, and reach out to them in love just as Jesus did. Whether or not we totally understand their experience, and whether or not we agree with the decisions they make, they need to find us offering a safe place in which they can experience the love of God. (Carlson 2020, 11)

Pope Francis, in his post-synodal exhortation, the Joy of Love (*Amoris Laetitia*) exemplifies through the Scriptures Jesus's evangelization in walking *with* people on their journeys. Pope Francis writes evangelization begins with *"the gaze of Jesus, and they spoke of how he looked upon the women and men whom he met with love and tenderness, accompanying their steps in truth, patience and mercy as he proclaimed the demands of the Kingdom of God"* (Francis 2016, 60). Jesus did not just command his ideology. He first met, accompanied, and proclaimed. Jesus accompanied people with *"truth, patience, and mercy,"* of these three virtues, only one left to discuss is mercy. St. Thomas wrote, *"But of all the virtues which relate to our neighbor, mercy is the greatest, even as its act surpasses all others"* (IIa–IIae 30, a. 4). Mercy is a step away from the personal virtues and individual transformation towards its social implications. Mercy is the social dimension whereby the virtues are manifested in the world. When reflecting on how pastors of the church and Christian leaders within society should respond to the *"transgender moment,"* all virtues, especially mercy, are necessary. Archbishop Carlson quoted Pope Francis, stating: *"What we say matters. But how we say it matters too. It's possible to violate our fidelity to God in what we say or fail to say. It's also possible to violate that fidelity in how we say things"* (Carlson 2020,10).

Fr. Cessario states, *"Growth in the moral life cannot happen apart from an effective, personal union with Christ in the church of faith and sacraments."* He continues, *"Those who provide good moral teachings recognize this truth, and so refrain from imposing moral obligations without giving a clear explanation about how these demands may be suitably met"* (Cessario 2001, 225–226). Fr. Cessario also challenges, *"Indeed, the Gospel itself requires such an inquiry, for in imitation of her Lord, the Church as a whole must respond to the question, 'And who is my neighbor?' (Lk 10: 29)"* (Cessario 2002, 75). The *communio* of believers is a challenge to the individual and a challenge to the communion as it exists. Since human flourishing is contingent on *communio*, is the *communio* open for members to enter communion with it? Fr. Cessario warns about creating impositions and obligations without creating a pathway to achieve them. When approaching the ethical dilemma of addressing gender dysphoria, it is not enough to have good intentions. In the Letter of St. James, he writes, *"If one of the brothers or one of the sisters is in need of clothes and has not enough food to live on, and one of you says to them, 'I wish you well; keep warm and eat plenty,' without giving them these bare necessities of life, then what good is that?"* (Jm 2:15–16 NJB)

The Christian communion can establish impositions and obligations on homosexual and transgender people, but a *praxis* of how holiness appears for them is much less clear. Dr. Vanier challenges the church to avoid creating a divided community, where each person only cares about his or her own holiness. This attitude is a counter-witness to the resurrection. He taught,

> *Often community stops crying to God when it has itself stopped hearing the cry of the poor when it has become self-satisfied and found a way of life which is not too insecure… When the community makes a covenant with the poor people, their cry becomes its own.* (Vanier 1989, 196)

Parents of a transgender child, when interviewed, recalled their own struggle to find community, *"When [her son] first told us we felt like we were the only people in our area that has this issue of a child that wants to be a female. When we went to the PFLAG (Parents and Friends of Lesbians and Gays support group), we met others [with transgender children]. There is so much involved in transgender child [sic]... We all went for quite a while, and they were very helpful"* (Yarhouse et al., 2016, 203). Having a PFLAG support network for parents of transgender children may benefit some, but it is incomplete. The church may be missing an opportunity to better serve her people by offering a parental support system steeped in medical science, the practice of virtues, prayer, and the openness to grace.

The reader may also consider what the church loses by not encountering transgender people and the families of transgender people. By remaining isolated from the neighbor's suffering, the community has lost an opportunity to be transformed. Pope Francis wrote in his encyclical, Fraternity and Social Friendship (Fratelli Tutti), "We cannot be indifferent to suffering; we cannot allow anyone to go through life as an outcast. Instead, we should feel indignant, challenged to emerge from our comfortable isolation and to be changed by our contact with human suffering. That is the meaning of dignity" (Francis 2020, sec. 68).

The work of *communio* is a challenge for transgender people and a new challenge for the church not to ignore the cry of the suffering in its midst—our brothers and sisters in Christ. The church faces a poor man Lazarus moment when the community will be judged by how well they respond to the poor's needs at the church's door. St. John Chrysostom warned, *"If you cannot find Christ in the beggar at the church door, you will not find Him in the chalice."*[6] Dr. Vanier further warns, *"The broken body of Christ in the Eucharist is only clearly understood when it is seen in relation to the broken bodies and hearts of the poor; and their broken bodies and hearts find the meaning in the broken Body of Christ"* (Vanier 1989, 198). This message of Dr. Vanier is echoed in the words of St. Thomas Aquinas in the *Summa, "Mercy signifies grief for another's distress"* (ST IIa–IIae 30, a. 3). Jesus calls his followers to manifest His desire for mercy rather than sacrifice (Matthew 19:13) when He calls his followers to open their eyes and their hearts to the suffering of people with disabilities and

---

[6] Popular paraphrase of *Homily 50* on Matthew 14:23, 24.

accompany them on their journey of healing. Fidelity to religious rituals is essential, but the Word did not become flesh to institute a liturgical reform; instead, He came to remind people who they were created to be.

Jesus establishes in Matthew 19 two pathways for holiness: marriage and eunuchs for the sake of the Kingdom of Heaven. John Paul II echoes these two pathways throughout the *Theology of the Body*. The original solitude was Adam, who was alone, so God took from his side a rib to make Eve. After the two-fold creation, Adam no longer experienced the original solitude, but the original unity was destroyed in the process. To regain the original unity, the two become one flesh again. This unity occurs in the Christian era through the Sacrament of Marriage and the self-giving of one to another, bringing forth offspring, the embodiment of the two flesh becoming one. St. Paul also establishes the theology of the Body (of Christ) found in first Corinthians 12: 27. In this spiritual body, a person married, single, homosexual, transsexual, or any other type of sexual are invited to enter into Christ and receive a new identity not defined by personal feelings of identity or sexual attraction.

Paradoxically, when offspring are born, the original unity is both destroyed and created. The offspring is the two-flesh made one, but it also means Adam's unity is now three. In every subsequent generation, the original unity becomes even more distant. With 6 billion people on the planet, anthropological disunity appears permanent. The reunification of the original unity cannot be in the flesh but is instead in Spirit. As God punished the people of Babel with division, the Holy Spirit at Pentecost recreates a single person, a single chosen people who are not dependent on class, culture, nationality, age, sex, or any other worldly feature.

Through baptism, one is adopted into the Body of Christ; one next receives the Eucharist to become what one receives, which is again the Body of Christ. Finally, as a member of the Body of Christ, one unites their suffering to that of Christ, one makes up for what is lacking in the suffering of Christ, and one picks up one's cross to follow Christ to Golgotha. Dying with Christ, afterward, one rises with Christ at the resurrection. Thus, the mystery of faith becomes the story of Christian salvation but also *communio* and *beatitudio*. This narrative works equally well for St. Paul unmarried as for St. Peter, who was married, and St.

Agnes, the virgin or St. Perpetua, the mother. One's status in life, even to the extent of being St. Onesimus, the slave or St. Philemon, the slave owner, St. Philip the apostle, or St. Simeon, the Black the eunuch,[7] is irrelevant compared to the unity of the Body of Christ.

Within John Paul II's *Theology of the Body*, the pontiff presents married people, naturally born eunuchs, those having been made so by others, and those who have become eunuchs for the sake of the Kingdom of Heaven. Natural eunuchs and those made so by others are not clearly placed within either of those two categories of a sacramental union by marriage or consecrated life. Has the church considered how a Christian vocation for a homosexual and transgender person would appear? Similarities exist between these natural eunuchs of Matthew 19 and present-day sexual outcasts.

The Church has promulgated in the Second Vatican Council *Apostolicam Actuositatem* (Decree on the Apostolate of the Laity). The church declares that each person has a vocation according to his or her *particular character* of life. As the document proclaims,

> This plan for the spiritual life of the laity should take its particular character from their married or family state or their single or widowed state, from their state of health, and from their professional and social activity. They should not cease to develop earnestly the qualities and talents bestowed on them in accord with these conditions of life, and they should make use of the gifts which they have received from the Holy Spirit. (*AA* 4)

Homosexuals and transgender people, like all Christians, are called to find holiness within their specific state of life. Diversity of expression is consistent with St. Paul's theology of the Body of Christ since not every person can be a foot or a hand. Unity through diversity comprises the Body of Christ. The Dogmatic Constitution on the Church, *Lumen Gentium* (Light of the Nations), also states, all Christians are *"called to the fulfillment of the Christian life and the perfection of charity"* (LG 5, 40). Most Christians find holiness within married life. The church recognizes the family as the *"first and vital cell of society"* (AA 11), but marriage is not the only vocation.

---

[7] Ethiopian Orthodox tradition for the Ethiopian Eunuch found in Acts 8 and 13.

When administering the sacrament of baptism, Bishop Robert Barron of Los Angeles (Barron 2020) recalls the story of an eagle hatched among chickens. The eagle begins copying the chickens' behavior until an older eagle flies over and witnesses this young eagle pecking the ground. The older eagle lands and tells the young eagle he is not a chicken and has the ability to soar in the sky. That old one teaches the young one how to be an eagle. Likewise, many children are baptized into Christ and possess the potential to be tremendous saints. Unfortunately, they are never told of their potential and are instead pecking the dirt like chickens. This message applies to all Christians, whether transgender or cisgender. The church militant's vocation is to remind one another of their calling to be tremendous saints and stop pecking at the world.

Dr. Vanier asks Christians to consider, *"Now this fire of the Holy Spirit is given, not to the wise and the powerful, but to the weak and the smallest ones, to the poor, to the gentle, to the pure of heart and the persecuted. To these, Jesus shows himself as the Spouse"* (Vanier 1985, 103). Becoming the spouse of Christ is not easy to accept as a vocation, as can be attested to by many great saints. For most Christians, their married parents have been their formators in Christian life. Religious, priests, or married people have no shortage of exemplars for holy life; however, the examples for single holy laypeople and, in particular, homosexual and transgender people are far more limited. Chapter VI of *Apostolicam Actuositatem* (Decree on the Apostolate of the Laity) is dedicated to the formation of the laity. It claims the necessity for moral formation,

> Since formation for the apostolate cannot consist in merely theoretical instruction, from the beginning of their formation, the laity should gradually and prudently learn how to view, judge, and do all things in the light of faith as well as to develop and improve themselves along with others through doing, thereby entering into active service to the Church. (AA 29)

According to the Magisterium, homosexual acts are disordered, and therefore Christian marriage is not possible for these church members. Suppose a homosexual person were to marry a person of the opposite sex and the marriage were to fail. Homosexuality is grounds for an annulment since the marriage would have been impossible from the beginning of the marriage. Canon law states homosexual desires may be an *"incapacity to assume the essential obligations of marriage"* (*Canon Law*, 1095, 3).

Reparative therapy has also been unsuccessful and damaging to people. The Congregation for Catholic Education has deemed homosexuals are not to enter into holy orders in 2005 (Congregation for Catholic Education 2005), following an earlier 1961 directive (Sacred Congregation for Religious 1961). The only vocation remaining is a celibate single life. Transgender people face a similar dilemma. If the church requires the vocation for a transgender person to be the celibate single life, what formation and support does the church hope to offer for transgender people? *Apostolicam Actuositatem* (Decree on the Apostolate of the Laity) is aware that formation is needed, but none is currently provided. Celibacy is not easily obtained within the priesthood and religious life without a strong formation, a supportive community, spiritual directors, confessors, prayer, and robust sacramental life. This system for religious and clerical celibates has not been replicated for single laity, although the church recognizes this state of life as a vocation.

At the height of Catholicism within the United States in 1965, approximately 45 million Catholics and 180,000 religious sisters were in the church. Presently, about 76 million Catholics and 31,350 sisters reside in the United States (McKay 2020). If levels of devotion and rates of vocations persisted, 337,800 sisters should be around today. So where did these 306,000 women go who would have become sisters in 60 years? Much of this is attributed to the increase in the *"nones,"* those who identify as not religiously affiliated.

If Catholic men and women who experience gender identity considered lay states of religious life, this would produce an additional 230,000 religious sisters and an equal number of religious brothers. Religious abandon their gender-specific secular garb and stereotypes of their sex to become bound to Christ Himself. Objections will be that religious life is designed for healthy and whole people who seek God, and community life is not a place to abandon the broken. This is a fair point, but one should consider that people with gender dysphoria are not mentally ill and can otherwise fully integrate into society if given the opportunity.

A large group of late-onset gender dysphoric youth are looking for direction and being part of something meaningful. Instead of entering into a form of life that is unnatural and self-destructive to find meaning, a gender dysphoric young Catholic woman could consider formation to support her throughout her life. Many religious explain that they never believed they were like the other kids, and they had different desires in life while growing up. They also experienced a convent or monastery's counter-cultural and community element and felt drawn to this life. Religious fully live their sexuality through restraint and self-control. Their lives become offerings to God and in service of the world. Dysphoric youth may be too focused inward and may be called to religious life, which sends them out with meaning.

The vocation of the church members by nature of their baptism is to welcome to the table new Christians. Dr. Vanier reflects on community stating, *"We are also "missionaries"– that is, people who are sent— when we welcome someone to our table when we show them that they are loved and appreciated when we tell them with love how we have been called by Jesus to live when we make them feel at home. At that moment, we are also truly announcing the good news"* (Vanier 1989, 271–272). The transgender person's vocation is not a particular vocation within the church as transgender people were in pagan cultures (*supra*-2.6), yet it requires unique formation. The goal of all Christians is the final beatitude, which is not achieved in earthly life.

Fr. Cessario, in his explanation, *communio* disposes believers to accept *"the mystery of Christ, even as [the church] instructs about that authentic 'contempt for the world' which attends the exercise of a spiritual life"* (Cessario 2001, 225). This final beatitude leads St. Augustine to write, *"You have made us for yourself, O Lord and our hearts are restless until they rest in thee"* (Augustine, *The Confessions,* Chap. 1). According to Christian theology, fully realized and contented humans are not designed for this world.

Transfeminist Rachel Anne Williams, who does not identify as a Christian, recognizes the fall in her own words, *"My body is not enough for me. It just doesn't cut it"* (R. A. Williams 2019, 121). The *not enough-ness* at the heart of Rachel Anne Williams' transgender identity is at the center of the Christian narrative. When one views one's body through the lens of materialism, one's body is never enough because the body does not effortlessly manifest the greatness to which humanity is called. Blaise Pascal imagined,

> There was once in man a true happiness, of which all that now remains is the empty print and trace? This he tries in vain to fill with everything around him, seeking in things that are not there the help he cannot find in those that are, though none can help, since this infinite abyss can be filled only with an infinite and immutable object; in other words by God himself. (Pascal *Pensees*, 148)

Man tries to fill this vacuum in his heart with every distraction, but only God can fill the void of happiness.

American Evangelical Christian theologian Dr. Mark Yarhouse proposes that the church needs to decide which model they prefer (Yarhouse 2015, 147). The traditional Protestant model is:

Behave →Believe →Belong

This model attracts people who believe and think as they do. One should not be surprised that white Republican gun-owning farmers attend parishes with culturally similar members. Likewise, traditional black communities attract other black members. Similarly, one should not be surprised that liberal, pro-choice, social justice individuals attend the United Church of Christ parishes or LGBT Christians attend the Metropolitan Community Church. Their faith does not unite them to practice; instead, their practice unites them to a denomination or parish. The other church model is the missional church approach:

Belong →Believe →Become

In this model, a person enters a community allowing the faith to transform belief, transforming action and identity. This model is appealing since the process allows the Holy Spirit to inform the intellect and provide the grace to affect the will so the righteous living can be possible. This model's challenge is that the church welcomes people to belong who do not yet act as they belong. This model is inevitable with infant baptisms when a child belongs to a community before being aware. Some members who belong do not yet believe the creed. How long do people have to belong to a community before their beliefs and behavior match the teachings of the faith? The grace of the life of faith is sometimes instantaneous and other times unfolds slowly.

The secondary challenge to allowing members to belong without fully believing or becoming/behaving according to the church's teachings is the degree of participation. Who is allowed to be a reader, greeter, or catechist? Since full belief and becoming is not complete until the other side of the tomb, the church is left with imperfect members. How imperfect can people be? Often the practical metric is public scandal and controversy. Many inconsistencies are tolerated so long as their actions do not lead to public confusion.

Dr. Yarhouse proposes a challenge for the church to move beyond comfort and become missionary. Can space for mercy and communio for transgender people be provided during re-evangelization without scandalizing the rest of the faithful? Is the Body of Christ broad enough to encompass sexual outcastes?

11.2 Step 5: Grace

D ue to the world's fallen nature, the redemption of the body will not occur until the resurrection. Therefore, man depends on God's grace and salvation for his ultimate happiness.

a. ***Redemption*** means, in fact, a *"new creation,"* as it were, it means *taking up all that is created* to express in creation the fullness of justice, equity, and holiness planned for it by God and to express that fullness above all in man, created male and female *"in the image of God."* (John Paul II 2006, sec. 99.7)

The Second Vatican Council declared in *Gaudium et Spes* (Church in the Modern World), *"Since human freedom has been weakened by sin, it is only by the help of God's grace that people can properly orientate their actions towards God"* (GS 17). Similarly, when asked, Jesus told his disciples who can be saved, *"For human beings, this is impossible, but for God, all things are possible"* (Mt 5:26 NAB).

The Exultete reminds Catholics each year with the magnanimous prayer, *Father, how wonderful your care for us! How boundless your merciful love! To ransom a slave, you gave away your Son. O happy fault, O necessary sin of Adam, which gained for us so great a Redeemer!* The brokenness of man's body and his inability to reach inner perfection is not a barrier to God's love but instead an invitation to enter God's mercy. Venerable Catherine McAuley taught her Sisters, "Mercy receives the ungrateful again and again, and is never weary in pardoning them" (McAuley 1888, 137). Mercy is a highway to the Father.

Dr. Vanier wrote, *"Yes, the Word was made flesh because of the cry of the poor"* (Vanier 2019, 133). So long as man believes he or she can overcome human error alone, man can never accept healing. St. Ambrose wrote, *"My guilt became for me the cause of redemption, through which Christ came to me"* (Ambrose *De Jacob et vita beata*, I. 6. 21). When a Christian recognizes the inability to reach perfection and the uneasiness of being within one's own body, this is a recognition of the human condition and an invitation to accept Christ's message of hope.

The Catechism teaches, *"Grace is a participation in the life of God"* (*CCC*, 1997). The calling of grace is not just a matter of living a contented life on earth but adoption into the divine life. Grace is not God's participation in the natural world but man's participation in God's life. The church has an in-depth theology on grace, which started with St. Augustine's battle with Pelagius and was further developed during the Council of Trent's battle with Calvinism and Lutheranism. The types of grace necessary for a transgender person's life are *sanctifying grace, habitual grace*, and *actual grace*.

St. Paul admits, *"I was given a thorn in the flesh, a measure from Satan to batter me and prevent me from getting above myself. About this, I have three times pleaded with the Lord that it might leave me, but he has answered me, 'My grace is enough for you: for power is at full strength in weakness"* (2 Cor 12: 7–9 NAB). St. Paul also wrote, *"Therefore, if anyone is in Christ, he is a new creation; the old has passed away, behold, the new has come. All this is from God, who through Christ reconciled us to himself"* (2 Cor 5: 17–18 NAB). This Pauline theology of grace explains sanctifying grace, a gift from God which carries out the work of salvation with the human soul. Sanctifying grace is a *"habitual gift, a stable and supernatural disposition that perfects the soul itself to enable it to live with God, to act by his love"* (*CCC*, 2000). Whereas habitual grace is a permanent disposition, actual grace is God's *"interventions, whether at the beginning of conversion or in the course of the work of sanctification"* (*CCC*, 2000). Although sanctifying and habitual grace are immensely important since they lead to eternal life, they have a less specific application in the transgender topic. These forms of grace are necessary for every sanctified Christian. Transgender people are not specially equipped or ill-equipped to receive God's sanctifying grace.

Concerning actual grace, this is a special grace God gives each person specifically for his or her own life as an invitation into the life of Christ or in *any particular way* God chooses to bring the person to perfection. This grace explains how each person receives a particular call, like the apostles in the Gospels, to *"come follow me."* In the third hour, the call comes early in life for some Christians (Mt 20:1–16). For others, they are the laborers who are called at the eleventh hour, but all are called at their own time and in their own way. Similarly, a person with a transgender identity, like each Christian before him or her, will receive the grace necessary to bring forth vocation. St. Augustine, in his treatises on nature and grace, points out,

> Indeed, we also work, but we are only collaborating with God who works, for his mercy has gone before us. It has gone before us so that we may be healed and follows us so that once healed, we may be given life; it goes before us so that we may be called, and follows us so that we may be glorified; it goes before us so that we may live devoutly, and follows us so that we may always live with God: for without him we can do nothing. (Augustine *De Natura et gratia*, 31)

Christians rely on grace to answer the call of holiness. Grace is also necessary to maintain the vocation and to bring virtue to fruition. Grace is supernatural, but not magic. Instead, grace is rooted in God's love for humanity and requires *"man to prepare his soul, since he does this by his free will. And yet he does not do this without the help of God moving him and drawing him to Himself"* (*ST* Ia–IIae q.109, a.6, ad. 4). Br. Jacques Maritain, P.F.J., explains St. Thomas's *preparation* of the soul in more detail in *The Person and the Common Good.* He writes,

> The deepest layer of the human person's dignity consists in the property of resembling God—not in a general way after the manner of all creatures, but in a proper way. It is the image of God. For God is spirit, and the human person proceeds from Him as having a principle of life, a spiritual soul capable of knowing, loving, and being uplifted by grace to participation in the very life of God. (Maritain 1947, 32)

Søren Kierkegaard's theology heavily leans on the passage "Come to me, all you who are weary and burdened, and I will give you rest" (Mt 11:28) (Kierkegaard *Training in Christianity*, 9). Jesus of the Gospels, rather than Christendom, comes not as a judge and creator of political Christian infrastructures but as a savior for the weak. In 1848, in a letter to his paralyzed cousin, Kierkegaard wrote, *"when everything has been forgotten, it is inwardness that still matters"* (Kierkegaard *Journals and Papers*, 83). Søren focuses on the inward life of people with a disability. He wrote to his cousin,

> Above all, do not forget your duty to love yourself; do not permit the fact that you have been set apart from life in a way, been prevented from participating actively in it, and that you are superfluous in the obtuse eyes of a busy world, above all do not permit this to deprive you of your idea of yourself, as if your life if lived in inwardness, did not have just as much meaning and worth as that of any other human being in the loving eyes of an all-wise Governance, and considerably more than the busy, busier, busiest haste of busyness—busy with wasting life and losing itself. (Kierkegaard *Journals and Papers*, 83)

Søren, like St. Thomas in his reflections on *monstrous* births, can see the divine providence found within a vocation of otherness. Within one's brokenness is found grace.

11.3 CONCEPT REVIEW

Chapter eleven offered the practical heuristic application in chapter ten, extending a practical guide for addressing gender dysphoria in adults. This chapter used Scripture and the church fathers to offer practical advice about how a gender dysphoric individual can approach desire using the *habitus* of acquired virtues. This chapter also raised the theological principles of infused virtues and grace—and how conformity to Christ brings true freedom. The backbone of this chapter was St. Augustine and St. Thomas Aquinas, and Thomist commentators like Cardinal Cajetan and Fr. Cessario. This methodology respects the different pathways of knowledge and expertise while providing a holistic approach towards healing using a combination of science, nature, virtue, and grace.

Within the theological approach towards gender dysphoria, no attempt to repress emotions or actions is advisable since they would be contrary to the best medical and spiritual practices. Instead, moral theology aims to conform one's life to the *imago Christi* and allow God's grace to transform a person by infusing virtues and the gift of grace. St. Augustine wrote, *"God created us without us: but he did not will to save us without us"* (*CCC*, 1847; Augustine *Sermo*, 169, 11).

CONCLUSION

Brief Summary

In the mid-twentieth century, Dr. Harry Benjamin began a revolution, combining innovations in cosmetic surgery with developments in endocrinology to treat a small but determined group suffering from gender dysphoria who believed that a medical approach was the best solution. Although health is a blessing of both God and science, the medicalized approach is not always the best approach for healing feelings of desire. From the 1950s through the 1970s (and arguably still today), society has maintained an intense sense of modernity whereby human intelligence can solve all worldly problems.

René Descartes' *cogito* approach views the human person as a disembodied mind, detached from nature. Dr. Money and others believed the body and sex were moldable to any schema which the surgeon could skillfully create. This non-realist approach proved to be

522

a failure in the 1980s and 1990s. As a result, many children were given sex reassignment surgeries due to sexual ambiguities while later desisting and returning to their natal sex. Although doctors like Paul McHugh, M.D., Jon Meyer, and Lawrence Mayer, M.D., concluded the experimental surgeries performed for sex reassignment were failures from a psychological perspective, the practice of sex reassignment has increased fifty-fold since the 1980s.

Recent medical studies have identified key factors that point to a medical etiology for many forms of gender dysphoria. For example, Milton Diamond, Ph.D.,'s twins' study suggests a genetic link to transgender identities. When studying identical twins, he found that when one member identified as transgender, 20% of the time, the other twin also identified as transgender. In addition, Dr. Diamond found that none of the other siblings co-identified as transgender in cases of fraternal twins. This connection demonstrates a likely epigenetic causality since if gender dysphoria were entirely genetic, 100% of identical twins would co-identify as transgender if the gene were present.

The neurodevelopmental argument is confirmed by the significant rates of comorbidity between transgender identification and other neurodevelopmental disorders. These rates would be too high a probability if the conditions were based on independent variables. Transgender people are diagnosed with autism and other psychosis at a higher rater than non-transgender people. These disorders may be the etiology for gender dysphoria, but most transgender people are not autistic or psychotic, so this can not be the primary cause. Although many scientific literature reviews contain a wide range of comorbidity rates, all these studies show rates of correlation much higher than the control group. These results suggest a likely common neurodevelopmental etiology.

The final breakthrough was the 2016 discovery that brain matrixes of MtF and FtM had their own standard features. Despite this anomaly, subjects' brains were most like their natal sex. The Guillamon study discounts the narrative that an MtF individual has a female brain, and an FtM individual has a male brain. The matrix of features that create a male or female is too numerous and complex to interpret which combination of features determines sexual identity. Are the differences in the transgender brains significant enough to trigger a crisis in sexual identity? The answer is not medically certain, but the experience of gender dysphoric people suggests some anomalies affect identity.

The recognition of gender dysphoria as a medical condition means transgender people need to be treated as people with a disability, while transgenderism is a political ideology for others. The practical response from a purely rational perspective is straightforward. In cases of early-onset gender dysphoria, the majority (63 to 84%) will desist on their own by the time they reach fifteen years old. Performing any type of surgery or providing hormone blockers or cross-sex supplements on children would ignore the natural sexual development of the adolescent brain. Yet, in the state of California, doctors are performing double mastectomies on thirteen-year-olds and prescribing hormone blockers without thorough physical and psychological evaluations.

The human brain does not fully mature until after the age of 20 years. When teenagers take hormone blockers, the flow of estrogen and testosterone, which are necessary to finish feminizing or masculinizing their brains, ceases. The hormone blockers may permanently freeze the sexual maturation of the brain and cause permanent gender dysphoria, which might not have otherwise existed.

For youth with late-onset gender dysphoria, they are likely experiencing ROGD. Parents are typically aware of normal sexual development and can identify if a child had persisting gender dysphoria from childhood or a late teen rapid onset. If the child's gender dysphoria is ROGD, the best approach is to wait and see. The more a parent makes ROGD an act of rebellion and an identity, the more the disorder is reinforced.

Youth in every generation creates subcultures to give themselves a unique identity. In a post-Christian postmodern society, the world is uncertain for young people, and dysphoria has become commonplace. Young adults fear gun violence in schools and the instability of institutions like the family, government, and the church. Besides, social media is obsessed with the illusions of reality, which young people cannot fully rationalize. Post-Christianity leads to a lack of a cohesive cosmology, epistemology, and anthropology.

Teens face an existential crisis and have little guidance from the adults in their lives. Seeking belonging in any type of community becomes a way of escaping uncertainty. Helping a teen adopt a healthy personal Christian identity could help a child avoid seeking false idols, which do not help the young person transition into an emotionally mature adult. Youth left unsupported by their family and church are left to figure out their emotions with the aid of strangers and predators.

One transgender Christian recommends, *"Don't give them bumper sticker theology. Teens are in flux. Wouldn't it be great to introduce them to the wonders of the mystery of our faith? That God resides in the unanswerable places"* (Yarhouse and Houp 2016, 61). The Christian cosmology does not need to provide definitive answers to complicated situations to provide young transgender people with adequate relief. Studies have found that transgender youth who engage in faith-based counseling have increased rates of suicide. Also, LGBT youth from religious families experience elevated rates of suicide. Not based on sound medical science, religious counseling is potentially deadly for people with psychological medical disorders.

For adults with gender dysphoria, the worry for one's well-being is lessened since adults will be a better fit to make mature decisions and are prudently adapted to discerning real dysphoria from a social ideology. Presumably, if adults experience gender dysphoria, they better understand these feelings. If a person has experienced gender dysphoria for decades and still has significant concerns, this should be considered a grave medical condition. At this stage, the heuristic developed in chapters ten and eleven should be considered. The current approach is a rush to medicalization, a solution studies show does not cure many underlying conditions.

Considerable evidence points to ultimate dissatisfaction—the medical approach fails to relieve the feelings of dysphoria while increasing risks for cancer, heart disease, blood clots, and psychological hospitalization. In addition, the low participation rates in aftercare studies and the still high suicide rates suggest the medicalized approach is not sufficient on its own to bring healing for the individual. The heuristic does not reject modern medicine but instructs medical professionals that the process should aim to *restore the natural order* and be *the least invasive intervention possible.*

Aristotle claims that to achieve *eudaimonia,* one typically needs virtue but equally important, beneficial circumstances or good luck. He claims bad moral luck affects people's ability to flourish, but he also considers bad luck as an opportunity to express one's virtues. Virtue is not a virtue if one only has virtue during easy times or when no opportunities for extraordinary character arises. Magnanimity and magnificence can never be actualized when life is simple. Bad moral luck creates the opportunity to offer honor and glory to God.

The embrace of virtues is necessary for happiness in every Christian's life, not just for gender dysphoric individuals. C.S. Lewis wrote, *"Virtue—even attempted virtue – brings light; indulgence brings fog"* (Lewis 2016, 102). The theological virtues energize the infused moral virtues. The life of virtue is an imitation of Christ's life through which one becomes the *imago Christi*. Fr. Cessario connects virtue with the divine image, *"The love of Christ opens up the way for the final perfection of each man and woman created in the image of God"* (Cessario 2002, 105).

The finality of the moral life, which leads to the greatest opportunity to realize one's position in the world, is grace. Through salvation, the brokenness of humanity will be glorified with the redemption of the body. Christ did not come to heal the sick on Earth for the sake of a few dozen people in the first century. If He did, what benefit would be for Christians today? Instead, raising the dead, feeding the hungry, and healing the sick were signs of the Kingdom of God partially realized. The hope of humanity is not a partially realized Kingdom, but the fullness of the Kingdom after the eschaton. Like Jesus' body broken and glorified after the resurrection, each saved Christian will be made whole with glorified wounds. Although the church militant does not realize this, faith in the Kingdom hopes that the suffering will soon pass and peace will come. To end with a passage on the Christian life from St. Augustine,

> From the law comes knowledge of sin, by faith the reception of grace against sin, by grace the soul is healed of the imperfection of sin; a healthy soul possesses freedom of choice; freedom of choice is ordered to love of righteousness; love of righteousness is the accomplishment of the law. (Augustine *De doctrina christiana*, 30, 52)

Conclusions Drawn from Research

The research into the outcomes for individuals with gender dysphoria raises questions about the efficacy of a purely medicalized approach to transgender issues. Similarly, the efficacy of a purely religious response to people with gender dysphoria is similarly dangerous. Upon studying individuals who claim a gender identity other than which is ascribed at birth based on biological features, depression, anxiety, and suicide rates are exceedingly elevated.

Although ample evidence suggests transgender identities are related to neurodevelopmental and epigenetic origins, youth taken up with emotivist gender ideologies raise key questions about being transgender. Although proponents of certain gender theory ideologies seek to liberate society from the binary system's *"oppression,"* the result for most individuals surveyed self-identified as less happy and peaceful than their cisgender counterparts. The research on outcomes from these two categories of *"trans"* people concludes that neither the medicalized approach of hormone treatments and surgeries nor the liberatory efforts of some gender theorists result in *eudaimonia*—human flourishing.

Given the limitations of current strategies for addressing gender dysphoria, Thomistic realism may provide extra support. The church has a supplemental means of healing by using the normativity of creation, realist epistemology, the practice of virtue, and a cohesive cosmology that unites brokenness to grace. The Thomistic approach is not intended to replace medical science but instead enhance medical treatments. The church's principles guide moral decisions are also helpful in creating attainable goals and appropriate expectations. Presently, no one has a medical cure for gender dysphoria; therefore, managing the symptoms is the primary importance.

When coping with psychological challenges, the use of heuristics can bring a person step by step through the healing process. The heuristic created in this book reduces the emphasis placed on one's own desires and examines one's subjective beliefs in the light of reason and grace. The Twelve-Step program inspired this heuristic in its approach to healing the person through becoming a better person.

Despite biological causes for the feelings and desires of the transgender person, the practice of spirituality helps refocus the ego to otherness and thus reduces the dysphoria. Medical research has also confirmed that prayer, self-care, and volunteering are the best methods for coping with gender dysphoria. Suppose coping can replace less natural and more invasive treatments for dealing with this disorder. Is the coping approach always better than the use of surgeries and opposite-sex hormone treatments? One cannot know the consequences; however, this heuristic approach could never harm a patient and can only help to enhance the outcomes.

Importance of Research

The research on the transgender topic is timely since the rate of transgender surgeries has increased fifty-fold since the 1980s, and currently, 1.4 million Americans identify as transgender. In June of 2020, the Supreme Court included transgender people are a protected class of people under the 1964 civil rights act; yet, the Obama administration in 2016 concluded that sex reassignment surgeries are ineffective in treating the underlying conditions attributed to gender dysphoria. Although interested in how the inclusion of transgender people will affect a society's laws, the more critical issue for the church is the pastoral care of gender dysphoric individuals who are diagnosed with high levels of anxiety, depression, and attempted suicide. A vast need for support arises when a person decides to desist after their hopes have fallen short. Suppose the church uses this historical moment to attack a strawman version of transgender people. In that case, she will waste a valuable opportunity to show how faith and science can collaborate for the patient's good. On the contrary, if the church uses this moment to care for the needs of people who are not comforted by medical science alone nor nominalist gender theory, the church will have an opportunity to extend the hand of Christ to those most in need. The church needs books written from a foundation of faith that engages the best science to meet the needs of transgender people currently.

Future Research

As medical science continues to unfold, this research needs to continue. Dr. McHugh was correct in his conclusion that we do not know enough about this subject to come to any definitive conclusions. Care for transgender people is insufficient at this time, so any added information which can help create treatment plans for transgender people is essential. A critical study is needed to determine if MtF and FtM individuals apply ethics like males or females. Carol Gilligan, Ph.D., (1936–) *In a Different Voice*, 1982 determined men and women approach ethics differently. If Dr. Gilligan is correct, studies can determine if transgender people think like people of the opposite sex. The research in this book accepts that certain parts of the transgender brain are like that of the other sex. However, medical researchers do not know the effect those sections of the brain have on an individual. Do these brain sections affect only gender identity, or do they affect how a transgender person views the world? Two studies in this book have inadvertently suggested adolescent transgender youth approach stressful situations through the lens of their natal sex rather than their sexual identities (Human Rights Campaign 2018) (Toomey, Syvertsen, and Shramko 2018). Can a person who is genetically male, hormonally male, physically male, and approaches the world ethically as a male be deemed feminine because she wishes to be one?

Conclusion of the Conclusion

After visiting a psychiatric hospital for children, Jean Vanier, Ph.D., wrote, *"When they realize that nobody cares, that nobody will answer them, children no longer cry. It takes too much energy. We cry out only when there is hope that someone may hear us"* (Vanier 1998, 9). The American Academy of Pediatrics reports suicide ideation rates for transgender adolescents as high as 73.9%. Yet, the children are still crying out. Does the church respond to them before it is too late? Will the church respond before her children go silent?

Pope John Paul II, in the months leading up to his five-year catechesis on the *Theology of the Body*, addressed the crowds of Puebla, Mexico, with the teaching, *"The truth that we owe to man is, first and foremost, a truth about man"* (John Paul II 1979b, I.9). As the church searches for its voice again, she must respond with love to this *Transgender Moment*.

APPENDIX

Figures 7.1 and 7.2 reprinted by permission from Oxford University Press: *Cerebral Cortex*. Sex Differences in Adult Human Brain: Evidence from 5216 UK Biobank Participants, Stuart Ritchie and Simon Cox, 2018.

Figure 7.3 reprinted by permission from PNAS. Sex beyond the genitalia: The human brain mosaic, Daphna Joel et al., 2015.

Figure 9.2 reprinted by permission from Transgender Trend. The Surge in Referral Rates of Girls to the Tavistock Continues to Rise, The Transgender Trend Team, 2019.

Figures 10.2 and 10.3 are reprinted with permission from *PLoS One*. Long-term follow-up of transsexual persons undergoing sex reassignment surgery: A cohort study in Sweden, Cecilia Dhejne et al., 2011.

BIBLIOGRAPHY

ACLU. 2019. Twitter Post. November 19, 3:46 PM
https://twitter.com/ACLU/status/1196877415810813955.

adamandeve.com. "Adamandeve.com Asks: Would You Be Open To
Dating Someone Transgendered?" *PRNewswire*. August 4,
2016. Accessed July 22, 2020.
https://www.prnewswire.com/news-
releases/adamandevecom-asks-would-you-be-open-to-dating-
someone-transgendered-300309316.html.

Allen, Mary Prudence. 2014. "Gender Reality." *Solidarity: The Journal of
Catholic Social Thought and Secular Ethics* 4: 25–27.

———. 1985. *The Concept of Woman, vol. 1*. Grand Rapids, MI: W.B.
Eerdmans Publishing.

Ambrose. 1970. "De Jacob et vita beata." In *Seven Exegetical Works
(The Fathers of the Church, Volume 65*, by The Catholic
University of America Press, translated by Bernard Peebles.
Washington, DC: Catholic University of America Press.

———. 2018. *Exposition of the Christian Faith: St. Ambrose of Milan*.
Edited by Paul Boer. Translated by H Romestin. Veritatis
Splendor Publication.

American Academy of Pediatrics Committee on Adolescence. 2013.
"Policy Statement: Office-Based Care for Lesbian, Gay,
Bisexual, Transgender, and Questioning Youth." *Pediatrics*
132, no. 1: e198–203. https://doi.org/10.1542/peds.2013-
1282.

American Medical Association House of Delegates. 2016. *Removing
Financial Barriers to Care for Transgender Patients*. Resolution 122,
Chicago, IL: American Medical Association.

American Psychiatric Association. 2011. "American Psychological Association, "Answers to Your Questions About Transgender People, Gender Identity and Gender Expression." *American Psychiatric Association*. Accessed June 17, 2020. https://www.apa.org/topics/lgbt/transgender.pdf.

———. 2013. *Diagnostic and Statistical Manual of Mental Disorders- 5*. Philadelphia, PA: American Psychiatric Association.

———. *What Are Dissociative Disorders?* 2018. Edited by Philip Wang. August. Accessed June 30, 2020. https://www.psychiatry.org/patients-families/dissociative-disorders/what-are-dissociative-disorders#:~:text=Suicide%20attempts%20and%20other%20self,identity%20disorder%20have%20attempted%20suicide.

American Society of Plastic Surgeons. 2017a. "Gender Confirmation Surgeries Rise 20% in First Ever Report." *American Society of Plastic Surgeons*. May 22. Accessed December 15, 2019. https://www.plasticsurgery.org/news/press-releases/gender-confirmation-surgeries-rise-20-percent-in-first-ever-report.

———. 2017b. "2017 Plastic Surgery Statistics Report." *American Society of Plastic Surgeons*. Accessed June 23, 2020. https://www.plasticsurgery.org/documents/News/Statistics/2017/body-contouring-gender-confirmation-2017.pdf.

———. 2018. "2017 Plastic Surgery Statistics Report." *American Society of Plastic Surgeons*. Accessed June 23, 2020. https://www.plasticsurgery.org/documents/News/Statistics/2017/plastic-surgery-statistics-full-report-2017.pdf.

Amnesty International. 2014. "The State Decides: Lack of legal gender recognition for transgender people in Europe." *Amnesty International*. Accessed June 17, 2020. https://www.amnesty.org/download/Documents/8000/eur0 10012014en.pdf.

———. n.d. "LGBTQI Glossary." *Amnesty International*. Accessed January 22, 2020. https://www.amnestyusa.org/pdfs/AIUSA_Pride2015Glossa ry.pdf.

Anderson, Ryan. 2018b. "A New York Times Writer's Reckless Hit Piece on My Transgender Book." *The Daily Signal.* February 27. Accessed June 09, 2020. *https://www.dailysignal.com/2018/02/27/new-york-times-writers-reckless-hit-piece-transgender-book/.*

———. 2018c. "Transgender Ideology Is Riddled with Contradictions. Here Are the Big Ones." *The Heritage Foundation.* February 9. Accessed June 17, 2020. https://www.heritage.org/gender/commentary/transgender-ideology-riddled-contradictions-here-are-the-big-ones.

———. 2018a. *When Harry Became Sally: Responding to the Transgender Moment.* New York: Encounter Books.

Andreano, Joseph, Bradford Dickerson, and Lisa Feldman-Barrett. 2014. "Sex differences in the persistence of the amygdala response to negative material." *Social Cognitive and Affective Neuroscience.* vol. 9, no. 9 (September): 1388–1394. http://doi:10.1093/scan/nst127.

Apostolicam Actuositatem. 1965. "Decree on the Apostolate of the Laity." *The Second Vatican Council.* Vatican City: Promulgated by Pope Paul VI.

Aquinas Thomas. 2013. *Commentary on the Gospel of Matthew 13–28.* Translated by Jeremy Holmes. Steubenville, OH: Emmaus Academic.

———. 1994. *De Anima: Commentary on Aristotle's De Anima.* Chicago, IL: St. Augustine's Dumb Ox Books.

———. 1999. *Quaestio disputata de spe [Disputed Questions on Virtue].* Translated by Ralph McInerny. Notre Dame, IN: St. Augustine's Press.

———. 2019. *Summa Contra Gentiles.* Steubenville, OH: Emmaus Academic.

———. 1948. *Summa Theologica.* Translated by Fathers of the English Dominican Province. V vols. New York: Benzinger Bros.

Aristotle. 1966. *Aristoteles Latinus, XVII.* Edited by Drossaart Lulofs. Bruges, BE: Desclee de Brouwer.

————. 1984. "Categories." In *The Complete Works of Aristotle*, by Aristotle, translated by The Revised Oxford Translation, 1b 10–20. Princeton, NJ: Princeton University Press.

————. 1984. "Generation of Animals." In *The Complete Works of Aristotle*, by Aristotle, translated by The Revised Oxford Translation. Princeton, NJ: Princeton University Press.

————. 1984. "History of Animals." In *The Complete Works of Aristotle*, by Aristotle, translated by The Revised Oxford Translation, 538a 22 – 38b 10; 608b 8. Princeton, NJ: Princeton University Press.

————. 1924. *Metaphysics.* Translated by W.D. Ross. Oxford, UK: Oxford Press.

————. 1999. *Nicomachean Ethics.* Translated by Terence Irwin. Indianapolis, IN: Hackett Publishing.

————. 1984. "On the Soul." In *The Complete Works of Aristotle*, by Aristotle, translated by Jonathan Barnes, 412a 6–9. Princeton, NJ: Princeton University Press.

————. 1984. "Parts of Animals." In *The Complete Works of Aristotle*, by Aristotle, 4,10,687a10. Princeton, NJ: Princeton University Press.

————. 1984. "Physics." In *The Complete Works of Aristotle*, by Aristotle, translated by The Revised Oxford Translation, 194b 20–35. Princeton, NJ: Princeton University Press.

————. 2004. *Rhetoric.* Translated by W. Rhys Roberts. New York: Dover Publications.

————. 2011. *The Eudemian Ethics.* Translated by Anthony Kenny. Oxford, UK: Oxford World's Classics.

————. 1984. "Topics." In *The Complete Works of Aristotle*, by Aristotle, translated by Jonathan Barnes, 102a 15–25. Princeton, NJ: Princeton University Press.

Bibliography

Aschwanden, Christie. 2019. "Trans Athletes Are Posting Victories and Shaking Up Sports." *Wired.* October 29. Accessed June 27, 2020. https://www.wired.com/story/the-glorious-victories-of-trans-athletes-are-shaking-up-sports/.

Ashley, Benedict. 1985. *Theologies of the Body: Humanist and Christian.* Boston, MA: Pope John Center.

ASPS National Clearinghouse of Plastic Surgery. 2019. "Americans Spent More than $16.5 Billion on Cosmetic Plastic Surgery in 2018." *American Society of Plastic Surgeons.* April 10. Accessed January 19, 2020. https://www.plasticsurgery.org/documents/News/Statistics/2018/plastic-surgery-statistics-full-report-2018.pdf.

Associated Press. 1982. "Transgender." *Appeal-Democrat,* May 11: A 10. Accessed September 29, 2020. https://i1.wp.com/research.cristanwilliams.com/wp-content/uploads/2012/02/page.png.

Athenaeus. 1927. *The Deipnosophists xii.* Translated by C.D. Yonge. London, UK: Loeb Classical Library.

Augustine. 1978. *A Treatise on the merits and Forgiveness of Sins, and on the Baptism of Infants.* Vol. 5, in *The Nicene and Post-Nicene Fathers,* by Philip Schaff, 27–28. Grand Rapids, MI: Wm. B. Eermans Publishing.

———. 1954. *Augustinus Magister.* Paris, FR: Etudes Augustiniennes.

———. 1995. *De doctrina christiana.* Notre Dame, IN: University of Notre Dame Press.

———. 1966. *De moribus ecclesiae Catholicae et de moribus Manichaeorum.* Washington, DC: Catholic University of America Press.

———. 2005. *De Natura et gratia.* Whitefish, MT: Kessinger Publishing.

———. 1895. *Enarrationes in Psalmos.* Vol. 8, in *Nicene and Post-Nicene Fathers,* by Henry Wace, & Philip Schaff, translated by Bloomfield Jackson. Buffalo, NY: Christian Literature Publishing.

—. 1990. *Epistola 100–155*. Translated by Boniface Ramsey. Hyde Park, NY: New City Press.

—. 2019. *Sancti Aurelii Augustini ... Opera Omnia, Castigata Denuo Studio Monachorum Ordinis Sancti Benedicti E Congregatione Sancti Mauri*. Vol. 4 part 1. Sydney, AU: Wentworth Press.

—. 1888. *Sermo, 87*. Vol. VI, in *Nicene and Post-Nicene Fathers*, by Philip Schaff, translated by R.G. MacMullen. Buffalo, NY: Christian Literature Publishing.

—. 1887. *The Confessions*. Vol. 1, in *Nicene and Post-Nicene Fathers*, by Philip Schaff, translated by J.G. Pilkington. Buffalo, NY: Christian Literature Publishing.

—. 1888. *Tractate 26*. Vol. VII, in *Nicene and Post-Nicene Fathers*, by Philip Schaff, translated by John Gibb, 4–6. Buffalo, NY: Christian Literature Publishing.

Austriaco, Nicanor. 2013. "The Specification of Sex/Gender in the Human Species." *Blackfriars*, November: 701–715. https://doi.org/10.1111/nbfr.12028.

Bailey, John Michael, and Kiira Triea. 2007. "What many transgender activists don't want you to know: And why you should know it anyway." *Perspectives in Biology and Medicine* 50, no. 4: 521–534. https:// doi.org/10.1353/pbm.2007.0041.

Bailey, John Michael. 2003. *The Man Who Would Be Queen: The Science of Gender-Bending and Transsexualism*. Washington, DC: National Academies Press.

Bailey, John Michael, Ray Blanchard. 2017. "Gender dysphoria is not one thing." *4thWaveNow*. December 7. Accessed June 10, 2021. https://4thwavenow.com/tag/autohomoerotic-gender-dysphoria/.

Barbier, Patrick. 1996. *The world of the castrati: The history of an extraordinary operatic phenomenon*. London, UK: Souvenier Press.

Barford, Vanessa. 2008. *Iran's 'Diagnosed Transsexuals' [BBC News]*. February 25. Accessed January 6, 2020. http://news.bbc.co.uk/2/hi/7259057.stm.

Bibliography

Barlow, David, Gene Abel, and Edward Blanchard. 1977. "Gender Identity Change in transsexual: An exorcism." *Archives of Sexual Behavior* 6, no. 5 (September): 387–395. https://doi.org/10.1001/archpsyc.1979.01780090087009

Baron-Cohen, Simon. 2003. *The Essential Difference.* New York: Basic Books.

Barringer, Felicity. 1992. "Many Surgeons Reassure Their Patients on Implants." *The New York Times,* January: C12.

Barringer, M, and David Gay. 2017. "Happily, Religious: The Surprising Sources of Happiness Among Lesbian, Gay, Bisexual, and Transgender Adults." *Sociological Inquiry* 87, no. 1: 75–96. https://doi.org/10.1111/soin.12154.

Barron, Robert. 2015. "Bruce Jenner, The "Shadow Council," and St. Irenaeus." *Word on Fire.* June 9. Accessed June 27, 2020. https://www.wordonfire.org/resources/article/bruce-jenner-the-shadow-council-and-st-irenaeus/4785/.

———. 2020. "Stop Being a Chicken: Bishop Barron on the Realities of Baptism." *YouTube.* September 25. Accessed September 27, 2020. https://www.youtube.com/watch?v=1jUQd4UH1Zs.

Bartky, Sandra Lee. 1990. *Femininity and Domination.* New York: Routledge.

Basic Right Oregon. 2016. " *Oregon Health Plan Coverage of Gender Dysphoria: LGBTQ Community Partners Frequently Asked Questions (FAQ).*" March. Accessed June 8, 2021.

Basil. 1895. *The Letters, 115.* Vol. 8, in *Nicene and Post-Nicene Fathers,* by Henry Wace Philip Schaff, translated by Blomfield Jackson. Buffalo, NY: Christian Literature Publishing.

———. 1950. *The Long Rules.* Vol. IX, in *Ascetical Works,* by Inc. Fathers of the Church, translated by MM Wagner, 232. Washington, DC: Fathers of the Church.

Batty, David. 2004. *Mistaken identity.* July 30. Accessed January 7, 2020.

https://www.theguardian.com/society/2004/jul/31/health.s
ocialcare.

Baumeister, Roy, and Kathleen Vohs. 2013. "Recent Empirical
Findings on Meaning and How it Differs from Happiness."
The International Forum for Logotherapy 36: 87–94.

Bautista, Delfin, Quince Mountain, and Heath Mackenzie-Reynolds.
2014. "Religion and Spirituality." In *Trans Bodies, Trans Selves*,
by Laura Erickson-Schroth, 62–79. Oxford, UK: Oxford
University Press.

BCC Media Centre. 2017. *No More Boys and Girls: Can Our Kids Go
Gender Free?* August. Accessed January 8, 2020.
https://www.bbc.co.uk/mediacentre/proginfo/2017/33/no-
more-boys-and-girls.

BBC News. 2018. *Trans inmate jailed for Wakefield prison sex offenses.*
October 11. Accessed June 8, 2021.
https://www.bbc.com/news/uk-england-leeds-45825838.

BBC Newsnight. 2019. *Detransitioning: Reversing a gender transition - BBC
Newsnight.* November 26. Accessed June 8, 2021.
https://www.youtube.com/watch?v=fDi-jFVBLA8.

Bechard, Melanie, Doug VanderLaan, Hayley Wood, Lori
Wasserman, and Kenneth Zucker. 2017. "Psychosocial and
Psychological Vulnerability in Adolescents with Gender
Dysphoria: A 'Proof of Principle' study." *Journal of Sex and
Marital Therapy* 43, no. 7: 678–688. https://doi.org/
10.1080/0092623X.2016.1232325.

Bedford, Elliott Louis, and Jason Eberl. 2016. "Is the Soul Sexed?"
Health Care Ethics USA 24, no. 3 (Summer): 18–33.

Beemyn, Genny. n.d. *Transgender Terminology.* Accessed January 20,
2020.
https://hr.cornell.edu/sites/default/files/trans%20terms.pdf.

Beier, Klaus, H Bosinski, and K Loewit. 2005. *Sexual Medicine (Vol.
II).* Munchen, DE: Urban & Ficher Verlag.

Bibliography

Beilby, James, and Paul Rhodes Eddy. 2019. "Understanding Transgender Experiences and Identities: An Introduction." In *Understanding Transgender Identities*, by James Beilby, & Paul Rhodes Eddy, 1–54. Grand Rapids, MI: Baker Academic.

Becker, Christoph, Isadora Kirchmaier, and Stefan Trautmann. 2019. "Marriage, parenthood and social network: Subjective well-being and mental health in old age." *Plos One*, July 24: https://doi.org/10.1371/journal.pone.0218704.

Belli, Melvin. 1978. "Transsexual surgery: A new tort?" *Journal of the American Medical Association* 239, no. 20: 2143–2148. https://doi.org/10.1001/jama.1978.03280470055022.

Bello, Angela Ales. 2016. *"Neutral" Human Being to Gender Difference: Phenomenological and Dual Anthropology in Edith Stein.* Vol. 4, chap. 2 in *Edith Stein: Women, Social-Political Philosophy, Theology, Metaphysics and Public History*, by A. Calcagno, 11–23. Boston, MA: Springer International Publishing.

Benedict XIV, Pope. 2012. "Pope: faith, science must cooperate to protect people, planet." *The Eastern Tennessee Catholic.* November 8. Accessed 12 15, 2019. https://etcatholic.org/2012/11/pope-faith-science-must-cooperate-to-protect-people-planet/.

———. 2011. *Address at the Reichstag Building.* Performed by Pope Benedict XVI. Reichstag Building, Berlin, DE. September 22.

———. 2012. "Address to the Roman Curia." Vatican City: The Holy See, December 21.

Benjamin, Harry. 1966. *The Transsexual Phenomenon.* New York: Julian Press Books.

Bernard of Clairvaux. 1971. *On the Song of Songs I.* Translated by Kilian Walsh. Vol. IV. Spencer, MA: Cistercian Fathers Series.

Best, L, and K Stein. 1998. *Surgical gender reassignment for male to female transsexual people.* DEC Report No. 88, Southampton, UK: Wessex Institute for Health Research and Development, University of Southampton.

Beyrer, Christ, Robert Blum, and Tonia Poteat. 2017. "Hopkins faculty disavow 'troubling' report on gender and sexuality." *The Baltimore Sun.* September 28. Accessed June 06, 2020. https://www.baltimoresun.com/opinion/op-ed/bs-ed-lgbtq-hopkins-20160928-story.html.

Blackless, Melanie, Anthony Charuvastra, Amanda Derryck, Anne Fausto-Sterling, Karl Lauzanne, and Ellen Lee. 2000. "How sexually dimorphic are we? Review and synthesis." *American Journal of Human Biology*, February 11: https://doi.org/10.1002/(SICI)1520-6300(200003/04)12:2<151: AID-AJHB1>3.0.CO;2-F.

Black Lives Matter. 2020. Accessed July 25, 2020. *What we believe.* https://blacklivesmatter.com/what-we-believe/.

Blanchard, Ray. 1990. "Clinical Management of Gender Identity Disorders in Children and Adults." *American Psychiatric Publication* 49 (September): Preface.

———. 1991. "Clinical Observations and Systematic." *Journal of Sex & Marital Therapy* 17, no. 4: 235–251.https://doi.org/10.1080/00926239108404348.

———. 2013. Interview by Motherboard. *How the Psychiatrist Who Co-Wrote the Manual on Sex Talks About Sex* (April 11). Accessed September 29, 2020. https://www.vice.com/en_us/article/ypp93m/heres-how-the-guy-who-wrote-the-manual-on-sex-talks-about-sex.

———. 20000. "Part II: The case for publicly funded transsexual surgery." *Psychiatric Rounds* (University of Toronto) 4, no. 2 (April): 4–6.

———. 1985. "Typology of male-to-female transsexualism." *Archives of Sexual Behavior* 14, no. 3 (June): 247–261.

Blanchard, Ray, Line Clemmensen, and Betty Steiner. 1987. "Heterosexual and Homosexual Gender Dysphoria." *Archives of Sexual Behavior* 16: 139–152.

Blanke, Olaf, Florence Morgenthaler, Peter Brugger, and Landis Overney. 2008. "Preliminary evidence for a frontal-parietal dysfunction in able-bodied participants with a desire for limb amputation." *Journal of Neuropsychology*: 1–13. https://doi.org/10.1348/174866408X318653.

Blum, Deborah. 1998. *Sex on the Brain*. New York: Penguin Press.

Body Dysmorphic Disorder Foundation. n.d. *Problems related to BDD*. Accessed January 5, 2020. https://bddfoundation.org/helping-you/problems-related-to-bdd/.

———. n.d. *What is BDD?* Accessed January 5, 2020. https://bddfoundation.org/.

Boellstorff, Tom. 2004. "Playing Back the Nation: Waria, Indonesian Transvestites." *Cultural Anthropology* 19, no. 2: 159–195. https://doi.org/10.1525/can.2004.19.2.159.

Bonfatto, Marina, and Eva Crasnow. 2018. "Gender/ed identities: an overview of our current work as child psychotherapists in the Gender Identity Development Service." *Journal of Child Psychotherapy* 44, no. 1: 29–46. https://doi.org/10.1080/0075417X.2018.1443150.

Bonos, Lisa. 2016. "LGBTQ singles are split on marriage, kids and dating someone who's transgender." *Washington Post*. May 26. Accessed July 22, 2020. https://www.washingtonpost.com/news/soloish/wp/2016/05/26/lgbtq-singles-are-split-on-marriage-kids-and-dating-someone-whos-transgender/.

Book Ngram Viewer. 2019. *Identity*. Accessed June 16, 2021. https://books.google.com/ngrams/graph?content=identity&year_start=1800&year_end=2019&corpus=26&smoothing=7&direct_url=t1%3B%2Cidentity%3B%2Cc0#t1%3B%2Cidentity%3B%2Cc0

Bornstein, Kate. 1995. *Gender Outlaw: On Men, Women, and the Rest of Us*. New York: Vintage Books.

Bossi, Paul. 2019. "Transgender Statement." *100% Raw Powerlifting Federation*. Press Release May 1. Accessed May 21, 2021. https://rawpowerlifting.com/wp-content/uploads/2019/05/Transgender-statement-05.2019.pdf.

Bossuet, Jacques. 1900. *Traité de la connaissance de dieu et de soi-même.* Edited by L Rossigneux. Paris, FR: Lacaffee.

Bostock, John, and Henry Riley. 1857. *The Natural History of Pliny* Vol. 6. London, UK: Henry G. Bohn.

Bote, Joshua. 2018. "'Love, Simon' Actor Keiynan Lonsdale Talks About Preferred Pronouns: 'I Just Want to Go by Tree.'" *Billboard.* September 26. Accessed January 14, 2020. https://www.billboard.com/articles/news/pride/8477100/ke iynan-lonsdale-preferred-pronouns-tree

Bowles, Josephine, and Peter Koopman. 2013. "Precious cargo: regulation of sex-specific germ cell development in mice." *Sex Development* 7: 46–60. https://doi.org/10.1159/000342072.

Boylan, Jennifer Finney. 2018. "It's Not a Disaster Movie. It's Reality." *The New York Times.* February 27. Accessed June 09, 2020. https://www.nytimes.com/2018/02/27/opinion/transgender -rights.html.

Bränström, Richard, and John Pachankis. 2020. "Reduction in Mental Health Treatment Utilization Among Transgender Individuals After Gender-Affirming Surgeries: A Total Population Study." *American Journal of Psychiatry*, August 1: 727–734. https://doi.org/10.1176/appi.ajp.2019.19010080.

Brewer, Erin. 2021. *Always Erin.* Independently Published.

Brock, Brian. 2012. "Augustine's Hierarchies of Human Wholeness and Their Healing." In *Disability in the Christian Tradition*, by Brian Brock, & John Swinton, 65–100. Grand Rapids, MI: Wm. B. Eerdmans Publishing.

Brooks, Jon. 2018. "The Controversial Research on 'Desistance' in Transgender Youth." *KQED Science.* May 23. Accessed 12 15, 2019. https://www.kqed.org/futureofyou/441784/the-controversial-research-on-desistance-in-transgender-youth.

Brown, Michael. 2015. "Marry For Love: Aydin and Jo Olson-Kennedy – The love story of one transgender couple." *Gay Weddings & Marriage Magazine*. September 22. Accessed June 1, 2021. https://www.gayweddingsmag.com/marry-for-love-aydin-and-jo-olson-kennedy-the-love-story-of-one-transgender-couple/.

Brucculieri, Julia. 2018. "'Snapchat Dysmorphia' Points To A Troubling New Trend In Plastic Surgery." *The Huffington Post*. February 22. Accessed January 25, 2021. https://www.huffpost.com/entry/snapchat-dysmorphia_n_5a8d8168e4b0273053a680f6.

Brugger, E. Christian. 2016. "Response to Bayley and Gremmels on Transgender Ethics." *Health Care Ethics USA* 24, no. 3 (Summer): 12–17.

Brusman, Liza. 2019. "Sex isn't binary, and we should stop acting like it is." *Massive Science*. June 14. Accessed June 16, 2020. https://massivesci.com/articles/sex-gender-intersex-transgender-identity-discrimination-title-ix/.

Bullough, Vern, and Bonnie Bullough. 1993. *Cross Dressing, Sex, and Gender*. Philadelphia: University of Pennsylvania Press.

Burkeman, Oliver, and Gary Younge. 2004. "Being Brenda [Book review of "As Nature Made Him" by John Colapinto]." *The Guardian*. May 12. Accessed January 3, 2020. https://www.theguardian.com/books/2004/may/12/scienceandnature.gender.

Butler, Gary. 2017. "Child and Adolescent Endocrinology." In *Genderqueer and Non-Binary Genders*, by Christina Richards, Walter Bouman, and Meg-John Barker, 171-182. London: Palgrave Macmillan.

———.Butler, Gary. n.d. "Professor Gary Butler." *NHS University College London Hospitals*. Accessed June 10, 2021. https://www.uclh.nhs.uk/our-services/find-consultant/professor-gary-butler.

Butler, Judith, interview by Diana Tourjée. 2015. *Why Do Men Kill Trans Women? Gender Theorist Judith Butler Explains* Vice, (December 16).

————. 1988. "Performative Acts and Gender Constitution: An Essay in Phenomenology and Feminist Theory." *Theatre Journal* 40, no. 4: 519–531. https://doi.org/10.2307/3207893.

Cajetan, Thomas Cardinal. 2003. *Commentary on Summa Theologiae IIa–IIae*. Hildesheim, DE: Georg Olms.

Cameron, David. 1999. "Caught Between: An Essay on Intersexuality." In *Intersex in the Age of Ethics*, by Alice Domurat, 91–98. Hagerstown, MD: University Publishing Group.

Cantor, James. 2017. "How many transgender kids grow up to stay trans?" *PsyPost*. December 30. Accessed June 11, 2020. https://www.psypost.org/2017/12/many-transgender-kids-grow-stay-trans-50499.

Carr, Lucien. 1883. "The Mounds of the Mississippi Valley, Historically Considered." In *Memoirs of the Kentucky Geological Survey Vol. II*, by NS Shaler, 33, footnote. 143. Oxford, UK: Oxford University.

Cashman, Eion, and Andrew Walters. 2016. "The Genders We Live: Transgender Youth and Young Adults in an Era of Expanding Gender Paradigms." In Transgender Youth, by Shemya Vaughn, 1–36. New York: Nova Publishers.

Carlson, Robert. 2020. "Compassion and Challenge." *Archdiocese of St. Louis*. June 1. Accessed September 23, 2020. http://www.archstl.org/Portals/0/Pastoral%20letters/Compassion%20and%20Challenge%20-%20letter%20size.pdf.

Carter, Rita. 1998. *Mapping the Mind*. Berkeley: University of California Press.

Catechism of the Catholic Church. 1994. *The Holy See*. Edited by Promulgated by Pope John Paul II. London, UK: Geoffrey Chapman.

Bibliography

Cauldwell, David Oliver. 1949. "Psychopathia transsexualis." *Sexology* 16: 274–280.

Caviness, Verne. 1996. "The Human Brain Age 7–11 Years: A Volumetric Analysis Based on Magnetic Resonance Differences." *Cerebral Cortex* 6: 726–736. https://doi.org/ 10.1093/CERCOR/6.5.726.

Center for Disease Control and Prevention. 2014. "Lesbian, gay, bisexual, and transgender health." *CDC*. Accessed July 20, 2020. www.cdc.gov/lgbtheath/youth.htm.

———. 2016. "Sexual Identity, Sex of Sexual Contacts, and Health-Risk Behaviors Among Students in Grades 9–12: Youth Risk Behavior Surveillance." *Department of Health and Human Services*, August 12: Accessed June 20, 2020. https://www.cdc.gov/mmwr/volumes/65/ss/pdfs/ss6509.p df.

Cessario, Romanus. 2001. *Introduction to Moral Theology*. Washington, DC: Catholic University of America Press.

———. 1991. *The Moral Virtues and Theological Ethics*. Notre Dame, IN: University of Notre Dame Press.

———. 2002. *The Virtues, or the Examined Life*. New York: Continuum International Publishing Group.

Chan, STH, and Oo Wai-Sum. 1981. "Environmental and Non-genetic Mechanisms in Sex Determination." In *Mechanisms of Sex Differentiation in Animals and Men*, by CR Austin, & RG Edwards. New York: Academic Press.

Chang, Larry. 2007. *Wisdom for the Soul of Black Folk*. Washington, D.C.: Gnosophia Publishers.

Chapin Hall. 2018. "Missed Opportunities: LGBTQ Youth Homelessness in America." Chapin Hall. April. Accessed July 20, 2020. https://voicesofyouthcount.org/wp-content/uploads/2018/05/VoYC-LGBTQ-Brief-Chapin-Hall-2018.pdf.

Charlevoix, Pierre Francis Xavier. 1851. *Historical Journal of Father Pierre François Xavier de Charlevoix: in letters addressed to the Dutchess of Lesdiguières.* New York: Historical collections of Louisiana.

Chase, Cheryl. 2006. "Hermaphrodites with Attitude: Mapping the Emergence of Intersex Political Activism." In *Transgender Studies Reader,* by Susan Stryker, & Stephen Whittle, 300–314. New York: Routledge.

Cherry, Kittredge. 2019. *Cross-dressing warrior-saint and LGBTQ role model.* May 30. Accessed 12 30, 2019. http://qspirit.net/joan-of-arc-cross-dressing-lgbtq/.

Chesterton, G.K. 1933. *Saint Thomas Aquinas.* New York: Sheed.

Chokshi, Niraj. 2016. "Transgender Woman Is Charged With Voyeurism at Target in Idaho." *The New York Times.* July 14. Accessed June 8, 2021. https://www.nytimes.com/2016/07/15/us/target-transgender-idaho-voyeurism.html.

Chrysostom, John. 1854. *The Homilies of St. John Chrysostom Archbishop of Constantinople.* Translated by John Henry Parker. Oxford, UK: F. & J. Rivington.

Chung, Wilson, and Anthony Auger. 2013. "Gender differences in neurodevelopment and epigenetics." *Pflügers Archive: European Journal of Physiology* 465, no. 5: 573–584.

Clark, Marianne. 2011. "Whose Eyes?: Women's Experiences of Changing in a Public Change Room." *Phenomenology & Practice* 5, no. 2: 57–69.https://doi.org/10.29173/pandpr19845.

Clark, Nathan. 2021. "Transgender woman sues prison after allegedly being raped by cellmate in male prison." *M Live.* March 8. Accessed June 8, 2021. https://www.mlive.com/news/jackson/2021/03/transgender-woman-sues-prison-after-allegedly-being-raped-by-cellmate-in-male-prison.html.

Clarke, W. Norris. 2016. *Person and Being.* Milwaukee, WI: Marquette University Press.

Cohen, Deborah and Hannah Barnes. 2019. "Transgender treatment: Puberty blockers study under investigation." *BBC Newsnight.* July 22. Accessed June 15, 2021. https://www.bbc.com/news/health-49036145

Cohen, Leo, Corine de Ruiter, Heleen Ringelberg, and Peggy Cohen-Kittenis. 1977. "Psychological functioning of adolescent transsexuals: Personality and psychopathology." *Journal of Clinical Psychology* 53, no. 2: 187–196. https://doi.org/10.1002/(sici)1097-4679(199702)53:2<187::aid-jclp12>3.0.co;2-g.

Cohen-Kettenis, Peggy, and Friedemann Pfäfflin. 2003. *Transgenderism and intersexuality in childhood and adolescence: Making choices.* Vol. 46. London, UK: Sage Publications.

Cole, Collier, Michael O'Boyle, Lee Emory, and Walter Meyer. 1997. "Comorbidity of gender dysphoria and other major psychiatric diagnoses." *Archives of Sexual Behavior* 26, no. 1 (February): 13–26. https://doi.org/10.1023/a:1024517302481.

Coleman, Eli, Philip Colgan, and Louis Gooren. 1992. "Male cross-gender behavior in Myanmar: A description of the acault." *Archives of Sexual Behavior* 21, no. 3: 313–321. https://doi.org/10.1007/BF01542999.

Coleman, Eli, Walter Bockting, Marsha Botzer, Peggy Cohen-Kettenis, Griet DeCuypere, and Jamie Feldman. 2012. "Standards of Care." *WPATH.* Accessed July 25, 2020. https://www.wpath.org/media/cms/Documents/SOC%20v7/Standards%20of%20Care_V7%20Full%20Book_English.pdf.

Collier, James Lincoln. 1973. "Man and Woman, Boy and Girl [Review]." *The New York Times*, February: 6.

Congregation for Catholic Education. 2005. *Instruction Concerning the Criteria for the Discernment of Vocations with Regard to Persons with Homosexual Tendencies in View of Their Admission to the Seminary and to Holy Orders.* for the formation of clergy, Vatican City: Congregation for Catholic Education. Accessed September

29, 2020.
http://www.vatican.va/roman_curia/congregations/ccathedu
c/documents/rc_con_ccatheduc_doc_20051104_istruzione_
en.html.

———. 2019. *Male and Female He Created Them.* for Educational
Institutions, Vatican City: Congregation for Catholic
Education. Accessed September 29, 2020.
https://www.vatican.va/roman_curia/congregations/ccathed
uc/documents/rc_con_ccatheduc_doc_20190202_maschio-
e-femmina_en.pdf.

Congregation for the Doctrine of the Faith. 1990. "Donum Veritatis
on the Ecclesial Vocation of the Theologian." Vatican.va.
Edited by Joseph Ratzinger. May 24. Accessed September 23,
2020.
http://www.vatican.va/roman_curia/congregations/cfaith/d
ocuments/rc_con_cfaith_doc_19900524_theologian-
vocation_en.html.

———. 1986. "Letter to the Bishops of the Catholic Church on the
Pastoral Care of Homosexual Persons." EWTN.com. Edited
by Joseph Ratzinger. October 1. Accessed September 23,
2020. https://www.ewtn.com/catholicism/library/letter-to-
the-bishops-of-the-catholic-church-on-the-pastoral-care-of-
homosexual-persons-2081.

———. 1975. "Persona Humana." Vatican.va. Edited by Franjo
Seper. December 29. Accessed September 23, 2020.
https://www.vatican.va/roman_curia/congregations/cfaith/
documents/rc_con_cfaith_doc_19751229_persona-
humana_en.html.

Cooke, Rachel. 2019. *The Gendered Brain by Gina Rippon review- demolition
of a sexist myth.* March 5. Accessed January 8, 2020.
https://www.theguardian.com/books/2019/mar/05/the-
gendered-brain-gina-rippon-review.

Council of Nicaea. 325. "The Canons of the First Council of Nicaea."
Constantinople. Canon 1.

Bibliography

Cretella, Michelle. 2016. "Gender Dysphoria in Children and Suppression of Debate." *Journal of American Physicians & Surgeons* 21, no. 2: 50–54.

Crews, David. 1994. "Animal Sexuality." *Scientific America*, November: 108–114. Accessed September 29, 2020. https://www.scientificamerican.com/article/animal-sexuality/.

Cronin, Helena. 2005. "The vital statistics." *The Guardian*. March 11. Accessed January 9, 2020. https://www.theguardian.com/world/2005/mar/12/gender. comment.

Cronin, Helena, Gina Rippon, and Simon Baron-Cohen, interview by Mark Salter. 2016. "How Men and Women Think." IAI, January 22. YouTube video, 10:17. Accessed 03 22, 2020. https://www.youtube.com/watch?v=31c48XUtwVg.

Cross Dreamers. 2018. *What the sexual fantasies of non-transgender people tell us about the dreams of those who are trans.* December 30. Accessed 12 17, 2019. https://www.crossdreamers.com/search?q=cross+sex+gend er+fantasy%E2%%80%9D.

Cross, Erin. n.d. "Respecting Pronouns in the Classroom." *The Educator's Playbook.* Accessed June 3, 2021. https://www.gse.upenn.edu/news/educators-playbook/erin-cross-pronouns-gender-identity.

Culp-Ressler, Tara. 2015. "Birth Control Goes Against Catholicism's Teachings, But Most Catholics Use It Anyway." *Think Progress.* August 4. Accessed July 24, 2020. https://archive.thinkprogress.org/birth-control-goes-against-catholicisms-teachings-but-most-catholics-use-it-anyway-d22f2da560a1/.

Cummings, Deborah, and Pauline Yahr. 1984. "Adult testosterone levels influence the morphology of a sexually dimorphic area in the Mongolian gerbil brain." *The Journal of Comparative Neurology* 224, no. 1 (March): 132-140. https://doi.org/10.1002/cne.902240112.

Cuypere, Griet De, Els Elaut, Gunter Heylens, and Georges van Maele. 2006. "Long-term follow-up: Psychological outcome of Belgian transsexuals after sex reassignment surgery." *Sexologies*, April: 126–133.

Daily News. 1952. "Ex-GI Becomes Blonde Beauty: Operation transforms Bronx youth." *Daily News*, December 1: 1,3.

David, Sister Monica. 2015. "A nun's underground ministry for the trans community." *U.S. Catholic* 80, no. 9 (September): 32–34. Accessed September 29, 2020. https://uscatholic.org/articles/201509/a-nuns-underground-ministry-for-the-trans-community/.

Davidson v. Aetna Life & Casualty Insurance Company. 1979. 101 Misc. 2d 1 (N.Y. Sup. Ct., August 9).

Davis, William David, and Dale Alloison.1988. *A Critical and Exegetical Commentary on the Gospel according to Saint Matthew.* Vol. 3. Edinburgh, UK: T. & T. Clark.

Declaration of Quentin L. Van Meter, M.D. 2016. 1:16-cv-00425-TDS-JEP (Middle District of North Carolina, August 17).

DeFranza, Megan. 2019. "Response to Owen Strachan." In *Understanding Transgender Identities,* by James Beilby, & Paul Rhodes Eddy, 90–94. Grand Rapids, MI: Baker Academics.

———. 2015. *Sex Difference in Christian Theology.* Grand Rapids, MI: Wm. B. Eerdmans Publishing.

Dennett, Daniel. 1996. *Darwin's Dangerous Idea.* New York: Simon and Schuster.

Denzinger, Heinricus, and Adolfus Schönmetzer. 1965. *Enchiridion Symbolorum.* Freiburg, CH: Herder.

Depalma, Anthony, and Laurie Goodstein. 2002. "Member of Sex Abuse Panel Upsets Some." *The New York Times.* July 26. Accessed June 15, 2020. https://www.nytimes.com/2002/07/26/us/member-of-sex-abuse-panel-upsets-some.html.

Bibliography

Derouen, Sister Luisa. 2019. *Listening to God's transgender people.* June 26. Accessed January 14, 2020. https://www.globalsistersreport.org/column/equality/listeni ng-gods-transgender-people-56286.

Descartes, René. 1999. *Discourse on Method and Meditations on First Philosophy.* Translated by Donald A. Cress. Indianapolis, IN: Hackett Publishing.

Descher, Jack, and Jack Pula. 2014. *Ethical Issues Raised by the Treatment of Gender-Variant Prepubescent Children.* Follow-Up Report, Garrison, NY: Hastings Center Report 44 [supplement].

Devor, Aaron. *Reed Erickson and the Erickson Educational Foundation.* n.d. Accessed January 5, 2020. http://web.uvic.ca/~erick123.

de Vries, Annelou, Thomas Steensma, Theo Doreleijers, and Peggy Cohen-Kettenis. 2011. "Puberty Suppression in Adolescents with Gender Identity Disorder: A Prospective Follow-Up Study." *The Journal of Sexual Medicine* 8, no. 8 (August): 2276–2283. https://doi.org/ 10.1111/j.1743-6109.2010.01943.x.

de Vries, Annelou. 2020. "Challenges in Timing Puberty Suppression for Gender-Nonconforming Adolescents." *Pediatrics,* 146 (4). DOI: https://doi.org/10.1542/peds.2020-010611.

Dewing, Phoebe, Tao Shi, Steve Horvath, and Eric Vilain. 2003. "Sexually Dimorphic Gene Expression in Mouse Brain Precedes Gonadal Differentiation." *Molecular Brain Research* 118: 82–90. https://doi.org/10.1016/s0169-328x(03)00339-5.

Dhejne, Cecilia, Katarina Öberg, Stefan Arver, and Mikael Landén. 2014. "An Analysis of All Applications for Sex Reassignment Surgery in Sweden, 1960–2010: Prevalence, Incidence, and Regrets." *Archives of Sexual Behavior,* November: 1535–1545. https://doi.org/10.1007/s10508-014-0300-8.

Dhejne, Cecilia, Paul Lichtenstein, Marcus Boman, Anna Johansson, Niklas Långström, and Mikael Landén. 2011. "Long-term follow-up of transsexual persons undergoing sex reassignment surgery: cohort study in Sweden." *PLoS One,* February 22. https://doi.org/ 10.1371/journal.pone.0016885.

Dhejne, Cecilia, Roy Van Vlerken, Gunter Heylens, and Jon Arcelus. 2016. "Mental Health and Gender Dysphoria: A review of literature." *International Review of Psychiatry* 28, no. 1: 44–57. https://doi.org/10.3109/09540261.2015.1115753.

Diamond, Milton. 2013. "Transsexuality among twins: Identity concordance, transition, rearing, and orientation." *International Journal Transgender Health* 14: 24–38. https://doi.org/10.1080/15532739.2013.750222.

Diamond, Milton, and Keith Sigmundson. 1997. "Sex Reassignment at Birth: A long term review and clinical implications." *Archives of Pediatrics and Adolescent Medicine* 151 (March): 298–304. https://doi.org/10.1001/archpedi.1997.02170400084015.

Dörner, Günter, Ingrid Poppe, F Stahl, J Kölzsch, and Ralf Uebelhack. 1991. "Gene and environment-dependent neuroendocrine etiogenesis of homosexuality and transsexuality." *Experimental and Clinical Endocrinology* 98, no. 2: 141–150. https://doi.org/10.1055/s-0029-1211110.

Dostoevsky, Fyodor. 2018. *The Brothers Karamazov.* Translated by Constance Garnett. New Delhi, IO: Om Books International.

Dreger, Alice. 1999. "A History of Intersex: From the age of gonads to the age of consent." In *Intersex in the Age of Ethics*, by Alice Dreger, 5–28. Hagerstown, MD: University Publishing Group.

———. 2015. *Galileo's Middle Finger.* London, UK: Penguin Press.

Dresher, Jack, and Jack Pula. n.d. *American Psychiatric Association.* Accessed 12 16, 2019. https://www.psychiatry.org/patients-families/gender-dysphoria/expert-q-and-a.

Drummond, Kelley, Susan Bradley, Michele Peterson-Badali, and Kenneth Zucker. 2008 "A Follow Up Study of Girls With Gender Identity Disorder." *Developmental Psychology* 44, no. 1 (February): 34–45. https://doi.org/10.1037/0012-1649.44.1.34.

Bibliography

Dr. Veronica Ivy. 2019. Twitter Post. October 20, 2:32 AM
https://twitter.com/SportIsARight/status/118580592994361
7537.

Du Bois, W.E.B. 1969. *The Souls of Black Folk.* New York: Signet
Classic.

Dulles, Avery. 2007. "God and Evolution." *First Things,* October: 19–
24.

Dumic, Miroslav, Karen Lin-Su, Natasha I. Leibel, Srecko Ciglar,
Giovanna Vinci, Ruzica Lasan. 2008. "Report of Fertility in a
Woman with a Predominantly 46 XY Karyotype in a Family
with Multiple Disorders of Sexual Development." *Journal of
Clinical Endocrinology and Metabolism* 93: 182–189.
https://doi.org/10.1210/jc.2007-2155.

Edgerton, Milton, Norman Knorr, and James Callison. 1970. "The
surgical treatment of transsexual patients: Limitations and
indications." *Plastic and Reconstructive Surgery* 45, no. 1: 38–50.

Edison, Avery. 2014. "I'm trans and on Tinder, but I am not a fetish
for your sexual bucket list." *The Guardian.* December 12.
Accessed July 22, 2020.
https://www.theguardian.com/commentisfree/2014/dec/12
/trans-tinder-sexual-bucket-list.

Edwards-Leeper, Laura, and Norman Spack. 2012. "Psychological
evaluation and medical treatment of transgender youth in an
interdisciplinary "Gender Management Service" (GeMS) in a
major pediatric center." *Journal of Homosexuality* 59: 321–336.
https://doi.org/ 10.1080/00918369.2012.653302.

Ehrenhalt, Jey. 2018. "Trans Rights and Bathroom Access Laws: A
History Explained." *Teaching Tolerance,* October 16: Accessed
September 29, 2020.
https://www.tolerance.org/magazine/transgender-bathroom-
laws-history.

Ehernstaf, Diane. 2021. "Fertility Issues for Transgender and
Nonbinary Youth." *UC San Francisco Child and Adolescent
Gender Center.* Zoom April 7. Accessed June 17, 2021.

https://drive.google.com/file/d/1SlpfbHRxf3mvbc7SdS5W GBav__3Tm3Vx/view.

Ehrhardt, Anke. 2007. "John Money, Ph.D." *The Journal of Sex Research* 44, no. 3 (August): 223–224. https://doi.org/10.1080/00224490701580741.

Ellul, Jacques. 1964. *The Technological Society.* Translated by John Wilkonson. New York: Vintage Books.

Ely, Robin, Debra Meyerson, and Martin Davidson. 2006. "Rethinking Political Correctness." *Harvard Business Review.* September. Accessed June 24, 2020. https://hbr.org/2006/09/rethinking-political-correctness.

Ennis, Dawn. 2016. "Queer singles survey reveals divisions on dating, marriage, and kids." LGBTQ Nation. June 2. Accessed July 22, 2020. https://www.lgbtqnation.com/2016/06/queer-singles-survey-reveals-divisions-dating-marriage-kids/.

Erickson-Schroth, Laura. 2014. *Trans Bodies, Trans Selves. A Resource for the transgender community.* Oxford, UK: Oxford University Press.

Ettner, Randi. 1999. *Gender Loving Care.* New York: WW Norton.

Ettner, Randi, Mark Schaht, J Brown, Craig Niederberger, and Eugene Schrang 1996. "Transsexualism: The phenotypic variable." *Fifteenth International Symposium on Gender Dysphoria.* Vancouver: Harry Benjamin International Gender Dysphoria Association. Poster session presentation.

Evans, Lydia. 2010. "Charleston, SC: Dr. Paul McHugh: "There Is No Gay Gene"." *Virtue Online.* January 26. Accessed June 15, 2020. https://virtueonline.org/charleston-sc-dr-paul-mchugh-there-no-gay-gene.

Family Policy Institute of Washington. 2016. *Trans-Activism Uncensored (Warning: Explicit Language).* YouTube video. June 22. Accessed June 10, 2021. https://www.youtube.com/watch?v=mFujpMxmUME.

Fausto-Sterling, Anne. 2000a. *Sexing the Body: Gender Politics and the Construction of Sexuality.* New York: Basic Books.

Fausto-Sterling, Anne. 2000b. "The five sexes revisited"." *The Sciences* 40, no. 4: 18–23.

Faustus. 2006. "Sermo 5, De Epiphania 2." *Documenta Catholica Omnia.* Accessed February 09, 2020. ://www.documentacatholicaomnia.eu/04z/z_0425-0490__Faustus_Rhegiensis_Episcopus__Sermones__MLT.pd f.html.

Favale, Abigail. 2019. "The Eclipse of Sex by the Rise of Gender." *Church Life* 22: 1–10. Accessed September 29, 2020. https://churchlifejournal.nd.edu/articles/the-eclipse-of-sex-by-the-rise-of-gender/.

Fernández, Rosa. 2014. "The (CA)n Polymorphism of ERβ Gene is Associated with FtM Transsexualism." *The Journal of Sexual Medicine* 11, no. 3 (March): 720–728. https://doi.org/10.1111/jsm.12398.

Fichtner, Joseph. 1963. *Theological Anthropology: The Science of Man in His Relations to God.* Notre Dame, IN: University of Notre Dame Press.

Field, Richard. 1984. "St. Thomas Aquinas on Properties and the Powers of the Soul." *Laval théologique et philosophique* 40, no. 2: 203–215. https://doi.org/10.7202/400093ar.

Finley, John. 2015. "The Metaphysics of Gender: A Thomistic Approach." *The Thomist: A Speculative Quarterly Review* 79, no. 4: 585–614. https://doi.org/ 10.1353/tho.2015.0031.

First, Michael. 2005. "Desire for amputation of a limb: paraphilia, psychosis, or a new type of identity disorder." *Psychological Medicine,* 35, no. 6 (June): 919–928. https://doi.org/10.1017/s0033291704003320.

Fisher, Alessandra, Elisa Bandini, Helen Casale, and Naika Ferruccio. 2013."Sociodemographic and Clinical Features of Gender Identity Disorder: An Italian Multicentric Evaluation." *The Journal of Sexual Medicine* 10, no. 2 (February): 408–419. https://doi.org/10.1111/j.1743-6109.2012.03006.x.

Fisk, Norman. 1973. *Gender dysphoria syndrome (the how, what, and why of a disease), in Proceedings of the Second Interdisciplinary Symposium on Gender Dysphoria Syndrome.* Edited by D Laub, & P Gandy. Palo Alto, CA: Stanford Press.

———. 1974. "Gender dysphoria syndrome – The conceptualization that liberalizes indications for total gender reorientation and implies a broadly based multi-dimensional rehabilitative regimen." *Western Journal of Medicine* 5, no. 120: 386–391.

Flier, Jeffrey. 2018. "As a Former Dean of Harvard Medical School, I Question Brown's Failure to Defend Lisa Littman." *Quillette.* August 31. Accessed June 30, 2020. https://quillette.com/2018/08/31/as-a-former-dean-of-harvard-medical-school-i-question-browns-failure-to-defend-lisa-littman/.

Flores, Andrew, Jody Herman, Gary Gates, and Taylor Brown. 2016."How Many Adults Identify as Transgender in the United States." *Williams Institute of Law UCLA.* June. Accessed 12 15, 2019. https://williamsinstitute.law.ucla.edu/wp-content/uploads/How-Many-Adults-Identify-as-Transgender-in-the-United-States.pdf.

Foot, Philippa. 2001. *Natural Goodness.* Oxford, UK: Clarendon.

Forbes, Catherine, Leslie Clark, and Huong Diep. 2016. "Positive attributes and risk behaviors in young transgender women." *Psychology of Sexual Orientation and Gender Diversity 3*, no. 1: 129–134. https://doi.org/10.1037/sgd0000148.

Ford, Zack. 2014. "Laverne Cox: 'Loving Trans People Is A Revolutionary Act'." *ThinkProgressive.org.* January 31. Accessed July 22, 2020. https://archive.thinkprogress.org/laverne-cox-loving-trans-people-is-a-revolutionary-act-2b79c142ae69/.

Forger, Nancy, James Strahan, and Alexandra Castillo-Ruiz. 2016. "Cellular and molecular mechanisms of sexual differentiation in the mammalian nervous system." *Frontiers in Neuroendocrinology* 40: 67–86. https://doi.org/10.1016/j.yfrne.2016.01.001.

Bibliography

Forrai, Judit. 2006. "History Ambroise Paré- The "Father of Surgery"." *Clinica e Pesquisa Odontológica, Curitiba*, July 10: 447–450.

Francis, Pope. 2017. "Address to the Participants in the General Assembly of the Members of the Pontifical Academy for Life." Vatican City, October 5. Accessed September 29, 2020. http://www.vatican.va/content/francesco/en/speeches/2017/october/documents/papa-francesco_20171005_assemblea-pav.html.

———. 2016a. Amoris Laetitia (The Joy of Love). Post- Synodal Apostolic Exhortation." Vatican City: The Holy See. Promulgated by Pope Francis, March 19. Accessed September 29, 2020. https://w2.vatican.va/content/dam/francesco/pdf/apost_exhortations/documents/papa-francesco_esortazione-ap_20160319_amoris-laetitia_en.pdf.

———. 2019. Aperuit Illis (He Opened). *Aperuit Illis Instituting the Sunday of the Word of God.* Vatican City: The Holy See. Promulgated by Pope Francis, September 30. Accessed September 29, 2020. http://www.vatican.va/content/francesco/en/motu_proprio/documents/papa-francesco-motu-proprio-20190930_aperuit-illis.html.

———. 2013b "Chrism Mass Homily." *Vatican.va.* March 28. Accessed September 28, 2020. http://w2.vatican.va/content/francesco/en/homilies/2013/documents/papa-francesco_20130328_messa-crismale.html.

———. 2013a. Evangelii Gaudium (The Love of the Gospel). "Apostolic Exhortation." Vatican City: The Holy See. Promulgated by Pope Francis, November 24. Accessed September 29, 2020. http://www.vatican.va/content/francesco/en/apost_exhortations/documents/papa-francesco_esortazione-ap_20131124_evangelii-gaudium.html.

———. 2020. Fratelli Tutti. (Fraternity and Social Friendship)."Encyclical Letter." Vatican City: The Holy See.

Promulgated by Pope Francis, October 3. Accessed October 5, 2020. http://www.vatican.va/content/francesco/en/encyclicals/do cuments/papa-francesco_20201003_enciclica-fratelli-tutti.html#_ftn187.

———. 2015b. "General Audience." *Vatican.va.* April 15. Accessed June 04, 2020. http://w2.vatican.va/content/francesco/en/audiences/2015 /documents/papa-francesco_20150415_udienza-generale.html.

———. 2016b. "Pope complains schools are telling children they can choose their gender." *Associated Press.* August 2. Accessed July 24, 2020. https://www.theguardian.com/world/2016/aug/02/pope-complains-gender-children-schools-telling-choose.

———. 2015a. Laudato Si' (Praise be to You)."Encyclical Letter." Vatican City: The Holy See. Promulgated by Pope Francis, May 24. Accessed September 29, 2020. http://www.vatican.va/content/francesco/en/encyclicals/do cuments/papa-francesco_20150524_enciclica-laudato-si.html.

———. 2018. "Pope's quotes: Peace builds bridges." *Vatican.va.* May 4. Accessed January 28, 2020. https://press.vatican.va/content/salastampa/en/bollettino/p ubblico/2016/07/28/160728c.html.

Frankl, Viktor. 2007. "Man's Search for Meaning." In *Virtue & Vice in Everyday Life,* by Christina Hoff Sommers, & Fred Sommers, 530–536. Boston, MA: Wadsworth Cengage Learning.

Freud, Sigmund. 2014. *Three Essays on the Theory of Sexuality.* Translated by James Strachey. Vol. 7. London, UK: Hogarth Press.

G.G. [Gavin Grimm v. Gloucester County School Board. 2018. 15–2056 (United States Court of Appeals for the Fourth Circuit, May 22).

Galanter, Marc, and Lee Anne Kaskutas. 2008. *Research on Alcoholics Anonymous and Spirituality in Addiction Recovery.* Berlin, DE: Springer Science & Business Media.

Garner, Bryan. 2019. "Black's Law Dictionary (11th ed.)." *Mayhem Definition*. Eagan: Thomson West, July.

Garofalo, Robert, Joanne Deleon, Elizabeth Osmer, Mary Doll, and Gary Harper. 2006. "Overlooked, misunderstood and at-risk: exploring the lives and HIV risk of ethnic minority male-to-female transgender youth." *Journal of Adolescent Health* 38, no. 3: 230–236. https://doi.org/10.1016/j.jadohealth.2005.03.023.

Gary-Smith, Mariotta and Judith Steinhart. 2016. "Transgender Youth: ways to be an ally and advocate" In *Transgender Youth*, by Shemya Vaughn, 209–221. New York: Nova Publishers.

Gates, Gary. 2011. "How many people are lesbian, gay, bisexual, and transgender?" *The Williams Institute at UCLA*. April. Accessed 12 15, 2019. http://williamsinstitute.law.ucla.edu/wp-content/uploads/Gates-How-Many-People-LGBT-Apr-2011.pdf.

Gaudium et Spes. 1965. "Pastoral Constitution on the Church in the Modern World." *The Second Vatican Council*. Vatican City: Promulgated by Pope Paul VI.

Geach, Peter. 1977. *Virtues*. Cambridge, UK: Cambridge University Press.

Gehring, John. 2019. "Why Catholic bishops need a year of abstinence on preaching about sexuality." *National Catholic Reporter*. June 26. Accessed January 15, 2020. https://www.ncronline.org/news/opinion/why-catholic-bishops-need-year-abstinence-preaching-about-sexuality.

Gender Identity Clinic. 1979. *The Johns Hopkins Medical Institutions News*. Press Release, Baltimore, MD: Johns Hopkins.

George, Robert. 2016. "Gnostic Liberalism." *First Things*. December. Accessed June 27, 2020. https://www.firstthings.com/article/2016/12/gnostic-liberalism.

Gettell, Oliver. 2016. "Little Axe illuminates transgender gospel singer Willmer Broadnax." *Entertainment Weekly*. March 1.

Accessed July 25, 2020.
https://ew.com/article/2016/03/01/little-axe-transgender-gospel-singer-short-film/.

Ghosh, Shuvo. 2020. "Gender Identity." *Medscape.* December 9. Accessed June 5, 2021. https://emedicine.medscape.com/article/917990-overview.

Gibbs, Jeremy, and Jeremy Goldbach. 2015. "Religious Conflict, Sexual Identity, and Suicidal Behaviors among LGBT Young Adults." *Archives of Suicide Research*, March 12: 472–488. https://doi.org/10.1080/13811118.2015.1004476

Gigerenzer, Gerd. 1999. *Simple Heuristics That Make Us Smart.* New York: Oxford University Press.

Gigerenzer, Gerd, and Wolfgang Gaissmaier. 2011. "Heuristic decision making." *Annual Review of Psychology* 62: 451–482. https://doi.org/ 10.1146/annurev-psych-120709-145346.

Gilchrist, Susan. 2015. "Deuteronomy 22:5 and its Impact on Gender." *tgdr.* November 15. Accessed 12 24, 2019. http://www.tgdr.co.uk/documents/022B-Deuteronomy22-5.pdf.

Gilligan, Andrew. 2019. "Surge in girls switching gender." *The Sunday Times.* June 29. Accessed September 28, 2020. https://www.thetimes.co.uk/article/surge-in-girls-switching-gender-c69nl57vt.

Gilson, Étienne. 1952. *Being and Some Philosophers.* Toronto: Pontifical Institute of Mediaeval Studies.

———. 1948. *The Philosophy of St. Thomas Aquinas.* Translated by Edward Bullough. New York: Dorset Press.

———. 2012. *Thomist Realism and the Critique of Knowledge.* Translated by Mark Wauck. San Francisco, CA: Ignatius Press.

GLAAD. 2019. Twitter Post. July 31, 12:14PM: https://twitter.com/glaad/status/1156599091096371207

Glanvill, Joseph. 1661. *Vanity of Dogmatizing.* London, UK: Printed by E.C. for Henry Eversden.

Bibliography

Goddard, Jonathan Charles. 2009. "Development of Feminizing Genitoplasty for Gender Dysphoria." *The Journal of Sexual Medicine: Goddard, Jonathan Charles MD,* "April 19: 981–989. https://doi.org/10.1111/j.1743-6109.2007.00480.x.

González, Ana Marta. 1999. "Depositum Gladius non Debet Restitui Furioso: Precepts, Synderesis, and Virtues in Saint Thomas Aquinas." *The Thomist,* April 2: 217–240. https://doi.org/10.1353/tho.1999.0029.

Grand View Research. 2020. "U.S. Sex Reassignment Surgery Market Size, Share & Trends Analysis Report By Gender Transition (Male To Female, Female To Male), And Segment Forecasts, 2020 - 2027." *Grand View Research.* December. Accessed March 15, 2021. https://www.grandviewresearch.com/industry-analysis/us-sex-reassignment-surgery-market.

Grant, Jaime, Lisa Mottet, Justin Tanis, and Jack Harrison. 2011. "Injustice at Every Turn." *National Center for Transgender Equality.* Accessed January 9, 2020. https://www.transequality.org/sites/default/files/docs/resources/NTDS_Report.pdf.

Grant, Jon, and Katherine Phillips. 2004. "Is Anorexia Nervosa a Subtype of Body Dysmorphic Disorder? Probably Not, but Read On …." *Harvard Review of Psychiatry* 12, no. 2: 123–126. https://doi.org/10.1080/10673220490447236.

Grayson Project. 2021. *I'm Detransitioning | My struggle with Gender and Self Acceptance.* June 9. YouTube video. Accessed June 10, 2021. https://www.youtube.com/watch?v=wNsIpF7g2lQ.

Green, Richard. 2008. "The Three Kings: Harry Benjamin, John Money, Robert Stoller." *Archives of Sexual Behavior,* June 21: 610–613. https://doi.org/10.1007/s10508-008-9392-3.

———. 1987. *The "Sissy Boy Syndrome" and the Development of Homosexuality.* New Haven. CT: Yale University Press.

Greenberg, Steve. 1993. "The Next Wave." *The Advocate,* July 13: 51–52.

Greer, Germaine, interview by Krishnan Guru-Murthy. 2018. "Germaine Greer on women's liberation, the trans community and her rape." *Channel 4 News*, May 23. YouTube video, 45:01. Accessed 04 24, 2020. https://www.youtube.com/watch?v=aU_csXGfdVM&t=178 s.

Gremmels, Becket. 2016. "Sex Reassignment Surgery and the Catholic Moral." *Health Care Ethics USA* 24, no. 1 (Winter): 6–10.

Griswold, Alexander. 2014. "How to Shrink Your Church in One Easy Step." *The Federalist.* August 21. Accessed July 24, 2020. https://thefederalist.com/2014/08/21/how-to-shrink-your-church-in-one-easy-step/.

Gstalter, Morgan. 2019. "International sports court rules women with high testosterone can be required to take suppressants." *The Hill.* May 1. Accessed January 27, 2020. https://thehill.com/policy/international/441529-international-sports-court-rules-women-with-high-testosterone-can-be.

Guillamon, Antonio, Carme Junque, and Esther Gómez-Gil. 2016. "A Review of the Status of Brain Structure Research in Transsexualism." *Archives of Sexual Behavior* 45, no. 1: 1615–1648. https://doi.org/10.1007/s10508-016-0768-5.

Guillen, Matheus. 2018. *Gender-affirming surgery 'significantly improves quality of life,' study says.* April 11. Accessed February 7, 2020. http://www.nbcnews.com/feature/nbc-out/gender-affirming-surgery-significantly-improves-quality-life-study-says-n862361.

Gurian, Michael. 2017. *Saving Our Sons.* Spokane, WA: Gurian Institute.

Gurian, Michael, and Kathy Stevens. 2005. *The Minds of Boys.* San Francisco, CA: Jossey-Bass.

Guttmacher Institute. 2008. "Religion and Family Planning Tables." *Guttmacher Institute.* Accessed July 24, 2020.

https://www.guttmacher.org/religion-and-family-planning-tables.

Haas, Ann, Philip Rodgers, and Jody Herman. 2014. "Suicide Attempts among Transgender and Gender Non-Conforming Adults." *Williams Institute of Law UCLA.* January 2. Accessed January 11, 2020. https://williamsinstitute.law.ucla.edu/wp-content/uploads/AFSP-Williams-Suicide-Report-Final.pdf.

Hadro, Matt. 2020. *After AOC Decries Statue, Hawaiian Catholic Says St Damien 'Gave His Life' Serving Leper.* July 31. Accessed October 5, 2020. https://www.ncregister.com/news/after-aoc-decries-statue-hawaiian-catholic-says-st-damien-gave-his-life-serving-leper.

Haier, Richard, Rex Jung, Ronald Yeo, Kevin Head, and Michael Alkire. 2005. "The neuroanatomy of general intelligence: sex matters." *Neuroimage* 25, no. 1 (March): 320–327. https://doi.org/10.1016/j.neuroimage.2004.11.019.

Hake, Laura, and Claire O'Connor. 2008. "Genetic mechanisms of sex determination." *Nature Education*: 25.

Hamer, Dean. 2016. "New 'Scientific' Study on Sexuality, Gender Is Neither New nor Scientific." *The Advocate.* August 29. Accessed June 06, 2020. https://www.advocate.com/commentary/2016/8/29/new-scientific-study-sexuality-gender-neither-new-nor-scientific.

Hare, John. 2015. "Hermaphrodites, Eunuchs, and Intersex People: The witness of medical science in Biblical times and today." In *Intersex, Theology, and the Bible: Troubling bodies in Church text and society*, by Susannah Cornwall, 83–87. New York: Palgrave.

Hare, Lauren, Pascal Bernard, Francisco Sánchez, Paul Baird, Eric Vilain, Trudy Kennedy. 2009. "Androgen Receptor Repeat Length Polymorphism Associated with Male-To-Female Transsexualism." *Biological Psychiatry* 65, no. 1: 93–96. https://doi.org/ 10.1016/j.biopsych.2008.08.033.

Hartin v. Director of the Bureau of Records and Statistics. 1973. 347 N.Y.S. 2d 515 (N.Y. Sup. Ct.).

Hayes. 2014. "Hormone therapy for the treatment of gender dysphoria." *Hayes Medical Technology Directory,* May 14.

Hayton, Debbie interview by Madeleine Kearns. 2020. "One Transwoman Speaks Out on the Dangers of Trans Extremism." National Review. February 25. Accessed June 8, 2021. https://www.nationalreview.com/2020/02/debbie-hayton-transwoman-speaks-out-on-dangers-of-trans-extremism/.

———. 2021. "'Trans Women Are Men … Including Me' - Debbie Hayton." *Triggernomitry.* March 31. YouTube video. Accessed June 8, 2021. https://www.youtube.com/watch?v=q0DT1aBHheI.

Hembree, Wylie, Peggy Cohen-Kettenis, Louis Gooren, Sabine Hannema, Walter Meyer. 2017. "Endocrine Treatment of Gender-Dysphoric/Gender-Incongruent Persons: An Endocrine Society Clinical Practice Guideline." *The Journal of Clinical Endocrinology & Metabolism,* September 13: 3869–3903. https://doi.org/10.1210/jc.2017-01658.

Hendershott, Anne. 2015. "Digging deeper into the Pew data about nones, millennials, and Christians." *The Catholic World Report.* May 25. Accessed July 24, 2020. https://www.catholicworldreport.com/2015/05/25/digging-deeper-into-the-pew-data-about-nones-millennials-and-christians/.

Henningsson, Susanne, Lars Westberg, Staffan Nilsson, Bengt Lundström, Lisa Ekselius, and Owe Bodlund. 2005. "Sex steroid-related genes and male-to-female transsexualism." *Psychoneuro endocrinology* 30: 657–664. https://doi.org/10.1016/j.psyneuen.2005.02.006.

Hess, Jochen, Andreas Henkel, Joseph Bohr, Christian Rheme, Andrej Panic, and Linda Panic. 2018. "Sexuality after Male-to-Female Gender Affirmation Surgery." *Biomedical Research International:* 7 pgs. https://doi.org/10.1155/2018/9037979.

Hester, David. 2005. "Eunuchs and the Postgender Jesus: Matthew 19.12 and Transgressive Sexualities." *Journal for the Study of the*

New Testament 28, no. 1: 13–40.
https://doi.org/10.1177/0142064X05057772.

Heyer, Walt. 2020. "Another Women's Sport Is Letting Biological
Males Compete." *The Daily Signal.* January 16. Accessed June
27, 2020. https://www.dailysignal.com/2020/01/16/another-
womens-sport-is-letting-biological-males-compete/.

———. 2018. *Trans Life Survivors.* Lightning Source UK.

Hidalgo, Marco, Diane Ehrensaft, Amy Tishelman, and L Clarke.
2013. "The Gender Affirmative Model: What we know and
what we aim to learn." *Human Development* 56, no. 5 (October):
285–290. https://doi.org/10.1159/000355235.

Hirschfeld, Magnus. 1948. *Sexual Anomalies.* New York: Emerson
Books.

———. 2003. *The Transvestites: The Erotic Drive to Cross-dress.*
Translated by MA Lombardi-Nash. Buffalo, NY: Prometheus.

Holt, Alison. 2020. "NHS gender clinic 'should have challenged me
more' over transition." *BBC News.* March 1. Accessed May 25,
2021. https://www.bbc.com/news/health-51676020.

Horan, Dan. 2020. "The truth about so-called 'gender ideology'."
National Catholic Reporter, June 24. Accessed September 29,
2020. https://www.ncronline.org/news/opinion/faith-
seeking-understanding/truth-about-so-called-gender-ideology.

Hughes, Ieuan. 2006. "Consensus Statement on Management of
Intersex Disorders." *Archives of Disease in Childhood 2*, May:
488–500. https://doi.org/10.1136/adc.2006.098319.

Hulshoff, Hilleke. 2006. "Changing your sex changes your brain:
influences of testosterone and estrogen on adult human brain
structure." *European Journal of Endocrinology* 155: 107–114.
https://doi.org/10.1530/eje.1.02248.

Human Rights Campaign. 2018. "2018 Gender-Expansive Youth
Report." *Human Rights Campaign.* Accessed 12 18, 2019.
https://www.hrc.org/resources/2018-gender-expansive-
youth-report.

Hunt, Mary. 2015. "Vatican Council on Women Would Be Funny Were It Not So Insulting." *Religion Dispatches*. February 5. Accessed January 15, 2020. https://religiondispatches.org/vatican-council-on-women-would-be-funny-were-it-not-so-insulting/.

Hutchinson, Anna, Melissa Midgen, and Anastasis Spiliadis. 2020. "In Support of Research into Rapid-Onset Gender Dysphoria." *Archives of Sexual Behavior* 49: 79–80. https://doi.org/10.1007/s10508-019-01517-9.

Hutchinson, J. Benjamin. 1997. "Gender-specific Steroid Metabolism in Neural Differentiation." *Cellular and Molecular Neurobiology, 17(6),* 603–626.

Ihlenfeld, Charles. 2004. "Harry Benjamin and Psychiatrists." In *Transgender Subjectivities: A Clinician's Guide*, by Ubaldo Leli, & Jack Dresher, 147–152. Binghamton, NY: Hayworth Medical Press.

Inkwood Research. 2020. "Global Cosmetic Surgery and Procedure Market Forecast 2020-2028." *Inkwood Research*. September. Accessed December 13, 2020. https://inkwoodresearch.com/reports/cosmetic-surgery-and-procedure-market#.

International Theological Commission. 2002. "Communion and Stewardship: Human Persons Created in the Image of God." *Vatican.va*. Accessed June 27, 2020. http://www.vatican.va/roman_curia/congregations/cfaith/cti_documents/rc_con_cfaith_doc_20040723_communion-stewardship_en.html.

Intrusive Thoughts. *Living with Body Dysmorphic Disorder (BDD)*. n.d. Accessed January 8, 2020. https://www.intrusivethoughts.org/ocd-symptoms/body-dysmorphic-disorder/.

Isidore of Seville. 2010. *The Etymologies of Isidore of Seville*. Translated by Stephen A. Barney. Cambridge, UK: Cambridge University Press.

Bibliography

Jaeger, Werner. 1947. *Theology of Early Greek Philosophers.* Oxford, UK: Clarendon Press.

Jaffrey, Zia. 1996. *The Invisibles.* New York: Pantheon.

James, Sandy, Jody Herman, Susan Rankin, Mara Keisling, Lisa Mottet, and Ma'ayan Anafi. 2016. *The Report of the 2015 U.S. Transgender Survey.* Results of Survey, Washington, DC: National Center for Transgender Equality. Accessed September 29, 2020. https://www.transequality.org/sites/default/files/docs/UST S-Full-Report-FINAL.PDF.

Jensen, Steven. 2010. *Good & Evil Actions: A Journey through Saint Thomas Aquinas.* Washington, DC: Catholic University of America Press.

———. 2008. "Of Gnome and Gnomes: The Virtue of Higher Discernment and the Production of Monsters." *American Catholic Philosophical Quarterly* 82, no. 3: 411–428. https://doi.org/10.5840/acpq200882328.

Jensen, Tamara Syrek, Joseph Chin, James Rollins, Elizabeth Koller, Linda Gousis, and Katherine Szarama. 2016b. "Decision Memo for Gender Dysphoria and Gender Reassignment Surgery (CAG-00446N)." *Centers for Medicare & Medicaid Services.* August 30. Accessed January 7, 2020. https://www.cms.gov/medicare-coverage-database/details/nca-decision-memo.aspx?NCAId=282&bc=ACAAAAAAQAAA&.

———. 2016a. "Proposed Decision Memo for Gender Dysphoria and Gender Reassignment Surgery (CAG-00446N)." *Centers for Medicare & Medicaid Services.* June 2. Accessed January 7, 2020. https://www.cms.gov/medicare-coverage-database/details/nca-proposed-decision-memo.aspx?NCAId=282.

Joel, Daphna. 2019. "It's Time for a World without Gender." *Scientific American.* October 10. Accessed June 17, 2020. https://blogs.scientificamerican.com/observations/its-time-for-a-world-without-gender/?print=true.

———. 2012. "TEDxJaffa — Daphna Joel — Are brains male or female?" *TEDx Talks*. October 8. YouTube video, 14:47. Accessed January 10, 2020. https://www.youtube.com/watch?v=rYpDU040yzc.

Joel, Daphna, Zohar Berman, Ido Tavor, Nadav Wexler, Olga Gaber. 2015. "Sex beyond the genitalia: The human brain mosaic." *Proceedings of the National Academy of Sciences of the United States of America* 112, no. 50 (December): 15468-15473. https://doi.org/10.1073/pnas.1509654112.

John Paul II, Pope. 1979a. "Address of His Holiness John Paul II to High School Students." *Vatican.va*. October 3, 1979. Accessed December 12, 2020. http://www.vatican.va/content/john-paul-ii/en/speeches/1979/october/documents/hf_jp-ii_spe_19791003_ny-madison-square-garden.html.

———. 1991. "Centesimus Annus." *The hundredth anniversary of Rerum novarum*. Vatican City: The Holy See. http://www.vatican.va/content/john-paul-ii/en/encyclicals/documents/hf_jp-ii_enc_01051991_centesimus-annus.html (accessed September 29, 2020).

———. 2006. *Man and Woman, He Created Them: A Theology of the Body*. Translated by Michael Waldstein. Boston, MA: Pauline Books and Media.

———. 1996. "Message of St. John Paul II to the Pontifical Academy of Sciences." *Vatican.va*. October 22. Accessed December 15, 2019. http://www.vatican.va/content/john-paul-ii/fr/messages/pont_messages/1996/documents/hf_jp-ii_mes_19961022_evoluzione.html.

———. 1979b. "Third General Conference of the Latin American Episcopate." Puebla, Mexico: The Holy See, January 28. Accessed September 29, 2020. http://www.vatican.va/content/john-paul-ii/en/speeches/1979/january/documents/hf_jp-ii_spe_19790128_messico-puebla-episc-latam.html.

———. 1993. The Splendor of the Truth (Veritatis Splendor), London, UK: Catholic Truth Society.

Joint Commission. 2011. *Advancing effective communication, cultural competence, and patient and family centered care for the gay, lesbian, bisexual and transgender (lgbt) community: A field guide.* Oak Brook, IL: Joint Commission.

Jones, Bethany Alice, Jon Arcelus, Walter Pierre Bouman, and Emma Haycraft. 2017. "Sport and Transgender People: A Systematic Review of the Literature Relating to Sport Participation and Competitive Sport Policies." *Sports Medicine,* 47, no. 4: 701–716. https://doi.org/ 10.1007/s40279-016-0621-y.

Jones, David Albert. 2018. "Truth in transition? Gender Identity and Catholic Anthropology." *Blackfriars*, November: 756–774. https://doi.org/10.1111/nbfr.12380.

———. 2019. "One More Way to be Human." *The Tablet*, April 6: 4–5.

Jones, Morgan. 2017. "LDS Church issues statement of support for LGBTQ concert event." *Deseret News.* August 16. Accessed July 24, 2020. https://www.deseret.com/2017/8/16/20617692/lds-church-issues-statement-of-support-for-lgbtq-concert-event#dan-reynolds-of-imagine-dragons-performs-at-the-staples-center-on-monday-april-3-2017-in-los-angeles.

Jones, Robert, Daniel Cox, and Juhem Navarro-Rivera. 2014. *A Shifting Landscape.* A Decade of Change in American Attitudes about Same-sex Marriage and LGBT Issues, Washington, DC: Public Religion Research Institute.

Jones, Zinnia. 2013. *"That was dysphoria?" 8 signs and symptoms of indirect gender dysphoria.* September 10. Accessed February 15, 2021. http://genderanalysis.net/articles/that-was-dysphoria-8-signs-and-symptoms-of-indirect-gender-dysphoria/.

———. 2016. *Myth: Pimozide and gender dysphoria [Gender Analysis].* December 30. Accessed January 4, 2020. https://genderanalysis.net/2016/12/myth-pimozide-and-gender-dysphoria-gender-analysis/.

———. 2021 Twitter Post. July 21, 6:49 AM: https://twitter.com/ZJemptv/status/1417798800903659520.

———. 2020. Twitter Post. December 2, 11:35 AM: https://twitter.com/ZJemptv/status/1334159240466997249.

Jordan, Crimson. 2018. "The Gender Affirmative Model: APA Publishes Groundbreaking Book on Care for Trans and Gender Expansive Youth." *Spectrum South.* June 20. Accessed July 1, 2020. https://www.spectrumsouth.com/gender-affirmative-model/.

Jordan-Young, Rebecca. 2010. *Brain Storm: The Flaws in the Science of Sex Differences.* Cambridge, MA: Harvard University Press.

Jost, Alfred. 1978. "Basic sexual trends in the development of vertebrates." *Ciba Foundation symposium* (14) 16: 5–18. https://doi.org/10.1002/9780470720448.ch2.

Kahneman, Daniel. 2011. *Thinking, Fast and Slow.* New York: Farrar, Strauss, Giroux.

Kahneman, Daniel, Alan Krueger, David Schkade, Norbert Schwarz, and Arthur Stone. 2004. "A Survey Method for Characterizing Daily Life Experience: The Day Reconstruction Method." *Science*, December 3: 1776–1780. https://doi.org/ 10.1126/science.1103572.

Kailas, Maya, Hsun Ming Simon Lu, Emily Rothman, and Joshua Safer. 2017. "Prevalence and types of gender-affirming surgery among a sample of transgender endocrinology patients prior to state expansion of insurance coverage." *Endocrine Practice* 23, no. 7 (July): 780–786. https://doi.org/10.4158/EP161727.OR.

Kay, Jackie. 1998. *Trumpet.* London, UK: Picador.

Kalin, Ned. 2020. "Reassessing Mental Health Treatment Utilization Reduction in Transgender Individuals After Gender-Affirming Surgeries: A Comment by the Editor on the Process." *American Journal of Psychiatry*, August 1: 176. https://doi.org/10.1176/appi.ajp.2020.20060803.

Bibliography

Kavanaugh, James and Vamik Volkan. 1979. "Transsexualism and a New Kind of Psychosurgery." *International Journal of Psychoanalytic Psychotherapy* 7: 366–372. PMID: 738821.

Keating, Shannon. 2019. *Gender Dysphoria Isn't A "Social Contagion," According to A New Study.* April 19. Accessed June 15, 2020. https://www.buzzfeednews.com/article/shannonkeating/rap id-onset-gender-dysphoria-flawed-methods-transgender.

Keefe, Donald. 1999. "The Relation of Nuptial symbolism to Eucharistic Realism." *The Pacific Journal of Theology, Series II* 21: 89–119.

Kellaway, Mitch. 2014. *Will the Catholic Church Accept Its First Openly Transgender Nun?* July 15. Accessed January 14, 2020. https://www.advocate.com/politics/religion/2014/07/15/wi ll-catholic-church-accept-its-first-openly-transgender-nun.

Kelleher, Patrick. 2020. "Trans woman raped 14 times by inmates and staff in men's prison speaks her truth about 'nightmare' existence." *Pink News.* November 25. Accessed June 8, 2021. https://www.pinknews.co.uk/2020/11/25/ashley-diamond-transgender-lawsuit-georgia-corrections-male-prison-sexual-assault/.

Keo-Meier, Colt, and Diane Ehrensaft. 2018. *The Gender Affirmative Model: An Interdisciplinary Approach to Supporting Transgender and Gender Expansive Children.* Worcester, MA: American Psychological Association.

Kerlin, Scott. 2005. "Prenatal Diethylstilbestrol Exposure in Males and Gender-related Disorders: Results from a 5-year study." Presented at the *International Behavioral Development Symposium.* (July). Minot, ND.

Kierkegaard, Søren. 1978. *Søren Kierkegaard's Journals and Papers.* Edited by Howard Hong & Edna Hong. Vol. 6. Indianapolis: Indiana University Press.

———. 1983. *The Sickness Unto Death: A Christian Psychological Exposition for Upbuilding And Awakening.* Princeton, NJ: Princeton University Press.

————. 2004. *Training in Christianity.* Translated by Walter Lowrie. London, UK: Vintage Spiritual Classics.

Kingkade, Tyler. 2015. "Mount Holyoke Cancels 'Vagina Monologues' For Not Being Inclusive Enough." *The Huffington Post.* January 16. Accessed July 25, 2020. https://www.huffpost.com/entry/vagina-monologues-mount-holyoke_n_6487302.

Kirkbride, James, Antonia Errazuriz, Tim Croudace, and Craig Morgan. 2012. *Systematic review of the incidence and prevalence of schizophrenia and other psychoses in England.* Systematic Review of Case Files, London, UK: The Department of Health.

Knight, Ema, and Matthew McDonald. 2013. "Recurrence and Progression of Meningioma in Male-to-Female Transgender Individuals During Exogenous Hormone Use." *International Journal of Transgenderism* 14: 18–23. https://doi.org/10.1080/15532739.2012.725563.

Knoll, Benjamin. 2016. "Youth Suicide Rates and Mormon Religious Context: An Additional Empirical Analysis." *Rational Faiths.* March 9. Accessed July 24, 2020. https://rationalfaiths.com/mormon-religious-context-and-lgbt-youth-suicides-an-additional-empirical-analysis/.

Kockott, Götz, and Eva-Maria Fahrner. 1987. "Transsexuals who have not undergone surgery: a follow-up study." *Archives of Sex Behavior* 16: 511–522. https://doi.org/10.1007/BF01541715.

Koyama, Emi. 2006. "From "Intersex" to "DSD": Toward a Queer Disability Politics of Gender." *Intersex Initiative.* February. Accessed January 7, 2020. http://www.intersexinitiative.org/articles/intersextodsd.html.

Kruijer, Frank, Jiang-Ning Zhou, Chris Pool, Michel Hofman, Louis Gooren, and Dick Swaab. 2000. "Male-to-Female Transsexuals Have Female Neuron Numbers in a Limbic Nucleus." *The Journal of Clinical Endocrinology & Metabolism* 85, no. 5 (May): 2034–2041. https://doi.org/10.1210/jcem.85.5.6564.

Bibliography

Kuefler, Mathew. 2001. *Manly Eunuchs: Masculinity, gender ambiguity, and Christian Ideology in Late Antiquity*. Chicago, IL: Chicago University Press.

Kuhn, Thomas. 2012. *The Structure of Scientific Revolutions*. Chicago, IL: University of Chicago Press.

Kuiper, Abraham, and Peggy Cohen-Kettenis. 1995. "Factors influencing post-operative "regret" in transsexuals." *Fourteenth International Symposium on Gender Dysphoria*. Ulm, Germany: Harry Benjamin International Gender Dysphoria Association. Paper Presented. Accessed September 29, 2020. https://kinseyinstitute.org/pdf/HBIGDA_S14_1995OCR.pdf.

———. 1988. "Sex reassignment surgery: A study of 141 Dutch transsexuals." *Archives of Sexual Behavior* 17: 439–457.

Kvam, Kristen, Linda Schearing, and Valarie Ziegler. 1999. *Eve and Adam: Jewish, Christian, and Muslim Readings on Genesis and Gender*. Bloomington: Indiana University Press.

Laidlaw, Michael, Michelle Cretella, and G Donovan. 2019. "The Right to Best Care for Children Does Not Include the Right to Medical Transition." *American Journal of Bioethics* 19, no. 2: 75. https://doi.org/10.1080/15265161.2018.1557288.

Lambda Legal. 2018. *Professional Organization Statements Supporting Transgender People in Health Care*. New York: Lambda Legal. Accessed September 29, 2020. https://www.lambdalegal.org/sites/default/files/publications/downloads/resource_trans-professional-statements_09-18-2018.pdf.

Lamminmäki, Annamarja, Melissa Hines, Tanja Kuiri-Hänninen, Leena Kilpeläinen, Leo Dunkel, and Ulla Sankilampi. 2012. "Testosterone measured in infancy predicts subsequent sex-typed behavior in boys and in girls." *Hormones and Behavior* 61, no. 4 (April): 611–616. https://doi.org/10.1016/j.yhbeh.2012.02.013.

Larsen, Karin. "Estheticians don't have to wax male genitalia against their will, B.C. tribunal rules." *CBC*. October 22. Accessed

June 8, 2021. https://www.cbc.ca/news/canada/british-columbia/transgender-woman-human-rights-waxing-1.5330807.

Last, Jonathan. 2017."We Have Ways to Make You Conform." *Washington Examiner.* April 17. Accessed June 11, 2020. https://www.washingtonexaminer.com/weekly-standard/we-have-ways-to-make-you-conform.

Laub, Gillian. 2014. "The Transgender Tipping Point [Cover Photo]." *Time*, May 29: Cover.

Lawrence, Anne. 2012. *Men Trapped in Men's Bodies: Narratives of Autogynephilic Transsexualism.* New York: Springer Books.

Lawrence, Anne, Elizabeth Latty, Merideth Chivers, and John Michael Bailey. 2005. "Measurement of sexual arousal in postoperative male-to-female transsexuals using vaginal photoplethysmography." *Archives of Sexual Behavior* 34, no. 2 (April): 135-145. https://doi.org/10.1007/s10508-005-1792-z.

Leahy, Robert. 2008. "How Big a Problem is Anxiety?" *Psychology Today.* April 30. Accessed July 15, 2021. https://www.psychologytoday.com/us/blog/anxiety-files/200804/how-big-problem-is-anxiety.

Leavitt, Berger. 1990. "Clinical patterns among male transsexual candidates with erotic interest in males." *Archives of Sexual Behavior*, October: 491–505. https://doi.org/10.1007/BF02442350.

Leo XIII, Pope. 1879. *Aeterni Patris* (Of the Eternal Father). "Encyclical Letter." Vatican City: The Holy See, Promulgated by Pope Leo XIII. Accessed September 29, 2020. http://www.vatican.va/content/leo-xiii/en/encyclicals/documents/hf_l-xiii_enc_04081879_aeterni-patris.html.

———. 1893. Providentissimus Deus (On the Study of Holy Scripture). "Encyclical Letter." *Vatican.va.* November 18. Accessed December 15, 2019. http://w2.vatican.va/content/leo-

xiii/en/encyclicals/documents/hf_l-
xiii_enc_18111893_providentissimus-deus.html.

———. 1891. Rerum Novarum (On the Condition of the Working
Class). "Encyclical Letter." Vatican City: The Holy See.
Promulgated by Pope Leo XIII. Accessed September 29,
2020. http://www.vatican.va/content/leo-
xiii/en/encyclicals/documents/hf_l-
xiii_enc_15051891_rerum-novarum.html.

Levine, Stephen and Anna Solomon. 2009. "Meanings and political
implications of "psychopathology" in a gender identity clinic:
a report of 10 cases." *Journal of Sex & Marital Therapy* 35, no.
1: 40–57. https://doi.org/10.1080/00926230802525646.

Lewis, C.S. 2016. *Mere Christianity.* London, UK: William Collins.

Licht, Hans. 1932. *Sexual Life in Ancient Greece.* London, UK: George
Routledge & Sons.

Liese, Sharon. 2020. *Transhood.* [online] HBO. June 4. Accessed June
3, 2021. https://www.hbo.com/documentaries/transhood.

Lilly, Silly. 2019. Twitter Post. December 19, 5:09 AM:
https://twitter.com/jk_rowling/status/120764616281310003
3

Lind, Earl. 1975. *Autobiography of an Androgyne.* New York: Arno Press.

Lindenfors, Patrik, Charles Nunn, and Robert Barton. 2007. "Primate
brain architecture and selection in relation to sex." *BMC
Biology* 5 (20). https://doi:10.1186/1741-7007-5-20.

Lipka, Michael. 2015. "Most U.S. Catholics hope for change in
church rule on divorce, Communion." *Pew Research Center.*
October 26. Accessed July 24, 2020.
https://www.pewresearch.org/fact-tank/2015/10/26/most-
u-s-catholics-hope-for-change-in-church-rule-on-divorce-
communion/.

Littman, Lisa. 2019. "Correction: Parent reports of adolescents and
young adults perceived to show signs of a rapid onset of

gender dysphoria." *PLoS One*, March: 1–7.
https://doi.org/10.1371/journal.pone.0214157.

———. 2018. "Rapid-onset gender dysphoria in adolescents and young adults: A study of parental reports." *PLoS One* 13, no. 8 (August): 1–44.
https://doi.org/10.1371/journal.pone.0214157.

Lopez, Mario, interview by Candace Owens. 2019. "The Candace Owens Show: Mario Lopez." *PragerU*, June 23. YouTube video, 40:02. Accessed March 11, 2020.
https://www.youtube.com/watch?v=FSDlx23uiDY.

Lothstein, Leonard. 1979. "Psychodynamics and sociodynamics of gender-dysphoric states." *The American Psychiatric Association* 33, no. 2 (April): 214–238.
https://doi.org/10.1176/appi.psychotherapy.1979.33.2.214.

———. 1984. "Psychological testing with transsexuals: a 30-year review." *Journal of Personality Assessment* 48, no. 5: 500–507.
https://doi.org/10.1207/s15327752jpa4805_9.

Lorber, Judith. 2018. "The social construction of gender." In *Inequality Reader: Contemporary and Foundational Readings in Race, Class, and Gender*, by David Grusky, & Szonja Szelenyi, Chapter 36. New York: Perseus Books.

Lowry, Rich. 2019. "Trans athletes are making a travesty of women's sports." *New York Post.* March 4. Accessed June 27, 2020.
https://nypost.com/2019/03/04/trans-athletes-are-making-a-travesty-of-womens-sports/.

Luders, Eileen, Francisco Sanchez, Christian Gaser, Arthur Toga, and Katherine Narr. 2009. "Regional gray matter variation in male-to-female transsexualism." *NeuroImage*: 904–907.
https://doi.org/10.1016/j.neuroimage.2009.03.048.

Lumen Gentium. 1964. "Light of the Nations." *The Second Vatican Council.* Vatican City: Promulgated by Pope Paul VI.

MacIntyre, Alasdair. 1984. *After Virtue*. Notre Dame, IN: University of Notre Dame Press.

Bibliography

Mallory, Christy, Taylor Brown, and Kerith Conron. 2019. "Conversion Therapy and LGBT Youth." *Williams Institute of UCLA*. June. Accessed July 23, 2020. https://williamsinstitute.law.ucla.edu/publications/conversion-therapy-and-lgbt-youth/.

Mansfield, Caroline, Suellen Hopfer, and Theresa Marteau. 1999. "Termination rates after prenatal diagnosis of Down syndrome, spina bifida, anencephaly, and Turner and Klinefelter syndromes: A systematic literature review." *Prenatal Diagnosis,* 19, no. 9: 808–812. PMID: 10521836.

Marano, Hara. 2003. "The Opposite Sex: The New Sex Scorecard." *Psychology Today*, July/August: 38–44. Accessed September 29, 2020. https://www.psychologytoday.com/us/articles/200307/the-new-sex-scorecard.

Maritain, Jacques. 1955. *An Essay on Christian Philosophy.* Translated by Edward Flannery. New York: Philosophical Library.

———. 1968. *Integral Humanism: Temporal and Spiritual Problems of a new Christendom.* Translated by Joseph Evans. New York: Charles Scribner's Sons.

———. 2001. *Natural Law: Reflections on Theory & Practice.* South Bend, IN: St. Augustine Press.

———. 1959. *The Degrees of Knowledge.* New York: Charles Scribner's Sons.

———. 1968. *The Peasant of the Garonne.* New York: Holt, Rinehart, and Winston.

———. 1947. *The Person and the Common Good.* Translated by John Fitzgerald. New York: Charles Scribner's Sons.

Marshall, Francis. 1937. "Forward to A.L. Peck." In *De partibus animalium,* by Aristotle, 3. Cambridge, UK: Loeb Classic Library.

Marx, Karl. 1975. *Economic and Philosophical Manuscripts of 1844.* Vol. 3, in *Karl Marx and Frederick Engels, Collected Works,* by Karl Marx,

& Frederick Engels, 305–306. New York: International Publishers.

Masiello, Shawna. 2021. "Twitter defends gross 'little girls are kinky' tweet by Alok Vaid-Menon." *PopTopic*. March 8. Accessed July 15, 2021. https://poptopic.com.au/tech/twitter-defends-gross-little-girls-are-kinky-tweet-by-alok-vaid-menon/.

Masterson, Matt. 2020. "Lawsuit: Female Prisoner Says She Was Raped by Transgender Inmate." *WTTW*. February 19. Accessed June 8, 2021. https://news.wttw.com/2020/02/19/lawsuit-female-prisoner-says-she-was-raped-transgender-inmate.

Mathew, Teresa. 2017. "When Nuns Tried to Kick-Start India's First Transgender School." *The Atlantic*. March 27. Accessed January 14, 2020. https://www.theatlantic.com/international/archive/2017/03/when-nuns-tried-to-kickstart-indias-first-transgender-school/519957/.

Maxouris, Christina. 2020. "3 Connecticut high school girls are suing over a policy that allows trans athletes to compete in girls' sports." *CNN*. February 15. Accessed June 8, 2021. https://edition.cnn.com/2020/02/14/us/transgender-athletes-connecticut-lawsuit/index.html.

McAuley, Catherine. 1888. *Familiar Instructions*. Dulin, IR: Ev. E. Carreras.

McCarthy, Justin. 2021. Mixed Views Among Americans on Transgender Issues. *Gallup*. May 26. Accessed July 12, 2021. https://news.gallup.com/poll/350174/mixed-views-among-americans-transgender-issues.aspx.

McHugh, Paul. 2014a. "Brief of Amicus Curiae." *SupremeCourt.gov*. April 04. Accessed June 30, 2020. https://www.supremecourt.gov/DocketPDF/18/18-107/113262/20190822151939369_TO%20PRINT%2019-8-22%20Dr.%20Paul%20McHugh%20Amicus%20Brief%20FINAL.pdf.

———. 2015. "Transgenderism: A Pathogenic Meme." *Public Discourse*. June 05. Accessed June 30, 2020. https://www.thepublicdiscourse.com/2015/06/15145/.

———. 2014b. "Transgender Surgery Isn't the Solution." *Wall Street Journal*, June 12. Accessed September 29, 2020. https://www.wsj.com/articles/paul-mchugh-transgender-surgery-isnt-the-solution-1402615120.

———. 2004. "Surgical Sex: Why we stopped doing sex change operations." *First Things*. November. Accessed June 11, 2020. https://www.firstthings.com/article/2004/11/surgical-sex.

———. 2006. *The Mind Has Mountains: Reflections on Society and Psychiatry*. Baltimore, MD: Johns Hopkins University Press.

McHugh, Paul, and Lawrence Mayer. 2016. "Sexuality and Gender: Findings from the Biological, Psychological, and Social Sciences." *The New Atlantis*: Special Report. https://www.jstor.org/stable/43893424.

McKay, Hollie. 2020. "Keeping the sisterhood from extinction: The struggle to save nuns in America." *Fox News*. Accessed June 8, 2021. https://www.foxnews.com/us/keeping-the-sisterhood-from-extinction-the-struggle-to-save-nuns-in-america.

Mead, Christina. n.d. "What the Catholic Church Wants the Transgender Community to Know," *Life Teen* (blog). Accessed January 12, 2021. https://lifeteen.com/blog/catholic-church-wants-transgender-community-know/

Medical Accidents Group. 2014. *Two thirds of Brits regret having cosmetic surgery*. May 28. Accessed June 11, 2021. https://www.medicalaccidentgroup.co.uk/news/two-thirds-brits-regret-cosmetic-surgery/.

Melina, Livio. 2001. *Sharing in Christ's Virtues*. Translated by William May. Washington, DC: Catholic University of America Press.

Meybodi, Azadeh, Ahmad Hajebi, Atefeh Jolfaei. 2014. "Psychiatric Axis I Comorbidities among Patients with Gender

Dysphoria." *Psychiatric Journal*: 1–5.
http://doi.org/10.1155/2014/971814.

Meyer, Ilan, Merilee Teylan, and Sharon Schwartz. 2014. "The role of
help-seeking in preventing suicide attempts among lesbians,
gay men, and bisexuals." *Suicide and Life Threatening Behavior* 45,
no. 1: 35–36.

Meyer, Jon, and D Reter. 1979. "Sex Reassignment: follow-up."
Archives of General Psychiatry 36: 1010–1015.
https://doi.org/10.1001/archpsyc.1979.01780090096010.

Meyer-Bahlburg, Heino. 2002. "Gender Identity in Young Boys: A
parent- and peer-based treatment protocol." *Clinical Child
Psychology and Psychiatry* 7, no. 3: 361.
https://doi.org/10.1177/1359104502007003005.

Meyerowitz, Joanne. 2002. *How Sex Changed: A history of transsexuality in
the United States*. Cambridge, MA: Harvard University Press.

Migeon, Claude, Amy Wisniewski, John Gearhart, Heino Meyer-
Bahlburg, John Rock. 2002. "Ambiguous Genitalia With
Perineoscrotal Hypospadias in 46, XY Individuals: Long-term
Medical, Surgical, and Psychosexual Outcome." *Pediatrics* 110:
e31. https://doi.org/DOI: 10.1542/peds.110.3.e31.

Milanovich, Anita. 2019. "Transgender athletes deserve compassion,
but not the right to transform women's sports." *USA Today*.
September 19. Accessed June 27, 2020.
https://www.usatoday.com/story/opinion/voices/2019/09/
27/transgender-athletes-supreme-court-sex-equality-
column/2421776001/.

Mineo, Liz. 2019. "Schuyler Bailar races toward his authentic self."
The Harvard Gazette. May 15. Accessed February 13, 2021.
https://news.harvard.edu/gazette/story/2019/05/ncaas-
first-openly-transgender-swimmer-schuyler-bailar-finds-his-
real-self-and-flourishes-at-harvard/.

Mirasol. n.d. Eating Order Statistics. Accessed September 22, 2020.
https://www.mirasol.net/learning-center/eating-disorder-
statistics.php.

Bibliography

Moir, Anne, and David Jessel. 1989. *Brain Sex.* New York: Dell.

Money, John. 1955. "Hermaphroditism, Gender and Precocity in Hyperadrenocorticism: Psychological Findings." *Bulletin of the Johns Hopkins Hospital* 96: 253–264. PMID: 14378807.

Money, John, Joan Hampson, and John Hampson. 1957. "Imprinting and the Establishment of Gender Role." *American Medical Association Archives of Neurology & Psychiatry* 77, no. 3: 333–336. https://doi.org/10.1001/archneurpsyc.1957.02330330119019 .

Montgomery, Stephen H., and N. I. Mundy. 2013. "Microcephaly genes and the evolution of sexual dimorphism in primate brain size." *Journal of Evolutionary Biology* 26: 906-911. doi:10.1111/jeb.12091.

Morandini, James. n.d. "10) Nature versus Nurture: What other factors besides "innate gender identity" contribute to trans identification in young people." *Gender Health Query.* Accessed January 24, 2020. https://www.genderhq.org/trans-nature-vs-nurture-innate-gender-identity-culture.

Moreau, Danielle. 2019. "What is 'gender critical' anyway? On essentialism and transphobia." *Overland.* May 8. Accessed 02 16, 2020. https://overland.org.au/2019/05/what-is-gender-critical-anyway-on-essentialism-and-transphobia/comment-page-1/.

Morgan, Robin. 1973. "Lesbianism and Feminism: Synonyms or Contradictions?" *The Lesbian Tide*, April 14: 37–38. Accessed September 29, 2020. http://www.onearchives.org/wp-content/uploads/2015/02/Lesbianism-and-Feminism-Synonyms-or-Contradictions-by-Robin-Morgan-April-14-1973.pdf.

Moser, Caroline. 2010. "Blanchard's Autogynephilia Theory: a critique." *Journal of Homosexuality* 57, no. 6 (July): 790–809. https://doi.org/10.1080/00918369.2010.486241.

Moss, Decker.2013. "Hey Doc, some boys are born girls: Decker Moss at TEDxColumbus." October 11. Accessed 02 16, 2020. YouTube video, 17:02.

https://www.youtube.com/watch?v=nOmstbKVebM&t=73 0s.

Munro, Alistair. 1980. "Monosymptomatic hypochondriacal psychosis." *British Journal of Hospital Medicine* 24: 34–38. https://doi.org/10.1192/S0007125000298978.

Murad, Mohammad Hassan, Mohamed Elamin, Magaly Zumaeta Garcia, Rebecca Mullan. 2010. "Hormonal Therapy and Sex Reassignment: A Systematic Review and Meta-Analysis of Quality of Life and Psychosocial Outcomes." *Clinical Endocrinology*, February. 214–231. https://doi.org/10.1111/j.1365-2265.2009.03625.x.

Murchison, Gabe. 2016. "Supporting and Caring of Transgender Children." *Human Rights Campaign.* Accessed January 8, 2020. https://www.aap.org/en-us/Documents/solgbt_resource_transgenderchildren.pdf.

Murib, Zein. 2015. "Transgender: Examining an Emerging Political Identity Using Three Political Processes." *Politics, Groups, and Identities* 3, no. 3: 381–397. https://doi.org/10.1080/21565503.2015.1048257.

Murphy, Heather. 2019. "Always Removes Female Symbol From Sanitary Pads.*" The New York Times.* October 22. Accessed November 23, 2020. https://www.nytimes.com/2019/10/22/business/always-pads-female-symbol.html.

Murphy, Peter. 2006. "Prudential Gnome, Right Judgments and Diagnostic Tests." *The Linacre Quarterly* 73, no. 2 (May): 190–193. https://doi.org/10.1080/20508549.2006.11877778.

Murray, James. 1985. "Borderline Manifestations in the Rorschachs of Male Transsexuals." *Journal of Personality Assessment* 49, no. 5 (November): 454–466. https://doi.org/10.1207/s15327752jpa4905_1.

Meyerowitz, Joanne. 1998. "Sex change and the popular press: Historical notes on transsexuality in the United States, 1930–1955." *GLQ: A Journal of Lesbian and Gay Studies* 4, no. 2: 159–187. https://doi.org/10.1215/10642684-4-2-159.

Bibliography

National Center for Transgender Equality.2016. *2015 U.S. Transgender Survey.* Washington, DC: National Center for Transgender Equality. Accessed September 29, 2020. http://www.ustranssurvey.org/.

Naylor, Dave. "Yaniv now suing Ontario beauty pageant for not letting her in." *Western Standard.* October 26. Accessed June 8, 2021. https://westernstandardonline.com/2020/10/yaniv-now-suing-ontario-beauty-pageant-for-not-letting-her-in/.

Nazianzus, Gregory. 2006. *Gregory of Nazianzus. The early church fathers.* Translated by Brian Daley. London, UK: Routledge.

Neenan, Mary Angelica. 20017. *The Nature of the Human Soul.* Nashville, TN: Cluny Media.

Newman, Larry. 1976. "Treatment for the Parents of Feminine Boys." *American Journal of Psychiatry* 133, no. 6: 683–687. https://doi.org/10.1176/ajp.133.6.683.

Newport, Frank. 2017. "Wyoming, North Dakota and Mississippi Most Conservative." *Gallup.* January 31. Accessed December 31, 2019. https://news.gallup.com/poll/203204/wyoming-north-dakota-mississippi-conservative.aspx.

Nicholas I, Pope. 1925. "The Responses of Pope Nicholas I to the Questions of the Bulgars A.D. 866 (Letter 99)." Edited by W.L. North. Epistolae VI: 568–600.

Nickell, Amy interview by Pierce Morgan. 2019. "Piers Gets in a Furious Debate on Whether or Not Men Can Be Mothers | Good Morning Britain." *Good Morning Britain.* March 26. YouTube video. Accessed June 8, 2021. https://www.youtube.com/watch?v=UnB7Bi4DfBk.

Nolan, Ian, Christopher Kuhner, and Geolani Dy. 2019. "Demographic and temporal trends in transgender identities and gender confirming surgery." *Translational Andrology and Urology* 8, no. 3 (June): 184–190. https://doi.org/10.21037/tau.2019.04.09.

Nolan, Michael. 1995. "Passive and Deformed? Did Aristotle Really Say This?" *Blackfriars*, May: 237. https://doi.org/10.1111/j.1741-2005.1995.tb07100.x.

North Carolina Department of Health and Human Services. 2016. "Myths vs. Facts: What the New York Times, Huffington Post and other media outlets aren't saying about common-sense privacy laws." *North Carolina Department of Health and Human Services.* March 25. Accessed January 27, 2020. https://www.ncdhhs.gov/news/press-releases/myths-vs-facts-what-new-york-times-huffington-post-and-other-media-outlets-arent.

Novak, Kelly. 2018. *Let Harry Become Sally: Responding to the Anti-Transgender Movement.* Andover, MA: Hypothesis Press.

Nussbaum, Martha. 1986. *The Fragility of Goodness: Luck and Ethics in Greek Tragedy and Philosophy.* Cambridge, UK: Cambridge University Press.

O'Brien, Jennifer. 2018. "The Psychology of Drag." *Psychology Today.* January 30. Accessed June 11, 2020. https://www.psychologytoday.com/us/blog/all-things-lgbtq/201801/the-psychology-drag.

O'Keefe, Benjamin. 2014. *Retract Your Disgusting and Transphobic Op-Ed on Laverne Cox.* Accessed January 12, 2020. https://www.change.org/p/chicago-sun-times-retract-your-disgusting-and-transphobic-op-ed-on-laverne-cox.

O'Leary, Siobhan. 2018. "The Rejection of 'Conversion Therapy' Isn't Motivated by Politics—It's Motivated by Science." *Rewire News.* November 21. Accessed June 27, 2020. https://rewire.news/article/2018/11/21/the-rejection-of-conversion-therapy-for-trans-kids-isnt-motivated-by-politics-its-motivated-by-science/.

Olson, Kristina, Lily Durwood, Madeleine DeMeules, and Katie McLaughlin. 2015. "Mental Health of Transgender Children Who Are Supported in Their Identities." *Pediatrics* 137, no. 3: 1098–4275. https://doi.org/10.1542/peds.2015-3223.

Bibliography

Olson-Kennedy, Johanna, Jonathan Warus, Vivian Okonta, Marvin
    Belzer, and Leslie Clark. 2018. "Chest Reconstruction and
    Chest Dysphoria in Transmasculine Minors and Young
    Adults." *JAMA Pediatrics*, May: 431–436.
    https://doi.org/10.1001/jamapediatrics.2017.5440

Olson-Kennedy, Johanna. 2014. *Johanna Olson, MD, Talks About
    Research on Transgender Youth.* Edited by Children's Hospital
    Los Angeles. February 12. YouTube video. Accessed October
    4, 2020.
    https://www.youtube.com/watch?v=jjtRJsC16HE&feature=
    emb_title.

Operario, Don, Toho Soma, and Kristen Underhill. 2008. "Sex work
    and HIV status among transgender women: systematic review
    and meta-analysis." *Journal of Acquired Immune Deficiency
    Syndromes* 48, no. 1: 97–103.
    https://doi.org/10.1097/QAI.0b013e31816e3971.

Oppenheimer, Mark. 2015. "Catholics, Plastic Surgery, and 'the Truth
    of the Feminine Self'." *The New York Times.* March 14.
    Accessed June 11, 2020. https://advance-lexis-com.ez-
    salve.idm.oclc.org/api/document?collection=news&id=urn:c
    ontentItem:5FH7-DP11-JBG3-63W2-00000-
    00&context=1516831.

Ostgathe, Antonia, Thomas Schnell, and Erich Kasten. 2014. "Body
    integrity identity disorder and Gender Dysphoria: A pilot
    study to investigate similarities and differences." *American
    Journal of Applied Psychology* 3, no. 6: 138–143.
    https://doi.org/10.11648/j.ajap.20140306.14.

Owens, Christian. 2019. Twitter Post. February 12, 6:59 AM
    https://twitter.com/SgtCOwens/status/10952761720936038
    40.

Pape, Madeleine. 2019. "I was sore about losing to Caster Semenya.
    But this decision against her is wrong." *The Guardian.* May 1.
    Accessed June 27, 2020.
    https://www.theguardian.com/commentisfree/2019/may/01
    /losing-caster-semenya-decision-wrong-women-testosterone-
    iaaf.

Parker, Posie interview by Konstantin Kisin and Francis Foster. 2019. "Posie Parker: "Trans Women Aren't Women." *Triggernometry*. November 17. YouTube video. Accessed June 8, 2021. https://www.youtube.com/watch?v=Pdpc2r4cBxQ.

Pascal, Blaise. 1995. *Pensees*. London, UK: Penguin Classics.

Pauly, Ira. 1992. "Terminology and Classification of gender identity disorders." In *Gender Dysphoria: Interdisciplinary approaches in clinical management*, by WO Bockting, & E Coleman, 1–11. New York: Haworth.

Peirce, Birnberg. 2020. "Sexual assault victim challenge to transgender prisoners policy." *Press Release*. October 27. Accessed June 8, 2021. https://fairplayforwomen.com/wp-content/uploads/2020/10/0097320003-FDJ-v-SSJ-Press-Release-Birnberg-Peirce-27.10.20.pdf.

Pellegrini, Massimiliano Matteo, Lamberto Zollo Cristiano Ciappei, and Andrea Boccardi. 2016. "Finding the extraordinary and creating the unexpected: Gnome and genius combined in an exceptional ethical heuristic." *Journal of Management Development* 35, no. 6: 789–801. https://doi.org/10.1108/JMD-09-2015-0130.

Pentin, Edward. 2010. "Plastic Surgery: Not Just for the Rich and Famous." *National Catholic Register*, February 14. Accessed September 29, 2020. http://www.ncregister.com/daily-news/plastic_surgery_not_just_for_the_rich_and_famous.

Peterson, Jordan. 2018. "Jordan Peterson debate on the gender pay gap, campus protests, and postmodernism.' *Channel 4 News*. January 16. YouTube Video. Accessed June 28, 2021. https://www.youtube.com/watch?v=aMcjxSThD54

———. 2021. "Abandon Ideology | Gad Saad - The Jordan B. Peterson Podcast #S4E6." *Jordan P. Peterson*. February 15. YouTube Video. Accessed June 28, 2021. https://www.youtube.com/watch?v=5eBcKlBaaoc.

Petri, Thomas. 2016. *Aquinas and the Theology of the Body*. Washington, DC: Catholic University of America Press.

Bibliography

Philadelphia Fight Community Health Centers. *Eating Disorders Awareness Week*. February 22, 2019. Accessed September 28, 2020. https://fight.org/eating-disorders-awareness-week/.

Phillips, Katharine. n.d. *Prevalence of BDD*. Accessed January 8, 2020. https://bdd.iocdf.org/professionals/prevalence/.

Piacenza, Joanna, and Robert Jones. 2017. "Most American Religious Groups Support Same-sex Marriage, Oppose Religiously Based Service Refusals." *PRRI*. February 3. https://www.prri.org/spotlight/religious-americans-same-sex-marriage-service-refusals/ (accessed July 24, 2020).

Pieper, Josef. 1986. *Hope*. San Francisco, CA: Ignatius Press.

———. 1966. *The Four Cardinal Virtues*. Translated by R & C Wilson. Notre Dame, IN: University of Notre Dame.

Pius IX, Pope. 1864. The Syllabus of Errors *(Syllabus Errorum)*. "Encyclical Letter." Vatican City: The Holy See. Promulgated by Pope Pius IX, December 8.

Pius XII, Pope. 1953a. "Address to the Participants of the 26th Congress of the International Society of Urology." Translated by Becket Gremmels. Vatican City, October 8.

———. 1952. "Address to the Participants of the International Congress of Histopathology of the Nervous System." Vatican City: The Holy See, September 13. https://www.chausa.org/publications/health-care-ethics-usa/archives/issues/winter-2016/sex-reassignment-surgery-and-the-catholic-moral-tradition-insight-from-pope-pius-xii-on-the-principle-totality (Accessed September 29, 2020).

———. 1953b. "Fifth International Congress of Psychotherapy and Clinical Psychology." Vatican City: Osservatore Romano, April 16.

———. 1950. Humani Generis (On the Human Race). "Encyclical Letter." Vatican City: The Holy See. Promulgated by Pope Pius XII, August 12.

Plato. 2009. *Phaedrus*. Oxford, UK: Oxford World Classics.

———. 1989. *Symposium.* Indianapolis, IN: Hackett Publishing.

Ponticus, Evagrius. 1972. *Evagrius Ponticus: The Praktikos. Chapters on Prayer.* Translated by John Eudes Bamberger. Kalamazoo, MI: Cistercian Publications.

Pontifical Council for Culture. 2015. *Women's Cultures: Equality and Difference.* "Plenary Assembly document." Outline Document, Rome: The Holy See. http://www.cultura.va/content/dam/cultura/docs/pdf/Trac cia_en.pdf (Accessed September 29, 2020).

Preves, Sharon. 2003. *Intersex and Identity.* New Brunswick, CA: Rutgers University Press.

Prince, Virginia. 1969. "Change of Sex or Gender." *Transvestia,* 10, no. 60: 53–65.

———. 1978. "Transsexuals and Pseudotranssexuals." *Archives of Sexual Behaviour* 7, no. 4: 263–272.

Przywara, Erich. 1929. *Das Geheimnis Kierkegaards.* München, DE: R. Oldenbourg.

Puri, Basant, and Iqbal Singh. 1996. "The successful treatment of a gender dysphoric patient with pimozide." *Australian and New Zealand Journal of Psychiatry* 30, no. 3: 422–425. https://doi.org/10.3109/00048679609065010.

Pymnts. 2021. *Reality Check: Paycheck-to-Paycheck Report.* June Accessed July 14, 2021. https://www.pymnts.com/wp-content/uploads/2021/06/PYMNTS-Reality-Check-Paycheck-to-Paycheck-June-2021.pdf.

Quincy Bell and Mrs. A v. The Tavistock And Portman NHS Foundation Trust. 2020. EWHC 3274 (High Court of Justice Administrative Court, December 21).

r/asktransgender. 2015. "Existence precedes essence: how I know that I am definitely transgender." *Reddit.* December 14. https://www.reddit.com/r/asktransgender/comments/3wsid 6/existence_precedes_essence_how_i_know_that_i_am/.

Radcliffe, Daniel. 2020. "Daniel Radcliffe Responds to J.K. Rowling's Tweets on Gender Identity." *Trevor Project.* June 8. https://www.thetrevorproject.org/2020/06/08/daniel-radcliffe-responds-to-j-k-rowlings-tweets-on-gender-identity/ (Accessed June 28, 2020).

Raines, Jamie. 2020. "Trans Guy Reacts to Anti-Trans Feminist." *Jammidodger.* November 18. YouTube Video. Accessed June 15, 2021. https://www.youtube.com/watch?v=fxCxZWFUSgY.

Rajkumar, Ravi. 2014. "Gender Identity Disorder and Schizophrenia: Neurodevelopmental Disorders with Common Causal Mechanisms?" *Schizophrenia Research and Treatment:* 1-8. https://doi.org/ 10.1155/2014/463757.

Rametti, Giuseppina, Beatriz Carrillo, Esther Gómez-Gil, Carme Junque, Santiago Segovia, Ángel Gomez, Antonio Guillamon. 2011. "White Matter Microstructure in Female to Male Transsexuals Before Cross-Sex Hormonal Treatment." *Journal of Psychiatric Research* 45: 199–204. https://doi.org/10.1016/j.jpsychires.2010.05.006.

Ramphul, Kamleshun, and Stephanie Mejias. 2018. "Is "Snapchat Dysmorphia" a Real Issue?" *Cureus,* March 3. https://doi:10.7759/cureus.2263.

Rand, Ayn. 1979."Introduction to Objectivist Epistemology." *The Tomorrow Show,* New York, NY: NBC Universal, July 2. Accessed January 11, 2020. from NBC Learn: https://archives.nbclearn.com/portal/site/k-12/browse/?cuecard=41640

Rashi, Shlomo Yizchaki. 1985. *Tractate Nazir / Sotah.* Edited by I. Epstein. Translated by B. Klien. London, UK: Soncino Press.

Ratzinger, Joseph. 1992. "Catechism of the Catholic Church." *L' Obsservatore Romano,* December 16: 4.

———. 1987. "The Gift of Life." (Donum Vitae). *Introduction on Respect for Human Life in its origin and on the dignity of Procreation Replies to Certain Questions of the Day.* Vatican City: Congregation for the Doctrine of the Faith, February 22.

———. 2005. "Homily of his eminency Joseph Cardinal Ratzinger to the College of Cardinals." *Vatican.va.* April 15. Accessed June 27, 2020. http://www.vatican.va/gpII/documents/homily-pro-eligendo-pontifice_20050418_en.html.

Raymond, Janice. 1994. "Introduction to the 1994 Edition." In *The Transsexual Empire,* by Janice Raymond, i–xxxv. New York: Teachers College Press.

Reardon, Sarah. 2016. "Transgender youth study kicks off." *Nature* 531: 560.

Redtube. 2016. "Trans Porn In the USA." *RedTube Blog.* June 2. Accessed July 25, 2020. https://blog.redtube.com/2016/06/trans-porn-usa/.

Reiner, William, and John Gearhart.2004. "Discordant Sexual Identity in Some Genetic Males with Cloacal Exstrophy Assigned to Female Sex at Birth." *The New England Journal of Medicine* 350 (January): 333–341.

Rekers, George, Mark Kilgus, and Alexander Rosen. 1990. "Long-Term Effects of Treatment for Gender Identity Disorder of Childhood." *Journal of Psychology and Human Sexuality* 3: 121–153. https://doi.org/10.1300/J056v03n02_09.

Reynolds, Mark. 2018. "Gender Identity issues for Brighton high school's 76 pupils." *Express.* November 28. Accessed June 8, 2021. https://www.express.co.uk/news/uk/1051523/Gender-identity-Brighton-school-gender-fluid-education-transgender.

Rhoads, Steven. 2004. *Taking Sex Differences Seriously.* San Francisco, CA: Encounter Books.

Rider, Nicole, Barbara McMorris, Amy Gower, Eli Coleman, and Marla Eisenberg. 2018. "Health and Care Utilization of Transgender and Gender Nonconforming Youth: A Population-Based Study." *Pediatrics* 141, no. 3 (March). https://doi.org/10.1542/peds.2017-1683.

Bibliography

Ringrose, Kathryn. 2004. *The Perfect Servant: Eunuchs and the social construction of gender in Byzantium.* Chicago, IL: University of Chicago Press.

Rippon, Gina. 2019. *The Gendered Brain: The New Neuroscience that Shatters the Myth of the Female Brain.* New York: Pantheon.

Risman, Barbara. 2018. *Where the Millennials Will Take Us: A New Generation Wrestles with the Gender Structure.* Vol. 61. Oxford, UK: Oxford University Press.

Ritchie, Stuart, Simon Cox, Xueyi Shen, Michael Lombardo, Lianne Reus, Clara Alloza. 2018. "Sex Differences in the Adult Human Brain: Evidence from 5216 UK Biobank Participants." *Cerebral Cortex,* 28, no. 8 (August): 2959–2975. https://doi.org/10.1093/cercor/bhy109.

Robertson, Carol. 1989. "The Mahu of Hawaii." *Feminist Studies* 15: 313–327.

Robins, Jane. 2018. *U.S. Doctors Are Performing Double Mastectomies on Healthy 13-Year-Old Girls.* September 12. Accessed September 27, 2020. https://thefederalist.com/2018/09/12/u-s-doctors-performing-double-mastectomies-healthy-13-year-old-girls/.

Rogan, Joe. 2018. "Joe Rogan Reflects on Fallon Fox Controversy." *JRE Clips.* July 26. YouTube Video. Accessed June 8, 2021. https://www.youtube.com/watch?v=KQpQmNhya14.

Romano, Aja. 2019. *J.K. Rowling's latest tweet seems like transphobic BS. Her fans are heartbroken.* December 19. Accessed January 12, 2020. https://www.vox.com/culture/2019/12/19/21029852/jk-rowling-terf-transphobia-history-timeline.

Romey, Kristen. 2018. "Exclusive: Ancient Mass Child Sacrifice May Be World's Largest." *National Geographic.* April 26. Accessed February 27, 2021. https://www.nationalgeographic.com/science/article/mass-child-human-animal-sacrifice-peru-chimu-science.

591

Rose of Dawn. 2019. "Rose of Dawn: Trans Activists Don't Speak for Me." *Tiggernometry*. December 15. Accessed June 9, 2021. https://www.youtube.com/watch?v=ak8v1LxdavY.

Rosen, Danni/y. n.d. "Gender-neutral bathrooms are radical, but now how you think." *GLSEN*. Accessed June 10, 2021. https://www.glsen.org/blog/gender-neutral-bathrooms-are-radical-not-how-you-think.

Rowling, J.K. 2019. "Twitter Post." 4:57AM: https://twitter.com/jk_rowling/status/12076461628131000 3, December 19.

Rude, Mey Valdivia. 2014. "It's Time for People to Stop Using the Social Construct of "Biological Sex" to Defend Their Transmisogyny." *Autostraddle*. June 5. Accessed January 9, 2020. https://www.autostraddle.com/its-time-for-people-to-stop-using-the-social-construct-of-biological-sex-to-defend-their-transmisogyny-240284/.

Russo, Francine. 2016. "Debate is growing about how to meet the urgent need of transgender kids." *Scientific American Mind*, January/February: 27–35.

Russo, Francine. 2016. "There Something Unique about the Transgender Brain?" *Scientific American*. January 1. Accessed June 29, 2020. https://www.scientificamerican.com/article/is-there-something-unique-about-the-transgender-brain/.

Ryan, Hugh. 2014. "What Does Trans* Mean, and Where Did It Come From?" *Slate*. January 10. Accessed June 27, 2020. https://slate.com/human-interest/2014/01/trans-what-does-it-mean-and-where-did-it-come-from.html.

Sacred Congregation for Religious. 1961. *Instruction on the Careful Selection and Training of Candidates for the States of Perfection and Sacred Orders.* for the formation of clergy, Vatican City: Sacred Congregation for Religious. Accessed September 29, 2020. https://adoremus.org/1961/02/religiosorum-institutio/.

Salve Regina University Ph.D. in Humanities Department. *Ph.D. in Humanities Program Handbook.* Handbook, Newport, RI: Salve Regina University, 2019–2020.

San Martín, Inés. 2016. "Pope says walk with trans persons, but fight gender theory." *Crux.* October 16. Accessed January 14, 2020. https://cruxnow.com/global-church/2016/10/pope-says-walk-trans-persons-fight-gender-theory/.

———. 2017. "Nun ministering to transgender women gets thumbs-up from Pope." *Crux.* July 25. Accessed January 14, 2020. https://cruxnow.com/global-church/2017/07/nun-ministering-transgender-women-gets-thumbs-pope/.

Sarah, Robert. 2016. "National Catholic Prayer Breakfast 2016." *Amazon News.* May 26. Accessed July 24, 2020. https://s3.amazonaws.com/ncpb/platform/wp-content/uploads/Cardinal-Sarah-Keynote_2016-NCPB.pdf.

Saraswat, Aruna, Jamie Weinand, and Joshua Safer. 2015. "Evidence supporting the biologic nature of gender identity." *Endocrine Practice* 21, no. 2 (February): 199–204. https://doi.org/10.4158/EP14351.RA.

Sartre, Jean Paul. 1965. "Critique de la raison dialectique." In *Marxism and Existentialism*, by Walter Odajnyk, 139. Garden City, NY: Doubleday Anchor Books.

Schaefer, Leah, and Connie Wheeler. 1995. "Harry Benjamin's First Ten Cases (1938–1953): A Clinical Historical Note." *Archives of Sexual Behavior*, February 24: 73–93. https://doi.org/10.1007/BF01541990.

Schaffer, Kay, and Sidonie Smith. 2000. *The Olympics at the Millennium: Power, Politics, and the Games.* New Brunswick: Rutgers University Press.

Schmitt, David, Anu Realo, Voracek Martin, and Jüri Allik. 2008. "Why can't a man be more like a woman? Sex differences in Big Five personality traits across 55 cultures." *Journal of Personality and Social Psychology* 94, no. 1: 168–182. https://doi.org/10.1037/0022-3514.94.1.168.

Schore, Allan. 2001. "effects of a Secure Attachment Relationship on Right Brain Development, Affect Regulation, and Infant Mental Health." *Infant Medical Health* 22: 7–66. https://doi.org/10.1002/1097-0355(200101/04)22:1<7::AID-IMHJ2>3.0.CO;2-N

Scott, Daryl Michael. 1997. *Contempt and Pity: Social policy and the image of the damaged black psyche, 1880–1996*. Chapel Hill: University of North Carolina Press.

Scott, Walter Sidney. 1956. *The Trial of Joan of Arc, Being the verbatim report of the proceedings from the Orleans Manuscript*. London: Folio Society.

Seal, Leighton. 2017. "Adult Endocrinology." In *Genderqueer and Non-Binary Genders*, by Christina Richards, Walter Bouman, and Meg-John Barker, 183-223. London: Palgrave Macmillan.

Searle, John. 1984. *Minds, Brains, and Science*. Cambridge, MA: Harvard University Press.

Sedda, Anna and Gabriella Bottini. 2014. "Apotemnophilia, body integrity identity disorder or xenomelia? Psychiatric and neurologic etiologies face each." *Neuropsychiatric Disease and Treatment* 10, July 7: 1255–1265. https://doi.org/10.2147/NDT.S53385.

Serano, Julia. 2013. *Gender Is More Than Performance*. Emeryville, CA: Seal Press.

———. 2010a. "Performance Piece." In *Gender Outlaws: The Next Generation*, by Kate Bornstein, & S. Bear Bergman, 85–88. Emeryville, CA: Seal Publishing.

———. 2010b. "The Case Against Autogynephilia." *International Journal of Transgenderism* 12, no. 3: 176–187.

———. 2007. *Whipping Girl: A transsexual woman on sexism and the scapegoating of femininity*. Emeryville, CA: Seal Press.

Shafer, Jeff. 2017. "Supreme Incoherence: Transgender Ideology and the End of Law." *First Things*, March. Accessed September 29, 2020. https://www.firstthings.com/web-exclusives/2017/03/supreme-incoherencetransgender-ideology-and-the-end-of-law.

Shapiro, Ben, interview by David Ruben. 2018. "Jordan Peterson and Ben Shapiro: Religion, Trans Activism, and Censorship." *The Ruben Report*, November 30. YouTube video, 2:01:04. Accessed 02 25, 2020. https://www.youtube.com/watch?v=1opHWsHr798&t=69s.

Shapiro, Judith. 1991. "Transsexualism: Reflections on the Persistence of Gender and the Mutability of Sex." In *Body Guards: The Cultural Politics of Gender Ambiguity*, by Julia Epstein, & Kristina Straub, 248–262. New York: Routledge.

Shaw, Diana. 2020. "Transgender Teen With Pattern of Violence Against Women 'Anxious' to be Jailed With Women." *Women are Human*. September 26. Accessed June 10, 2021. https://www.womenarehuman.com/transgender-teen-charged-with-making-death-threats-against-two-individuals/.

Shea, John Gilmary. 2015. *Discovery and Exploration of the Mississippi Valley*. London, UK: Scholar Select.

Shostak, Art. 2015. *Viable Utopian Ideas: Shaping a Better World: Shaping a Better World*. London, UK: Routledge.

Shrier, Abigail. 2021. "Science, the Transgender Phenomenon, and the Young | Abigail Shrier." *Hillsdale College*. May 12. Accessed June 3, 2021. YouTube video, https://www.youtube.com/watch?v=DWbxIFC0Q2o.

Shucart, Brenden. 2016. "The Empty "Choice" Argument." *The Advocate*: 16.

Shupe, Jamie. 2019. "First Legally "Non-Binary" Individual Detransitions | Interview with Jamie Shupe." *Benjamin A Boyce*. March 5. YouTube Video. Accessed July 1, 2021. https://www.youtube.com/watch?v=0l-b7Ke8qBk&t=1425s.

Sigall, David. 2017. "Buyer's Remorse: The consequences of your decisions." *Psychology Today*. August 17. Accessed October 5, 2020. https://www.psychologytoday.com/us/blog/wishful-thoughts/201708/buyer-s-remorse.

Silberner, Joanne. 2006. "The Legacy of Sex Researcher John Money." *Obituaries.* Compiled by NPR. All Things Considered, July 11. Accessed September 29, 2020. https://www.npr.org/templates/story/story.php?storyId=55 49668.

Silverberg, Corey. 20013. "From Pathology to Pride: Supporting Gender Non-Conforming Children." *Contemporary Sexuality,* 47, no. 8: 1, 3–6.

Singal, Jesse. 2016. "A False Accusation Helped Bring Down Kenneth Zucker, a Controversial Sex Researcher." *The Cut.* January 27. Accessed January 8, 2020. https://www.thecut.com/2016/01/false-charge-helped-bring-down-kenneth-zucker.html.

———. 2016. "How the Fight over Transgender Kids Got a Leading Sex Researcher Fired." *The Cut.* February 7. Accessed January 8, 2020. https://www.thecut.com/2016/02/fight-over-trans-kids-got-a-researcher-fired.html.

———. 2015. *Why Some of the Worst Attacks on Social Science Have Come from Liberals.* New York Magazine. December 30. Accessed 12 17, 2019. https://www.thecut.com/2015/12/when-liberals-attack-social-science.html.

Sky News. 2019. *Special Report: NHS 'over-diagnosing' transgender children.* December 12. Accessed June 19, 2021. https://www.youtube.com/watch?v=qXvdrSkBFqw.

Smaers, Jeroen, Poppy Mulvaney, Christophe Soligo, Karl Zilles, Katrin Amunts. 2012, and 79(3):205-12. 2012. "Sexual dimorphism and laterality in the evolution of the primate prefrontal cortex." *Brain, Behavior, and Evolution* 79 (3): 205-212. https://doi:10.1159/000336115.

Smith, Michael, and Jeffrey Wilhelm. 2002. *Reading Don't Fix No Chevys: Literacy in the Lives of Young Men.* Portsmouth, NH: Heinemann.

Socarides, Charles. 1970. "A psychoanalytic study of the desire for sexual transformation ('transsexualism'): the plaster-of-paris man." *The International Journal of Psycho-Analysis* 51, no. 3: 341–349. PMID: 5503634.

———. 1969. "Dr. Socarides replies, [Letter to the editor]." *American Journal of Psychiatry* 126, no. 2: 156.

———. 1978. "Transsexualism and Psychosis." *International Journal of Psychoanalytic Psychotherapy* 7: 373–384.

Soh, Debra. 2020. *The End of Gender: Debunking the Myths about Sex and Identity in Our Society.* New York, NY: Threshold Editions.

———.2021. "Debra Soh | Full Address and Q&A | Oxford Union Web Series." *OxfordUnion.* April 10. Accessed June 15, 2021. https://www.youtube.com/watch?v=epm_2oC0tus.

Sommers, Christina Hoff. 2013. "What 'Lean In' Misunderstands About Gender Differences." *The Atlantic.* March 19. Accessed June 11, 2020. www.theatlantic.com/sexes/archive/2013/03/what-lean-in-misunderstands-about-gender-differences/274138/.

Spinoza, Baruch. 2001. *Theological-Political Treatise.* Translated by Samuel Shirley. Indianapolis. IN: Hackett Publishing.

St. Thomas, John of. 1885. "De donis Spiritus Sancti." In *Curses Theologicus, Disputatio XVIII*, by Vives. Paris, FR: Vives.

Stahl, Lesley. 2021. "Transgender Healthcare." *60 Minutes.* CBS, WCBS, May 23.

Stebbins, George Ledyard. 1966. *Processes of Organic Evolution.* Englewood Cliffs, NJ: Prentice-Hall.

Steensma, Thomas, Peggy Cohen-Kettenis, and Annelou de Vries. 2011a. "Treatment of Adolescents with Gender Dysphoria in the Netherlands." *Child Adolescent Psychiatric Clinics of North America* 20, no. 4 (October): 689–700. https://doi.org/10.1016/j.chc.2011.08.001.

Steensma, Thomas, Roseline Biemond, Fijgje de Boer, and Peggy Cohen-Kettenis. 2011b. "Desisting and Persisting Gender Dysphoria After Childhood: A Qualitative follow-Up Study."

Clinical Child Psychology and Psychiatry, January 7. https://doi.org/10.1177/1359104510378303.

Steensma, Thomas, and Peggy Cohen-Kettenis. 2018. "A critical commentary on "A critical commentary on follow-up studies and "desistence" theories about transgender and gender non-conforming children"." *International Journal of Transgenderism*, May 29: 225–230. https://doi.org/10.1080/15532739.2018.1468292

Steensma, Thomas, Jenifer McGuire, Baudewijntje Kreukels, Anneke Beekman, and Peggy Cohen-Kettenis. 2013. "Factors associated with desistence and persistence of childhood gender dysphoria: a quantitative follow-up study." *Journal of the American Academy of Child & Adolescent Psychiatry* 52, no. 6 (June): 582–590. https://doi.org/10.1016/j.jaac.2013.03.016,

Stephens, Travis. 2016. "The Principle of Totality Does Not Justify Sex Reassignment Surgery." *Ethics & Medics,* 41, no. 11 (November): 1–4. Accessed September 29, 2020. https://www.ncbcenter.org/em-openaccess/ethics-medics-november-2016.

Stewart, Conor. 2020. *Hospital admissions involving a diagnosis of anorexia nervosa in England in 2019/20, by age.* September 25. Accessed September 28, 2020. https://www.statista.com/statistics/987224/england-anorexia-diagnoses-by-age/.

Stewart, Milo. 2020. Twitter Post. May 11, 2:07AM. https://twitter.com/genderthrash/status/1259726894800535553

Stoller, Robert. 1968. *Sex and Gender: On the development of masculinity and femininity.* New York: Science House.

Strang, John, Lauren Kenworthy, Aleksandra Dominska, Jennifer Sokoloff, Laura Kenealy, Madison Berl, Karin Walsh. 2014. "Increased Gender Variance in Autism Spectrum Disorders and Attention Deficit Hyperactivity Disorder." *Archives of Sexual Behavior*, November: 1525–1533. https://doi.org/10.1007/s10508-014-0285-3.

Bibliography

Swain, Smarak. 2006. "Problems of third gender." In *Social Issues of India*, by Smarak Swain, 57–59. New Delhi, IO: New Vishal Publications.

Synesius of Cyrene Bishop of Ptolemais. 1985. "Synesii Cyrenaei Calvitii encomium." In *In Praise of Baldness*, by J.G. Krabinger, translated by George Kendal, 1–44. Vancouver, CA: Pharmakon Press.

Szasz, Thomas. 1979. "Male and Female Created He Them." *The New York Times*, June: 3.

Talusan, Meredith. 2017. "Why Can't My Famous Gender Nonconforming Friends Get Laid?" *Vice*. June 22. Accessed February 15, 2021. https://www.vice.com/en/article/wjq99z/why-cant-my-famous-gender-nonconforming-friends-get-laid.

Tanis, Justin. 2016. "The Power of the 41%: A glimpse into the life of a statistic." *Journal of Orthopsychiatry* 86, no. 4: 373–377. https://doi.org/10.1037/ort0000200.

Tannehill, Brynn. 2016. "The End of the Desistance Myth." *The Huffington Post*. January 01. Accessed June 11, 2020. https://www.huffpost.com/entry/the-end-of-the-desistance_b_8903690.

Tauler, John. 1910. *The Sermons and Conferences of John Tauler*. Translated by Maria Shrady. Washington, DC: Apostolic Mission House.

Taylor, Timothy. 1996. *The pre-history of sex: Four million years of human sexual culture*. New York: Bantam.

Taylor & Francis. 2020. *Article Metrics*. June 26. Accessed June 26, 2020. https://www.tandfonline.com/doi/abs/10.3109/00048679609065010#metrics-content.

Tetelepta, Berendien. 2021. *More research is urgently needed into transgender care for young people: "Where does the large increase of children come from?"*. February 27. Accessed June 12, 2021. https://www.voorzij.nl/more-research-is-urgently-needed-into-transgender-care-for-young-people-where-does-the-large-increase-of-children-come-from/.

Temple Newhook, Julia, Jake Pyne, Cindy Holmes, Jemma Tosh, and Sarah Pickett. 2018. "A Critical Commentary on Follow-Up Studies and "Desistance" Theories about Transgender and Gender-Nonconforming Children." *International Journal of Transgenderism* 19, no. 2 (April): 212-224. https://doi.org/10.1080/15532739.2018.1456390.

Terruwe, Anna, and Conrad Baars. 1981. *Psychic Wholeness and Healing.* New York: Alba House.

Tertullian. 1971. *Adversus Valentinianos.* Translated by Mark Riley. Ann Arbor, MI: Bell & Howell.

———. 1885. *On the Apparel of women.* Vol. 4, in *Ante-Nicene Fathers,* by James Donaldson, A. Cleveland Coxe Alexander Roberts, translated by S. Thelwall. Buffalo, NY: Christian Literature Publishing.

Tessman, Lisa. 2005. *Burdened Virtues: Virtue Ethics for Liberatory Struggles.* Oxford, UK: Oxford University Press.

The Barna Group. 2007. *A New Generation Expresses its Skepticism and Frustration with Christianity.* Research Releases in Millennials & Generations, Ventura, CA: Barna Group.

The Ethicists of The National Catholic Bioethics Center. 2016. "Brief Statement on Transgenderism." *The National Catholic Bioethics Quarterly*, Winter: 599–603.

The Leader. 2012. "Exploring Sexual and Gender Identities." *The Leader.* May 1. Accessed June 28, 2020. https://ecleader.net/2012/tag/Benjamin.

The Mayo Clinic. n.d. *Gender dysphoria.* Accessed June 19, 2020. https://www.mayoclinic.org/diseases-conditions/gender-dysphoria/diagnosis-treatment/drc-20475262.

The Roman Missal. 1973. *Exsultet.* Vatican City: International Commission on English in the Liturgy.

Bibliography

The Royal Institution. 2016. "How Neurononsense Keeps Women in Their Place- with Gina Rippon." June 1. YouTube video, 53:26. Accessed January 8, 2020. https://www.youtube.com/watch?v=uqR4cw9Amlg.

The United States Department of State. 2017. *2017 Country Reports on Human Rights Practices: Iran.* Country Report, Washington, DC: Bureau of Democracy, Human Rights and Labor.

The World Conservation Union. 2014. *Numbers of threatened species by major groups of organisms (1996–2014).* November 13. Accessed December 24, 2019. http://cmsdocs.s3.amazonaws.com/summarystats/2014_3_S ummary_Stats_Page_Documents/2014_3_RL_Stats_Table_1 .pdf.

The World Professional Association for Transgender Health. 2012. *Standards of Care written by the World Professional Association for Transgender Health.* Minneapolis, MN: WPATH.

Thérèse. *The Story of a Soul.* 1996. Translated by John Clarke. Charmouth, UK: C.S. Publications.

Toomey, Russell, Amy Syvertsen, and Maura Shramko. 2018. "Transgender Adolescent Suicide Behavior." *Pediatrics* 42, no. 4 (October): https://doi.org/10.1542/peds.2017-4218.

Totenberg, Nina. 2020. "Supreme Court Delivers Major Victory to LGBTQ Employees." *NPR.* June 15. Accessed June 28, 2020. https://www.npr.org/2020/06/15/863498848/supreme-court-delivers-major-victory-to-lgbtq-employees.

Tougher, Shaun. 2004. "Holy Eunuchs! Masculinity and Eunuch Saints in Byzantium." In *Holiness and Masculinity in the Middle Ages*, by PH Cullum, & Katherine Lewis, 94. Cardiff, UK: University of Wales Press.

Trans Student Educational Resources. n.d. *The Gender Unicorn.* Accessed January 9, 2020. https://www.transstudent.org/gender.

———. n.d. *Why We Used Trans* and Why We Don't Anymore.* Accessed January 23, 2020. https://www.transstudent.org/asterisk.

Transgender Law Center. 2015. "Ten tips for working with transgender patients: An information and resource publication for healthcare providers." *Transgender Law Center.* Accessed July 20, 2020. http://transgenderlawcenter.org/wp-content/uploads/2011/12/01.06.2016-tips-healthcare.pdf.

Travers, Robb, Greta Bauer, and Jake Pyne. 2012. *Impacts of Strong Parental Support for Trans Youth.* Children's Aid Society of Toronto and Delisle Youth Services, Toronto, ON: Trans Pulse.

Tur, Zoey. 2015. "The moment this transgender debate got heated." *HLN.* July 17. Accessed July 16, 2021. https://www.youtube.com/watch?v=YgQy70_LPS4.

Ugalmugle, Sumant, and Rupali Swain. 2020. "Sex Reassignment Surgery Market Size By Gender Transition (Male to Female {Facial, Breast, Genitals}, Female to Male {Facial, Chest, Genitals}), Industry Analysis Report, Regional Outlook, Application Potential, Price Trends, Competitive Market Share." *Global Market Insights.* March. Accessed December 13, 2020. https://www.gminsights.com/industry-analysis/sex-reassignment-surgery-market.

Ulrichs, Karl Heinrich. 1868. *Memnon.* Schleiz, DE: Hübscher.

United States Conference of Catholic Bishops. 2019. "U.S. Bishops' Chairman for Catholic Education Welcomes the Release of Male and Female He Created Them." *United States Conference of Catholic Bishops.* June 11. Accessed July 15, 2020. http://www.usccb.org/news/2019/19–109.cfm.

U.S. Department of Health and Human Services. 2013. *Child Maltreatment 2012.* Accessed July 12, 2021. http://www.acf.hhs.gov/programs/cb/research-data-technology/statistics-research/child-maltreatment.

Bibliography

Vaid-Menon, Alok. 2021. Twitter Post. March 7, 6:57 AM. https://twitter.com/WomenReadWomen/status/136851610 6520911874/photo/1

van de Grift, Tim, Els Elaut, Susanne Cerwenka, Peggy Cohen-Kettenis, and Baudewijntje Keukels. 2018. "Surgical Satisfaction, Quality of Life, and Their Association After Gender-Affirming Surgery: A Follow-up Study." *Journal of Sex & Marital Therapy* 44, no. 2: 138–148. https://doi.org/10.1080/0092623X.2017.1326190.

van Kesteren, Paul, Henk Asscheman, Jos Megens, and Louis Gooren. 1997. "Mortality and Morbidity in Transexual Subjects Treated with Cross-sex Hormones." *Clinical Endocrinology, 47*(3): 337–342.

van Mol, Andre, Michael Laidlaw, Miriam Grossman, and Paul McHugh. 2020. *Correction: Transgender Surgery Provides No Mental Health Benefit.* September 13. Accessed September 27, 2020. https://www.thepublicdiscourse.com/2020/09/71296/.

van Straalen, Wouter, J. Joris Hage, and Elisabeth Bloemena. 1995. "The inframammary ligament: myth or reality?" *Annals of Plastic Surgery* 35, no. 3 (September): 237–241.

Vanier, Jean. 2019. *A Cry is Heard: My path to peace.* Toronto, ON: Darton, Longman, and Todd.

———. 1998. *Becoming Human.* Toronto, ON: Anansi.

———. 1989. *Community and Growth.* New York: Paulist Press.

———. 1985. *Man and Woman He Made Them.* Mahwah, NJ: Paulist Press.

———. 1997. *Our Journey Home.* Translated by Maggie Parham. London, UK: Novalis/ Orbis.

———. 1988. *The Broken Body.* New York: Paulist Press.

Vatsyayana. 1961. *Kama Sutra.* Translated by Upadhyaya. Bombay, IO: D.B. Traraporevala Sons.

Vincent, Ben, and Ana Manzano. 2017. "History and Cultural Diversity." In *Genderqueer and Non-Binary Genders*, by Christina Richards, Walter Pierre Bouman, 11–30. London, UK: Palgrave Macmillan.

Vincent, Par Alizée. 2020. "Sylvia Rivera, la Rosa Parks des trans." *Causette.* May 20. Accessed June 13, 2021. https://www.causette.fr/feminismes/figures/sylvia-rivera-la-rosa-parks-des-trans.

von Balthasar, Hans Urs. 1974. "Nine Theses in Christian Ethics." *Vatican.va,* Accessed February 12, 2020. http://www.vatican.va/roman_curia/congregations/cfaith/ct i_documents/rc_cti_1974_morale-cristiana_en.html.

von Hildebrand, Dietrich, Mary Shivanandan, and Mark S. Latkovic. 2013. "Sex." In *New Catholic Encyclopedia Supplement 2012–2013: Ethics and Philosophy*, by Catholic University of America, translated by Robert L. Fastiggi, 1405. Detroit, MI: Gale.

von Krafft-Ebing, Richard. 1906. *Psychopathia Sexualis: With Especial Reference to the Antipathic Sexual Instinct [12th ed.].* Translated by FJ Rebman. New York: Physicians and Surgeons Book; reprint.

Walch, Tad. 2018. "LDS Church donates 25K to LGBT advocacy group in effort to prevent suicide." *KSL.com.* July 11. Accessed July 24, 2020. https://www.ksl.com/article/46358409/lds-church-donates-25k-to-lgbt-advocacy-group-in-effort-to-prevent-suicide.

Wallace, William. 1999. "Quantification in the Sixteenth Century Natural Philosophy." In *Recovering Nature: Essays in Natural Philosophy, Ethics, and Metaphysics in Honor of Ralph McInerny*, by O'Callaghan, & Thomas Hibbs, 11–24. Notre Dame, IN: University of Notre Dame Press.

Wallien, Madeleine, and Peggy Cohen-Kettenis. 2008. "Psychosexual outcome of gender-dysphoric children." *Journal of the American Academy of Child and Adolescent Psychiatry*: 1414–1423. https://doi.org/10.1097/CHI.0b013e31818956b9.

Watson, Diane, and Stanley Coren. 1992. "Left-handedness in male-to-female transsexuals [letter]." *Journal of the American Medical Association* 267, no. 10: 1342.

Warrier, Varun, David M. Greenberg, Elizabeth Weir, Clara Buckingham, Paula Smith, Meng Chuan Lai, Carrie Allison & Simon Baron-Cohen. 2020. "Elevated rates of autism, other neurodevelopmental and psychiatric diagnoses, and autistic traits in transgender and gender-diverse individuals." *Nature Communications* 11, 3959. https://doi.org/10.1038/s41467-020-17794-1.

Watson, Rebecca. 2019. "Correction or Censorship? An Anti-Trans Study Sparks Controversy." March 29. YouTube video, 7:28. Accessed 12 16, 2019. https://www.youtube.com/watch?v=rIiFQ5UJCJQ.

Watts, Fraser. 2002. "Transsexualism and the Church." *Theology and Sexuality* 9: 63–85. https://doi.org/10.1177/135583580200900105.

White, Blaire. 2017. "Live Debate w/ Trans Activist" *Blaire White*. February 20. YouTube video, 58:20. Accessed January 15, 2021. https://www.youtube.com/watch?v=7mamVI4UPYQ.

———. 2018. "DEBATE: Ben Shapiro & Blaire White." *Blaire White*. January 10. YouTube video, 14:35. Accessed January 21, 2020. https://www.youtube.com/watch?v=hbTwoLah2VY.

———. 2019a. "Why I'm Not Getting "The Surgery." *Blaire White*. March 7. YouTube video. Accessed January 21, 2020. https://www.youtube.com/watch?v=z1ZWX5r_0MI.

———. 2019b. "Exposing Jessica Yaniv: Trans Predator." *Blaire White*. July 23. YouTube video. Accessed June 8, 2021. https://www.youtube.com/watch?v=MI_lXO7zrAQ.

———. 2020. "'I Regret Transitioning' - Talk w/ Teen De-transitioner." *Blaire White*. January 21. YouTube video, 9:00. Accessed January 21, 2020. https://www.youtube.com/watch?v=tPBLyb8H_iE

————. 2021a. "'My Life Felt Ruined' - Talk w/ Detransitioned Woman" *Blaire White*. May 26. YouTube video, Accessed January 21, 2021. https://www.youtube.com/watch?v=xJNAD6dJanA.

————. 2021b. "Responding to 'Blaire White Hates Non-Binary People'" Blaire *White*. May 14. YouTube video, Accessed May 15, 2021. https://www.youtube.com/watch?v=_CUf2vIz2Y4.

White, Tonya. 1997. "Gender Identity Disorder: Nature, Nurture and A Common Final Pathway." *The Second International Congress on Sex & Gender Issues*. King of Prussia, PA: The Renaissance Education Association, 1997. Saturday, June 21.

Whyte, Stephen, Robert C. Brooks, and Benno Torgler. 2018. "Man, Woman, "Other": Factors Associated with Nonbinary Gender." *Archives of Sexual Behavior*, November 1: 2397–2406. https://doi.org/10.1007/s10508-018-1307-3.

Wilhelmsen, Frederick. 2012. "Forward." In *Thomist Realism and the Critique of Knowledge*, by Étienne Gilson, 7–21. San Francisco, CA: Ignatius Press.

Williams, Bernard. 1981. *Moral Luck*. Cambridge, UK: Cambridge University Press.

Williams, Cristan. 2012a. "1971: Transsex Added to the Dictionary." *Cristan Williams*. February 10. Accessed June 27, 2020. http://research.cristanwilliams.com/2012/02/10/1971-transsex-added-to-dictionary/.

————. 2012b. "Tracking Transgender: The Historical Truth." *Cristan Williams*. March 27. Accessed June 27, 2020. http://www.cristanwilliams.com/2012/03/27/tracking-transgender-the-historical-truth/.

Williams, Rachel Anne. 2019. *Transgressive: A Trans Woman on Gender, Feminism, and Politics*. London, UK: Jessica Kingsley Publishers.

Williamson, Kevin. 2014. "National Review." *Laverne Cox Is Not a Woman: Facts are not subject to our feelings*. May 30. Accessed

January 12, 2020.
https://www.nationalreview.com/2014/05/laverne-cox-not-woman/.

Willoughby, India. 2019. "India Willoughby on Being Trans, Trans Athletes and Women's Spaces." *Triggernometry*. April 14. Accessed June 9, 2021. https://www.youtube.com/watch?v=jWuNG5tXNS4.

Wilson, Erin, Ellen Iverson, Robert Garofalo, and Marvin Belzer. 2012. "Parental support and condom use among transgender female youth.*" Journal of the Association of Nurses in AIDS Care* 23, no. 4: 306–317. https://doi.org/10.1016/j.jana.2011.09.001.

Wilson, Erin, Robert Garofalo, Robert Harris, Amy Herrick, Miguel Martinez, Jaime Martinez. 2009. "Transgender Female Youth and Sex Work: HIV Risk and a Comparison of Life Factors Related to Engagement in Sex Work." *AIDS and Behavior* 13, no. 5: 902–913. https://doi.org/ 10.1007/s10461-008-9508-8.

Wischik, Claude. 2020. "Neuropathology, the Brain, and Spirituality." Keynote Address. Elgin, UK: Pluscarden Abbey, January 29.

Witt, Charlotte. 1989. *Substance and Essence in Aristotle: An Interpretation of Metaphysics VII-IX*. Ithica, NY: Cornell University Press.

———. 2011. *The Metaphysics of Gender*. Oxford, UK: Oxford Press.

Wojtyla, Karol. 1981. *Love & Responsibility*. Translated by H.T. Willetts. London, UK: Collins.

———. 1979. *The Acting Person*. Translated by Andrzej Potocki. Boston, MA: Reidel.

Wood. Graeme. 2019. "Genital waxing complainant's topless-OK youth LGBTQ2S+ swim proposal delayed by Township of Langley." *North Shore News*. July 25. Accessed June 8, 2021. https://www.nsnews.com/local-news/genital-waxing-complainants-topless-ok-youth-lgbtq2s-swim-proposal-delayed-by-township-of-langley-3104138.

Wooden, Cindy. 2016. "Pope Francis deplores 'global war' on marriage." *Catholic Herald*. October 1. Accessed January 14, 2020. https://catholicherald.co.uk/news/2016/10/01/pope-deplores-global-war-on-marriage/.

Wright, Colin. 2020. "'Sex is NOT a Spectrum' - Colin Wright." *Triggernometry*. October 7. Accessed June 10, 2021. https://www.youtube.com/watch?v=ncF-ZbfVR2w.

Wright, N.T. 2017. "Letter to the Editor." *The Times of London*, August 3.

Wu, Chengliang. 1995. "Ancient Crocodile Chomped on Plants." *Science News*, August: 132. Accessed September 29, 2020. https://www.sciencenewsforstudents.org/article/ancient-crocodiles-may-have-preferred-chomping-plants-not-meat.

Wu, Katherine. 2016. *Between the (Gender) Lines: Science of Transgender Identity*. December. Accessed 12 15, 2019. http://sitn.hms.harvard.edu/flash/2016/gender-lines-science-transgender-identity/.

Wynn, Natalie. 2019. ""Transtrenders" | ContraPoints." ContraPoints, July 1. YouTube video, 34:43. Accessed December 17, 2019. https://www.youtube.com/watch?v=EdvM_pRfuFM.

———. 2018. "Autogynephilia | ContraPoints." ContraPoints, February 1. YouTube, 48:54. Accessed 12 16, 2019. https://www.youtube.com/watch?v=6czRFLs5JQo.

Yarhouse, Mark. 2015. *Understanding Gender Dysphoria*. Downers Grove, IL: IVP Academic, 2015.

Yarhouse, Mark, and Dara Houp. 2016. "Transgender Christians: Gender Identity, Family Relationships, and Religious Faith." In *Transgender Youth*, by Shemya Vaughn, 51–65. New York: Nova Publishers.

Yarhouse, Mark, Dara Houp, Julia Sadusky, and Olya Zaporozhets. 2016. "Christian Parents' Experiences of Transgender Youth During the Coming Out Process" In *Transgender Youth*, by Shemya Vaughn, 193–208. New York: Nova Publishers.

Yarhouse, Mark, and Julia Sadusky. 2019. "The Complexities of Gender Identity." In *Understanding Transgender Identities*, by James Beilby, & Paul Rhodes Eddy, 101–146. Grand Rapids, MI: Baker Academic.

Yeo, Margaret. 1938. *A Prince of Pastors: St. Charles Borromeo.* London, UK: Catholic Book Club.

Yerke, Adam, and Ashley Fortier. 2016. "Leveling the Playing Field for All: safe, fair, and equal inclusion of transgender youth athletes part one." In Transgender Youth, by Shemya Vaughn, 143–163. New York: Nova Publishers.

Zeigler, Cyd. 2016. "Exclusive: Read the Olympics' new transgender guidelines that will not mandate surgery." *Out Sports.* January 21. Accessed July 23, 2020. https://www.outsports.com/2016/1/21/10812404/transgender-ioc-policy-new-olympics.

Zell, Michael. 1986. "Suicide in pre-industrial England." *Social History,* 11, no. 3 (October): 303–317. http://www.jstor.org/stable/4285541.

Zhou, Jiang-Ning, Michael Hofman, Louis Gooren, and Dick Swaab. 1995. "A sex difference in the human brain and its relation to transsexuality." *Nature* 68: 68–70. https://doi.org/10.1038/378068a0.

Zinn, Andrew. 2016. "Turner Syndrome—the Basics, Genetic Overview." In *Sex, Gender, and Sexuality: The New Basics*, by Abby Ferber, Kimberly Holcomb, & Tre Wentling, 540. Oxford, UK: Oxford University Press.

Zucker, Kenneth, Anne Lawrence, and BPC Kreukels. 2016. "Gender dysphoria in adults." *Annual Review of Clinical Psychology* 12: 217–247. https://doi.org/10.1146/annurev-clinpsy-021815-093034.

Zucker, Kenneth. 2007. "Gender Identity Disorder in Children and Adolescents." In *Gabbard's treatments of psychiatric disorders*, by G.O. Gabbard, 683–701. Washington, DC: American Psychiatric Press.

INDEX

Index

Index

Index